CONTEMPORARY FILM AND TELEVISION SERIES

IMITATIONS of LIFE

edited by Marcia Landy

IMITATIONS of LIFE

a reader on FILM & TELEVISION

MELODRAMA

 Wayne State University Press Detroit

95 94 93 92 91 5 4 3 2 1

Library of Congress Cataloging-in-Publication Data

Imitations of life : a reader on film and television melodrama
edited by Marcia Landy.
p. cm.—(Contemporary film and television series)
Includes bibliographical references.
ISBN 0-8143-2064-3 (alk. paper).—ISBN 0-8143-2065-1 (pbk. : alk. paper)
1. Melodrama in motion pictures. 2. Melodrama in television. 3. Melodrama—History and criticism. I. Landy, Marcia, 1931– II. Series.
PN1995.9.M45I45 1991
791.43'655—dc20 90-34379
CIP

Manufactured in the United States of America

Contents

III

HISTORY AND IDEOLOGY 193

IV

PSYCHOANALYSIS, GENDER, AND RACE 263

V

DIRECTORS AND STARS 349

Preface

Because of the wide-ranging critical concerns expressed in the study of melodrama, touching all aspects of film study—history, genre, narrativity, style, representations of sexual difference, authorship, the nature and role of stars, spectatorship, audience response, and popular culture—a reader on melodrama is a timely and useful critical text, serving to bring together writings that until now have been scattered among various journals and books on the subject. The essays included in this volume are organized around current theoretical, historical, and methodological concerns. They represent contesting points of view and different historical moments in the history of cinema. Because of the range of concerns expressed by the authors, this book will be useful for classes in popular culture, genre, film and ideology, and women's studies. In teaching graduate and undergraduate courses, I felt the need of a text that would represent the best work to date on melodrama. This volume is my attempt to meet that need.

I would like especially to express my gratitude to Lucy Fischer for her invaluable comments on several versions of the book and for being an exemplary colleague. Busy as she is, she always finds time to support other people's scholarship. I would also like to thank Dana Polan for commenting on the preliminary manuscript. Patricia Erens, the general editor of the series, offered helpful suggestions about format and style. My thanks to Jamie Shepherd, who, during a long hot summer, helped both with the correspondence concerning permissions and with proofreading the manuscript, and to Dr. Alberta Sbragia, Director of the Western European Program, and her assistant, Dr. Ursual Davis, for providing necessary funds for work in time of need. Above all, I am indebted to Stanley Shostak for his criticism and his friendship.

Introduction

She took a deep, brave breath and told him. "My mother was a Frenchwoman. I only knew that her name was Solange Bertrand, a 'commoner' as you would put it. My father met her when he liberated Paris with the Allied forces. I know nothing more. My father was an actor, a well-known one, much respected, named Sam Walker. They were said to be very much in love, and they had three daughters, of which I am the second one. And then. . . ." She almost choked on her words as she told him, but in an odd way it was a relief to say the words. ". . . as a result of some madness he killed her. And when he was convicted of the crime, he committed suicide in his cell, leaving me and my sisters penniless and orphaned. We were left with an aunt for a few months, and then a friend of the family, an attorney, found homes for us and got us adopted, two of us anyway. I was very fortunate in that I was given to Margaret and her first husband, a lawyer named George Gorham. I was five at the time. I was apparently four when my father killed my mother which is why I don't recall it. And I don't know anything about the man named George Gorham. Apparently six months later he died, and my mother . . . Margaret, that is, came to France to recover and met my father . . . Pierre. . . . He adopted me as soon as he married my mother . . . and then you came along."

—Danielle Steele, *Kaleidoscope*

Things are like this throughout the film [*Imitation of Life*]. They are always making plans for happiness, for tenderness, and then the phone rings, a new part and Lana revives. The woman is a hopeless case. So is John Gavin. He should have caught on pretty soon that it won't work. But he pins his life on that woman just the same. For all of us it's the things that won't

> work that keep our interest. Lana Turner's daughter then falls in love with John, she is exactly what John would like Lana to be—but she's not Lana. This is understandable. Only Sandra Dee doesn't understand. It could be that when one is in love one doesn't understand too well. Annie, too, loves her daughter and doesn't understand her at all. Once, when Sarah Jane is still a child, it is raining and Annie takes her an umbrella at school. Sarah Jane has pretended at school that she is white. The truth comes out when her mother shows up with the umbrella. Sarah Jane will never forget. And when Annie, shortly before her death, wants to see Sarah Jane for the last time, her love still prevents her from understanding. It seems to her to be a sin that Sarah Jane should want to be taken for white. The most terrible thing about this scene is that the more Sarah Jane is mean and cruel the more her mother is poor and pathetic. But in actual fact, exactly the reverse is true. It is the mother who is brutal, wanting to possess her child because she loves her. And Sarah Jane defends herself against her mother's terrorism, against the terrorism of the world. The cruelty is that we can understand them both, both are right and no one will be able to help them. At this point all of us in the cinema cried. Because changing the world is so difficult. Then they come together again at Annie's funeral, and behave for a few minutes as though everything was all right. It's this "as though" that lets them carry on with the same old crap, underneath they have an inkling of what they are really after, but they soon forget it again.
>
> —Rainer Werner Fassbinder, *Douglas Sirk*

The passage from Danielle Steele's *Kaleidoscope* and Fassbinder's commentary on Douglas Sirk's film, *Imitation of Life,* expose the content of melodrama: a constant struggle for gratification and equally constant blockages to its attainment. Melodramatic narratives are driven by the experience of one crisis after another, crises involving severed familial ties, separation and loss, misrecognition of one's place, person, and propriety. Seduction, betrayal, abandonment, extortion, murder, suicide, revenge, jealously, incurable illness, obsession, and compulsion—these are part of the familiar terrain of melodrama. The victims are most often females threatened in their sexuality, their property, their very identity. Often orphaned, subjected to cruel and arbitrary treatment at the hands of domineering paternal and maternal figures or their surrogates, they experience a number of trials, until, if they are fortunate, they are rescued by a gentle and understanding lover, the "happy, unhappy ending" in Douglas Sirk's terms.

Illness and criminality are often the marks of the protagonist's inevitable transgression against societal expectations, and the presence of physicians, psychiatrists, and representatives of the law is a commonplace. These figures serve a contradictory role in the narrative. They are agents for recuperation, helping the protagonists to take their appropriate place in the social and domestic order, disciplining their unruly passions and desires, or reconciling them to their difference, in which case the resolution is not domestic containment but isolation or death. Their presence also provides a means for exposing how gender and sexuality are instruments of social power, ensuring compliance through both coercion and consent. The external landscape is a correlative for an internal landscape of hysteria, schizophrenia, depression, obsession-compulsion, and misdirected desire. In most instances, tensions in personal relationships are generated from power and domination which take the form of class, property, generational, sexual, and racial struggles. The narratives generate emotional intensity involving not only the figures within the melodrama but the external audience, and affect is conveyed primarily through gesture, music, and iconography which are indicative of the limitations of conventional verbal language to express the intense psychic and bodily pains or pleasures experienced by the characters.

Melodrama is not unique to the cinema but is deeply rooted in Western culture since the eighteenth century in prose fiction and in the theater. That the ideology it represents is alive and well within the culture can also be seen in the transference of the "melodramatic imagination" to television in the popular daytime soap operas as well as in such prime-time programs as "Dynasty," "Falconcrest," and "Dallas." Some critics argue, though, that the impetus to melodrama is stronger during times of ideological crisis. For example, in the last years of Italian fascism, from 1939 to 1943, melodrama served to dramatize cultural conflicts. The films exploded with irresolvable contradictions involving tensions between the personal and the public spheres, within the family, and within the individual. Similarly, the Hollywood melodramas of the 1950s are intimately linked to the unsettled ideological milieu of post–World War II society and the Cold War in particular.

Melodramatic texts have constituted an important source of pleasure, learning, and even resistance to prevailing social attitudes. Yet, until recently, melodrama has suffered from either negative esteem or almost complete disregard by critics. With the assault on the hegemony of the classics and of high culture and with the feminist reevaluations of popular culture, critics have begun to recognize the importance of understanding how profoundly the popular theater, cinema, radio, and television have shaped modern society and how great a role the melodramatic imagination has played in these media. Melodrama traverses a number of genres—romances, narratives of crime and espionage, thrillers, and historical narratives. Moreover, the protagonists of melodrama vary. In the women's narratives such as the women's novel and film, as well as the soap opera, the protagonists are females, and the conflicts are often seen from a woman's vantage point. In other genres ranging from the action-oriented westerns to the family melodramas, the perspective is more likely to be associated with conflicts involving male identity and power. In all cases, though, what is at stake are questions of personal and cultural identity, social power, and continuity. One can identify the strategies of melodrama in its dichotomizing of the world, its Manicheanism, its emphasis on sensibility and sentiment, its inflation of personal conflicts, and its internalization of external social conflicts.

Given the effectiveness of melodrama in exposing the mechanisms of power inherent in bourgeois representations, it is important to question why there have been so few studies of the genre until very recently. One reason for the low esteem in which melodrama has been held is its identification with mass, or what has been termed "low culture," in contrast to "high culture." Low culture has been identified with escapism, vulgarity, sensationalism, excess, and exaggeration, regarded as corrupting by critics who have upheld the values of high seriousness, universality, timelessness, and especially realism. The separation between high and low cultures is tied to political and cultural struggles which took place in the last part of the nineteenth century and continued unabated through the early twentieth century, revealing sharp divergences concerning the impact of cultural artifacts on their audiences. For liberals such as Matthew Arnold, literature and theater, in order to maintain their high mission, must not pander to the masses but must seek to raise their intellectual level.

The bias against low culture, whether of an ethical or aesthetic cast, has generally been linked to a class and gender bias. The audiences have been characterized in degraded intellectual terms as untutored and indicative of the debased tastes of the "masses." More particularly, as Andreas Huyssens writes, "Time and time again documents from the nineteenth century ascribe pejorative feminine characteristics to mass culture."[1] Moreover, he adds, "The fear of the masses in this age of declining liberalism is always a fear of woman, a fear of nature out of control, a fear of the unconscious, of sexuality, of the loss of identity and of stable ego boundaries in the mass."[2] The fear of the masses has therefore been instrumental in creating a resistance to critically exploring the needs and desires which are deeply embedded in the mass culture.

Even in the examinations of critics committed to studies of social change and to an examination of mass culture, such as those of the Frankfurt school, assessments of the "culture industry" have been negative. Theodor W. Adorno wrote:

> Just as culture sprang up in the marketplace, in the traffic of trade, in communication and negotiation, as something distinct from the immediate struggle for individual self-preservation, just as it was closely tied to trade in the era of mature capitalism, just as its representatives were counted among the class of "third persons" who supported themselves in life as middle men, so culture, considered "socially necessary" acording to classical rules, in the sense of reproducing itself economically, is in the end reduced to that as which it began, to mere communication. Its alienation from human affairs terminates in its absolute docility before a humanity which has been transformed into clientele by the suppliers. In the name of the consumer, the manipulators suppress everything in the culture which enables it to go beyond the total immanence in the existing society and allow only that to remain which serves society's equivocal purpose.[3]

The writings of Gyorgy Lukacs, too, concerned as they were to identify "progressive" cultural production reproduced the middle-class predilection for the classics and tended to regard mass culture (as well as avant-garde texts) as symptomatic of cultural decadence.[4] However, Lukacs's linking of mass and modernist culture acknowledges the relationship between the two where other critics have tended to keep them apart. In more recent terms, both Fredric Jameson and Andreas Huyssens have argued for the ideological nature of these divisions and the relationship between "mass" and "elitist" cultures, the latter being a reaction to the former. High art has thus been seen as a purer expression of cultural values, untainted by the vulgar world of commerce. Yet in their reaction against mass culture, elitist works of art have been complicit in denying, if not censoring, knowledge about the culture. In the wholesale condemnation of mass culture, the opportunity for understanding the needs and desires of marginal groups within the culture has been retarded.

By the same token, the popular novel, cinema, and television are not devoid of their own complicity. They are not on the side of the angels but are blatantly commercial. They appear to reinforce dominant values. Yet, like all forms of cultural expression, they are not monolithic. They, too, are rife with contradictions. In their seemingly seamless narratives, they reveal contradictions. Inevitably, contradictions surface in the texts' attempts to reconcile irreconcilable conflicts. Their "resolutions" are built on an edifice of opposing elements which on close examination reveal themselves to be in conflict not only with each other but with the events they seek to resolve. The study of popular narratives has become a laboratory for examining the persistence of dominant cultural attitudes. It has also become a way of exploring how narratives are also the locus for resistance to the status quo. Hence, forms of representation are not only the source of repetition; they are also the story of change, resistance, and even subversion.

The most persistent complaint about the media has been that they distort "reality," implying that they are indicative of a "bread and circus" mentality and of a reproduction of the meaningless consumption of capitalist society. Nowhere is this attitude more prevalent than in the treatment of mass cultural production. In the past, when culture critics referred to Hollywood as the "dream factory," they tended to use the term *dream* in a pejorative rather than a Freudian sense. In this context, dream and fantasy are insubstantial and vacuous. Escapism implies that the texts are removed from "reality" and have no contact with the needs, desires, or struggles of individuals. Melodrama has been high on the list of escapist works, regarded as the consummate form of evasion.

Yet an examination of popular literature, cinema, and television challenges these attitudes, exposing them as judgments rather than analysis. First of all, the notion that the audiences for these texts are merely passive consumers has been questioned by contemporary critics who argue that these texts, by virtue of their longevity and phenomenal success, make contact with the audience and, as such, with immediate and everyday problems. Moreover, if the texts thrive on fantasies, then it is imperative to explore the possibility that these fantasies have substance, that they have, as Fredric Jameson says, "as their underlying impulse—albeit in what is often distorted and repressed, unconscious form—our deepest fantasies about the nature of social life; both as we live it now, and as we feel in our bones that it ought rather to be lived."[5]

These fantasies are not alien to reality but are constituted within the culture. This is not to say, however, that the texts are not manipulative and exemplary of the fetishization of commodities but is rather a reminder that they are not total distortions of human needs and desires. The challenge is to understand how and why mass culture has been regarded as a monolith and as antithetical to reality. Some critics, such as Antonio Gramsci, have suggested that cultural works are not monolithic, any more than individuals are, and that it is necessary to identify the nature of the mass culture in order to understand the ways that ideology, or common sense as he called it, is a pastiche of contradictory attitudes, geared toward survival. Cultural artifacts contain the marks of dominance and subordination in their strategies of containment, but they also provide the clues to opposition.[6]

The implications of such a position are crucial to the study of cultural texts, raising questions about how to trace the relationship between economic and social reality and cultural production. The text is not merely a direct response to or reflection of social life; it is also a determinant of social reality. In an attempt to understand how form and meaning in a work are inextricably, though often indirectly, tied to their conditions of production, critics have turned their attention to the domain of ideology as the carrier of social values and attitudes. Ideological analysis is by no means new. What distinguishes contemporary investigations of ideological operations is their refusal to assert a direct connection between social determinations, their relationship to the institutions of social power, and the nature of artistic representation.

Ideology is no longer regarded as false consciousness or the coercive imposition of values, attitudes, and beliefs on innocent victims by the apparatuses of power. Ideology is now assumed to be more pervasive and less obvious as such. In order to be effective, ideology has to function by consent; and in order to gain assent, it must be made to appear natural, inevitable, and personally enhancing. Above all, it does not appear as coercion. Rather, it appears as transparent, as consonant with the the way things are or should be. One of the most transportable means of ideology is through myths, images, and symbols which are deeply rooted in the culture. Specifically, these myths and symbols are linked to questions of class, gender, and racial identity; authority and power; and the family and private property. However, since these issues are clothed in the language of myth and fantasy, they do not immediately lend themselves to historical analysis. The critic's work has thus become one of decipherment, of locating how the seemingly ahistorical narratives are, in fact, intimately linked to social experience.

A major complaint about melodrama has been its assumed antirealistic style. This assessment has been based on notions of realism which are derived from naturalism with its privileging of "objective" social reality and a fidelity to character and setting. The writings on realism in recent decades have suggested, however, that the assessments of cultural production are themselves ideological. What is realism in one era may become escapism in another. The criterion of fidelity to external reality is a latecomer in aesthetics and in no way need preclude other forms of representation. The concept of realism demands not only reexamination but the critique of realism as well. For example, the confusion over the nature and role of realism has been further compounded in critical theory with the introduction of the concept of the "classic realist text." This concept, as developed by the critics of *Screen* magazine in the last decade, is based on the nineteenth-century novel and its reproduction in the Hollywood cinema of genres.

"A classic realist text," Colin MacCabe says, "may be defined as one in which there is a hierarchy of discourses which compose the text and this hierarchy is defined in terms of an empirical notion of truth."[7] MacCabe's notion of the unified text has been challenged by David Bordwell, who finds that "Far from attempting to provide an unmediated literary representation of reality, the novel tends to criticize discourses which reduce reality in univocal ways."[8] Following the work of Bakhtin, Bordwell finds a variety of discourses at work in the text which challenge the notion of a monolithic text. Such a view raises the possibility of examining texts for their lapses, illogicalities, and contradictions, for the ways they can be read against the grain. Feminists in particular have found this way of reading films useful as they seek to locate alternative voices in the texts.

Melodrama, therefore, which seems so obviously to call attention to itself and its modes of construction to the point of ridicule, provides a test case for undermining the traditional critical predilection for the unified text. Its obvious strategies for polarizing issues, for fragmenting voices in the text, and for violating the language of rationality and empiricism call attention to the text's struggle with itself. Furthermore, the audience is assigned a more active role in the process of engaging with the text as opposed to the traditional assumption of audience passivity. The notion of a more dynamic relationship to the text does not, however, imply that melodrama is necessarily a progressive or revolutionary mode, but it does suggest that the text can be seen more clearly as negotiating in complex ways its relationship to the world and to its audience.

An examination of the popular literature of the late eighteenth and early nineteenth centuries exposes the ways in which melodramas are inextricable from social conflicts, revealing, obliquely or directly, class, gender, and generational conflicts. Even when the literature and drama appear to be reinforcing the values and attitudes of the class in ascendancy—the middle class—the works often betray their strategies, providing insights into the ways they deform and seek to contain culturally oppositional elements. Whether the works express a sense of conformity or opposition, it is clear that they contend with questions of social and class identity, and critics have increasingly been able to demonstrate the social basis of literature. In the case of the commercial cinema, an analysis of its social basis has been more problematic. On the one hand, reinforced by the existence of censorship, there has always been the assumption that cinema exerts a powerful role in the shaping of social values and attitudes. On the other hand, there has also been a resistance on the part of critics to exploring the specific social determinants of cinematic representation.

In the post–World War II cinema, as in literature, the predilection for realism obscured the importance of melodrama, suggesting that it, like so much of the genre work associated with the commercial cinema, was a retreat from politics, a form of expression that not only pandered to the popular taste but was responsible for corrupting the hearts and minds of audiences. To the supporters of Italian neorealism, this type of cinema would be associated with fascism, while the realist aesthetic would be associated with the struggle against fascism. Because of the emphasis on location settings, the use of nonprofessional actors, and the use of loosely constructed plots, the concern with the present and with overtly political conflicts, neorealism appeared as a harbinger of the liberation of Western culture from the decadent forms that were closely integrated with the structures of domination.

In the cinemas of Western Europe, as well as in Hollywood, the realist aesthetic took hold, producing films that were social in nature, that appeared to address and redress the social issues that were considered to have been obscured by Hollywood, the "dream factory." With the reexamination of the genre films produced under fascism, it became obvious that the judgment of these films as escapist vehicles could not be sustained. In fact, critics began to recognize that the notion of escapism was itself ideologically based. The films were not merely a rubber stamp for prevailing political attitudes. The notion of escapism could no longer be regarded as a sign of vacuousness and absence of meaning. Rather, escapism would come to signify a retreat into the private sphere. The highly stylized form of representation characteristic of genre films dependent on set conventions and codes allowed for the entertainment of issues that were politically circumscribed in direct discourse. Moreover, the antirealist cast of the narratives allowed for more psychologically focused conflicts which touched at the heart of discontents concerning patriarchy, the family, and personal and sexual identity. Couched in highly florid language and in terms of conflicts that seemed removed in time and space from the external appearances of everyday life, the film language ironically often came closer to dramatizing the contradictions of immediate life under fascism than many realist texts.

In general, the study of film genres has done much to redeem these texts from the charge of superficiality. Genre study has called attention to the reciprocal function of texts, that they are a contract between the audience and the film, thus challenging the notion that audiences are totally passive victims manipulated by the culture industry. Moreover, genres are not static. They make concessions to their changing audiences through the renewal and transformation of their filmic conventions. The assumption that audiences are totally identified with the films and hence robbed of any critical insights cannot be borne out by the role audiences play in the survival or demise of particular genres. Equally important is the long-held assumption that under the spell of cinema, spectators confuse reality and fiction. Just as texts are not monolithic, neither are the responses of the audience. With the assistance of psychoanalytic theory, it is possible to speculate on the complex ways in which genres and their audiences negotiate orders of reality. For example, the style of genre films, like the language of dreams, is a collage of the real and the fantastic, of remote and the everyday experience. Most often, threatening aspects of experience are concealed in order to be entertained. Conflicts that are unresolvable in daily life are clothed in the form of wish-fulfillment. There are clues in the texts to their underlying conflicts, moments when the language of the text appears to be saying more than what it intends. It is possible to see what Freud termed overdeterminations in his analysis of discourse, those heavily freighted moments that intentionally or unintentionally call attention to the nature of problems which are, within the context of the narration, unresolvable though the narrator has sought to disguise or overcome them.

Because of its highly affective nature, its specializing in psychological conflicts, the family melodrama has become an important site for investigating the properties of genre, the nature of audience involvement, and the psychosocial issues that underpin the films. The study of genre has most often been associated with specific directors. For example, the impetus for the study of family melodrama was generated by the critical reexamination of the films of Douglas Sirk, along with other Hollywood directors such as Nicholas Ray and Vincente Minnelli. The examination of the stylistic excesses of Sirk's family melodramas led critics to assert that his films actively subvert conventional bourgeois values, attitudes, and beliefs. The analysis of Sirk's films served several important functions in film studies. First of all, these studies reinforced the critical work linking film production to ideological practices and, in particular, the tendency to see ideology in less monolithic terms. Narratives can thus be seen as a pastiche or collage of received knowledge, of strategies for survival, of idiosyncratic markings, and of conformity and resistance to prevailing ideas. Second, the criticism led to a historicizing of narrative. By focusing on the 1950s through Sirk's films, the critics could entertain questions about the convergence of the family melodrama and the social milieu which became a model for further studies of melodrama. The 1950s was a time of ideological crisis. Public issues such as the Korean War, the Cold War, and the dangers of nuclear holocaust paled alongside more immediate private concerns about the sanctity of the family as a haven from a threatening social environment. The family melodrama has been described as dramatizing the retreat into the private sphere. The films also dramatize the impossible burdens and expectations placed on the family. Most importantly, these films provide an example of how the seemingly escapist aspects of melodrama are intimately tied to pressing social concerns. Moreover, the privileging of these films for study has motivated feminist critics to raise specific questions about how these films position women in contrast to the women's films of the 1930s and 1940s.

The essays in this book, though they may differ in point of view, are concerned with similar issues. The writers seek to identify the nature of melodrama from a number of perspectives. Is melodrama a genre like the detective narrative, the musical, the romance, or is it more all-embracing? Is there a way to identify the appeal that the various forms of melodrama exercise on the audience? Is melodrama an example of how the culture industry exercises a hold on the minds and hearts of the audience, serving to contain forces for social change, reproducing traditional attitudes which militate against alternative views of society, the family, sexual difference, personal identity, economic inequality? Or is it possible to locate in melodrama an expression of social discontents and of unresolvable conflicts in contemporary social life? Is it possible to read these texts "against the grain," surfacing ways in which they subvert conventional notions of behavior and beliefs?

In addressing these questions, the writers inevitably become involved in questions of method. For example, is it enough to merely interpret a text? Are there strategies of analyzing the texts that enable the texts to yield up their secrets? What is the role of film and television production in determining the nature of the text and the ways in which it seeks to garner audience involvement? What role do the screen and television writers play in these texts? What about studios, stars, sponsors of television programs, publicity, advertising? How sensitive are these films and programs to the flow of everyday life, to political and social changes? And, above all, what is the basis of pleasure in melodrama?

The essays are organized so as to provide a broad historical and theoretical context. There is by no means a consensus about any of these questions, though the writers seem to agree on the importance of reevaluating the productions of mass culture and removing the stigma placed on them. Moreover, they seem to agree that melodrama is one of the major modes of mass cultural expression. At the same time that the writers are attempting to develop a genealogy of melodrama, to account for its specific properties and strategies, to situate it in relation to the particular media in which it appears, there is more disagreement about the nature of its impact on the audience.

Part I of this volume, "The Melodramatic Context," addresses the cultural importance of melodrama. The writers examine the history of melodrama, linking that history to significant social developments. John G. Cawelti's "The Evolution of Social Melodrama" is a major attempt to recuperate popular literary forms, to compensate for their neglect and stigmatization. He examines the evolution of social melodrama, accounting for its historical appearance. He traces the formulaic elements of the social melodrama, identifying how the aesthetics of melodrama is closely intertwined with cultural values. The appearances of Peter Brooks's "The Melodramatic Imagination" and Thomas Elsaesser's "Tales of Sound and Fury: Observations on the Family Melodrama" were important moments in the move to take a popular form of representation and examine it seriously. Brooks characterizes melodrama as verbal and visual excess and traces its lineage to the eighteenth- and nineteenth-century theater, to popular forms of literary and theatrical expression. He relates its appearance to historical events, providing a much-needed language to assess the workings of melodrama.

While Brooks traces the melodramatic imagination to the eighteenth-century novel, Elsaesser explores its cinematic expressions and probes its political and ideological underpinnings. A major strategy of melodrama resides in its mystification of social class and of political power and powerlessness. Since the film texts reveal a tendency to displace historical, political, and economic issues onto the private sphere and onto psychological conflict, critical analysis seeks to identify how ideological displacement can be exposed in the melodramatic text. Elsaesser tends to see melodrama as dynamic, altered in relation to differing historical situations. Differences in melodramatic expression can be identified in the silent cinema, the pre–World War II cinema, the postwar cinema, and contemporary film and television. These differences can be linked to changing ideological imperatives. However, not all melodramas provide an auto-critique or contain subversive elements. Some melodramas, depending on historical factors, may serve to recuperate cultural and social values and ideology.

"Genre, Style, and Affect," Part II of this volume, addresses the specific techniques and strategies through which melodramas generate response from audiences. Given the negative status of melodrama in the past and the tacit assumptions that the language of melodrama was obvious to all, very little study was devoted to exploring how melodrama is constructed. Moreover, the question of whether melodrama is a genre or a style is contingent on being able to identify differences between style and genre. On the one hand, melodrama cuts across genres, appearing in different forms of narratives, thus suggesting that it is more akin to a worldview, a specific and pervasive mode of confronting social conflict. On the other hand, it is possible to identify specific melodramatic genres with their own stylistic properties.

Charles Affron's study of linkages between cinema and sentiment provides a language to describe the workings of melodrama, in particular how viewers are involved in narratives and "made to recognize their feelings in cinematic fictions as they now recognize them in life." With the aid of psychoanalytic and reader response theories, he explores the affective designs of the "tearjerker." Daniel Gerould's formalist examination of melodramatic strategies draws on Russian formalist theories of melodrama to identify the techniques of the melodramatic text and its aesthetic principles. In "Ways of Melodrama," Raymond Durgnat examines the differing ways in which character, action, and emotion contribute to the workings of melodrama.

Much of the recent work on melodrama has been connected to the study of genre, and the essays in this section also present different assessments of its generic characteristics. Thomas Schatz's "The Family Melodrama" describes the particular nature of that genre, distinguishing such subgenres as the family aristocracy variation, the male intruder-redeemer in the world of women, and the male weepie. Schatz's discussion is sensitive to changes in style that relate to social and historical developments, though his specific focus is on the melodramatic texts of the 1950s. He does not, however, accord much attention to the women's film.

By contrast, Christian Viviani in "Who Is Without Sin: The Maternal Melodrama in American Film, 1930–1939," explores the genre of the women's film, a popular genre in the 1930s but largely neglected until resurrected by feminist theorists. These films center on a female protagonist and her conflicts with deviance and conformity. Viviani traces the rise, characteristics, transformation, and reception of the maternal melodrama, a genre common to both the European cinema and Hollywood. The essay provides an introduction to the psychoanalytic discussions of the women's film that are included in this volume. Moreover, Viviani's examination of the films treats the ideological implications of the genre delicately, refusing to indict them as mere examples of conformity and women's suppression.

Noël Carroll's essay provides an alternative example of genre analysis. His discussion of melodrama relies heavily on what he terms "the moral ecology of melodrama." He challenges those critics who read melodramas against the grain. Applying the methods of generic and stylistic analysis to Douglas Sirk's *Magnificent Obsession*, Carroll finds more evidence for reading the films as expressions of conformity rather than subversion. His essay crystallizes a dominant conflict in media analysis; namely, the possibility of recuperating popular and commercial texts.

Part III, "History and Ideology," addresses Carroll's reservations by attempting to move from a purely textual analysis to a consideration of the convergences between the text and social history. At stake are two questions: whether melodrama converges with social life, and whether melodrama is a reproduction of the dominant and traditional values within the culture or whether it is subversive, undermining prevailing attitudes through its deployment of genre strategies and its style. The essays in this section examine the melodramas of the 1940s and 1950s in relation to women's position, representations of the family, and notions of social class. Their analysis of the films' ideological impact leads the critics to see the films as exposing underlying social contradictions.

Chuck Kleinhans, in "Notes on Melodrama and the Family under Capitalism," identifies conjunctures between class relations, sexuality, and the positioning of the family as a way in which melodrama works on the audience. By linking melodramatic expression to the complex role of the family under capitalism, Kleinhans makes a case for melodramas as a response to complex social needs. The implications of his position are several. First of all, he sees the films as addressing pressing social problems rather than merely reproducing mindless conformity. Moreover, in his method, he demonstrates that texts are not one thing or another, not purely progressive or purely regressive, but that, like the social reality of which they are a part, they, too, are characterized by conflicting attitudes.

Since the film texts reveal a tendency to displace historical, political, and economic issues onto the private sphere and onto psychological conflict, critical analysis seeks to identify the ways in which ideological displacement can be exposed in the melodramatic text. Charles Eckert's study of Warner's *A Marked Woman* addresses a major dilemma of narrative analysis; namely, how to translate the static and seemingly unhistorical aspects of genre into recognizable social conflicts. Through a close analysis of the text, Eckert exposes textual strategies which through melodrama mask the social and historical conflicts embedded in the text.

Focusing particularly on the immediate post–World War II cinema, Michael Renov, in his analysis of *Leave Her to Heaven*, examines how the film positions the woman in a double-bind situation which is exemplary of the conflicting and contradictory messages communicated to women immediately after the war. Examining the setting and in particular the representation of the family, Renov makes a case for the interface between women's representation and post–World War II ideology.

David N. Rodowick's essay, "Madness, Authority, and Ideology in the Domestic Melodrama of the 1950s," carefully and ambitiously orchestrates the formal, historical, psychological, and social convergences in the Hollywood domestic melodramas of the 1950s. His study, like the others in this section, is exemplary for its attempt to open up the text to a number of social considerations. Unlike many studies that focus on the formal properties of a genre and exclude historical considerations, Rodowick's essay regards an understanding of social history and psychology as essential for understanding stylistic choices.

Pam Cook's "Melodrama and the Women's Picture" rehearses current definitions and theories of melodrama. In particular, following the work of Laura Mulvey, who is skeptical about the attempt to find the progressive elements in the women's picture, Cook seeks to distinguish two types of melodramas—the women's picture and the tragic melodrama. The women's picture (a term coined by Molly Haskell in *From Reverence to Rape*) addresses women and their problems. The tragic melodrama is associated with male identity conflicts, in particular with the conflict between fathers and sons. In the 1930s and during World War II in the United States and in Britain, the women's film flourished. Cook's essay focuses on that branch of British melodrama produced by the Gainsborough studios in the 1940s, its historical context, themes, and visual codes, and specifically how those melodramas produced contradictory representations of sexual difference.

The essays in Part IV, "Psychoanalysis, Gender, and Race," are representative of critical work that is heavily dependent on psychoanalytic theory for developing concepts specifically related to the deciphering of film texts. In both current feminist and Marxist criticism, psychoanalytic theory has provided a way to get beneath the text's surface not only to explore the affective and stylistic aspects of melodramatic representation but also to address specifically how texts have a knowledge of their audiences. In its emphasis on the unconscious and the mechanisms of repression, in its linking of repression and loss to the construction of the human subject and the mechanisms of desire, psychoanalysis redeems the ostensible banality of the melodramatic text.

Geoffrey Nowell-Smith reads melodramatic excess in terms of the family romance, the construction of subjectivity, and the language of hysteria. He relates these to bourgeois ideology, not in a direct cause-effect relationship but as symptomatic of the positioning of the subject within bourgeois culture. Reading the melodramatic text in this fashion exposes expectations about the flow of narrativity, the unity of the text, and hence the unity of expectations relating to power, social class, sexuality, and sexual difference.

Because of its highly coded mode of representation, melodrama has been a congenial medium for testing psychoanalytic theory and the ways in which this theory can or cannot be historicized. Griselda Pollock's comments on the uses of psychoanalytic theory point to its deficiencies in historical analysis and in theorizing the nature of family in relation to the position of women. While psychoanalysis has aided in providing feminist theory with a working model of subjectivity from which to explore the nature of sexual difference, while it has taken feminist theory beyond conventional sociological studies of women's image and "role," Pollock's essay points to difficulties of remaining too rigidly within a psychoanalytic model, especially when that model does not accommodate itself to the concerns of women.

Mary Ann Doane's "The Moving Image: Pathos and the Maternal" draws on psychoanalytic theory to explore women's representation though she attempts to historicize her discussion of melodramas from the 1930s and 1940s. Rehearsing recent theoretical work on melodrama, she traces how melodrama and women's conflicts can be seen to coincide in the discourse of the mother and particularly in the pathetic affect so characteristic of melodrama. She describes the maternal melodrama as a drama of separation and return in which the mother is the site of multiple contradictions. The convergence of the maternal and the language of melodrama, Doane claims, arises in their "mutual reinforcement of certain semes: presence, immediacy, readability."

Through psychoanalysis and semiotics, feminist critics have sought to locate a female discourse in the women's films. Since many melodramas are either addressed to a female spectator or involve the issue of female sexuality, the issue of spectatorship has been central to exploring the ways in which the melodramatic text addresses female spectators and situates them within or against certain conceptions of sexuality, power, and even social class. Linda Williams's analysis of the maternal conflict in *Stella Dallas* outlines various theoretical aspects of the mother-daughter relationship. Williams's reading of the language of melodrama in King Vidor's film identifies moments of resistance to the ideology of patriarchy. She finds that in certain melodramas of which *Stella Dallas* is a prime example, one can locate a female discourse.

Jane Gaines's discussion of *The Scar of Shame* introduces the question of race in relation to melodrama. Her essay raises questions about the ideology of films addressed to black audiences and containing black subjects. Unlike the maternal melodramas which appear to subvert the representations of women and allow for a female discourse, *The Scar of Shame* is a closed text, inscribing the ideology of racism and only admitting of counterhegemonic positions on the part of the informed spectator. Gaines's interrogation of the strategies of the text also raises a question about the degree to which feminist theory in its quest for an alternative discourse needs further impetus from reception rather than from psychoanalytic theory.

Part V, "Directors and Stars," offers representative examples of auteur criticism, an examination of the limitations of such critical treatment, and samples of criticism that identify other elements in production such as the role of stars. Excepting studies of genre, the discussion of melodrama has been heavily dependent on the concept of the auteur, focusing on the "personal" styles of such directors as D. W. Griffith, Frank Borzage, King Vidor, Douglas Sirk, Vincente Minnelli, and Nicholas Ray. Hence, analyses of influences, studio production, and historical and social issues have been discussed within the context of a particular artist's oeuvre. Moreover, the role of the auteur has been central to discussions of melodrama. The films of D. W. Griffith are, therefore, an important moment not only in the development of narrative cinema but also in the development of cinematic melodrama, as A. Nicholas Vardac's examination of Griffith's films indicates. Alan Casty examines Griffith's melodramas for the ways they represent a fusion of motion picture techniques, personal sensibility, and cultural assumptions. John Belton's study of Frank Borzage's films distinguishes Borzage's melodramas from Griffith's. Borzage avoids the extreme polarization so characteristic of Griffith's work. Moreover, his treatment of conflict tends to transpose events from the material onto the spiritual plane, focusing on the emotional states of his characters as opposed to their social contexts.

While studies of 1930s melodramas have increased, particularly those which deal with the woman's film and the treatment of gender in these films, much of the critical work has been generated by an examination of the films of the 1950s, including the works of such directors as Vincente Minnelli, Nicholas Ray, and Douglas Sirk. Their melodramas have been identified as self-consciously using style as a way of subversively probing and exposing the contradictions of social class, sexuality, and materialism in American culture. Sirk's films utilize color, music, choreography, costume, and mise-en-scène as a means of undercutting identification with the characters and their situations. Christopher Orr, in his study of Sirk's *Written on the Wind*, "Closure and Containment: Marylee Hadley in *Written on the Wind*," takes a slightly different direction. While acknowledging the role of style as a means of undercutting the content, he also focuses on ways that content and style work together to provide a social critique. He examines the privotal and excessive nature of Marylee Hadley as the disruptive force in the melodrama which undermines the legitimization and containment of the bourgeois ideology that the film seeks to subvert.

As most studies of genre indicate, genre is not a static system but sensitive to historical and social changes. The work of Hollywood directors such as Francis Ford Coppola and Michael Cimino has introduced a different content and different stylistic approach to melodrama which Naomi Greene in her essay "Copola, Cimino: The Operatics of History" has described as operatic and historical. Greene links the work of these directors to the political, ideological, and stylistic concerns of the 1970s cinema, and, in particular, to the political and social climate of the post-Vietnam war era.

As these essays on various directors indicate, the search for a single voice in the text continues to animate film criticism, and in particular the position of the director has been considered preeeminent. Drawing on the work of Roland Barthes and John Caughie, Christine Saxton in her essay "The Collective Voice as Cultural Voice" takes issue with the search for a single voice and proposed to identify the text as a cultural collaboration between producers and consumers. She sees the text as a collection of voices, a "juncture of multiple codes," and her essay attempts to account for other voices in the text.

In the overwhelming critical preoccupation with the director as author of the film, the role of the star has been given scant attention. Yet an examination of particular melodramas, especially remakes of popular narratives, reveals significant differences in point of view based on performances by the films' stars. For example, though there are several versions of *Stella Dallas*, it is the Barbara Stanwyck version that is most examined. The presence of particular stars is crucial to an understanding of a film's melodramatic strategies, but what is necessary is a method for describing and analyzing the star's functions within the text. Richard Dyer's study of four Lana Turner films opens up ways of discussing how the star image is an important but neglected aspect of film language and how, in the case of the Turner melodramas he examines, her role is instrumental in providing for a certain ideological coherence, if not subversiveness, in the texts.

"Faces of the American Melodrama: Joan Crawford," by Jean-Loup Bourget, offers a way of reading a cinematic text, in this instance melodrama and in particular women's films, through the perspective of the star's contribution to the thematics of the text. Bourget contends that the distinct style of actresses like Crawford is part of the landscape and ideology of melodrama. The personality and physical appearance of Crawford are linked to the textual tensions between nature and culture so prevalent in the melodramas in which she stars. Bourget is trying not to invent a category of the star to replace that of auteurist criticism but rather to open up an area of study that has been only feebly investigated; namely, the filmic and extrafilmic contributions of the star to the style and meaning of melodrama.

If melodrama moved into the cinema from the theater and from prose fiction, becoming a dominant aspect of film narrative and style, it is now the case that television, which is the newest form of mass culture, has also found melodrama a profitable cultural item of consumption. The soap opera, originally a creation of radio, was transferred to daytime television and has gradually found its way in a new, more lavish format in prime-time television. The essays in Part VI examine the various forms of television melodrama.

In "The Search for Tomorrow in Today's Soap Operas," Tania Modleski provides an unusually complex perspective on television. Her examination of soap operas addresses the characteristics of these programs as well as their specific terms of reception. In charting the strategies of the soap opera, Modleski is particularly concerned to position the female characters and the female spectator in relation not only to the programs themselves but to the historical and ideological imperatives that are an intrinsic part of the experience of the soap opera. Modleski does not regard the programs as tightly controlling the viewer's vision but sees them rather as offering a space for women's pleasure and addressing real needs and desires.

Like Modleski, Brunsdon questions whether the audience for soap operas is a gendered audience and whether this is a useful hypothesis. In her essay, "*Crossroads:* Notes on Soap Opera," she explores the context for the soap opera, its textual strategies, and its discontinuities, commenting particularly on the program's uses of space, the fractured framework in the form of a plurality of story lines, the role of interruptions and the deferment of knowledge and resolutions, and the importance of deceit in establishing a relationship between spectator and text. Brunsdon affirms Modleski's view that the form of soaps is particularly geared to female viewers, an issue that Robert C. Allen will challenge in his discussion of the soap opera.

While television studies of soap opera have concentrated on distinguishing the formal effects of television from those of cinema, critics have also concentrated on television treatments of genre. Ien Ang's study, "*Dallas* and the Melodramatic Imagination," examines the prime-time soap opera within the context of recent theories of melodrama. Like Modleski and Brunsdon, Ang identifies how elements of continuity and discontinuity characteristic of serialization and the deployment of multiple narratives contribute to an inhibiting of identification with a single central character and to a diffusion of interest among several, creating a sense of community. It is the soap opera community that is the source of melodrama, not the individual characters. In "Dallas," melodramatic conflict and excess is conveyed through the metaphors of alcoholism and illness, which present the nuclear family in terms of crisis and breakdown rather than idealization. For Ang, the "melodramatic imagination does not reside in great public tragedies but in the tragedies of daily life so congenial to prime time soap operas."

Too often, assumptions about responses to film narratives are carried over to a discussion of television. Robert C. Allen's "A Reader-Oriented Poetics of the Soap Opera" distinguishes between cinematic and television style. In describing the textual system of soap operas, Allen pays particular attention to the codes that govern the television narratives. Moreover, his distinction between modes of viewing in cinema and television is useful for distinguishing different audience responses to the melodramatic. Adopting concepts from reader response theory, Allen attempts to account for the nature of audience responses to soap operas and for gendered responses, in particular.

Focusing on the late 1970s Ellen Seiter explores contemporary expressions of melodrama in both cinema and television in "Men, Sex, and Money in Recent Family Melodramas." Commenting on the resurgence of the family melodrama in the 1970s, it popularity among audiences, Seiter addresses differences among daytime and prime time soap operas, and films. She finds that the cinema, in particular, has been most marked in moving away from an earlier emphasis in family melodrama on women and on class conflict and toward a concern with male issues and with upper-class characters, a situation she regards as a loss for women, for whom melodrama had constituted a channel of expression in popular culture.

Most of the essays in this anthology are concerned with Anglo-American melodrama, since the preponderance of critical work has focused on it, but melodrama is also evident in European and Latin American cinema and television. Part VII, the final section, addresses the appearance of melodrama in the early French cinema and in the Italian cinema of the 1940s, the existence of modernist forms of melodrama exemplified in the European and Latin American cinema of the 1960s and 1970s, and popular expressions of melodrama in recent Latin American television.

Richard Abel's essay, "French Film Melodrama: Before and After the Great War," explores the connection between the first bourgeois film melodramas and the French theatre. The cinema soon supplanted the theatre as a source for melodrama, but it was the wartime melodramas, in particular, exemplified in such films as Abel Gance's *Mater Dolorosa*, that were a primary influence on the post World War I French avant-garde narrative cinema. My own discussion of the Italian film melodrama during the late 1930s and 1940s explores how the melodramas of the period can be read so as to shed light on fascist ideology. Visonti's *Ossessione* dissects the immediate and everday structures of life under fascism, exploring familial relations and the violence they generate, a violence that converges with the more public aspects of fascist life.

In a contemporary context, the films of Rainer Werner Fassbinder utilize melodramatic narratives. Fassbinder found Douglas Sirk's films influential in the development of his own attempt to create popular and political films that addressed the convergences of family, sexuality, social class, and history. Ruth McCormick's essay, "Fassbinder's Reality: An Imitation of Life," examines the thematics in Fassbinder's films and his struggle to develop a style that was capable of communicating how his characters are victimized by their own melodramatic scenarios. Katherine S. Woodward, in her essay "European Anti-Melodrama: Godard, Truffaut, and Fassbinder," discusses modernist appropriations of melodrama. Calling the films of these directors "anti-melodramas," she examines how their work self-consciously and critically seeks to undermine traditional melodramatic representation. Finally, Ana Lopez, in her essay, "The Melodrama in Latin America: Films, Telenovelas, and the Currency of a Popular Form," discusses the popularity of melodrama in Latin American countries from the silent cinema to the present, with the exception of the sixties and seventies, when the New Latin American cinema rejected many of the popular melodramas as petit bourgeois and sought to create a new anti-bourgeois form. However, with the expansion of television, melodrama has reappeared as a popular form in the *telenovelas* which, unlike the American soap operas, are clearly demarcated narratives. Like the writers whose studies of American and British television are represented in this book, Lopez views the telenovelas as responding to certain needs of the audience which are not purely regressive.

The essays in this volume were selected to represent some of the major concerns of film and television study over the past two decades. The writings testify to the intellectual ferment that characterizes contemporary media study. Above all, it should be apparent that the essays proceed from a position of active intellectual engagement in their concern not merely to characterize and describe the forms of melodrama but to analyze its impact on the audience. The role of the media in contemporary society is not a matter of indifference but a crucial factor in understanding social relationships and the potential for social change. By no means have the questions raised by these writers been definitively answered, but the essays challenge the reader to understand what is at stake in the study of melodrama.

Notes

1. Andreas Huyssen, "Mass Culture as Woman: Modernism's Other," in *Studies in Entertainment*, ed. by Tania Modleski (Bloomington: Indiana University Press, 1986), p. 193.
2. Ibid., p. 196.
3. Theodor Adorno, *Prisms* (London: Neville Spearman, 1967), pp. 25–26.
4. Gyorgy Lukacs, "The Historical Novel of Democratic Humanism," in *Marxism & Art.*, ed by Berel Lang and Forest Williams (New York: David McKay, 1972), pp. 372–89.
5. Fredric Jameson, "Reification and Utopia in Mass Culture," *Social Text*, no. 1 (1979), p. 147.
6. Antonio Gramsci, *Miscellanea, Quadernie del carcere*, Vol. 3, ed. by Valentino Gerratana (Turin: Einaudi, 1975), pp. 2193–95.

7. Colin MacCabe, *Theoretical Essays: Film, Linguistics, Literature* (Manchester: Manchester University Press, 1985), p. 34.
8. David Bordwell, *Narration in the Fiction Film* (Madison: University of Wisconsin Press, 1985), p. 19.

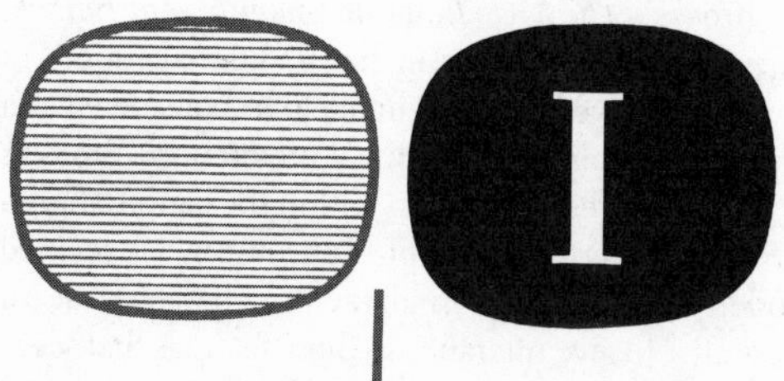

I

THE MELODRAMATIC CONTEXT

Until the last two decades, melodrama was regarded as a sensational and theatrical form of manipulation of the audience's emotions. Little attention was paid to its genealogy, its particular stylistic properties, and its social significance. The essays in this section are characteristic of an attempt to correct this deficiency. They seek not only to identify the specific features of melodramatic representation but to situate this mode of representation in a historical and social context. The *melodramatic imagination* is a term that has become useful for signifying this broader approach. The term suggests that melodrama is a way of perceiving the world, a response to specific social pressures which can be located in literature and drama as well as in the cinema. The term also suggests that the focus of critical work on melodrama extends beyond the study of an individual author or text, focusing rather on its general character and, above all, on its pervasiveness as a sociohistorical phenomenon.

John G. Cawelti's essay charts the evolution of melodrama in literature, beginning with Dickens's work in the nineteenth century and ending with the recent writings of Irving Wallace. He isolates and describes melodramatic conventions and suggests their connection to dominant social themes and conflicts which he finds inextricably tied to the essence of melodrama. He is concerned with the ways in which melodrama increasingly challenged traditional views of order and orthodoxy in society, noting changes in women's representation and the increasing introduction of issues of criminality and the pursuit of success and of power. But certain formulas remain constant in social melodrama despite changing historical conditions: its middle-class orientation and its emphasis on romantic love, the monogamous family, and ethical considerations of power and success.

The appearance in 1985 of Peter Brooks's *The Melodramatic Imagination: Balzac, Henry James, and the Mode of Excess* signaled changes in the traditional modes of literary study and the fact that the time had arrived for melodrama to be considered as a serious rather than pejorative treatment of literary and theatrical production. Brooks's analysis of the melodramatic imagination exposes how writers within the canon of high cultural production were drawn to melodrama as a way of expressing what seemed inexpressible within the realist mode, finding that a fundamental characteristic of melodrama is the tendency "to express all," to give utterance to those feelings that seem inaccessible within the ordinary modes of discourse. For Brooks, these feelings are tied to the moral occult, to a vision of the world as a scene of polarized moral conflict.

In effect, melodrama seems within this context to be a striving for a transcendent reality, an overcoming of the inertness of things, an expression of spirituality in the face of an increasingly meaningless, desacralized existence. Brooks identifies the language of melodrama as primarily gestural, related most particularly to the music with which it is associated, the *melos* of melodrama. Not only is music inextricably linked to the genealogy of the form, but it also is an essential ingredient in melodrama's straining to evoke the ineffable, to articulate that which seems inaccesible to verbal language. For Brooks, melodrama is an inescapable fact of modern life which he traces to a human need for meaning and significant action.

By contrast, Thomas Elsaesser's "Tales of Sound and Fury: Observations on the Family Melodrama" seeks to link the history of melodrama to periods of social and ideological crisis, in particular to the eighteenth century and the rise to power of the bourgeoisie. Elsaesser traces a transformation in melodrama from tragic to conformist representations that seem to converge with the rise and the later consolidation of bourgeois power. In the nineteenth century, with growing industrialization and class struggle, the melodrama thrived as a locus for the expression of social and political conflict, as exemplified in the novels of Dickens in England and Hugo in France. The crux of the melodrama as a vehicle of social expression lies in its tendency to fuse social and economic conflicts with psychological and spiritual intensity.

Elsaesser, like Brooks, extends the term *melos* to cover all the stylistic strategies of melodrama that create its expressivity and are enhanced in the cinema by means of camera, lighting, mise-en-scène, the use of objects, montage, color, and, in the sound cinema, verbal and musical sound. The films of the 1950s, particularly those of Douglas Sirk and Vincente Minnelli, are exemplary of a tendency of some melodramas to allow themselves to be read against the grain, as subverting the very attitudes that they seem superficially to be endorsing. The handling of decor and the architectonic use of people and objects produce a dramatic discontinuity, a jarring sense of excess, signaling class and sexual tensions that call attention to the elements of repression, linking the personal to the political and inviting both Freudian and Marxian analysis. Many current studies of cinema melodrama have followed Elsaesser's lead in exploring the family melodrama as a crucial site for the convergence of aesthetics and ideology.

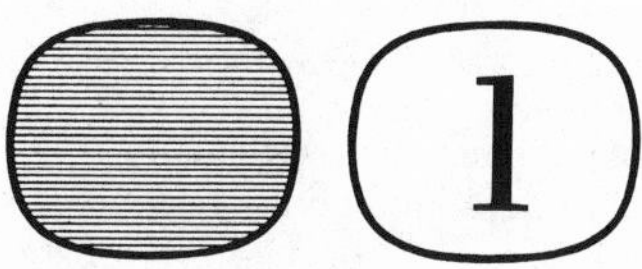

The Evolution of Social Melodrama

JOHN G. CAWELTI

If he did not invent it, Charles Dickens developed the formula for social melodrama into one of the most successful fictional genres of the nineteenth and twentieth centuries. Dickens showed conclusively that a writer could represent society in a fairly complex and critical way yet still achieve tremendous popular success if he synthesized social criticism with the archetype of melodrama and thereby gave readers the pleasure of seeing the follies of men and institutions combined with the satisfaction of witnessing the triumph of virtue and the punishment of vice.

The melodramatic conventions on which Dickens drew were the product of earlier developments in both fiction and the theater. In the last decade of the eighteenth century, a new kind of melodrama had become increasingly popular with the growing public for books and theater. The central figure in this formulaic pattern was usually a virtuous young lady of some lower or ambiguous status—village maiden, orphan, daughter of parents in reduced circumstances—who was pursued by a male character of higher status and dubious intentions, a figure of aristocratic, erotic, financial, and social power; in other words, some form of the stereotypical squire with curling mustaches. The sorely beset heroine commonly loved a more worthy and innocent young man, who was himself enmeshed in status difficulties, often because his true parentage was concealed for one reason or another. This primary triangle was the essence of melodrama and was capable of two major permutations, corresponding loosely to comic and tragic modes of action. In the first case, the heroine resisted the entreaties

John Cawelti, "The Best-Selling Social Melodramas," from *Adventure, Mystery, and Romance: Formula Stories as Art and Popular Culture* (Chicago: University of Chicago Press, 1976). Reprinted by permission of the author and the University of Chicago Press.

and threats of the villain and was ultimately united in marriage with the noble young man. In Richardson's seminal *Pamela*, the villain and the good hero were combined as phases of a single character, but in most instances hero and villain exemplified moral principles in a more stereotypical fashion. In the tragic melodrama, the heroine succumbed to the villain's plots. "When this happened," as David Grimsted puts it,

> repentance, madness, and death were all that awaited her, except in a few instances where after long suffering she was allowed a modicum of happiness. Such unhappy fate was inevitable even if the heroine had been "unfortunate, rather than guilty"—if she had been raped or deceived by a "false marriage." These were favorite plot devices because the woman's total purity of intent made her fall more pathetic, but no less inevitable.[1]

This dramatic and narrative formula, which set a supreme symbol of virtue (the beleaguered village maiden) against a potent embodiment of evil (the wicked squire), and then arranged in a particularly suspenseful and exciting manner for the success of virtue and the punishment of evil, was a highly effective version of the archetype of melodrama. But in tracing the evolution of social melodrama we must also look at the particular social and cultural themes involved. Melodrama, as we have seen, is particularly dependent on a sense of what is a proper, acceptable, and plausible means for insuring the triumph of virtue in spite of the terrible strength of vice. This sense of the proper order of things justifies the coincidences and accidents of melodramatic action and reveals, in a striking way, the conventional moral vision that a particular culture and period wishes to see affirmed by the striking reversals of fortune that characterize the structure of melodrama.

In the melodramas of the early nineteenth century, the principle of proper order reflected an intertwining of religious and social values. The single most important outcome of any melodrama was the marriage of the virtuous heroine to the right man—or, in the tragic version of melodrama, the degradation and death of the fallen heroine. In general, the right man was somewhat above the virtuous heroine in social status, though at the beginning of the story he may have been poor or a lost heir. When a relationship developed between a poor young man and a woman above him in status, something unfortunate usually came of it, unless by the operation of melodramatic coincidence the noble hero turned out to be the rightful heir to a still larger fortune. If a wealthy girl became involved with a hero beneath her station she often exemplified one of the favorite secondary characters of the early nineteenth-century melodramatic formula, the "other woman," who was normally more like the villain than the heroine. In fact, the "other woman," wealthy, decadent, and lustful, increasingly took on the role of villain, as later melodramatists cast about for ways to give new vitality to what were, by midcentury, somewhat tired conventions.

These stereotypes of character and action indicate the degree to which social dominance, the ideas of middle-class domesticity, the dream of romantic love, and the drive for social mobility were unified in the popular moral vision of early nineteenth-century England and America. After being threatened with a fate worse than death by an upper-class villain, the virtuous heroine settled into happy domesticity with a solidly respectable young man with whom she also, coincidentally, was in love, thus neatly affirming in one stroke the nineteenth-century middle-class values of love, domesticity, social respectability, masculine dominance, and feminine purity. In the later nineteenth century, this ideal union became increasingly precarious and melodrama began to change in relation to new cultural tensions.

The other basic principle of the melodramatic vision in this period was the primacy of religion. Religion was, in effect, the cement tying together the other social and moral ideas. The heroine's faith in God not only helps her to endure the trials and tribulations she is subjected to by the villain, but it also leads her to make the proper romantic choice of the good hero who can share her profound faith. Moreover, the hero and heroine's Christian dedication sanctifies their union and insures that it will be a truly proper and respectable one. Above all, it is the sense of divine providence operating in the world that insures that virtue and vice will achieve their appropriate rewards. In Mrs. Southworth's *The Curse of Clifton*, Archer Clifton is deceived by the wicked "other woman" into thinking that his wife has married him for his money. Driven by suspicion, he subjects his loving and virtuous helpmeet to two years of brutal indifference. His suspicions are finally cleared up (a) through an especially selfless and heroic act on the heroine's part, (b) through Clifton's chance encounter with an even wealthier gentleman she had earlier rejected, and (c) through a deathbed confession by the villainess. Somewhat embarrassed by his lack of trust, as well he might be, Archer Clifton laments to his wife,

> "And, oh, Catherine to think that all this trouble I have suffered, and have inflicted upon you, should have been so unnecessary."

But she, knowing better, and deeper in her faith, replies,

> "Oh, no! it was *not* unnecessary. God suffered it to be, and it was well—*very* well! All things work together for good, to them that love the Lord! And every pang that has ploughed our hearts in the past, will make them fruitful of good in the future. One fruit is, that the suffering of the last two years has drawn our hearts together as nothing else could have done."[2]

Thus, the murky melodramatic triangle of virtuous heroine, noble hero, and dastardly villain was a drama of providence in which suffering and doubt challenge the heroine's religious faith, but insure that, if she remains chaste and true and submits herself to God's will, not only will she become a respectable wife and the center of a happy domestic circle but this social and romantic achievement will be sanctified and blessed by the hand of God. Thus the melodramatic formula of this period dramatized the congruence between the social ideas of domesticity, romantic love, and respectable mobility and the religious faith in the divine governance of the world. In these stories, melodramatic coincidence and apparent chance take on a special emotional and moral force because they are understood to be results of God's operative providence. When rightly understood, they show us that every worldly event is controlled by His benevolent interest and power. Henry Nash Smith is right in calling this a "cosmic success story."[3]

Beyond the basic formula of virtuous hero and heroine entangled in the toils of an aristocratic villain and saved by a providential series of revelations or happenstances, the melodrama was fleshed out by a variety of minor figures:

> The gallery of rogues was increased by such stock characters as the designing governess, preferably French; the hardhearted landlady, the cruel stepmother, the inhuman creditor, the flinty jailor, the vile procuress, and the mercenary wet nurse. Upon the side of the angels were to be found, with wearisome monotony, the noble soldier dispensing good cheer out of a meager pension, with a gesture or two borrowed from Uncle Toby; and the generous sailor endowed with some of the more genial characteristics of Smollett's seamen. The [melodramatist's] contention that sympathy is the mainspring of human nature was exemplified in numerous instances of the good apprentice, the philanthropic merchant, the chivalrous rustic, the noble savage, the highborn benefactress, and the long-suffering wife.[4]

Grimsted points out that the serious melodramatic triangle was often paralleled by a low comedy situation and characters whose attitudes and actions burlesqued and even sometimes cast an ironic light on the turbulent posturings of the major characters, as if, to achieve its highest effectiveness, melodramatic moralism had to be served up with a dash of comic realism. Indeed, the ideal vision of melodrama with its fundamental principle of a supremely just universe often seems a little too much for its audience to accept without some sense of basic evil or comic ridicule lurking in the wings.

Thus, from the very beginning of the nineteenth century, melodrama tended to add at least a dash of spice to its portrayal of virtue triumphant and evil defeated.[5] More sophisticated audiences were probably more responsive to the kind of story that could balance some of the satisfactions of melodrama against the claims of their sense of reality. The village virgin, her noble young swain, and the mustachioed villain may have been satisfying enough for the simpler audiences of the popular theater, but for melodrama to reach out to the more educated public as well it had to find ways of setting its stories of virtue versus vice in a context of more plausibly complex representations of the world. The result was the emergence, first in Dickens[6] and then in an almost unbroken tradition of best-sellers since his time, of what I have called social melodrama, with its basic structure of a melodramatic inner plot embodied in a more or less complex and critical treatment of society.

Perhaps because of the way in which it depends on a complex balancing of quite disparate perceptions of the world, social melodrama shades over on one side into the nonmelodramatic novel as when, in some of the novels of Dickens and almost all of Dostoevsky, strongly melodramatic elements are overpowered by a nonmelodramatic social vision. On the other side, social melodrama is closely related to other melodramatic formulas of similar character: the historical, the gothic, the religious, or the sensation melodramas. These other modes of melodramatic expression share with social melodrama the structure of a melodramatic action embedded in a more complex imaginative vision, but the nature and source of that vision reflect a religious or historical rather than a primarily social concern. Thus a truly adequate treatment of the evolution of melodrama in the nineteenth and twentieth centuries is a task of great complexity. Here I can only make a few observations about major changes in the complex of moral attitudes underlying the development of social melodrama by analyzing some exemplary works.

The basic combination of social criticism and melodramatic plot that Dickens so brilliantly articulated was embodied in hundreds of novels and plays in mid-nineteenth-century England and America. None was more powerful and striking than Harriet Beecher Stowe's *Uncle Tom's Cabin*, which in both printed and theatrical form was the greatest nineteenth-century best-seller.

The extraordinary impact of *Uncle Tom's Cabin*—perhaps the only book other than the Bible that has been held responsible for a major war—was a testimony to Mrs. Stowe's ability to express her sense of deeply felt social wrongs in terms of the melodramatic conventions her readers were predisposed to respond to. Most important, she extended these melodramatic conventions to cover black characters as well as white and thereby accomplished one of the first major acts of racial integration on the imaginative level. Just as Dickens forced his audience to a new awareness of the urban poor by cutting through the class separation between high and low character stereotypes that had been the rule in early melodrama, Mrs. Stowe took the even more daring imaginative step of treating black characters as high melodramatic heroes and heroines. Her carefully documented account of the system of slavery and its outrages against human decency and the Christian faith was given added force by her insistence on presenting black characters as serious melodramatic protagonists. Her characterization of Eliza drew upon two of the strongest melodramatic traditions, the virtuous heroine persecuted by the brutal seducer and the suffering mother. George Harris was the noble upwardly mobile hero suddenly confronted with a dastardly plot against the woman he loved and prevented by his situation from going to her aid until it was almost too late. Uncle Tom himself embodied the convention of the benevolent father and moral spokesman who suffered and died as a martyr to the cause of Christian faith and feminine purity. Mrs. Stowe's white characters also grew out of melodramatic stereotypes: the dastardly, lascivious, mustache-twirling villain, Simon Legree; the pure and innocent young girl; the peevish spinster.

The action, too, was of the essence of melodrama. Specific scenes like Eliza's flight across the frozen river, the death of Little Eva, the sudden attack on Augustine St. Clare and the ultimate confrontation of Uncle Tom and Simon Legree possessed those qualities of suspenseful excitement, seemingly miraculous coincidence, and intensity of emotion that are essential to melodramatic incident. The overall action of *Uncle Tom's Cabin* was constructed of two large movements: the daring flight, pursuit, and eventual escape of George and Eliza Harris to the North, and the bondage, suffering, and martyrdom of Uncle Tom as he moved deeper and deeper into the hell of the slavery system of the plantation South. The happy outcome of the trials of George and Eliza obviously demonstrated the operation of providence. Not only did they escape from bondage, but they kept encountering kindly and decent people who, as agents of a higher plan, helped them on their way to freedom. The martyrdom of Uncle Tom was a less obvious but deeper portrayal of the divine governance of the world, for, in his hopeless suffering, Tom's Christian resignation to the will of God insured that he would meet his terrible fate with dignity, faith, and a growing certainty of his eternal salvation. Tom's victory was substantiated by the narrator's frequent and explicit comments on the subject, and by the two major incidents that marked important stages in the process of Tom's martyrdom: the death of Little Eva and the degeneration and damnation of Simon Legree. The manner of Little Eva's demise perfectly exemplified the striking change of tears resolved in ultimate joy that was the essence of nineteenth-century melodrama. Eva's translation to heaven—an episode that later generations with different moral and religious attitudes would see as the quintessence of archaic melodramatic absurdity—was a scene that deeply moved nineteenth-century readers and theatrical audiences who were evidently supersensitive to the combination of childhood innocence and purity with suffering, death, and the certainty of heaven. But it also played a vital symbolic role in Tom's story, assuring us that whatever his temporal suffering might be, he was certain to join his beloved little mistress in eternal bliss. Legree's progressive deterioration was lovingly detailed by Mrs. Stowe. After Tom's death, Legree sees a diabolical figure of death beckoning to him, a vision that we are certainly intended to take as the sign of God's justice striking down the guilty.

Mrs. Stowe's work was unique in its power and impact because she integrated her attack on the social evil of slavery with the prevailing melodramatic vision of the world. Yet *Uncle Tom's Cabin* was typical of mid-nineteenth-century social melodrama in its emphasis on divine providence as the agency of a benevolent moral order that rewards the good and punishes the wicked, bringing about the melodramatic triumph. The mid-nineteenth-century vision of a Christian, providential world implied several other themes. It meant that feminine purity and the ideal of motherhood were dominant symbols of virtue, the chief objects of the noble hero's protection and the villain's attack. Closely associated with the ideal of purity was the value of Christian resignation and submission to God's will. Heroine and hero both had to learn faith in God's operative providence in order to be assured of a happy resolution to their problems. The central role of the villain as seducer also grew out of this complex of values. The ideal moral order that God's providence ultimately established for the virtuous and denied to the wicked was a happy synthesis of traditional Protestant religious ideals and the middle-class social values of domesticity and respectability. The proper fate for the melodramatic hero or heroine was to learn Christian resignation by preserving moral purity in the face of great trials and temptations, with the assurance that this would lead to a happy and respectable marriage as a temporal prelude to eternal salvation in the afterlife.[7]

This divinely appointed moral order had many worldly enemies. Their attempts to draw the hero and heroine from the proper path constituted the major source of suspenseful excitement and virtuous suffering. Moreover, in social melodrama, the plots of the aristocratic rake were often supplemented or even replaced by the pressure of bad social institutions. Mrs. Stowe's analysis of the way in which the social system of slavery had corrupted government, the church, and the family was comparable to Dickens's attack on the Court of Chancery, the system of debtor's prison, the social treatment of the poor, and other institutions. These heavy indictments were echoed more thinly in Mrs. Southworth's attacks on aristocratic social prejudice and Susan Warner's pale criticisms of the worldliness and materialism of city society. It was also an important article of melodramatic faith that people were generally good when their hearts were simple and open to God's word and to love for their neighbor. Invariably the suffering, melodramatic protagonist found assistance and support among children, rural people, and the lowly, those yet uncorrupted by the artifices of society. Yet, at the same time, the successful hero or heroine was hardly fated to remain in lowly obscurity. On the contrary, having faced the dangers of social worldliness and corruption with moral purity and Christian resignation, the melodramatic protagonist typically achieved a marriage that placed him or her firmly within the genteel and respectable classes. Or, if the heroine ultimately succumbed to her trials, the result was a lingering death, usually among lowly, simple people who offered a final protection. If, like Uncle Tom, the tragic melodramatic protagonist had learned to accept martyrdom, the reader was usually assured in some fashion that the protagonist's death was only the prelude to a more glorious resurrection.

Culturally, the social melodrama of the mid-nineteenth century can best be interpreted as an attempt to reconcile the increasing conflict between traditional Christian views of the world and the secular values of a rapidly changing society. The formula that dominated the period's social melodrama resolved the tension between religion and the values of mobility and success by making its virtuous protagonists examples of both and by asserting a fundamental unity between the operation of God's providence and the creation of happy, prosperous, and respectable middle-class families. By the end of the nineteenth century, however, this equation of traditional religious attitudes and middle-class social values was no longer viable in the social melodrama. In the number one best-seller of 1913, Winston Churchill's *The Inside of the Cup*, the story begins with an apparent affirmation of the social and moral vision that we have just described, but the ironic tone of the narrative indicates that the traditional melodramatic version of the moral order has broken down:

> [Our story begins in] a city overtaken, in recent years, by the plague which has swept our country from the Atlantic to the Pacific—prosperity. Before its advent the [respectable families] lived leisurely lives in a sleepy quarter of shade trees and spacious yards and muddy macadam streets, now passed away forever. Existence was decorous, marriage an irrevocable step, wives were wives, and the Authorized Version of the Bible was true from cover to cover. So Dr. Gilman preached and so they believed.[8]

In this novel, the profession of religious piety represents a residue of stultifying orthodoxy and large-scale social hypocrisy. There is a deadening separation between religion and society: "[On Sundays] the city suddenly became full of churches, as though they had magically been let down from Heaven during Saturday night. They must have been there on weekdays, but few persons even thought of them."[9]

Increasing ambivalence about divine providence as the cornerstone of society was accompanied by doubts about the two other value complexes that were basic to the earlier melodramatic vision: the purity and domestic submissiveness of women and the ideal of the respectable, middle-class family. If feminine purity, piety, and submissiveness were no longer felt to be so important as to evoke the hand of God in their defense; if the direct operation of God's providence in worldly affairs was no longer felt as an imaginative reality; if the attainment of Christian resignation in a life of domestic piety and respectability was no longer conceived to be the highest ideal; then it was not possible for melodramatists to continue writing stories in which virtuous maidens were pursued by lascivious and aristocratic rakes, saved at the last minute by providential interventions, and happily married to a lost heir of the respectable gentry. Nor could they depend on stories in which Christian innocents accepted martyrdom in the assurance of eternal happiness in a palpable heaven.

The increasing pressure on the traditional vision was reflected in two significant late nineteenth-century developments in the formulas of social melodrama. One consisted of attempts to revitalize the traditions by expressing them in more modern terms. An example is what James Hart calls the "Gates Ajar" school in which writers tried to integrate the traditional view of divine providence and the conception of heaven and hell with contemporary social values. Even more striking was a transformation of the virtuous Christian heroine by writers like Augusta Jane Evans, whose *Beulah* (1859) and *St. Elmo* (1867) were runaway best-sellers in the 1860s and early 1870s. In these stories, the heroine retained her Christian purity and faith, but, in contrast to the early nineteenth-century image of a meek and submissive female, became a veritable tigress in the defense of her religion against aggressive and agnostic men.[10] The typical plot pattern of Miss Evans's novels restructured the traditional melodramatic triangle by setting a virtuous and dominant heroine against an aristocratic but weak male, who, converted to Christian faith by the heroine's indomitable force of will, was miraculously transformed into a noble but submissive hero. St. Elmo, for example, began as a sort of Byronic decadent, but under the avalanche of heroine Edna Earl's purity and faith was eventually converted into a pious minister and devoted husband. E. P. Roe, a best-seller in the 1870s and one of the last major social melodramatists in the earlier tradition, updated his works by giving a greater topicality to his treatment of the contemporary social scene and by inverting the traditional moral roles of men and women. In his popular *Barriers Burned Away* (1872) the heroine, initially a high-living wealthy young lady, was eventually converted to virtue and purity by her love for the noble young hero. This happy event was brought about by the great conflagration of the Chicago fire.

A second major development was the emergence of new forms of melodramatic action, and of new ways of treating society. Most important, social change and upheaval became a primary background for melodramatic action. The earlier melodrama, however much it may have advocated some kind of social reform such as the abolition of slavery in *Uncle Tom's Cabin*, tended to portray society within the story as static. Individuals rose and fell, but society went on in much the same way. This is true of the earlier novels of Dickens as it is of mid-nineteenth-century American social melodramas like those of Mrs. Southworth. For Dickens, a growing sense of social upheaval meant that his later novels would become less melodramatic, and increasingly dominated by a dark sense of social chaos. Later melodramatists concerned with social change developed stories in which the protagonist was morally regenerated by a new and better understanding of what was happening to society. By the end of the nineteenth century, this had become one of the standard patterns of social melodrama. The protagonist, faced with a rapidly changing society, finds his traditional religious and moral orthodoxy inadequate and finally wins through to a better relationship to the world around him. Late nineteenth- and early twentieth-century social melodramas are full of ministers who are converted from a narrow orthodoxy to a new and more humane social gospel, capitalists who recognize the narrow materialism of their goals and discover a new fullness of spirit in service to mankind, of tired and jaded aristocrats who sense the emptiness and futility of their lives and go west to become part of a new life.

The best-selling social melodramatists of the early twentieth century—writers like Harold Bell Wright and Winston Churchill—evolved a new melodramatic synthesis to deal with tensions between the traditional Christian moral universe and the new sense of social change. Their works are a mélange of the leading social and philosophical currents of the time—Spencerian Social Darwinism, the social gospel, political reformism and progressivism, the institutional church, the new sociology of environmentalism, even, in some writers, the intellectual and philosophical racism of the period—all stated in such a way that they can be ultimately harmonized with a more socially oriented Christianity. For these writers the traditional orthodoxies of Christian thought had to be revitalized to correspond with new realities, but they see no fundamental conflict between a religious view of the world and the new social currents. Indeed, their stories show that a regenerated religious perspective can bring about a meaningful understanding of social change. Thus Harold Bell Wright wrote in his enormously popular *Shepherd of the Hills* (1907) about a minister who had lost touch with his faith in the increasing swirl of materialism and change that characterized his fashionable urban world. His quest for regeneration takes him to the primitive Ozarks, where he learns to reaffirm his faith in a newly virile and passionate manner, freed from the sterile orthodoxies of the past. Winston Churchill's *The Inside of the Cup* (1913) told the same basic story, except that his ambivalent minister found a vital social gospel among the urban poor who lived on the margins of his upper-class parish. With his newfound strength, Churchill's John Hodder is able to confront his wealthy congregation with their selfishness and materialism while winning the love of the rebellious daughter of the city's wealthiest capitalist. In the social melodramas of the early twentieth century, the traditional plot of the embattled virgin and the lascivious seducer was typically replaced by the story of the young man or woman who recognizes the failure of success and seeks a higher ideal than material wealth and power. The aristocratic seducer was transformed into the figure of the selfish capitalist or the corrupt political boss who seeks to persuade the protagonist to give up the quest for a more humane religion and a higher concept of service to suffering mankind. The extent to which the novels of Wright and Churchill remained within the orbit of melodrama is evident by comparison with such contemporaries as Stephen Crane, Frank Norris, and Theodore Dreiser, in whose works there is no possible resolution between the traditions of Christianity and the new naturalistic determinism. Even William Dean Howells, close as he sometimes comes to social melodrama in his attempts to balance an increasingly critical view of contemporary society with a due representation of "the smiling aspect of life," cannot bring himself to the melodramatic reaffirmation of a benevolent moral order. For example, his novel *The Minister's Charge* (1887) deals like Wright's *Shepherd of the Hills* and Churchill's *The Inside of the Cup* with a minister's attempt to revitalize his faith by a concern for human suffering in the midst of social change, but ends up in a much more ambiguous sense of genteel futility. One might also compare Howells's *A Hazard of New Fortunes* (1890) with Wright's *Winning of Barbara Worth* (1911) as stories about the failure of capitalistic selfishness. Where Howells's Dryfoos comes to recognize an irreconcilable conflict between the power of wealth and his human needs, Wright's Jefferson Worth establishes a higher harmony between the service of God and Mammon in the gospel of the social ministry of capital.

Just as the melodramatists of the early twentieth century found ways of dramatizing the harmony between social change and Christian tradition in a vision of Christian progressivism, they also worked out new patterns for resolving the tensions created by changing conceptions of the feminine character and of relations between the sexes. In place of the traditional melodramatic incarnation of feminine purity and submissiveness, the social melodramatists of the later nineteenth century gradually evolved a morally sympathetic portrait of the new woman. While the divorcée, the promiscuous, and the prostitute remained beyond the pale and were still usually allocated an unfortunate fate, they were often treated with considerable sympathy and understanding and sometimes were even allowed to take a role as secondary heroine until their tragic fate caught up with them. The official heroine, though still usually characterized by sexual purity, gradually lost much of her submissiveness and was even granted a certain degree of wildness. One of the most popular heroines of the early twentieth century, Wright's Barbara Worth, was a vigorous horsewoman and the companion of rugged cowboys and railroad workers. Much of the drama of her romance with the upper-class eastern engineer Willard Holmes derived from the conflict between his love for her and his feeling that she was not quite respectable enough to bring home to his snobbish family, a conflict that was easily overcome when he recognized her true purity and moral worth as well as her vigor and courage. Winston Churchill went even further in the treatment of independent and self-reliant heroines. Some of his leading women were in their early thirties and had already achieved a degree of professional accomplishment before they met and fell in love with their future husbands.

Despite the greater vigor and force of the new melodramatic heroine and an increasing physicality and sensuality in her makeup, the social melodramatists of the early twentieth century strove mightily to balance these new feminine qualities with a residue of the purity and gentility so important to the traditional feminine ideal. In *Shepherd of the Hills*, Wright drew a much-loved portrait of Sammy Lane, the wild mountain girl, who, underneath her primitive and passionate exterior, has a deep desire to be a cultivated Christian lady. Before her marriage she achieves this goal under the Shepherd's tutelage. Even the free and easy Barbara Worth has a fundamental substructure of instinctive feminine modesty. Her first meeting with the man she will eventually marry goes like this:

> It was no flimsy, two-fingered ceremony, but a whole-hearted, whole-handed grip that made the man's blood move more quickly. Unconsciously, as he felt the warm strength in the touch of the girl's hand, he leaned towards her with quick eagerness. And Barbara, who was looking straight into his face with the open frankness of one man to another, started and drew back a little, turning her head aside.[11]

Zane Grey, who would carry the early twentieth-century tradition of social melodrama forward into the twenties and thirties, elaborated still further on this combination of wildness and femininity in his heroines. For example, in his *Code of the West* (1934) the heroine is a flapper from the East who is visiting her married sister in the Tonto

Basin in Arizona. Her high jinks and flirtations nearly lead to tragedy until she falls deeply in love with a young westerner and changes her attitudes toward life. Yet her original wildness is only sublimated into a new and more proper form, for in the novel's climactic scene this regenerated flapper faces down the villain and so shames him that he is forced to leave the territory. In general, the melodramatic heroine of the early twentieth century was clearly evolving in the direction of what would become a favorite feminine stereotype in the novels and films of the thirties and forties: what has been labeled the "good-bad girl," a heroine who appears at the beginning of the story to be wild and even immoral but who is eventually revealed to be a truly chaste and loving woman.

In addition to its emphasis on social change, a new heroine, and the regeneration of traditional values, the early twentieth-century social melodrama explored a variety of new subjects, the most important of which were various forms of sensational crime and scandals, particularly among the upper classes, as well as the material that had been made available through the evolution of the western formula. Wister, Emerson Hough, and Zane Grey made a great success out of the western formula in the early twentieth century by giving it some important elements of social melodrama such as the multiple plot, the complex analysis of society, and an elaborate treatment of the romance between hero and heroine, qualities that were not an indispensable part of the western formula but, in this period, helped writers like Wright and Grey to achieve best-seller status. The melodramatic vision of the early twentieth century with its concern for the regeneration of traditions in the midst of a changing conception of society and sexuality was made to order for the western setting. Here it seemed appropriate that the heroine should be a more vigorous and openly aggressive type than the traditional heroine. Similarly, the portrayal of a jaded, overly genteel easterner revitalized into true manliness (or womanliness) by an encounter with the simpler and more "natural" society of the West was one effective way of dramatizing the theme of regeneration.

To sum up, the prevailing formula of social melodrama in the late nineteenth and early twentieth centuries was based on the representation of social and moral regeneration. Whether fairly conservative and orthodox in inclination like Harold Bell Wright or liberal like Winston Churchill, the social melodramatists portrayed a society that had moved from the proper course and needed to rediscover what was most important about life. In this society religion had become a sterile orthodoxy. The leading citizens had lost their humanity in the pursuit of wealth and power. Yet, underneath it all, there was an evolutionary force working to bring about a truer spirituality and a more direct and loving relationship between people. Those who discovered and aligned themselves with this deeper force were sure to become spiritually regenerated and find happiness. As a dramatization of cultural ideologies, this formula can be interpreted as a way of resolving the conflict between social and religious traditions and the new intellectual and social currents of the later nineteenth century. The social melodramas of Wright, Churchill, and many of their contemporaries were expressions in fictional form of some of the same impulses behind the more popular forms of the social gospel and the moralistic aspects of Progressive reformism. Indeed, the same emphasis on the rediscovery and revitalization of Christian ideals that we find in the social melodramas of this period is also central in the enormously popular religious best-seller of 1897,

Charles Sheldon's *In His Steps*, which told the story of a group of people who sought to transcend the sterility and hypocrisy of the traditional Christian orthodoxies by applying basic Christian principles to modern social life. This was essentially the moral vision of the leading social melodramatists of the early nineteenth century: the affirmation of a new and vital social Christianity based on the spirit of love and service rather than on submission to God's will. The new vision also attempted to resolve increasing anxieties and ambiguities about the moral nature and proper social role of women by creating an active and even aggressive heroine who discovered her rightful place in a passionate and deep attachment to a morally revitalized and loving man.

To discuss the complex developments of social melodrama in the twentieth century even in the most general terms is beyond my present intention. Instead, to complete this tentative analysis of the changing formulas of social melodrama, I will consider the social melodramas of a group of writers who have dominated the best-seller lists since the mid-1960s: Irving Wallace, Harold Robbins, Arthur Hailey, and Jacqueline Susann. These writers are clearly in the tradition of social melodrama, since they typically combine a detailed and often critical analysis of contemporary society with a melodramatic plot full of surprise and suspense that brings a group of characters through a series of trials and tribulations to their appropriate rewards. Indeed, the continuity between these writers and such earlier social melodramatists as Winston Churchill and even Charles Dickens goes beyond the general synthesis of social realism and melodramatic action to specific types of melodramatic plot. Jacqueline Susann's most recent novel *Once Is Not Enough* (1973) is a classic tragic melodrama in modern dress where a heroine is "seduced" (i.e., unable to make a proper sexual adjustment because of a perverse love for her father) and goes to a lingering degradation and death, a mid-twentieth-century Charlotte Temple or Clarissa Harlowe. Irving Wallace specializes in the regeneration plot in which a hero is revitalized by new moral discoveries. Harold Robbins tends to write stories of the failure of success. His central characters pursue the phantoms of wealth and power only to discover that true fulfillment can only come through love, loyalty, and compassion. Arthur Hailey usually combines a number of these basic melodramatic plots in multiple subplots growing out of the various characters involved in the institutions his novels center upon: a hotel, an airport, a large automobile corporation.

Despite these formulaic continuities, the social melodrama of the 1960s depends upon a very different conception of the moral universe than its early twentieth-century predecessors. First of all, the religious concerns so prominent in earlier periods are almost totally absent from the contemporary best-selling blockbuster. Neither the traditional vision of God's providence nor the early twentieth century's sense of harmony between the evolution of society and the manifestation of God's will is embodied in the current formulas. God seems to have been largely banished from the world of Robbins, Wallace, and their colleagues. This does not mean that these writers have no conception of a moral order. Melodrama would be impossible without some vision of poetic justice shaping the development of the story. But for the contemporary melodramatist, the assumption that faith in God is the ultimate test of virtue and the means by which worldly problems can be resolved is no longer tenable. Indeed, the central problem that these writers dramatize over and over again is whether modern secular man is doomed to a life without transcendent meaning or whether there is something on the human level that can offer the same sense of ultimate significance as the conception of God's providence gave to earlier generations. One of the most interesting recent social melodramas, Irving Wallace's *The Word* (1972), offered a fairly complex exploration of the meaning of religion in the modern world by confronting a representative group of modern men and women with a new gospel supposedly written by a brother of Christ. Some choose only to exploit the new gospel as a highly profitable publishing enterprise, but many people's lives are transformed by the way in which the new gospel seemingly substantiates both the historicity and the divinity of Christ. The protagonist encounters inconsistencies and anachronisms that lead him to a bitter old man who claims to have forged the document for revenge upon the church. Mysteriously, the old man dies in an accident—possibly murdered by the publishing syndicate to protect their profits—before he can give the protagonist definitive proofs of the forgery. The protagonist, a successful but frustrated public relations man who has been commissioned to direct the publicity for the new gospel, must finally decide whether to seek the truth about the forgery or to accept the fact that belief in the new gospel—even if false—has benefited many people. That he chooses in the end to commit himself to the hard road of truth is a sign both of his personal regeneration and of the ultimate inadequacy of unquestioning religious faith as a basic principle of moral order.

The Word has an unusual philosphical depth and articulateness as well as a compelling melodramatic plot. It may be Wallace's best work to the present time and the outstanding example of contemporary social melodrama. The novel illustrates the quest for order that dominates the contemporary formula: a search for transcendent significance in a secular, naturalistic age when religious faith has lost its power to inspire a basic belief in the benevolence of the world order and has come to seem only a complex psychological phenomenon. In order to fulfill the archetype of melodrama with its basic affirmation of moral significance and order in the universe, the contemporary social melodramatist has had to turn to other sources of transcendence. The most important area he looks to is that of human relations and sexuality.

It has been often observed of the writings of Wallace, Robbins, Susann, et al., that they exemplify a contemporary obsession with sexuality, and this is true. Sexual relationships of all sorts constitute the primary narrative interest in their works to the degree that one is partly constrained to agree with the critics who see such novels as *The Love Machine* (1969), *The Carpetbaggers* (1961), and *The Seven Minutes* (1969) as elaborate exercises in soft-core pornography.[12] Certainly, there is a connection between the emphasis on sexuality in these contemporary social melodramas and the flourishing in the sixties and seventies of many different kinds of pornography. Yet there is a great difference between a straight work of pornography with its primary purpose of sexual excitement and the novels of Wallace, Susann, Robbins, and Hailey where sexuality is part of a larger moral context. The contemporary social melodramatists seek to integrate new ideas of sexual liberation with traditional conceptions of romantic love and monogamy. The ideal of a full and satisfying sexuality based on a deep and lasting romantic relationship is one moral cornerstone of the new melodramatic vision. Those characters who seek and achieve this kind of experience are contemporary analogues of the pure young women and virtuous heroes who found happiness in Christian piety and faith. But those who exploit sexuality as a means to power, who deny sexual fulfillment to others, or who fail to understand the necessary relationship between sex and love are doomed to failure as contemporary incarnations of the impure heroine who yields to seductive temptation, or as melodramatic villains. In this moral universe, purity may be a form of repression, but promiscuity is still the primrose path to unhappiness. The truly virtuous are those who, like the heroine of *The Seven Minutes*, realize that happiness lies in a synthesis of full sexuality and deep love. Those who fail to find the fullness of human love and sexuality either because they are repressed or because they seek for false goals like fame, wealth, and power are on their way to "The Valley of the Dolls."

The union of romantic love and sexuality is one source of transcendent moral order in the contemporary social melodrama. The other is a concept of true success and integrity set against the evils of the unrestrained pursuit of wealth and power in the glamorous and exciting world of modern business, advertising, and the media. The novels of Wallace, Robbins, Hailey, and Susann teem with men and women who have achieved a brilliant success in glamorous careers but have not found that their accomplishment is either morally satisfying or responsive to their real human needs. Robin Stone, the hero of Susann's *The Love Machine*, rises to the top of the television industry and has innumerable casual affairs, but he does not find happiness until he gives up his position of power to become a writer and accepts his need for a woman who truly loves him. Essentially the same thing is true of the heroes of Robbins's *The Carpetbaggers* and *The Adventurers*. The lawyer protagonist of Wallace's *The Seven Minutes* is tempted by the offer of a lucrative corporate legal post and the empty and repressive sexual beauty of the tycoon's daughter, but his courageous defense of a controversial erotic novel makes him realize that he is on the path to degradation:

> For Barrett [the novel] had exposed to him the ugly truth that in [the tycoon's daughter] he had sought not love but success, and the uglier truth that his goals in life were empty and that by achieving them he would find nothing that could sustain a lifetime of remaining years.[13]

True success, as opposed to the pursuit of wealth and power for their own sake, is marked by personal integrity, satisfying human relationships, and the opportunity to be of service to others. It also usually involves a fulfilling romantic sexual relationship with a loving partner. In the world of the contemporary social melodrama, those who come to realize the meaning of true success and seek wholeheartedly usually become regenerated and their lives take on a new significance and meaning. The central antagonist, contemporary analogue to the traditional melodramatic villain, is usually not a person but the soulless modern corporation that seduces the protagonist with false ambitions and then turns him into an ulcer-ridden manipulator without the capacity for human feeling, until he has the good fortune to realize the error of his ways and turn toward a true ideal of success. No doubt the public for the contemporary melodrama takes some pleasure in vicarious participation in the protagonist's wheeling and dealing, but it has the additional satisfaction of discovering that only by a return to the basic human values of romantic love and true success that are available to everyone can the protagonist finally gain happiness.

In many ways this contemporary parable of regeneration is similar to the quest for a new sense of morality in the early twentieth-century social melodramas of Harold Bell

Wright and Winston Churchill without the latter's attempt to integrate the new ideals with a revitalized sense of religious meaning. But from another point of view the novels of Robbins, Wallace, and Susann might be seen as melodramatic transformations of the naturalistic muckraking novel, as attempts to domesticate or conventionalize the naturalistic view of social, economic, and sexual determinism by leaving out its pessimistic vision and its tendency toward a radical critique of the inequities and contradictions of "the system." In general, the contemporary social melodrama arrives at its vision of a meaningful moral order by resolving the conflict between secular naturalism and the traditional faith in transcendent verities by dramatizing the process through which protagonists arrive at regeneration and happiness by discovering ultimate significance in a totally fulfilling love and a true ideal of success, both of which are viewed as possible despite the disorder, unhappiness, and corruption of modern American society. Because writers like Wallace, Robbins, Susann, and Hailey can provide this assurance and reaffirm this ultimate sense of moral order and significance in the context of what appears to be a realistic portrayal of society with all its injustices and frustrations, its glittering temptations and overwhelming constellations of wealth, power, and corruption, they have been able to hold the high but probably ephemeral place on the best-seller lists that effective social melodramatists have been able to command since the beginning of the nineteenth century.

Looking back over the evolution of the best-selling social melodrama, it appears that the type gradually shifts its formulas as each generation seeks its own means of resolving the tension between changing perceptions of the social scene and the moral ideals that define what is right and significant in life. Thus, in the mid-nineteenth century the formula of social melodrama dramatized the operation of God's providence as the primary means through which the virtuous found happiness and the evil were punished. By the beginning of the twentieth century, a new formula of social melodrama had developed emphasizing the protagonist's discovery of a revitalized Christianity that could encompass the drastic social changes threatening the religious and moral tradition. Finally, in the mid-twentieth century, the prevailing formula of social melodrama has turned away from religion to seek for other means of affirming transcendent moral truths in a secular, naturalistic world.

Despite these considerable changes in the formulas of social melodrama, there are certain basic continuities of theme and structure such as the emphasis on romantic love as an ultimate value, the defense of monogamous, family-oriented relationships between men and women, and the attempt to define true and false conceptions of success and status. These themes, which seem to prevail through the whole period of the nineteenth and twentieth century, suggest, I think, that social melodrama is primarily a genre of the well-established middle class for whom these particular values are of most importance. If this speculation is correct, then the essential social-psychological dynamic of social melodrama is one of continually integrating new social circumstances and ideas to the developing middle-class sense of social value. Perhaps, then, the social melodrama has been one of the means by which the American and English middle classes have so successfully adjusted themselves to the drastic social and cultural changes of the last century and a half. If so, it will be interesting to see how the formulas of social melodrama evolve to confront the enormous changes that will face our society in the future.

Notes

1. David Grimsted, *Melodrama Unveiled: American Theater and Culture, 1800–1850* (Chicago: University of Chicago Press, 1968), p. 176.
2. Mrs. E. D. E. N. Southworth, *The Curse of Clifton* (New York: AMS Press, 1970), p. 465. This novel was first published in 1852.
3. Henry Nash Smith, "The Scribbling Women and the Cosmic Success Story," *Critical Inquiry*, 1, no. 1 (September 1974): 51.
4. Herbert R. Brown, *The Sentimental Novel in America, 1769–1860* (Durham, N.C.: Duke University Press, 1940), pp. 170–71.
5. This may be a major reason for the perennial popularity of the Clarissa Harlowe–Charlotte Temple type of tragic melodrama, which extends down to such present-day best-sellers as Susann's *Once Is Not Enough*, a modern version of this formula. The tragic melodrama plot type allows a sympathetic and spicy portrayal of sin without disrupting the vision of the moral order, since the sin is lovingly and sado-masochistically punished at great length.
6. There seems no need for me to comment on Dickens as the founding father of social melodrama, since his works are so well known and have been subjected to such a variety of critical analysis. Of course, in saying that Dickens was the first great master of social melodrama I am not saying that he did not also transcend the formula in many if not all of his works. To understand Dickens as social melodramatist is particularly useful in grasping the force for his contemporary readers of certain aspects of his work that twentieth-century taste tends to find dated or cloying. For instance, it is noteworthy that nineteenth-century readers were, on the whole, most enthusiastic about the earlier novels where melodramatic elements and resolutions play a much more dominant part, while more recent readers tend to approve more highly of later works like *Hard Times* and *Our Mutual Friend* where an increasingly bleak and critical view of society overpowers the melodramatic vision. *Bleak House* is perhaps a turning point in this development. In one sense we might say that melodrama and social criticism are perfectly balanced in that novel and that the two are encapsulated in the double narrative structure (i.e., the portions told by the anonymous narrator and the narrative of Esther Summerson). But the fact that the two visions are thus almost detached from each other in this structure indicates perhaps the extent to which Dickens is having more and more difficulty in holding them together in his work. Dickens himself was apparently aware of the degree to which his darker and more critical vision of society and his declining ability to qualify this with an effective sense of the benevolent order of melodrama were beginning to alienate his audience. That he turned at the last to experiment with the new structures of the sensation melodrama in the unfinished *Edwin Drood* suggests his search for a new principle of melodrama that might be more in harmony with his bleaker view of society. See the brilliantly suggestive treatment of this issue in Randolph Ivy, "The Victorian Sensation Novel: A Study in Formula Fiction," Ph.D. dissertation, University of Chicago, 1974.
7. Smith comments insightfully on the prevalence of this theme, pp. 53–66.
8. Winston Churchill, *The Inside of the Cup* (New York: Macmillan, 1913), p. 1.
9. Ibid., p. 2.
10. Dee Garrison, in a forthcoming article that I had the good fortune to see in manuscript, "Immoral Fiction in the Gilded Age Library," presents a detailed analysis of the emergence of the aggressive female and her defeat of the formerly dominant male in the melodramatic

novels of the later nineteenth century. Helen Papashvily, *All the Happy Endings* (New York: Harper, 1956), suggests that women enjoyed such stories because they were essentially fantasies of feminine heroism and even conquest within the still respectable framework of domesticity.

11. Harold Bell Wright, *The Winning of Barbara Worth* (Chicago: Book Supply Co., 1911), p. 243.
12. See the discussion of Harold Robbins as soft-core pornographer in Peter Michelsen, *The Aesthetics of Pornography* (New York: Herder and Herder, 1971), chap. 2.
13. Irving Wallace, *The Seven Minutes* (New York: Simon and Schuster, 1969), pp. 244–45.

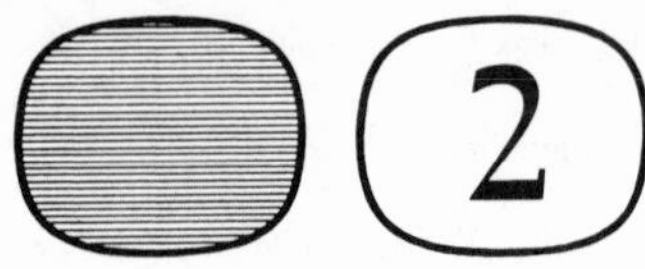

The Melodramatic Imagination

PETER BROOKS

Qu'on n'aille pas s'y tromper, ce n'était pas peu de chose que le mélodrame; c'était la moralité de la Révolution!

—Charles Nodier

Overture

There is at the start of Balzac's first major novel, *La Peau de chagrin*, a passage that indicates how we should read Balzac, how he locates and creates his drama, and, more generally, how the melodramatic imagination conceives its representations. When Raphaël de Valentin enters a gambling house to play roulette with his last franc, a shadowy figure crouched behind a counter rises up to ask for the young man's hat. The gesture of surrendering one's hat forthwith elicits a series of questions from the narrator:

> Is this some scriptural and providential parable? Isn't it rather a way of concluding a diabolical contract by exacting from you a sort of security? Or may it be to oblige you to maintain a respectful demeanour toward those who are about to win your money? Is it the police, lurking in the sewers of society, trying to find out your hatter's name, or your own, if you've inscribed it on the headband? Or is it, finally, to measure your skull in order to compile an instructive statistic on the cranial capacity of gamblers?[1]

Peter Brooks, "The Melodramatic Imagination," from *The Melodramatic Imagination: Balzac, Henry James, Melodrama, and the Mode of Excess* (New York: Columbia University Press, 1985). Reprinted by permission of the author.

The gestures of life call forth a series of interrogations aimed at discovering the meanings implicit in them. The narrative voice is not content to describe and record gesture, to see it simply as a figure in the interplay of persons one with another. Rather, the narrator applies pressure to the gesture, pressure through interrogation, through the evocation of more and more fantastic possibilities, to make it yield meaning, to make it give up to consciousness its full potential as "parable."

Throughout these opening pages of *La Peau de chagrin*, we can observe the narrator pressuring the surface of reality (the surface of his text) in order to make it yield the full, true terms of his story. In the face of the old man who takes the hat, we are told we can read "the wretchedness of hospital wards, aimless wanderings of ruined men, inquests on countless suicides, life sentences at hard labor, exiles to penal colonies." The gambling house itself elicits a contrast between the "vulgar poetry" of its evening denizens and the "quivering passion" of daytime gamblers. The crowd of spectators is like the populace awaiting an execution at the Place de Grève. Finally we reach this judgment: "Each of the spectators looked for a *drama* in the fate of this single gold piece, perhaps the final scene of a noble life" (9:17).

Use of the word *drama* is authorized here precisely by the kind of pressure which the narrator has exerted upon the surface of things. We have in fact been witnesses to the creation of drama—an exciting, excessive, parabolic story—from the banal stuff of reality. States of being beyond the immediate context of the narrative, and in excess of it, have been brought to bear on it, to charge it with intenser significances. The narrative voice, with its grandiose questions and hypotheses, leads us in a movement through and beyond the surface of things to what lies behind, to the spiritual reality which is the true scene of the highly colored drama to be played out in the novel. We have entered into the drama of Raphaël's last gold piece; that coin has become the token of a superdrama involving life and death, perdition and redemption, heaven and hell, the force of desire caught in a death struggle with the life force. The novel is constantly tensed to catch this essential drama, to go beyond the surface of the real to the truer, hidden reality, to open up the world of spirit.

One could adduce a multitude of other examples. There is always a moment in Balzac's descriptions of the world where the eye's photographic registration of objects yields to the mind's effort to pierce surface, to interrogate appearances. In *Le Père Goriot*, after a few initial lines of description of Mlle Michonneau, the narrator shifts into the interrogatory: "What acid had stripped this creature of her female forms? She must once have been pretty and well-built: was it vice, sorrow, greed? Had she loved too much, been a go-between, or simply a courtesan? Was she expiating the triumphs of an insolent youth?" (2:855). Reality is for Balzac both the scene of drama and mask of the true drama that lies behind, is mysterious, and can only be alluded to, questioned, then gradually elucidated. His drama is of the true, wrested from the real; the streets and walls of Paris, under pressure of the narrator's insistence, become the elements of a Dantesque vision, leading the reader into infernal circles: "as, step by step, daylight fades, and the song of the guide goes hollow when the visitor descends into the catacombs" (2:848).

The same process may be observed in Balzac's dramatizations of human encounters. They tend toward intense, excessive representations of life which strip the facade of manners to reveal the essential conflicts at work—moments of symbolic confrontation which fully articulate the terms of the drama. In *Gobseck*, for instance, the sinning Comtesse de Restaud, struggling to preserve an inheritance for her two illegitimate children, is caught in the act of trying to extort her husband's secrets from the oldest son (the legitimate child) when the comte rises from his deathbed:

> "Ah!" cried the comte, who had opened the door and appeared suddenly, almost naked, already as dried and shriveled as a skeleton. . . . "You watered my life with sorrows, and now you would trouble my death, pervert the mind of my own son, turn him into a vicious person," he cried in a rasping voice.
>
> The comtesse threw herself at the feet of this dying man, whom the last emotions of life made almost hideous, and poured out her tears. "Pardon, pardon!" she cried.
>
> "Had you any pity for me?" he asked. "I let you devour your fortune, now you want to devour mine and ruin my son."
>
> "All right, yes, no pity for me, be inflexible," she said. "But the children! Condemn your wife to live in a convent, I will obey; to expiate my faults toward you I will do all you command; but let the children live happily! Oh, the children, the children!"
>
> "I have only one child," answered the comte, stretching his shriveled arm toward his son in a gesture of despair. [2:665]

I have deliberately chosen an extreme example here, and in quoting it out of its context, I run the risk of simply confirming the view, popularized by Martin Turnell and others, that Balzac is a vulgar melodramatist whose versions of life are cheap, overwrought, and hollow. Balzac's use of hyperbolic figures, lurid and grandiose events, masked relationships and disguised identities, abductions, slow-acting poisons, secret societies, mysterious parentage, and other elements from the melodramatic repertory has repeatedly been the object of critical attack, as have, still more, his forcing of narrative voice to the breathless pitch of melodrama, his insistence that life be seen always through highly colored lenses. "His melodrama," Turnell comments, "reminds us not so much of Simenon or even Mrs. Christie as of the daily serial in the BBC's Light Programme." In his most waspish *Scrutiny* manner, Turnell adds, "It must be confessed that our experience in reading Balzac is not always very elevated and that his interests are by no means those of the adult."[2]

To the extent that the "interests of the adult" imply repression, sacrifice of the pleasure principle, and a refusal to live beyond the ordinary, Turnell is right, but his terms of judgment blind him to Balzac's characteristic drive to push *through* manners to deeper sources of being. Such representations as the scene I quoted from *Gobseck* are necessary culminations to the kind of drama Balzac is trying to evoke. The progress of the narrative elicits and authorizes such terminal articulations. The scene represents a victory over repression, a climactic moment at which the characters are able to confront one another with full expressivity, to fix in large gestures the meaning of their relations and existence. As in the interrogations of *La Peau de chagrin* we saw a desire to push through surface to a "drama" in the realm of emotional and spiritual reality, so in the scene from *Gobseck* we find a desire to make starkly articulate all that this family conflict has come to be about.

The desire to express all seems a fundamental characteristic of the melodramatic mode. Nothing is spared because nothing is left unsaid; the characters stand on stage and utter the unspeakable, give voice to their deepest feelings, dramatize through their heightened and polarized words and gestures the whole lesson of their relationship. They assume primary psychic roles, father, mother, child, and express basic psychic conditions. Life tends, in this fiction, toward ever more concentrated and totally expressive gestures and statements. Raphaël de Valentin is given a lesson by the old antiques dealer: "*Desire* sets us afire, and *power* destroys us"—terms which reveal the true locus and the stakes of his drama. Eugène de Rastignac, in *Le Père Goriot*, is summoned to choose between Obedience, represented by the family, and Revolt, represented by the outlaw Vautrin. The metaphoric texture of the prose itself suggests polarization into moral absolutes: Rastignac's "last tear of youth," shed over Goriot's grave, from the earth where it falls "rebounds into heaven." The world is subsumed by an underlying manichaeism, and the narrative creates the excitement of its drama by putting us in touch with the conflict of good and evil played out under the surface of things—just as description of the surfaces of the modern metropolis pierces through to a mythological realm where the imagination can find a habitat for its play with large moral entities. If we consider the prevalence of hidden relationships and masked personages and occult powers in Balzac, we find that they derive from a sense that the novelist's true subject is hidden and masked. The site of his drama, the ontology of his true subject, is not easily established: the narrative must push toward it, the pressure of the prose must uncover it. We might say that the center of interest and the scene of the underlying drama reside within what we could call the "moral occult," the domain of operative spiritual values which is both indicated within and masked by the surface of reality. The moral occult is not a metaphysical system; it is rather the repository of the fragmentary and desacralized remnants of sacred myth. It bears comparison to unconscious mind, for it is a sphere of being where our most basic desires and interdictions lie, a realm which in quotidian existence may appear closed off from us, but which we must accede to since it is the realm of meaning and value. The melodramatic mode in large measure exists to locate and to articulate the moral occult.

We shall return to these summary formulations. It is important first to extend our understanding of the kind of representation of social life offered by melodrama of manners, and to extend the demonstration beyond Balzac by calling upon his greatest admirer among subsequent novelists, Henry James. The melodramatic tenor of James's imagination was beautifully caught by his secretary, Theodora Bosanquet:

> When he walked out of the refuge of his study into the world and looked about him, he saw a place of torment, where creatures of prey perpetually thrust their claws into the quivering flesh of the doomed, defenseless children of light.[3]

James's moral manichaeism is the basis of a vision of the social world as the scene of dramatic choice between heightened moral alternatives, where every gesture, however frivolous or insignificant it may seem, is charged with the conflict between light and darkness, salvation and damnation, and where people's destinies and choices of life seem finally to have little to do with the surface realities of a situation, and much more to do with an intense inner drama in which consciousness must purge itself and assume the burden of moral sainthood. The theme of renunciation which sounds through James's novels—Isabel Archer's return to Gilbert Osmond, Strether's return to Woollett, Densher's rejection of Kate Croy—is incomprehensible and unjustifiable except as a victory within the realm of a moral occult which may be so inward and personal that it appears restricted to the individual's consciousness, predicated on the individual's "sacrifice to the ideal."

As Jacques Barzun has emphasized, James always creates a high degree of excitement from his dramatized moral dilemmas, partly because of his preoccupation with evil as a positive force ever menacing violent conflict and outburst.[4] Balzac did an apprenticeship in the *roman noir,* nourished himself with Gothic novel, melodrama, and frenetic adventure story, and invented cops-and-robbers fiction. These are modes which insist that reality can be exciting, can be equal to the demands of the imagination, which in Balzac's case means primarily the moral imagination, at play with large and basic ethical conflicts. With James, the same insistence has been further transposed into the drama of moral consciousness, so that excitement derives from the characters' own dramatized apprehension of clashing moral forces. A famous sentence from the preface to *The Portrait of a Lady* suggests James's intent. He is describing Isabel's vigil of discovery, the night she sits up and makes her mind move from discovery to discovery about Gilbert Osmond. "It is," says James, "a representation simply of her motionlessly *seeing*, and an attempt withal to make the mere still lucidity of her act as 'interesting' as the surprise of a caravan or the identification of a pirate."[5] The terms of reference in the adventure story are mocked; yet they remain the terms of reference: moral consciousness must be an adventure, its recognition must be the stuff of a heightened drama.

The excitement and violence of the melodrama of consciousness are obviously and derivatively Balzacian in such an early novel as *The American*. Christopher Newman's initiation into the epistemology of good and evil is represented through a dark ancestral crime hidden beneath, and suggested by, the gilded surface of Faubourg Saint-Germain society: depths open beneath the well-guarded social image of the Bellegarde family; crisis is revelation of sin, and Newman's consciousness must open to receive the lurid, flashing lights of melodrama. But even in James's latest and most subtle fiction—probably most of all in this fiction—the excitement of plot is generated almost exclusively from melodramatic conflict within the realm of the moral occult. There is a pressure similar to Balzac's on the textual surface, to make reality yield the terms of the drama of this moral occult. To take this time deliberately a low-keyed example—standing in apparent opposition to the quotation from *Gobseck* and thereby suggesting the range of the mode—from *The Ambassadors*: following the revelation of Mme de Vionnet's relationship with Chad, Strether goes to pay her a final visit. He stands for the last time in her noble apartment:

> From beyond this, and as from a great distance—beyond the court, beyond the *corps de logis* forming the front—came, as if excited and exciting, the vague voice of Paris. Strether had all along been subject to sudden gusts of fancy in connexion with such matters as these—odd starts of the historic sense, suppositions and divinations with no warrant but their intensity. Thus and so, on the eve of the great recorded dates, the days and nights of revolution, the sounds had come in, the omens, the beginnings broken out. They were the smell of revolution, the smell of the public temper—or perhaps simply the smell of blood.[6]

That this vision is ascribed to Strether's "gusts of fancy" does not really hedge the bet. James makes the "unwarranted" vision exist, wrests forth from "beyond" the facades of

Paris sinister implications of impending disaster and chaos, and pervades the final encounter of Strether and Mme de Vionnet with "the smell of blood." Their relation has all along been based on Strether's "exorbitant" commitment to "save her" if he could. Here, the evocation of bloody sacrifice, eliciting a state of moral exorbitance, authorizes the intensity of the encounter, where Strether sees Mme de Vionnet as resembling Mme Roland on the scaffold, and where he moves to his most penetrating vision of the realm of moral forces in which she struggles. "With this sharpest perception yet, it was like a chill in the air to him, it was almost appalling, that a creature so fine could be, by mysterious forces, a creature so exploited" (2:284). Strether, and James, have pierced through to a medium in which Mme de Vionnet can be seen as a child of light caught in the claws of the mysterious birds of prey. After this perception, when Strether speaks it is to say, "You're afraid for your life!"—an articulation that strikes home, makes Mme de Vionnet give up "all attempt at a manner," and break down in tears. This stark articulation, which clarifies and simplifies Mme de Vionnet's position and passion, which puts her in touch with elemental humanity ("as a maidservant crying for her young man," thinks Strether) and with the ravages of time, finally differs little from the exchanges of the Comte and Comtesse de Restaud in *Gobseck*. The Jamesian mode is subtler, more refined, but it aims at the same thing: a total articulation of the grandiose moral terms of the drama, an assertion that what is being played out on the plane of manners is charged from the realm of the moral occult, that gestures within the world constantly refer us to another, hyperbolic set of gestures where life and death are at stake.

There is a passage from James's 1902 essay on Balzac (he wrote five in all) that touches closely on the problem of melodramatic representation. A notable point about the passage is that it constitutes a reparation, for in his 1875 essay, in *French Poets and Novelists*, James had singled out, as an example of Balzac's ineptitude in portrayal of the aristocracy, the episode in *Illusions perdues* where Mme de Bargeton, under the influence of her Parisian relation the Marquise d'Espard, drops her young provincial attachment, Lucien de Rubempré. The two women desert Lucien, whose dress is ridiculous and whose plebeian parentage has become public knowledge, in the middle of the opera and sneak out of the loge. Aristocratic ladies would not so violate manners, James argues in the earlier essay, would not behave in so flustered and overly dramatic a fashion. His view in 1902 is more nuanced and marks an effort to come to terms with those features of Balzacian representation that he had previously criticized:

> The whole episode, in "Les Illusions perdues," of Madame de Bargeton's "chucking" Lucien de Rubempré, on reaching Paris with him, under pressure of Madame d'Espard's shockability as to his coat and trousers and other such matters, is either a magnificent lurid document or the baseless fabric of a vision. The great wonder is that, as I rejoice to put it, we can never really discover which, and that we feel as we read that we can't, and that we suffer at the hands of no other author this particular helplessness of immersion. It is *done*—we are always thrown back on that; we can't get out of it; all we can do is to say that the true itself can't be more than done and that if the false in this way equals it we must give up looking for the difference. Alone among novelists Balzac has the secret of an insistence that somehow makes the difference nought. He warms his facts into life—as witness the certainty that the episode I just cited has absolutely

> as much of that property as if perfect matching had been achieved. If the great ladies in question *didn't* behave, wouldn't, couldn't have behaved, like a pair of nervous snobs, why so much the worse, we say to ourselves, for the great ladies in question. We *know* them so—they owe their being to our so seeing them; whereas we never can tell ourselves how we should otherwise have known them or what quantity of being they would on a different footing have been able to put forth.[7]

James's somewhat baffled admiration here seems to arise from a perception of "surreality" in Balzac's representation of the episode: the fact that its hyperbolic mode and intensity make it figure more perfectly than would an accurate portrayal of manners what is really at stake for the characters and in their relationships. If reality does not permit of such self-representations, he seems to say, then so much the worse for reality. By the manner in which the thing is "done"—by the quality of the narrative performance—we know the characters essentially; we are, if not in the domain of reality, in that of truth.

James poses the alternative of judging Balzac's episode to be "either a magnificent lurid document or the baseless fabric of a vision," only to conclude that we cannot tell which it is. This alternative, and the admission of defeat in the attempt to choose, strikes close to the center of the problem of melodrama. The melodramatic imagination needs both document and vision, and it is centrally concerned with the extrapolation from one to another. When the Balzacian narrator pressures the details of reality to make them yield the terms of his drama, when he insists that Raphaël's gestures refer to a parabolic story, or when he creates a hyperbolic scene of Lucien de Rubempré's social defeat, he is using the things and gestures of the real world, of social life, as kinds of metaphors that refer us to the realm of spiritual reality and latent moral meanings. Things cease to be merely themselves, gestures cease to be merely tokens of social intercourse whose meaning is assigned by a social code; they become the vehicles of metaphors whose tenor suggests another kind of reality. In *The Ambassadors*, Strether's discovery of Mme de Vionnet's affair with Chad is essentially a vehicle for discovery of her entrapment and exploitation by "mysterious forces."

I. A. Richards has given an encompassing definition of metaphor as a "transaction between contexts," and in all these cases there is such a transaction: pressure on the primary context is such that things and gestures are made to release occult meanings, to transfer significance into another context.[8] Both Balzac and James weave a rich texture of metaphor in their prose, and the metaphors most often create an expanded moral context for the narrative. But it is not a question of metaphoric texture alone; it is rather that, to the melodramatic imagination, significant things and gestures are necessarily metaphoric in nature because they must refer to and speak of something else. Everything appears to bear the stamp of meaning, which can be expressed, pressed out, from it. The dandy de Marsay, refusing to recognize Lucien de Rubempré in *Illusions perdues*, lets his lorgnon fall "so singularly it seemed the blade of the guillotine" (4:624). In *Le Lys dans la vallée*, the narrator reads in the "forced smile" of the dying Mme de Mortsauf "the irony of vengeance, the anticipation of pleasure, the intoxication of the soul and the rage of disappointment" (8:1003). If with James we are tempted to believe that gestures receive their charge from social manners—this is after all the classic view of James—we find that, on the contrary, social signification is only the merest starting point for an immense construction of connotation. One could adduce this moment in *The Wings of the Dove* when Merton Densher learns from Milly Theale's servant that Milly can't receive him—his, and our, first indication that crisis is at hand:

> [Eugenio] now, as usual, slightly smiled at him in the process—but ever so slightly, this time, his manner also being attuned, our young man made out, to the thing, whatever it was, that constituted the rupture of peace.
>
> This manner, while they stood for a long minute facing each other over all they didn't say, played a part as well in the sudden jar to Densher's protected state. It was a Venice all of evil that had broken out for them alike, so that they were together in their anxiety, if they really could have met on it; a Venice of cold, lashing rain from a low black sky, of wicked wind raging through narrow passes, of general arrest and interruption, with the people engaged in all the water-life huddled, stranded and wageless, bored and cynical, under archways and bridges.[9]

The Jamesian prestidigitation is in full evidence here. Eugenio's slight, *too* slight smile is the detailed token which indicates a larger manner which in turn indicates a "rupture of peace"—already the vocabulary is taking on strong coloration—and this rupture then becomes the passageway for a flood of evil, conjuring into existence a new Venice of storm, darkness, and suppressed violence.

We will later pursue in more detail the questions posed by this metaphoricity of gesture that evokes meanings beyond its literal configuration. We may already be struck by the seeming paradox that the total expressivity assigned to gesture is related to the ineffability of what is to be expressed. Gesture is read as containing such meanings because it is postulated as the metaphorical approach to what cannot be said. If we often come perilously close, in reading these novelists, to a feeling that the represented world won't bear the weight of the significances placed on it, this is because the represented world is so often being used metaphorically, as sign of something else. If we consider in this light the implications of works like *The Beast in the Jungle* and *The Sacred Fount*, we find that the more elusive the tenor of the metaphor becomes—the more difficult it becomes to put one's finger on the nature of the spiritual reality alluded to—the more highly charged is the vehicle, the more strained with pressure to suggest a meaning beyond. The violence and extremism of emotional reaction and moral implication that we find in the prose of both James and Balzac may in part derive from their lack of clear foundation, their location in an ethical consciousness that cannot be shown to correspond evidently and necessarily to the way life is lived by most people. To the uncertainty of the tenor corresponds the exaggeration, the heightening of the vehicle. The heightening and hyperbole, the polarized conflict, the menace and suspense of the representations may be made necessary by the effort to perceive and image the spiritual in a world voided of its traditional Sacred, where the body of the ethical has become a sort of *deus absconditus* which must be sought for, postulated, brought into man's existence through the play of the spiritualist imagination. We cannot, however, go farther without saying more about melodrama, our understanding of the concept and use of the word, its historical and ideological situation, and its nature.

The Uses of Melodrama

I have tried, in the opening pages, to suggest the pervasive melodramatism of two such important novelists as Balzac and James—the very consubstantiality of melodrama with the mode and vision of their fiction. But I have not yet said anything in explication or justification of the word melodrama, its appropriateness as a critical term, the reasons for choosing a label that has a bad reputation and has usually been used pejoratively. The connotations of the word are probably similar for us all. They include: the indulgence of strong emotionalism; moral polarization and schematization; extreme states of being, situations, actions; overt villainy, persecution of the good, and final reward of virtue; inflated and extravagant expression; dark plottings, suspense, breathtaking peripety. The few critics who have given serious attention to melodrama have noted its psychological function in allowing us the pleasures of self-pity and the experience of wholeness brought by the identification with "monopathic" emotion, in Robert Heilman's phrase.[10] Eric Bentley in particular has argued the importance of melodrama as a concept opposed to naturalism, its expression of emotion in the pure histrionic form of dreams, its representation of the quintessentially dramatic.[11] In his discussion of four dramatic types (melodrama, farce, tragedy, comedy), Bentley sets melodrama first, because it embodies the root impulse of drama—the need for dramatization, we might say, for acting out. The term seems useful, even necessary, because it points, as no other word quite does, to a mode of high emotionalism and stark ethical conflict that is neither comic nor tragic in persons, structure, intent, effect. That the term covers and, in common usage, most often refers to a cheap and banal melodrama—to soap opera—need not decrease its usefulness: there is a range from high to low examples in any literary field, and the most successful melodrama belongs to a coherent mode that rewards attention, in its literal as well as in its "extrapolated" forms. What I will say about melodrama in general will, I think, be relevant to the low examples as well as the high, with the difference that, as in all art, the low is attempting less, risking less, is more conventional and less self-conscious. At its most ambitious, the melodramatic mode of conception and representation may appear to be the very process of reaching a fundamental drama of the moral life and finding the terms to express it.

It might be idle to use the term melodrama were not the literal reference of the word also relevant to our critical perspective. Working back from the adjective *melodramatic*, used to describe such novelists as Balzac and James, one finds that melodrama proper, stage melodrama, constitutes a viable and important context. Considering mainly the "classical" melodrama as it was first established in France at the dawn of the nineteenth century, we find a fully realized, coherent theatrical mode whose structures and characteristics, in their very purity and even crudity, can teach us to read a whole body of modern literature with a finer perception of its project. Without now entering into the characteristics of stage melodrama we can note that we find there an intense emotional and ethical drama based on the manichaeistic struggle of good and evil, a world where what one lives for and by is seen in terms of, and as determined by, the most fundamental psychic relations and cosmic ethical forces. The polarization of good and evil works toward revealing their presence and operation as real forces in the world. Their conflict suggests the need to recognize and confront evil, to combat and expel it, to purge the social order. Man is seen to be, and must recognize himself to be, playing on a theater that is the point of juncture, and of clash, of imperatives beyond himself that are non-mediated and irreducible. This is what is most real in the universe. The spectacular enactments of melodrama seek constantly to express these forces and imperatives, to bring them to striking revelation, to impose their evidence.

In considering melodrama, we are in a sense talking about a form of theatricality which will underlie novelistic efforts at representation—which will provide a model for the making of meaning in fictional dramatizations of existence. The nineteenth-century novel needs such a theatricality, as we shall see, to get its meaning across, to invest in its renderings of life a sense of memorability and significance. With the rise of the novel and of melodrama, we find the entry into literature of a new moral and aesthetic category, that of the "interesting." Its first theoretician may be Diderot, in his effort to establish the new genre of *drame,* which owes much to the novels of Richardson and in some ways prefigures melodrama. Diderot's definition of *le genre sérieux*, intermediate between tragedy and comedy—but explicitly not a mixture of the two—addresses itself to the "interesting" in life. What he proposes is a serious attention to the *drama* of the *ordinary:* the "picture of the misfortunes that surround us," the representation of "dangers concerning which you must have trembled for your parents, your friends, yourselves."[12] This should not be read as a recommendation of naturalistic "realism." On the contrary, Diderot wants to exploit the dramatics and excitement discoverable within the real, to heighten in dramatic gesture the moral crises and peripeties of life. The *drame* is characterized by its specific form of the sublime, which Diderot defines through examples of hypothetical speeches: the father who has been nursed by his son in old age pronounces, "My son, we are even. I gave you life, and you have restored it to me"; or again, "Always tell the truth. . . . I so beg you by these feet that I warmed in my hands when you were in the cradle."[13] These enunciations, like the situations that frame them, possess the precise "sublimity" of melodramatic rhetoric: the emphatic articulation of simple truths and relationships, the clarification of the cosmic moral sense of everyday gestures. We are near the beginnings of a modern aesthetic in which Balzac and James will fully participate: the effort to make the "real" and the "ordinary" and the "private life" interesting through heightened dramatic utterance and gesture that lay bare the true stakes.

The word melodrama means, originally, a drama accompanied by music. It appears to have first been used in this sense by Rousseau, to describe a play in which he sought a new emotional expressivity through the mixture of spoken soliloquy, pantomime, and orchestral accompaniment.[14] The word then came to characterize a popular drama derived from pantomime (itself accompanied by music) that did not fit within any of the accepted genres. Music was an important element in Diderot's aesthetics; it was given a durable role in nineteenth-century theatre and then became a staple in the contemporary form that most relayed and supplanted melodra[illegible] cinema. Jean-Paul Sartre has well described the effect of musical accompan[illegible] the silent film, the kind of clear identity it provided for character and incident, the rigorous necessity it conferred on plot;[15] and we are aware of how in the speaking film it still determines mode and meaning. Even though the novel has no literal music, this connotation of the term melodrama remains relevant. The emotional drama needs the desemanticized language of music, its evocation of the "ineffable," its tones and registers. Style, thematic structuring, modulations of tone and rhythm and voice—musical patterning in a metaphorical sense—are called upon to invest plot with some of the inexorability and necessity that in pre-modern literature derived from the substratum of myth.

One might be tempted to consider melodrama as a constant of the imagination and a constant among literary modes: it could be (as some critics have proposed for the terms *baroque and romanticism*) one typological pole, detectable at all epochs, as Heilman suggests in his discussions of Elizabethan and Jacobean dramatists. Such a conception of the term is no doubt valid; one could reasonably, for instance, talk of the melodramatic in Euripides in distinction to the tragic in Sophocles.[16] But melodrama as we need the term—as it demonstrates its usefulness—appears to be a peculiarly modern form, and there is a specific relevance in the genre labeled melodrama as it comes into being in an historical context. The origins of melodrama can be accurately located within the context of the French Revolution and its aftermath. This is the epistemological moment which it illustrates and to which it contributes: the moment that symbolically, and really, marks the final liquidation of the traditional Sacred and its representative institutions (Church and Monarch), the shattering of the myth of Christendom, the dissolution of an organic and hierarchically cohesive society, and the invalidation of the literary forms—tragedy, comedy of manners—that depended on such a society. Melodrama does not simply represent a "fall" from tragedy, but a response to the loss of the tragic vision. It comes into being in a world where the traditional imperatives of truth and ethics have been violently thrown into question, yet where the promulgation of truth and ethics, their instauration as a way of life, is of immediate, daily, political concern. When the revolutionary Saint-Just exclaims, "Republican government has as its principle virtue; or if not, terror,"[17] he is using the manichaeistic terms of melodrama, arguing its logic of the excluded middle, and imaging a situation—the moment of revolutionary suspension—where the word is called upon to make present and to impose a new society, to legislate the regime of virtue. A new world, a new chronology, a new religion, a new morality lay within the grasp of the revolutionary legislator and, particularly, in the power of his verbal representations. The Revolution attempts to sacralize law itself, the Republic as the institution of morality. Yet it necessarily produces melodrama instead, incessant struggle against enemies, without and within, branded as villains, suborners of morality, who must be confronted and expunged, over and over, to assure the triumph of virtue. Like the oratory of the Revolution, melodrama from its inception takes as its concern and raison d'être the location, expression, and imposition of basic ethical and psychic truths. It says them over and over in clear language, it rehearses their conflicts and combats, it reënacts the menace of evil and the eventual triumph of morality made operative and evident. While its social implications may be variously revolutionary or conservative, it is in all cases radically democratic, striving to make its representations clear and legible to everyone. We may legitimately claim that melodrama becomes the principal mode for uncovering, demonstrating, and making operative the essential moral universe in a post-sacred era.

This claim needs further attention. The Revolution can be seen as the convulsive last act in a process of desacralization that was set in motion at the Renaissance, passed through the momentary compromise of Christian humanism, and gathered momentum during the Enlightenment—a process in which the explanatory and cohesive force of sacred myth lost its power, and its political and social representations lost their legitimacy. In the course of this process, tragedy, which depends on the communal partaking of the sacred body—as in the mass—became impossible.[18] The crucial moment of passage could no doubt be located somewhere in the seventeenth century. Racine stands emblematically as the last tragic playwright (Milton as the last epic poet) and his career has much to tell us about the increasing difficulties encountered in the apprehension and representation of communal sacred imperatives. The Quarrel of the Ancient and the Moderns, at the close of the seventeenth century, was the symbolic annunciation of literature's divorce from the mythic substratum that had sustained it, its incipient privatization and desacralization.

Yet by the end of the Enlightenment, there was clearly a renewed thirst for the Sacred, a reaction to desacralization expressed in the vast movement we think of as Romanticism. The reaction both reasserted the need for some version of the Sacred and offered further proof of the irremediable loss of the Sacred in its traditional, categorical, unifying form. Mythmaking could not only be individual, personal; and the promulgation of ethical imperatives had to depend on an individual act of self-understanding that would then—by an imaginative or even a terroristic leap—be offered as the foundation of a general ethics. In fact, the entity making the strongest claim to sacred status tends more and more to be personality itself. From amid the collapse of order principles and criteria, the individual ego declares its central and overriding value, its demand to be the measure of all things. The *incipit* of modernity is the first page of Rousseau's *Confessions*, with its insistence on the uniqueness of his individual inner being, his difference from all other men, and on the necessity of expressing that being in its totality. The importance attached by Rousseau to his decision to "say all," *tout dire*, is a measure of the personalization and inwardness of post-sacred ethics, the difficulty of their location and expression.[19] A manic analogue can be found in Sade's effort to "say all" the possible crimes that are permitted in nature, in order to prove that the only principle to be observed is that of the individual's totalistic pleasure. Melodrama represents both the urge toward resacralization and the impossibility of conceiving sacralization other than in personal terms. Melodramatic good and evil are highly personalized: they are assigned to, they inhabit persons who indeed have no psychological complexity but who are strongly characterized. Most notably, evil is villainy; it is a swarthy, cape-enveloped man with a deep voice. Good and evil can be named as persons are named—and melodramas tend in fact to move toward a clear nomination of the moral universe. The ritual of melodrama involves the confrontation of clearly identified antagonists and the expulsion of one of them. It can offer no terminal reconciliation, for there is no longer a clear transcendent value to be reconciled to. There is, rather, a social order to be purged, a set of ethical imperatives to be made clear.

Of particular pertinence in any discussion of desacralization and the response to it are two early Romantic ("pre-Romantic") forms that in fact nourish one another, melodrama and the Gothic novel. The Gothic novel stands most clearly in reaction to desacralization and the pretensions of rationalism; it represents, in D. P. Varma's phrase, a "quest for the numinous."[20] It reasserts the presence, in the world, of forces that cannot be accounted for by the daylight self and the self-sufficient mind. Yet the Gothicists typically discover that this reassertion of spiritual forces and occult issues hidden in the phenomenal world cannot lead to the resacralization of experience. The status of the Sacred as "wholly other"—in Rudolf Otto's phrase—as a realm of being and value recognized to be apart from and superior to man, is gone and is irrecoverable. Of the *mysterium tremendum*, which Otto defines as the essence of the Holy, only the *tremendum* can be convincingly revived.[21] This issue, in fact, is given a dramatization in M. G. Lewis' *The Monk* (along with Mary Shelley's *Frankenstein* the most interesting and intelligent of the Gothic novels) in relation to the problem of guilt and its definition. The monk's temptress, Matilda, proposes to call upon diabolical aid in the seduction of the virginal Antonia; and Ambrosio, who still retains vestigial belief in the Christian paradox of salvation, resists: "No, no, Matilda, I will not ally myself with God's enemy." In reply, Matilda is fiercely logical in her description of the changed ontology of the supernatural and Ambrosio's altered relationship to it:

> Are you then God's friend at present? . . . Are you not planning the destruction of innocence, the ruin of a creature whom he formed in the mould of angels? If not of daemons, whose aid would you invoke to forward this laudable design? Will the seraphims protect it, conduct Antonia to your arms, and sanction with their ministry your illicit pleasures? Absurd! But I am not deceived, Ambrosio! It is not virtue which makes you reject my offer; you *would* accept it, but you *dare* not. 'Tis not the crime which holds your hand, but the punishment; 'tis not respect for God which restrains you, but the terror of his vengeance![22]

In her logic of the excluded middle (the very logic of melodrama), Matilda demonstrates that Ambrosio has moved out from under the mantle of the Sacred, and that ethics are now determined, not by virtue, but by terror. Her argument images a world in which God exists still, but no longer as holy mystery and as moral principle eliciting love, worship, and respect. No longer the source and guarantor of ethics, "God" has become an interdiction, a primitive force within nature that strikes fear in men's hearts but does not move them to allegiance and worship. Guilt, in the largest sense, may itself derive from an anxiety produced by man's failure to have maintained a relation to the Sacred; it must now be redefined in terms of self-punishment, which requires terror, interdiction of transgression, retribution. As with the revolutionary legislator Saint-Just, we have a new alternative basis for the ethical community: a sentimental virtue (of the type often urged in Diderot's aesthetics) or else a retributive, purgative terror.

The nature of the traditional idea of the Sacred is clarified in Clifford Geertz' definition of the status it maintains in "primitive" cultures: "The holy bears within it everywhere a sense of intrinsic obligation: it not only encourages devotion, it demands it; it not only induces intellectual assent, it enforces emotional commitment."[23] A true Sacred is evident, persuasive, and compelling, a system both of mythic explanation and implicit ethics. The traditional conception of the *mysterium tremendum* requires man's sense of dependence in relation to a "wholly other," and his feeling of being covered by it. The origin of religious feeling, according to Otto, lies in the "primal numinous awe," in a religious dread that may have at its root "demonic dread." The radical emotion is a feeling of the "eerie" and "uncanny," then elaborated into a concept in which the idea of awfulness and majesty exists in relation to the numen. Matilda's theology starts from the same point, but then evolves toward what a Christian theologian would see as a perversion, the belief in spooks and spirits, where "God" is merely one figure in a manichaeistic demonology. It is as if, coming out of the Enlightenment, man had to reinvent the sense of the Sacred from its source—but discovered it now skewed and narcissistically fascinated by its point of origin. There is a reassertion of magic and taboo, a recognition of the diabolical forces which inhabit our world and our inner being. Since these forces achieve no sacred status as wholly other, they appear, rather, to abide within nature and, particularly, within nature's creature, man. If the *tremendum* has reasserted its presence and force against the reductions of rationalism, the *mysterium* that it should modify has been displaced from without to within. We are led back to the sources of the "uncanny" in the processes of desire and repression analyzed by Freud.[24] The desacralization and sentimentalization of ethics leads us—as Diderot discovered in reading Richardson—into "the recesses of the cavern," there to discover "the hideous Moor" hidden in our motives and desires.[25]

The Gothic castle, with its pinnacles and dungeons, crenellations, moats, drawbridges, spiraling staircases and concealed doors, realizes an architectural approximation of the Freudian model of the mind, particularly the traps laid for the conscious by the unconscious and the repressed. The Gothic novel seeks an epistemology of the depths; it is fascinated by what lies hidden in the dungeon and the sepulcher. It sounds the depths, bringing to violent light and enactment the forces hidden and entrapped there. *The Monk*—in which all the major characters are finally compelled to descend into the sepulcher of St. Clare, there to perform their most extreme acts—belongs to a moment of "claustral" literature, fascinated by the constrained and hidden, determined to release its energies.[26] The content of the depths is one version of the "moral occult," the realm of inner imperatives and demons, and the Gothic novel dramatizes again and again the importance of bringing this occult into man's waking, social existence, of saying its meaning and acting out its force. The frenzy of the Gothic, the thunder of its rhetoric, and the excess of its situations image both the difficulty and the importance of the breaking through of repression, where victory is achieved, as in melodrama, by finding the true stakes of the drama.

The Monk, this exemplary Gothic novel written at the dead end of the Age of Reason, at the intersection of revolution and reaction, offers a particularly forceful dramatization of passage into an anxious new world where the Sacred is no longer viable, yet rediscovery of the ethical imperatives that traditionally depended on it is vital. Rediscovery would then be the task of the individual ethical consciousness in struggle with an occult domain. Melodrama shares many characteristics with the Gothic novel, and not simply in the subjects that were traded back and forth between the two genres. It is equally preoccupied with nightmare states, the claustration and thwarted escape, with innocence buried alive and unable to voice its claim to recognition. Particularly, it shares the preoccupation with evil as a real, irreducible force in the world, constantly menacing outburst. Melodrama is less directly interested in the reassertion of the numinous for its own sake than in its ethical corollaries. Melodrama starts from and expresses the anxiety brought by a frightening new world in which the traditional patterns of moral order no longer provide the necessary social glue. It plays out the force of that anxiety with the apparent triumph of villainy, and it dissipates it with the eventual victory of virtue. It demonstrates over and over that the signs of ethical forces can be discovered and can be made legible. It tends to diverge from the Gothic novel in its optimism, its claim that the moral imagination can open up the angelic spheres as well as the demonic depths and can allay the threat of moral chaos. Melodrama is indeed, typically, not only a moralistic drama but the drama of morality: it strives to find, to articulate, to demonstrate, to "prove" the existence of a moral universe which, though put into question, masked by villainy and perversions of judgment, does exist and can be made to assert its presence and its categorical force among men.

I am not making an argument for the direct influence of melodrama proper on novelists like Balzac and James (though this influence is in fact discernible), I am rather suggesting that perception of the melodramatic in their work can usefully be grounded and extended through reference to melodrama. Melodrama is the reductive, literalistic version of the mode to which they belong. The world of melodrama constitutes a temptation for such as Balzac and James because it offers a complete set of attitudes, phrases, gestures coherently conceived toward dramatization of essential spiritual conflict. It provides the expressive premises and the clear set of metaphors that they will exploit in extrapolated form, with a more problematical sense of the relation between vehicle and tenor.

Such writers as Balzac and James need melodrama because their deep subject, the locus of their true drama, has come to be what we have called the "moral occult": the domain of spiritual forces and imperatives that is not clearly visible within reality, but which they believe to be operative there, and which demands to be uncovered, registered, articulated. In the absence of a true Sacred (and in the absence indeed of any specific religious belief of their own) they continue to believe that what is most important in a man's life is his ethical drama and the ethical implications of his psychic drama. Yet here they are dealing in quantities and entities that have only an uncertain ontology and, especially, an uncertain visibility: they are not necessarily seen in the same manner, if perceived at all, by an audience, since the social cohesion of an earlier society with a greater community of belief no longer obtains. In the manner of the melodramatist, such writers must locate, express, demonstrate, prove the very terms in which they are dealing. They must wrest them forth from behind the facades of life, show their meaning and their operation. Precisely to the extent that they feel themselves dealing in concepts and issues that have no certain status or justification, they have recourse to the demonstrative, heightened representations of melodrama.

We might, finally, do well to recognize the melodramatic mode as a central fact of the modern sensibility (I take Romanticism to be the genesis of the modern, of the sensibility within which we are still living), in that modern art has typically felt itself to be constructed on, and over, the void, postulating meanings, and symbolic systems which have no certain justification because they are backed by no theology and no universally accepted social code. The mad quest of Mallarmé for a Book that would be "the Orphic explication of the earth," of Yeats for a synthetic mythology which would enable him to hold "in a single thought reality and justice," of Norman Mailer for dreams adequate to the moon—these are all versions of a reaction to the vertiginous feeling of standing over the abyss created when the necessary center of things has been evacuated and dispersed. Starting perhaps from Rousseau's decision that he must "say all" in his "enterprise without example," there is a desperate effort to renew contact with the scattered ethical and psychic fragments of the Sacred through the representation of fallen reality, insisting that behind reality, hidden by it yet indicated within it, there is a realm where large moral forces are operative, where large choices of ways of being must be made. The Promethean search to illuminate man's quotidian existence by the reflected flame of the higher cosmic drama constitutes one of the principal quests of the modern imagination. The melodramatic mode can be seen as an intensified, primary, and exemplary version of what the most ambitious art, since the beginnings of Romanticism, has been about.

What seems particularly important in the enterprise of the social melodramatists—and here one should include, beyond Balzac and James, Dickens, Gogol, Dostoevsky, Proust, Lawrence, to name only the most important—is their dual engagement with the representation of man's social existence, the way he lives in the ordinary, and with the moral drama implicated by and in his existence. They write a melodrama *of* manners. On the one hand, they refuse any metaphysical reduction of experience and refuse to reduce their metaphorical enterprise to the cold symbolism of allegory. They recognize, with Isabel Archer during her intense vigil, that "this base, ignoble world, it appeared, was after all what one was to live for" (2:197). On the other hand, they insist that life does make reference to a moral occult that is the realm of eventual value, and this insistence makes them more interesting and ambitious than more "behavioristic" novelists who, from Flaubert onwards, have suggested that there are not more things on earth than can be represented exclusively in terms of the material world. The melodramatists refuse to allow that the world has been completely drained of transcendence; and they locate that transcendence in the struggle of the children of light with the children of darkness, in the play of ethical mind.

It comes back, once again, to that alternative posed by James in reading Balzac, between the "magnificent lurid document" and the "baseless fabric of a vision." To make the fabric of vision into a document, to make the document lurid enough so that it releases the vision, to make vision document and document vision, and to persuade us that they cannot be distinguished, that they are necessarily interconnected through the chain of spiritual metaphor, that resonances are set up, electrical connections established whenever we touch any link of the chain, is to make the world we inhabit one charged with meaning, one in which interpersonal relations are not merely contacts of the flesh but encounters that must be carefully nurtured, judged, handled as if they mattered. It is a question, finally, of that attention to the significant in life that James captured in a famous line of advice to young novelists: "Try to be one of the people on whom nothing is lost."[27] To be so sensitized an instrument, one upon whom everything leaves a mark, with whom everything sets up a correspondence, is not simply to be an observer of life's surface, but someone who must bring into evidence, even into being, life's moral substance. So that the task of the writer is like that assigned by Balzac to the exiled Dante, in his tale *Les Proscrits*: "He closed himself in his room, lit his lamp of inspiration, and surrendered himself to the terrible demon of work, calling forth words from silence, and ideas from the night" (10:344).

Notes

1. Honoré de Balzac, *La Peau de chagrin*, in *La Comédie Humaine*, ed. Marcel Bouteron (Paris: Bibliothèque de la Pléïade, 1955–56), 9:11–12. All volume and page references to *La Comédie Humaine* are to the Pléïade edition and will henceforth be given in parentheses in the text. I refer to the Pléïade text for the sake of convenience, because it is relatively compact (11 volumes) and widely available. In some instances, its text needs emendation, and I have had recourse to the most reliable edition, the replica of the "Furne corrigé," published as Balzac's *Oeuvres complètes* (Paris: Les Bibliophiles de l'Originale, 1966–). All translations from the French are my own.
2. Martin Turnell, *The Novel in France* (New York: Vintage Books, 1958), p. 220.
3. Theodora Bosanquet, *Henry James at Work* (London: Hogarth Press, 1924), p. 32. This passage is also cited by Leo B. Levy, *Versions of Melodrama: A Study of the Fiction and Drama of Henry James, 1865–1897* (Berkeley and Los Angeles: University of California Press, 1957).
4. See Jacques Barzun, "Henry James, Melodramatist," in *The Question of Henry James*, ed. F. W. Dupee (New York: Holt, 1945).
5. Henry James, *The Portrait of a Lady* (New York: Scribner's, 1908), I:xxi. Following the original reference, page references to James's novels will be given in parentheses in the text.
6. Henry James, *The Ambassadors* (New York: Scribner's, 1909), 2:274.
7. Henry James, "Honoré de Balzac (1902)" in *Notes on Novelists* (New York: Scribner's, 1914), pp. 140–41.
8. I. A. Richards, *The Philosophy of Rhetoric* (New York: Oxford University Press, 1936), p. 94. We might note, in reference to the initial passage quoted from *La Peau de chagrin*, that *parable* has been defined as "teaching a moral by means of an extended metaphor" by Richard A. Lanham in *A Handlist of Rhetorical Terms* (Berkeley and Los Angeles: University of California Prss, 1968), p. 70.
9. Henry James, *The Wings of the Dove* (New York: Scribner's, 1909), 2:259.
10. *Tragedy and Melodrama: Versions of Experience*, p. 85.
11. "Melodrama," in *The Life of the Drama*, pp. 195–218.
12. Denis Diderot, "Entretiens sur *Le Fils naturel*," in *Oeuvres esthétiques*, ed. Paul Vernière (Paris: Garnier, 1959), pp. 148–49. For Diderot's discussion of the "interest" specific to the *genre sérieux*, see p. 136. The same aesthetic category is discernible in his discussion of Richardson (in "Eloge de Richardson") and in his comments on the paintings of Greuze (in "Salons").
13. Diderot, "Entretiens," p. 148.
14. The play was *Pygmalion*, "Scène lyrique," first staged in Lyon in 1770; and the word *mélodrame*, characterizing *Pygmalion*, is mentioned in Rousseau's "Observations sur l'*Alceste* Italien de M. le Chevalier Glück" (probably written in 1774 or 1775), in Jean-Jacques Rousseau, *Oeuvres* (Paris, 1801), 10:319–20.
15. Jean-Paul Sartre, *Les Mots* (Paris: Gallimard, 1964), pp. 101–2.

16. See Heilman, *Tragedy and Melodrama*, pasim. This usage is continued by James L. Smith, who subdivides the genre into melodrama of triumph, of defeat, and of protest.
17. Louis de Saint-Just, "Institutions républicaines," in *Oeuvres choisies* (Paris: Gallimard, 1968), p. 327.
18. I take this definition of tragedy from Northrop Frye, *Anatomy of Criticism* (Princeton: Princeton University Press, 1957), pp. 214–15. I find confirmation of my view of desacralization and its aftermath in a similar argument urged by Leslie Fiedler; see, in particular, *Love and Death in the American Novel* (1963; reprinted ed., London: Paladin Books, 1970), p. 34.
19. See, in particular, the closing paragraph of book 4 of Rousseau's *Confessions*.
20. Devendra P. Varma, *The Gotic Flame* (London: A. Barker, 1957), p. 211. On this aspect of the Gothic novel, see also Lowry Nelson, Jr., "Night Thoughts on the Gothic Novel," *Yale Review* 52 (1963); Eino Railo, *The Haunted Castle* (London: G. Routledge, 1927); Robert D. Hume, "Gothic versus Romantic: A Revaluation of the Gothic Novel," *PMLA* 84 (1969).
21. Rudolf Otto, *The Idea of the Holy* [*Das Heilige*], trans. John W. Harvey (Oxford: Galaxy Books, 1958), chaps. 4, 5.
22. Matthew Gregory Lewis, *The Monk* (New York: Grove Press, Evergreen Books, 1959), p. 266. For a more detailed discussion of this passage, of *The Monk* and the problem of the Sacred, see my article "Virtue and Terror: *The Monk*," *ELH* 40, no. 2 (1973).
23. Clifford Geertz, "Ethos, World View, and the Analysis of Sacred Symbolism," in *The Interpretation of Cultures* (New York: Basic Books, 1973), p. 126.
24. Sigmund Freud, "The Uncanny" ["Das Unheimliche"], in Standard Edition (London: Hogarth), 17:218–56.
25. Diderot, "Eloge de Richardson," in *Oeuvres esthétiques*, p. 32.
26. A prime example of claustral literature is *Les Victimes cloîtrées* (1791), a play by Boutet de Monvel which Lewis saw in Paris shortly before beginning work on *The Monk*, and which he translated as *Venoni*, staged in London. Another celebrated example, which Lewis may also have known, is *Le Couvent, ou les Voeux forcés*, by Olympe de Gouges (1790). And there are many more, particularly of the revolutionary period. See my discussion of Pixerécourt's *Latude, ou Trente-cinq ans de captivité* in chapter 2. See also Robert Shackleton, "The Cloister Theme in French Preromanticism," in *The French Mind: Studies in Honor of Gustave Rudler*, ed. Will Moore, Rhoda Sutherland, Enid Starkie (Oxford: Clarendon, 1952). The importance of *The Monk* and its exploration of psychological depths, as well as the close relation of the Gothic novel to the Revolution, was lucidly recognized by the foremost expositor of the claustral and its repressed content, the Marquis de Sade, in his essay "Idée sur les romans," in *Oeuvres* (Paris: Cercle du Livre Précieux, 1964), 10:15.
27. Henry James, "The Art of Fiction," in *The Future of the Novel*, ed. Leon Edel (New York: Vintage Books, 1956), p. 13.

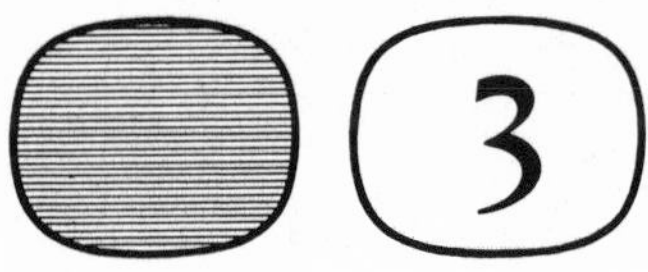

Tales of Sound and Fury: Observations on the Family Melodrama

THOMAS ELSAESSER

How to Make Stones Weep

Asked about the colour in *Written on the Wind*, Douglas Sirk replied: "Almost throughout the picture I used deep-focus lenses, which have the effect of giving a harshness to the objects and a kind of enamelled, hard surface to the colours. I wanted this to bring out the inner violence, the energy of the characters, which is all inside them and can't break through." It would be difficult to think of a better way of describing what this particular movie and indeed most of the best melodramas of the fifties and early sixties are about. Or for that matter, how closely, in this film, style and technique is related to theme.

In this article I want to pursue an elusive subject in two directions: to indicate the development of what one might call the melodramatic imagination across different artistic forms and in different epochs; secondly, Sirk's remark tempts one to look for some structural and stylistic constants in one medium during one particular period (the Hollywood family melodrama between roughly 1940 and 1963) and to speculate on the cultural and psychological context which this form of melodrama so manifestly reflected and helped to articulate. Nonetheless this isn't a historical study in any strict sense, nor a *catalogue raisonné* of names and titles, for reasons that have something to do with my general method as well as with the obvious limitation imposed on film research by unavailability. As a consequence I lean rather heavily on half a dozen

Thomas Elsaesser, "Tales of Sound and Fury: Observations on the Family Melodrama," originally published in *Monogram*, no. 4 (1972), pp. 2–15. Reprinted by permission of the author and the British Film Institute.

films, and notably *Written on the Wind*, to develop my points. This said, it is difficult to see how references to twenty more movies would make the argument any truer. For better or worse, what I want to say should at this stage be taken to be provocative rather than proven.

Bearing in mind that (whatever one's scruples about an exact definition) everybody has some idea of what is meant by "melodramatic," any discussion of the melodrama as a specific cinematic mode of expression has to start from its antecedents—the novel and certain types of "entertainment" drama—from which scriptwriters and directors have borrowed their models.

The first thing one notices is that the media and literary forms which have habitually embodied melodramatic situations have changed considerably in the course of history, and, further, they differ from country to country; in England, it has mainly been the novel and the literary gothic where melodramatic motifs persistently crop up (though the Victorian stage, especially in the 1880s and 1890s, knew an unprecedented vogue for the melodramas of R. Buchanan and G. R. Sims, plays in which "a footbridge over a torrent breaks under the steps of the villain; a piece of wall comes down to shatter him; a boiler bursts, and blows him to smithereens");[1] in France, it is the costume drama and historical novel; in Germany "high" drama and the ballad, as well as more popular forms like *Moritat* (street songs); finally, in Italy the opera rather than the novel reached the highest degree of sophistication in the handling of melodramatic situations.

Two currents make up the genealogy. One leads from the late medieval morality play, the popular *gestes* and other forms of oral narrative and drama, like fairy-tales and folk-songs to their romantic revival and the cult of the pictureseque in Scott, Byron, Heine and Victor Hugo, which has its low-brow echo in barrel-organ songs, music-hall drama, and what in Germany is known as Bänkellied, the latter coming to late literary honours through Brecht in his songs and musical plays, *The Threepenny Opera* or *Mahagonny.* The characteristic features for our present purposes in this tradition are not so much the emotional shock-tactics and the blatant playing on the audience's known sympathies and antipathies, but rather the non-psychological conception of the *dramatis personae*, who figure less as autonomous individuals than to transmit the action and link the various locales within a total constellation. In this respect, melodramas have a myth-making function, insofar as their significance lies in the structure and articulation of the action, not in any psychologically motivated correspondence with individualised experience.

Yet, what particularly marks the ballad or the *Bänkellied*, i.e., narratives accompanied by music, is that the moral/moralistic pattern which furnishes the primary content (crimes of passion bloodily revenged, murderers driven mad by guilt and drowning themselves, villains snatching children from their careless mothers, servants killing their unjust masters) is overlaid not only with a proliferation of "realistic" homey detail, but also "parodied" or relativised by the heavily repetitive verse-form or the mechanical up-and-down rhythms of the barrel organ, to which the voice of the singer adapts itself (consciously or not), thereby producing a vocal parallelism that has a distancing or ironic effect, to the extent of often criss-crossing the moral of the story by a "false," i.e., unexpected emphasis. Sirk's most successful German melodrama, *Zu Neuen Ufern*, makes excellent use of the street ballad to bring out the tragic irony in the court-room scene, and the tune which Walter Brennan keeps playing on the harmonica in King Vidor's *Ruby Gentry* works in a very similar way. A variation on this is the use of fairgrounds and carousels in films like *Some Came Running* and *Tarnished Angels*, or more self-consciously in Hitchcock (*Strangers on a Train, Stage Fright*) and Welles (*Lady from Shanghai* and *The Stranger*) to underscore the main action and at the same time "ease" the melodramatic impact by providing an ironic parallelism. Sirk uses the motif repeatedly in, for instance, *Scandal in Paris* and *Take Me to Town*. What such devices point to is that in the melodrama the *rhythm* of experience often establishes itself against its value (moral, intellectual).

Perhaps the current that leads more directly to the sophisticated family melodrama of the 40's and 50's, though, is derived from the romantic drama, which had its heyday after the French Revolution and subsequently furnished many of the plots for operas, but which is itself unthinkable without the 18th-century sentimental novel and the emphasis put on private feelings and interiorised (puritan, pietist) codes of morality and conscience. Historically, one of the interesting facts about this tradition is that its height of popularity seems to coincide (and this remains true throughout the 19th century) with periods of intense social and ideological crisis. The prerevolutionary sentimental novel—Richardson's *Clarissa* or Rousseau's *Nouvelle Héloise*, for example—go out of their way to make a case for extreme forms of behaviour and feeling by depicting very explicitly certain external constraints and pressures bearing upon the characters, and by showing up the quasi-totalitarian violence perpetrated by (agents of) the "system" (Lovelace who tries everything, from bribing her family to hiring pimps, prostitutes and kidnappers in order to get Clarissa to become his wife, only to have to rape her after all). The same pattern is to be found in the bourgeois tragedies of Lessing (*Emilia Galotti*, 1768) and the early Schiller (*Kabale und Liebe*, 1776), both deriving their dramatic force from the conflict between an extreme and highly individualised form of moral idealism in the heroes (again, non-psychological on the level of motivation) and a thoroughly corrupt yet seemingly omnipotent social class (made up of feudal princes and petty state functionaries). The melodramatic elements are clearly visible in the plots, which revolve around family relationships, star-crossed lovers and forced marriages. The villains (often of noble birth) demonstrate their superior political and economic power invariably by sexual aggression and attempted rape, leaving the heroine no other way than to commit suicide or take poison in the company of her lover. The ideological "message" of these tragedies, as in the case of *Clarissa*, is transparent: they record the struggle of a morally and emotionally emancipated bourgeois consciousness against the remnants of feudalism. They pose the problem in political terms and concentrate on the complex interplay of ethical principles, religious-metaphysical polarities and the idealist aspirations typical of the bourgeoisie in its militant phase, as the protagonists come to grief in a maze of economic necessities, *realpolitik*, family loyalties, and through the abuse of aristocratic privilege from a still divinely ordained, and therefore doubly depraved, absolutist authority.

Although these plays and novels, because they use the melodramatic-emotional plot only as their most rudimentary structure of meaning, belong to the more intellectually demanding forms of melodrama, the element of interiorisation and personalisation of primarily ideological conflicts, together with the metaphorical interpretation of class conflict as sexual exploitation and rape, is important in all subsequent forms of melodrama, including that of the cinema. (The latter in America, of course, is a stock theme of novels and movies with a "Southern" setting.)

Paradoxically, the French Revolution failed to produce a new form of social drama or tragedy. The Restoration stage (when theatres in Paris were specially licensed to play "melodramas") trivialised the form by using melodramatic plots in exotic settings, and providing escapist entertainment with little social relevance. The plays warmed up the standard motif of 18th-century French fiction and drama, that of innocence persecuted and virtue rewarded, and the conventions of melodrama functioned in their most barren form as the mechanics of pure suspense.

What before the Revolution had served to focus on suffering and victimization—the claims of the individual in an absolutist society—was reduced to ground-glass-in-the-porridge, poisoned handkerchiefs and last-minute rescues from the dungeon. The sudden reversals of fortune, the intrusion of chance and coincidence had originally pointed to the arbitrary way feudal institutions could ruin the individual unprotected by civil rights and liberties. The system stood accused of greed, wilfulness and irrationality through the Christ-like suffering of the pure virgin and the selfless heroism of the right-minded in the midst of court intrigue and callous indifference. Now, with the bourgeoisie triumphant, this form of drama lost its subversive charge and functioned more as a means of consolidating an as yet weak and incoherent ideological position. Whereas the prerevolutionary melodramas had often ended tragically, those of the Restoration had happy endings, they reconciled the suffering individual to his social position, by affirming an "open" society, where everything was possible. Over and over again, the victory of the "good" citizen over "evil" aristocrats, lecherous clergymen and the even more conventional villains drawn from the lumpenproletariat, was re-enacted in sentimental spectacles full of tears and high moral tones. Complex social processes were simplified either by blaming the evil disposition of individuals or by manipulating the plots and engineering coincidences and other *dei ex machina*, such as the instant conversion of the villain, moved by the plight of his victim, or suddenly struck by Divine Grace on the steps of Nôtre-Dame.

Since the overtly "conformist" strategy of such drama is quite evident, what is interesting is certainly not the plot structure, but whether the conventions allowed the author to dramatize in his episodes actual contradictions in society and genuine clashes of interests in the characters. Already during the Revolution plays such as Monvel's *Les Victimes cloîtrées* or Laya's *L'Ami des lois*, though working with very stereotyped plots, conveyed quite definite political sympathies (the second, for instance, backed the Girondist moderates in the trial of Louis XIV against the Jacobites) and were understood as such by their public.[2]

Even if the form might act to reinforce attitudes of submission, the actual working out of the scenes could nonetheless present fundamental social evils. Many of the pieces also flattered popular sympathies by giving the villains the funniest lines, just as Victorian drama playing east of Drury Lane was often enlivened by low comedy burlesque put on as curtain raisers and by the servants' farces during the intermission.

All this is to say that there seems a radical ambiguity attached to the melodrama, which holds even more for the film melodrama. Depending on whether the emphasis fell on the odyssey of suffering or the happy ending, on the place and context of rupture (moral conversion of the villain, unexpected appearance of a benevolent Capuchin monk throwing off his pimp's disguise), that is to say, depending on what dramatic mileage was got out of the heroine's perils before the ending (and one only has to think of Sade's *Justine* to see what could be done with the theme of innocence unprotected), melodrama would appear to function either subversively or as escapism—categories which are always relative to the given historical and social context.[3]

In the cinema, Griffith is a good example. Using identical dramatic devices and cinematic techniques, he could, with *Intolerance, Way Down East* or *Broken Blossoms*, create, if not exactly subversive, at any rate socially committed melodramas, whereas *Birth of a Nation* or *Orphans of the Storm* are classic examples of how melodramatic effects can successfully shift explicit political themes onto a personalised plane. In both cases, Griffith tailored ideological conflicts into emotionally loaded family situations.

The persistence of the melodrama might indicate the ways in which popular culture has not only taken note of social crises and the fact that the losers are not always those who deserve it most, but has also resolutely refused to understand social change in other than private contexts and emotional terms. In this, there is obviously a healthy distrust of intellectualisation and abstract social theory—insisting that other structures of experience (those of suffering, for instance) are more in keeping with reality. But it has also meant ignorance of the properly social and political dimensions of these changes and their causality, and consequently it has encouraged increasingly escapist forms of mass entertainment.

However, this ambivalence about the "structures" of experience, endemic in the melodramatic mode, has served artists throughout the 19th century for the depiction of a variety of themes and social phenomena, while remaining within the popular idiom. Industrialisation, urbanisation and nascent entrepreneurial capitalism have found their most telling literary embodiment in a type of novel clearly indebted to the melodrama, and the national liberals in Italy during the *Risorgimento*, for example, saw their political aspirations reflected in Verdi's operas (*cf.* the opening of Visconti's *Senso*). In England, Dickens, Collins and Reade relied heavily on melodramatic plots to sharpen social conflicts and portray an urban environment where chance encounters, coincidences, and the side-by-side existence of extreme social and moral contrasts were the natural products of the very conditions of existence—crowded tenement houses, narrow streets backing on to the better residential property, and other facts of urban demography of the time. Dickens in particular uses the element of chance, the dream/waking, horror/bliss switches in *Oliver Twist* or *Tale of Two Cities* partly to feel his way towards a portrayal of existential insecurity and moral anguish which fiction had previously not encompassed, but also to explore depth-psychological phenomena, for which the melodrama—as Freud was later to confirm—has supplied the dynamic motifs and the emotional-pictorial decor. What seems to me important in this form of melodrama (and one comes across a similar conception in the sophisticated Hollywood melodramas) is the emphasis Dickens places on discontinuity, on the evidence of fissures and ruptures in the fabric of experience, and the appeal to a reality of the psyche—to which the notions of sudden change, reversal and excess lend a symbolic plausibility.

In France it is the works of Sue, Hugo and Balzac that reflect most closely the relation of melodrama to social upheaval. Sue, for example, uses the time-worn trapdoor devices of cloak and dagger stage melodrama for an explicitly sensationalist, yet committed journalism. In a popular form and rendered politically palatable by the fictionalized treatment, his *Mystères de Paris* were intended to crusade on such issues as public heallth, prostitution, overcrowding and slum housing, sanitation, black-market racketeering, corruption in government circles, opium smoking and gambling. Sue exploited a "reactionary" form for reformist ends, and his success, both literary and practical, proved him right. Twenty years later Victor Hugo, who had learnt as much from Sue as Sue had picked up from *Nôtre-Dame de Paris*, produced with *Les Misérables* a super-melodrama spectacular which must stand as the crowning achievement of the genre in the novel. The career of Jean Valjean, from convict and galley slave to factory owner and capitalist, his fall and literal emergence from the sewers of Paris to become a somewhat unwilling activist in the 1848 Revolution, is staged with the help of mistaken identities, orphans suddenly discovering their noble birth, inconvenient reappearance of people long thought dead, hair-breadth escapes and rescues, multiple disguises, long-suffering females dying of consumption or wandering for days through the streets in search of their child—and yet, through all this, Hugo expresses a hallucinating vision of the anxiety, the moral confusion, the emotional demands, in short, the metaphysics of social change and urban life betwween the time of Waterloo and 1848. Hugo evidently wanted to bring together in a popular form subjective experiences of crises, while keeping track of the grand lines of France's history, and he succeeds singularly well in reproducing the ways individuals with different social backgrounds, levels of awareness and imaginations, respond to objective changes in the social fabric of their lives. For this, the melodrama, with its shifts in mood, its different tempi and the mixing of stylistic levels, is ideally suited: *Les Misérables*, even more so than the novels of Dickens, lets through a symbolic dimension of psychic truth, with the hero in turn representing very nearly the id, the superego and finally the sacrificed ego of a repressed and paranoid society.

Balzac, on the other hand, uses melodramatic plots to a rather different end. Many of his novels deal with the dynamics of early capitalist economics. The good/evil dichotomy has almost disappeared, and the Manichean conflicts have shifted away from questions of morality to the paradoxes of psychology and economics. What we see is a Schopenhauerian struggle of the will: the ruthlessness of industrial entrepreneurs and bankers, the spectacle of an uprooted, "decadent" aristocracy still holding tremendous political power, the sudden twists of fortune with no-good parasites becoming millionaires overnight (or vice versa) through speculation and the stock exchange, the antics of hangers-on, parvenus and cynical artist-intellectuals, the demonic, spellbinding potency of money and capital, the contrasts between abysmal poverty and unheard-of affluence and waste which characterized the "anarchic" phase of industrialisation and high finance, were experienced by Balzac as both vital and melodramatic. His work reflects this more in style than through direct comment.

To sum up: these writers understood the melodrama as a form which carried its own values and already embodied its own significant content: it served as the literary equivalent of a particular, historically and socially conditioned *mode of experience*. Even if the situations and sentiments defied all categories of versimilitude and were totally unlike anything in real life, the structure had a truth and a life of its own, which an artist could make part of his material. This meant that those who consciously adopted melodramatic techniques of presentation did not necessarily do so out of incompetence nor always from a cynical distance, but, by turning a body of techniques into a stylistic principle that carried the distinct overtones of spiritual crisis, they could put the finger on the texture of their social and human material while still being free to shape this material. For there is little doubt that the whole conception of life in 19th-century Europe and England, and especially the spiritual problems of the age, were often viewed in categories we would today call melodramatic—one can see this in painting, architecture, the ornamentation of gadgets and furniture, the domestic and public mise-en-scène of events and occasions, the oratory in parliament, the tractarian rhetoric from the pulpit as well as the more private manifestations of religious sentiment. Similarly, the timeless themes that Dostoyevsky brings up again and again in his novels—guilt, redemption, justice, innocence, freedom—are made specific and historically real not least because he was a great writer of melodramatic scenes and confrontations, and they more than anything else define that powerful irrational logic in the motivation and moral outlook of, say, Raskolnikov, Ivan Karamazov or Kirilov. Finally, how different Kafka's novels would be, if they did not contain those melodramatic family situations, pushed to the point where they reveal a dimension at once comic and tragically absurd—perhaps the existential undertow of all genuine melodrama.

Putting Melos into Drama

In its dictionary sense, melodrama is a dramatic narrative in which musical accompaniment marks the emotional effects. This is still perhaps the most useful definition, because it allows melodramatic elements to be seen as constituents of a system of punctuation, giving expressive colour and chromatic contrast to the storyline, by orchestrating the emotional ups and downs of the intrigue. The advantage of this approach is that it formulates the problems of melodrama as problems of style and articulation.

Music in melodrama, for example, as a device among others to dramatize a given narrative, is subjective, programmatic. But because it is also a form of punctuation in the above sense, it is both functional (i.e., of structural significance) and thematic (i.e., belonging to the expressive content) because used to formulate certain moods—sorrow, violence, dread, suspense, happiness. The syntactic function of music has, as is well known, survived into the sound film, and the experiments conducted by Hanns Eisler and T. W. Adorno are highly instructive in this respect.[4] A practical demonstration of the problem can be found in the account which Lilian Ross gives of how Gottfried Reinhard and Dore Shary reedited John Huston's *Red Badge of Courage* to give it a smooth dramatic shape, with build-ups and climaxes in the proper order, which is exactly what Huston had wanted to avoid when he shot it.[5]

Because it had to rely on piano accompaniment for punctuation, all silent film drama—from *True Heart Susie* to *Foolish Wives* or *The Lodger*—is "melodramatic." It meant that directors had to develop an extremely subtle and yet precise formal language (of lighting, staging, decor, acting, close-up, montage and camera movement), because they were deliberately looking for ways to compensate for the expressiveness, range of inflection and tonality, rhythmic emphasis and tension normally present in the spoken word. Having had to replace that part of language which is sound, directors like Murnau, Renoir, Hitchcock, Mizoguchi, Hawks, Lang, Sternberg achieved in their films a high degree (well recognised at the time) of plasticity in the modulation of optical planes and spatial masses which Panofsky rightly identified as a "dynamisation of space."

Among less gifted directors this sensitivity in the deployment of expressive means was partly lost with the advent of direct sound, since it seemed no longer necessary in a strictly technical sense—pictures "worked" on audiences through their dialogue, and the semantic force of language overshadowed the more sophisticated pictorial effects and architectural values. This perhaps helps to explain why some major technical innovations, such as colour, wide screen and deep-focus lenses, crane and dolly, have in fact encouraged a new form of sophisticated melodrama. Directors (quite a sizeable proportion of whom came during the 30s from Germany, and others were clearly indebted to German expressionism and Max Reinhardt's methods of theatrical mise-en-scène) began showing a similar degree of visual culture as the masters of silent film drama: Ophuls, Lubitsch, Sirk, Preminger, Welles, Losey, Ray, Minnelli, Cukor.

Considered as an expressive code, melodrama might therefore be described as a particular form of dramatic mise-en-scène, characterised by a dynamic use of spatial and musical categories, as opposed to intellectual or literary ones. Dramatic situations are given an orchestration which will allow for complex aesthetic patterns: indeed, orchstration is fundamental to the American cinema as a whole (being essentially a dramatic cinema, spectacular, and based on a broad appeal) because it has drawn the aesthetic consequences of having the spoken word more as an additional "melodic" dimension than as an autonomous semantic discourse. Sound, whether musical or verbal, acts first of all to give the illusion of depth to the moving image, and by helping to create the third dimension of the spectacle, dialogue becomes a scenic element, along with more directly visual means of the mise-en-scène. Anyone who has ever had the bad luck of watching a Hollywood movie dubbed into French or German will know how important diction is to the emotional resonance and dramatic continuity. Dubbing makes the best picture seem visually flat and out of sync: it destroys the flow on which the coherence of the illusionist spectacle is built.

That the plasticity of the human voice is quite consciously employed by directors for what are often thematic ends is known: Hawks trained Lauren Bacall's voice so that she could be given "male" lines in *To Have and Have Not*, an effect which Sternberg anticipated when he took great care to cultivate Marlene Dietrich's diction, and it is hard to miss the psychoanalytic significance of Robert Stack's voice in *Written on the Wind*, sounding as if every word had to be painfully pumped up from the bottom of one of his oil-wells.

If it is true that *speech* in the American cinema loses some of its semantic importance in favour of its material aspects as sound, then conversely lighting, composition, decor increase their semantic and syntactic contribution to the aesthetic effect. They become functional and integral elements in the construction of meaning. This is the justification for giving critical importance to the mise-en-scène over intellectual content or story-value. It is also the reason why the domestic melodrama in colour and wide screen, as it appeared in the 40's and 50's, is perhaps the most highly elaborated, complex mode of cinematic signification that the American cinema has ever produced, because of the restricted scope for external action determined by the subject, and because everything, as Sirk said, happens "inside." To the "sublimation" of the action picture and the Busby Berkeley/Lloyd Bacon musical into domestic and family melodrama corresponded a sublimation of dramatic conflict into decor, colour, gesture and composition of frame, which in the best melodramas is perfectly thematised in terms of the characters' emotional and psychological predicaments.

For example, when in ordinary language we call something melodramatic, what we often mean is an exaggerated rise-and-fall pattern in human actions and emotional responses, a from-the-sublime-to-the-ridiculous movement, a foreshortening of lived time in favour of intensity—all of which produces a graph of much greater fluctuation, a quicker swing from one extreme to the other than is considered natural, realistic or in conformity with literary standards of versimilitude: in the novel we like to sip our pleasures, rather than gulp them. But if we look at, say, Minnelli, who has adapted some of his best melodramas (*The Cobweb, Some Came Running, Home from the Hill, Two Weeks in Another Town, The Four Horsemen of the Apocalypse*) from generally extremely long, circumstantially detailed popular novels (by James Jones, Irving Shaw *et al.*), it is easy to see how in the process of having to reduce 7 to 9 hours' reading matter to 90-odd minutes, such a more violent "melodramatic" graph almost inevitably produces itself, short of the narrative becoming incoherent. Whereas in novels, especially when they are staple pulp fare, size connotes solid emotional involvement for the reader, the specific values of the cinema lie in its concentrated visual metaphors and dramatic acceleration rather than in the fictional techniques of dilation. The commercial necessity of compression (being also a formal one) is taken by Minnelli into the films themselves and developed as a theme—that of a pervasive psychological pressure on the characters. An acute sense of claustrophobia in decor and locale translates itself into a restless and yet suppressed energy surfacing sporadically in the actions and the behaviour of the protagonists—which is part of the subject of a film like *Two Weeks in Another Town*, with hysteria bubbling all the time just below the surface. The feeling that there is always more to tell than can be said leads to very consciously elliptical narratives, proceeding often by visually condensing the characters' motivation into sequences of images which do not seem to advance the plot. The shot of the Trevi fountain at the end of a complex scene where Kirk Douglas is making up his mind in *Two Weeks* is such a metaphoric condensation, and so is the silent sequence, consisting entirely of what might appear to be merely impressionistic dissolves, in the

Four Horsemen, when Glenn Ford and Ingrid Thulin go for a ride to Versailles, but which in fact tells and foretells the whole trajectory of their relationship.

Sirk, too, often constructs his films in this way: the restlessness of *Written on the Wind* is not unconnected with the fact that he almost always cuts on movement. His visual metaphors really ought to have a chapter to themselves: a yellow sports-car drawing up the gravelled driveway to stop in front of a pair of shining white Doric columns outside the Hadley mansion is not only a powerful piece of American iconography, especially when taken in a plunging high-angle shot, but the contrary associations of imperial splendour and vulgar materials (polished chrome-plate and stucco plaster) create a tension of correspondencess and dissimilarities in the same image, which perfectly crystallizes as the decadent affluence and melancholy energy that give the film its uncanny fascination. Sirk has a peculiarly vivid eye for the contrasting emotional qualities of textures and materials, and he combines them or makes them clash to very striking effect, especially when they occur in a non-dramatic sequence: again in *Written on the Wind*, after the funeral of Hadley Sr., a black servant is seen taking an oleander wreath off the front gate. A black silk ribbon gets unstuck and is blown by the wind along the concrete path. The camera follows the movement, dissolves and dollies in on a window, where Lauren Bacall, in an oleander-green dress, is just about to disappear behind the curtains. The scene has no plot significance whatsoever. But the colour parallels black/green, green/green, white concrete/white lace curtains provide an extremely strong emotional resonance in which the contrast of soft silk blown along the hard concrete is registered the more forcefully as a disquieting visual association. The desolation of the scene transfers itself onto the Bacall character, and the traditional fatalistic association of the wind reminds us of the futility implied in the movie's title.

These effects, of course, require a highly self-conscious stylist, but they are by no means rare in Hollywood. The fact that commercial necessities, political censorship and the various morality codes restricted directors in what they could tackle as a subject has entailed a different awareness of what constituted a worthwhile subject, a change in orientation from which sophisticated melodrama benefited perhaps most. Not only did they provide a defined thematic parameter, but they encouraged a conscious use of style-as-meaning, which is a mark of what I would consider to be the very condition of a modernist sensibility working in popular culture. To take another example from Minnelli: his existential theme of a character trying to cnstruct the world in the image of an inner self, only to discover that this world has become uninhabitable because it is both frighteningly suffocating and intolerably lonely (*The Long, Long Trailer, The Cobweb*) is transformed and given social significance in the stock melodrama theme of the woman who, having failed to make it in the big city, comes back to the small-town home in the hope of finding her true place at last, but who is made miserable by mean-mindedness and bigotry and then suffocated by the sheer weight of her none-too-glorious, still ruefully remembered past (*Hilda Crane, Beyond the Forest, All I Desire*).[6] But in Minnelli, it becomes an opportunity to explore in concrete circumstances the more philosophical questions of freedom and determinism, especially as they touch the aesthetic problem of how to depict a character who is not constantly externalising himself into action, without thereby trapping him in an environment of ready-made symbolism.

Similarly, when Robert Stack shows Lauren Bacall her hotel suite in *Written on the Wind*, where everything from flowers and pictures on the wall to underwear, nailpolish and handbag is provided, Sirk not only characterizes a rich man wanting to take over the woman he fancies body and soul, or the oppressive nature of an unwanted gift. He is also making a direct comment on the Hollywood stylistic technique that "creates" a character out of the elements of the decor, and that prefers actors who can provide as blank a facial surface and as little of a personality as possible.

Everyone who has at all thought about the Hollywood aesthetic wants to formulate one of its peculiar qualities: that of direct emotional involvement, whether one calls it "giving resonance to dramatic situations" or "fleshing out the cliché" or whether, more abstractly, one talks in terms of identification patterns, empathy and catharsis. Since the American cinema, determined as it is by an ideology of the spectacle and the spectacular, is essentially dramatic (as opposed to lyrical, i.e., concerned with mood or the inner self) and not conceptual (dealing with ideas and the structures of cognition and perception), the creation or reenactment of situations which the spectator can identify with and recognise (whether this recognition is on the conscious or unconscious level is another matter) depends to a large extent on the aptness of the iconography (the "visualisation") and on the quality (complexity, subtlety, ambiguity) of the orchestration for what are trans-individual, popular mythological (and therefore generally considered culturally "lowbrow") experiences and plot structures. In other words, this type of cinema depends on the ways "melos" is given to "drama" by means of lighting, montage, visual rhythm, decor, style of acting, music—that is, on the ways the mise-en-scène translates character into action (not unlike the pre-Jamesian novel) and action into gesture and dynamic space (comparable to 19th-century opera and ballet).

This granted, there seems to be a further problem which has some bearing on the question of melodrama: although the techniques of audience orientation and the possibility of psychic projection on the part of the spectator are as much in evidence in a melodrama like *Home from the Hill* or *Splendor in the Grass* as they are in a Western or adventure picture, the difference of setting and milieu affects the dynamic of the action. In the Western especially, the assumption of "open" spaces is virtually axiomatic; it is indeed one of the constants which makes the form perennially attractive to a largely urban audience. This openness becomes problematic in films that deal with potential "melodrama" themes and family situations. The complex father-son relationships in *The Left-Handed Gun*, the Cain-Abel themes of Mann's Westerns (*Winchester 73*, *Bend of the River*), the conflict of virility and mother-fixation in some of Tourneur's Westerns (*Great Day in the Morning*, *Wichita*) or the search for the mother (-country) in Fuller's *Run of the Arrow* seem to find resolution because the hero can act positively on the changing situations where and when they present themselves. In Raoul Walsh's adventure pictures, as Peter Lloyd has shown,[7] identity comes in an often paradoxical process of self-confirmation and overreaching—but always through direct action, while the momentum generated by the conflicts pushes the protagonists forward in an unrelentingly linear course.

The family melodrama, by contrast, though dealing largely with the same Oedipal themes of emotional and moral identity, more often records the failure of the protagonist to act in a way that could shape the events and influence the emotional environment, let alone change the stifling social milieu. The world is closed, and the characters are acted upon. Melodrama confers on them a negative identity through suffering, and the progressive self-immolation and disillusionment generally ends in resignation: they emerge as lesser human beings for having become wise and acquiescent to the ways of the world.

The difference can be put in another way. In one case, the drama moves towards its resolution by having the central conflicts successively externalised and projected into direct action. A jail-break, a bank robbery, a Western chase or cavalry charge, and even a criminal investigation lend themselves to psychologized, thematised representations of the heroes' inner dilemmas and frequently appear that way (Walsh's *White Heat* or *They Died with Their Boots On*, Losey's *The Criminal*, Preminger's *Where the Sidewalk Ends*). The same is true of the melodrama in the *série noire* tradition, where the hero is egged on or blackmailed by the *femme fatale*—the smell of honeysuckle and death in *Double Indemnity*, *Out of the Past* or *Detour*—into a course of action which pushes him further and further in one direction, opening a narrowing wedge of equally ineluctable consequences, that usually lead the hero to wishing his own death as the ultimate act of liberation, but where the mechanism of fate at least allows him to express his existential revolt in strong and strongly anti-social behavior.

Not so in the domestic melodrama: the social pressures are such, the frame of respectability so sharply defined that the range of "strong" actions is limited. The tellingly impotent gesture, the social gaffe, the hysterical outburst replaces any more directly liberating or self-annhilating action, and the cathartic violence of a shoot-out or a chase becomes an inner violence, often one which the characters turn against themselves. The dramatic configuration, the pattern of the plot makes them, regardless of attempts to break free, constantly look inwards, at each other and themselves. The characters are, so to speak, each others' sole referent, there is no world outside to be acted on, no reality that could be defined or assumed unambiguously. In Sirk, of course, they are locked into a universe of real and metaphoric mirrors, but quite generally, what is typical of this form of melodrama is that the characters' behaviour is often pathetically at variance with the real objectives they want to achieve. A sequence of substitute actions creates a kind of vicious circle in which the close nexus of cause and effect is somehow broken and—in an often overtly Freudian sense—displaced. James Dean in *East of Eden* thinks up a method of cold storage for lettuce, grows beans to sell to the Army, falls in love with Julie Harris, not to make a pile of money and live happily with a beautiful wife, but in order to win the love of his father and oust his brother—neither of which he achieves. Although very much on the surface of Kazan's film, this is a conjunction of puritan capitalist ethic and psychoanalysis which is sufficiently pertinent to the American melodrama to remain exemplary.

The melodramas of Ray, Sirk or Minnelli do not deal with this displacement-by-substitution directly, but by what one might call an intensified symbolisation of everyday actions, the heightening of the ordinary gesture and a use of setting and decor so as to reflect the characters' fetishist fixations. Violent feelings are given vent on "overdetermined" objects (James Dean kicking his father's portrait as he storms out of the house in *Rebel Without a Cause*), and aggressiveness is worked out by proxy. In such films, the plots have a quite noticeable propensity to form a circular pattern, which in Ray involves an almost geometrical variation of triangle into circle and vice versa,[8] whereas Sirk (*nomen est omen*) often suggests in his circles the possibility of a tangent detaching itself—the full-circle construction of *Written on the Wind* with its linear coda of the Hudson-Bacall relationship at the end, or even more visually apparent, the circular race around the pylons in *Tarnished Angels* broken when Dorothy Malone's plane in the last image soars past the fatal pylon into an unlimited sky.

It is perhaps not too fanciful to suggest that the structural changes from linear externalisation of action to a sublimation of dramatic values into more complex forms of symbolisation, and which I take to be a central characteristic of the melodramatic tradition in the American cinema, can be followed through on a more general level where it reflects a change in the history of dramatic forms and the articulation of energy in the American cinema as a whole.

As I have tried to show in an earlier article (*Monogram*, no. 1), one of the typical features of the classical Hollywood movie has been that the hero was defined dynamically, as the centre of a continuous movement, often both from sequence to sequence as well as within the individual shot. It is a fact of perception that in order to get its bearing, the eye adjusts almost automatically to whatever moves, and movement, together with sound, completes the realistic illusion. It was on the basis of sheer physical movement, for example, that the musicals of the 30's (Lloyd Bacon's *42nd Street* being perhaps the most spectacular example), the gangster movie and the B-thriller of the 40's and early 50's could subsist with the flimsiest of plots, an almost total absence of individual characterisation and rarely any big stars. These deficiencies were made up by focusing to the point of exaggeration on the drive, the obsession, the *idée fixe*, that is to say, by a concentration on the purely kinetic-mechanical elements of human motivation. The pattern is most evident in the gangster genre, where the single-minded pursuit of money and power is followed by the equally single-minded and peremptory pursuit of physical survival, ending in the hero's apotheosis through violent death. This curve of rise and fall—a wholly stylised and external pattern which takes on a moral significance—can be seen in movies like *Underworld*, *Little Caesar*, *The Roaring Twenties*, *Legs Diamond* and depends essentially on narrative pace, though it permits interesting variations and complexities, as in Fuller's *Underworld USA*. A sophisticated director, such as Hawks, has used speed of delivery and the pulsating energy of action to comic effect (*Scarface*, *20th Century*) and has even applied it to films whose dramatic structure did not naturally demand such a treatment (notably *His Girl Friday*). In fact, Hawks's reputed stoicism is itself a dramaturgical device, whereby sentimentality and cynicism are played so close together and played so fast that the result is an emotional hot-cold shower which is apt to numb the spectator's sensibility into feeling a sustained moral charge, where there is more often simply a very skilled switchboard manipulation of the same basic voltage. (I am thinking especially of films like *Only Angels Have Wings*).

This unrelenting internal combustion engine of physical and psychic energy, generically exemplified by the hard-boiled, crackling aggressiveness of the screwball comedy, but which Walsh diagnosed in his Cagney heroes as psychotic (*White Heat*) and a vehicle for extreme redneck republicanism (*A Lion in the Streets*), shows signs of a definite slowing-down in the 50's and early 60's, where raucous vitality and instinctual "lust for life" is deepened psychologically to intimate neuroses and adolescent or not so adolescent maladjustments of a wider social significance. Individual initiative is perceived as problematic in explicitly political terms (*All the King's Men*), after having previously been merely stoically and heroically anti-social, as in the *film noir*. The external world is more and more riddled with obstacles which oppose themselves to personal ambitions and are not simply overcome by the hero's assertion of a brawny or brainy libido. In Mann's Westerns the madness at the heart of the James Stewart character only occasionally breaks through an otherwise calm and controlled surface, like a strong subterranean current suddenly appearing above ground as an inhuman and yet somehow poetically apt thirst for vengeance and primitive Biblical justice, where the will to survive is linked to certain old-fashioned cultural and moral values—of dignity, honour and respect. In the films of Sirk, an uncompromising fundamentally innocent energy is gradually turned away from simple, direct fulfillment by the emergence of a conscience, a sense of guilt and responsibility, or the awareness of moral complexity, as in *Magnificent Obsession*, *Sign of the Pagan*, *All That Heaven Allows* and even *Interlude*—a theme which in Sirk is always interpreted in terms of cultural decadence.

Where Freud Left His Marx in the American Home

There can be little doubt that the postwar popularity of the family melodrama in Hollywood is partly connected with the fact that in those years America discovered Freud. This is not the place to analyse the reasons why the United States should have become the country in which his theories found their most enthusiastic reception anywhere, or why they became such a decisive influence on American culture, but the connections of Freud with melodrama are as complex as they are undeniable. An interesting fact, for example, is that Hollywood tackled Freudian themes in a particularly "romantic" or gothic guise, through a cycle of movies inaugurated possibly by Hitchcock's first big American success, *Rebecca*. Relating his Victorianism to the Crawford-Stanwyck-Davis type "women's picture," which for obvious reasons became a major studio concern during the war years and found its apotheosis in such movies as John Cromwell's *Since You Went Away* (to the front, that is), Hitchcock infused his film, and several others, with an unique intimation of female frigidity producing strange fantasies of persecution, rape and death—masochistic reveries and nightmares, which cast the husband into the role of the sadistic murderer. This projection of sexual anxiety and its mechanisms of displacement and transfer is translated into a whole string of movies often involving hypnosis and playing on the ambiguity and suspense of whether the wife is merely imagining it or whether her husband really does have murderous designs on her: Hitchcock's *Notorious* and *Suspicious*, Minnelli's *Undercurrent*, Cukor's *Gaslight*, Sirk's *Sleep My Love*, Tourneur's *Experiment Perilous*, Lang's *Secret Beyond the Door* all belong in this category, as does Preminger's *Whirlpool*, and in a wider sense Renoir's *Woman on the Beach*. What strikes one about this list is not only the high number of European émigrés entrusted with such projects, but that virtually all of the major directors of family melodramas (except Ray)[9] in the 50's had a (usually not entirely successful) crack at the Freudian feminist melodrama in the 40's.

More challenging, and difficult to prove, is the speculation that certain stylistic and structural features of the sophisticated melodrama may involve principles of symbolisation and coding which Freud conceptualised in his analysis of dreams and later also applied in his *Psychopathology of Everyday Life*. I am thinking less of the prevalence of what Freud called *Symptomhandlungen* or *Fehlhandlungen*, that is, slips of the tongue or other projections of inner states into interpretable overt behaviour. This is a way of symbolising and signalling attitudes common to the American cinema in virtually every genre. However, there is a certain refinement in the melodrama—it becomes part of the composition of the frame, more subliminally and unobtrusively transmitted to the spectator. When Minnelli's characters find themselves in an emotionally precarious or contradictory situation, it often affects the "balance" of the visual composition—wine glasses, a piece of china or a trayful of drinks emphasize the fragility of their situation—e.g., Judy Garland over breakfast in *The Clock*, Richard Widmark in *The Cobweb* explaining himself to Gloria Grahame, or Gregory Peck trying to make his girlfriend see why he married someone else in *Designing Women*. When Robert Stack in *Written on the Wind*, standing by the window he has just opened to get some fresh air into an extremely heavy family atmosphere, hears of Lauren Bacall expecting a baby, his misery becomes eloquent by the way he squeezes himself into the frame of the half-open window, every word his wife says to him bringing torment to his lacerated soul and racked body.

Along similar lines, I have in mind the kind of "condensation" of motivation into metaphoric images or sequences of images mentioned earlier, the relation that exists in Freudian dream-work between manifest dream material and latent dream content. Just as in dreams certain gestures and incidents mean something by their structure and sequence, rather than by what they literally represent, the melodrama often works, as I have tried to show, by a displaced emphasis, by substitute acts, by parallel situations and metaphoric connections. In dreams one tends to "use" as dream material incidents and circumstances from one's waking experience during the previous day, in order to "code" them, while nevertheless keeping a kind of emotional logic going, and even condensing their images into what, during the dream at least, seems an inevitable sequence. Melodramas often use middle-class American society, its iconography and the family experience in just this way as their manifest "material," but "displace" it into quite different patterns, juxtaposing stereotyped situations in strange configurations, provoking clashes and ruptures which not only open up new associations but also redistribute the emotional energies which suspense and tensions have accumulated, in disturbingly different directions. American movies, for example, often manipulate very shrewdly situations of extreme embarrassment (a blocking of emotional energy) and acts or gestures of violence (direct or indirect release) in order to create patterns of aesthetic significance which only a musical vocabulary might be able to describe accurately, and for which a psychologist or anthropologist might offer some explanation.

One of the principles involved is that of continuity and discontinuity (what Sirk has called the "rhythm of the plot"). A typical situation in American melodramas has the plot build up to an evidently catastrophic collision of counterrunning sentiments, but a string of delays gets the greatest possible effect from the clash when it does come. In Minnelli's *The Bad and the Beautiful* Lana Turner plays an alcoholic actress who has been "rescued" by producer Kirk Douglas giving her a new start in the movies. After the premier, flushed with success, self-confident for the first time in years, and in happy anticipating of celebrating with Douglas, with whom she has fallen in love, she drives to his home armed with a bottle of champagne. However, we already know that Douglas isn't emotionally interested in her ("I need an actress, not a wife," he later tells her) and is spending the evening with a "broad" in his bedroom. Lana Turner, suspecting nothing, is met by Douglas at the foot of the stairs, and she, at first too engrossed in herself to notice how cool he is, collapses when the other woman suddenly appears at the top of the stairs in Douglas's dressing gown. Her nervous breakdown in the car is conveyed by headlights flashing against her windscreen like a barrage of foot-lights and arc-lamps.

This letting the emotions rise and then bringing them suddenly down with a thump is an extreme example of dramatic discontinuity, and a similar, vertiginous drop in the emotional temperature punctuates a good many melodramas—almost invariably played out against the vertical axis of a staircase.[10] In one of the most paroxysmic montage sequences that the American cinema has known, Sirk has Dorothy Malone in *Written on the Wind* dance on her own, like some doomed goddess from a Dionysian mystery, while her father is collapsing on the stairs and dying from a heart-attack. Again, in *Imitation of Life,* John Gavin gets the brush-off from Lana Turner as they are going down the stairs, and in *All I Desire* Barbara Stanwyck has to disappoint her daughter about not taking her to New York to become an actress, after the girl has been rushing downstairs to tell her father the good news. Ray's use of the staircase for similar emotional effects is well known and most spectacular in *Bigger than Life,* but to give an example from another director, Henry King, I'd like to quote a scene from *Margie,* a film following rather closely Minnelli's *Meet Me in St. Louis,* where the heroine, Jeanne Crain, about to be taken to the graduation ball by a blind date (whom we know to be her father) since her poetry-loving bespectacled steady has caught a cold, comes tearing down from her bedroom when she hears that the French master, on whom she has a crush, has dropped in. She virtually rips the bouquet of flowers out of his hands and is overwhelmed by joy. With some embarrassment, he has to explain that he is taking somebody else to the ball, that he only came to return her papers, and Margie, mortified, humiliated and cringing with shame, has just enough time to get back upstairs before she dissolves in tears.

While this may not sound terribly profound on paper, the visual orchestration of such a scene can produce some rather strong emotional effects and the strategy of building up to a climax so as to throttle it the more abruptly is a form of dramatic reversal by which Hollywood directors have consistently criticised the streak of incurably naive moral and emotional idealism in the American psyche, first by showing it to be often indistinguishable from the grossest kind of illusion and self-delusion, and then by forcing a confrontation when it is most wounding and contradictory. The emotional extremes are played off in such a way that they reveal an inherent dialectic, and the undeniable psychic energy contained in this seemingly so vulnerable sentimentality is utilised to furnish its own antidote, to bring home the discontinuities in the structures of emotional experience which give a kind of realism and toughness rare if not unthinkable in the European cinema.

What makes these discontinuities in the melodrama so effective is that they occur, as it were, under pressure. Although the kinetics of the American cinema are generally directed towards creating pressure and manipulating it (as suspense, for example), the melodrama presents in some ways a special case. In the Western or the thriller, suspense is generated by the linear organisation of the plot and the action, together with the kind of "pressure" which the spectator brings to the film by way of anticipation and *a priori* expectations of what he hopes to see; melodrama, however, has to accommodate the later type of pressure, as already indicated, in what amounts to a relatively "closed" world.

This is emphasized by the function of the decor and the symbolisation of objects; the setting of the family melodrama almost by definition is the middle-class home, filled with objects, which in a film like Philip Dunne's *Hilda Crane*, typical of the genre in this respect, surround the heroine in a hierarchy of apparent order that becomes increasingly suffocating. From father's armchair in the living room and mother's knitting to the upstairs bedroom, where after five years' absence dolls and teddies are still neatly arranged on the bedspread, home not only overwhelms Hilda with images of parental oppression and a repressed past (which indirectly provoke her explosive outbursts that sustain the action), it also brings out the characteristic attempt of the bourgeois household to make time stand still, immobilise life and fix forever domestic property relations as the model of social life and a bulwark against the more disturbing sides in human nature. The theme has a particular poignancy in the many films about the victimisation and enforced passivity of women—women waiting at home, standing by the window, caught in a world of objects into which they are expected to invest their feelings. *Since You Went Away* has a telling sequence in which Claudette Colbert, having just taken her husband to the troop train at the station, returns home to clear up after the morning's rush. Everything she looks at or touches, dressing gown, pipe, wedding picture, breakfast cup, slippers, shaving brush, the dog, reminds her of her husband, until she cannot bear the strain and falls on her bed sobbing. The banality of the objects combined with the repressed anxieties and emotions force a contrast that makes the scene almost epitomise the relation of decor to characters in melodrama: the more the setting fills with objects to which the plot gives symbolic significance, the more the characters are enclosed in seemingly ineluctable situations. Pressure is generated by things crowding in on them, life becomes increasingly complicated because clutterd with obstacles and objects that invade their personalities, take them over, stand for them, become more real than the human relations or emotions they were intended to symbolise.

It is again an instance of Hollywood stylistic devices supporting the themes, or commenting on each other. Melodrama is iconographically fixed by the claustrophobic atmosphere of the bourgeois home and/or the small-town setting, its emotional pattern is that of panic and latent hysteria, reinforced stylistically by a complex handling of space in interiors (Sirk, Ray and Losey particularly excel in this) to the point where the world seems totally predetermined and pervaded by "meaning" and interpretable signs.

This marks another recurrent feature, already touched on, that of desire focusing on the unobtainable object. The mechanisms of displacement and transfer, in an enclosed field of pressure, open a highly dynamic yet discontinuous cycle of non-fulfilment, where discontinuity creates a universe of powerfully emotional but obliquely related fixations. In melodrama, violence, the strong action, the dynamic movement, the full articulation and the fleshed-out emotions—so characteristic of the American cinema—become the very signs of the characters' alienation, and thus serve to formulate a devastating critique of the ideology that supports it.

Minnelli and Sirk are exceptional directors in this respect not least because they handle stories with four, five or sometimes six characters all tied up in a single configuration, and yet give each of them an even thematic emphasis and an independent point of view. Such skill involves a particular "musical" gift and a very sensitive awareness of the harmonising potential contained in contrasting material and the structural implications of different characters' motives. Films like *Home from the Hill, The Cobweb, Tarnished Angels* or *Written on the Wind* strike one as "objective" films, since they do not have a central hero (even though there may be a gravitational pull towards one of the protagonists) and nonetheless they cohere, mainly because each of the characters' predicaments is made plausible in terms that relate to the problems of the others. The films are built architecturally, by a combination of structural tensions and articulated parts, and the overall design appears only retrospectively, as it were, when with the final coda of appeasement the edifice is complete and the spectator can stand back and look at the pattern. But there is, especially in the Minnelli movies, also a wholly "subjective" dimension. The films (because the parts are so closely organised around a central theme or dilemma) can be interpreted as emanating from a single consciousness, which is testing or experiencing in dramatic form the various options and possibilities flowing from an initially outlined moral or existential contradiction. In *The Cobweb* John Kerr wants both total self-expression and a defined human framework in which such freedom is meaningful, and George Hamilton in *Home from the Hill* wants to assume adult responsibilities while at the same time he rejects the standards of adulthood implied in his father's aggressive masculinity. In the latter the drama ends with a "Freudian" resolution of the father being eliminated at the very point when he has resigned himself to his loss of supremacy, but this is underpinned by a "Biblical" one which fuses the mythology of Cain and Abel with that of Abraham blessing his first-born. The interweaving of motifs is achieved by a series of parallels and contrasts. Set in the South, the story concerns the relations of a mother's boy with his tough father, played by Robert Mitchum, whose wife so resents his having a bastard son (George Peppard) that she won't sleep with him again. The plot progresses through all the possible permutations of the basic situation: lawful son/natural son, sensitive George Hamilton/hypochondriac mother, tough George Peppard/tough Robert Mitchum, both boys fancy the same girl, Hamilton gets her pregnant, Peppard marries her, girl's father turns nasty against the lawful son because of the notorious sex-life of his father, etc. However, because the plot is structured as a series of mirror-reflections on the theme of fathers and sons, blood ties and natural affinities, Minnelli's film is a psychoanalytical portrait of the sensitive adolescent—but placed in a definite ideological and social context. The boy's consciousness, we realise, is made up of what are external forces and circumstances, his dilemma the result of his social position as heir to his father's estate, unwanted because thought to be undeserved, and an upbringing deliberately exploited by his mother in order to get even with his father, whose own position as a Texan land-owner and local big-shot forces him to compensate for his wife's frigidity by proving his virility with other women. Melodrama here becomes the vehicle for diagnosing a single individual in ideological terms and objective categories, while the blow-by-blow emotional drama creates the second level, where the subjective aspect (the immediate and necessarily unreflected experience of the characters) is left intact. The hero's identity, on the other hand, emerges as a kind of picture-puzzle from the various pieces of dramatic action.

Home from the Hill is also a perfect example of the principle of substitute acts, mentioned earlier, which is Hollywood's way of portraying the dynamics of alienation. The story is sustained by pressure that is applied indirectly, and by desires that always chase unattainable goals: Mitchum forces George Hamilton to "become a man" though he is temperamentally his mother's son, while Mitchum's "real" son in terms of attitudes and character is George Peppard, whom he cannot acknowledge for social reasons. Likewise, Eleanor Parker puts pressure on her son in order to get at Mitchum, and Everett Sloane (the girl's father) takes out on George Hamilton the sexual hatred he feels against Mitchum. Finally, after his daughter has become pregnant he goes to see Mitchum to put pressure on him to get his son to marry the girl, only to break down when Mitchum turns the tables and accuses him of blackmail. It is a pattern which in an even purer form appears in *Written on the Wind*. Dorothy Malone wants Rock Hudson who wants Lauren Bacall who wants Robert Stack who just wants to die. *La ronde á l'américaine*. The point is that the melodramatic dynamism of these situations is used by both Sirk and Minnelli to make the emotional impact "carry over" into the very subdued, apparently neutral, sequences of images that so often round off a scene and which thereby have a strong lyrical quality.

One of the characteristic features of melodramas in general is that they concentrate on the point of view of the victim: what makes the films mentioned above exceptional is the way they manage to present *all* the characters convincingly as victims. The critique—the questions of "evil," of responsibility—is firmly placed on a social and existential level, away from the arbitrary and finally obtuse logic of private motives and individualised psychology. This is why the melodrama, at its most accomplished, seems capable of reproducing more directly than other genres the patterns of domination and exploitation existing in a given society, especially the relation between psychology, morality and class-consciousness, by emphasizing so clearly an emotional dynamic whose social correlative is a network of external forces directed oppressingly inward, and with which the characters themselves unwittingly collude to become their agents. In Minnelli, Sirk, Ray, Cukor and others, alienation is recognised as a basic condition, fate is secularised into the prison of social conformity and psychological neurosis, and the linear trajectory of self-fulfilment so potent in American ideology is twisted into the downward spiral of a self-destructive urge seemingly possessing a whole social class.

This typical masochism of the melodrama, with its incessant acts of inner violation, its mechanisms of frustration and over-compensation, is perhaps brought most into the open through characters who have a drink problem (cf. *Written on the Wind*, *Hilda*

Crane, Days of Wine and Roses). Although alcoholism is too common an emblem in films and too typical of middle-class America to deserve a close thematic analysis, drink does become interesting in movies where its dynamic significance is developed and its qualities as a visual metaphor recognised: wherever characters are seen swallowing and gulping their drinks as if they were swallowing their humiliations along with their pride, vitality and the life force have become palpably destructive, and a phoney libido has turned into real anxiety. *Written on the Wind* is perhaps the movie that most consistently builds on the metaphoric possibilities of alcohol (liquidity, potency, the phallic shape of bottles). Not only is its theme an emotional drought that no amount of alcohol, oil pumped by the derricks, or petrol in fast cars and planes can mitigate, it also has Robert Stack compensate for his sexual impotence and childhood guilt feelings by hugging a bottle of raw corn every time he feels suicidal, which he proceeds to smash in disgust against the paternal mansion. In one scene, Stack is making unmistakeable gestures with an empty Martini bottle in the direction of his wife, and an unconsummated relationship is visually underscored when two brimful glasses remain untouched on the table, as Dorothy Malone does her best to seduce an unresponsive Rock Hudson at the family party, having previously poured her whiskey into the flower vase of her rival, Lauren Bacall.

Melodrama is often used to describe tragedy that doesn't quite come off: either because the characters think of themselves too self-consciously as tragic or because the predicament is too evidently fabricated on the level of plot and dramaturgy to carry the kind of conviction normally termed "inner necessity." Now, in some American family melodramas the inadequacy of the characters' responses to their predicament becomes itself part of the subject. In Cukor's *The Chapman Report* and Minnelli's *The Cobweb*—two movies explicitly concerned with the impact of Freudian notions on American society—the protagonists' self-understanding as well as the doctors' attempts at analysis and therapy are shown to be either tragically or comically inadequate to the situations that the characters are supposed to cope with in everyday life. Pocket-size tragic heroes and heroines, they are blindly grappling with a fate real enough to cause intense human anguish, which as the spectator can see, however, is compounded by social prejudice, ignorance, insensitivity on top of the bogus claim to scientific objectivity by the doctors. Claire Bloom's nymphomania and Jane Fonda's frigidity in the Cukor movie are seen to be two different but equally hysterical reactions to the heavy ideological pressures which American society exerts on the relations between the sexes. *The Chapman Report*, despite having apparently been cut by Darryl F. Zanuck Jr., remains an extremely important film partly because it treats its theme both in the tragic and the comic mode without breaking apart, underlining thereby the ambiguous springs of the discrepancy between displaying intense feelings and the circumstances to which they are inadequate—usually a comic motif but tragic in its emotional implications.

Both Cukor and Minnelli, however, focus on how ideological contradictions are reflected in the characters' seemingly spontaneous behaviours—the way self-pity and self-hatred alternate with a violent urge towards some form of liberating action, which inevitably fails to resolve the conflict. The characters experience as a shamefully personal stigma what the spectator (because of the parallelisms between the different episodes in *The Chapman Report*, and the analogies in the fates of the seven principal figures of *The Cobweb*) is forced to recognise as belonging to a wider social dilemma. The poverty of the intellectual resources in some of the characters is starkly contrasted with a corresponding abundance of emotional resources, and as one sees them helplessly struggling inside their emotional prisons with no hope of realising to what degree they are the victims of their society, one gets a clear picture of how a certain individualism reinforces social and emotional alienation, and of how the economics of the psyche are as vulnerable to manipulation and exploitation as is a person's labour.

The point is that this inadequacy has itself a name, relevant to the melodrama as a form: irony or pathos, which both in tragedy and melodrama is the response to the recognition of different levels of awareness. Irony privileges the spectator vis-à-vis the protagonists, for he registers the difference from a superior position. Pathos results from non-communication or silence made eloquent—people talking at cross-purposes (Robert Stack and Lauren Bacall when she tells him she's pregnant in *Written in the Wind*), a mother watching her daughter's wedding from afar (Barbara Stanwyck in *Stella Dallas*) or a woman returning unnoticed to her family, watching them through the window (again Barbara Stanwyck in *All I Desire*)—where highly emotional situations are underplayed to present an ironic discontinuity of feeling or a qualitative difference in intensity, usually visualized in terms of spatial distance and separation.

Such archetypal melodramatic situations activate very strongly an audience's participation, for there is a desire to make up for the emotional deficiency, to impart the different awareness, which in other genres is systematically frustrated to produce suspense: the primitive desire to warn the heroine of the perils looming visibly over her in the shape of the villain's shadow. But in the more sophisticated melodramas this pathos is most acutely produced through a "liberal" mise-en-scène which balances different points of view, so that the spectator is in a position of seeing and evaluating contrasting attitudes within a given thematic framework—a framework which is the result of the total configuration and therefore inaccessible to the protagonists themselves. The spectator, say in Otto Preminger's *Daisy Kenyon* or a Nicholas Ray movie, is made aware of the slightest qualitative imbalance in a relationship and also sensitized to the tragic implications which a radical misunderstanding or a misconception of motives might have, even when this is not played out in terms of a tragic ending.

If pathos is the result of a skilfully displaced emotional emphasis, it is frequently used in melodramas to explore psychological and sexual repression, usually in conjunction with the theme of inferiority; inadequacy of response in the American cinema often has an explicitly sexual code: male impotence and female frigidity—a subject which allows for thematisation in various directions, not only to indicate the kinds of psychological anxiety and social pressures which generally make people sexually responsive, but as metaphors of unfreedom or a quasi-metaphysical "overreaching" (as in Ray's *Bigger Than Life*). In Sirk, where the theme has an exemplary status, it is treated as a problem of "decadence"—where intention, awareness, yearning, outstrip performance—sexual, social, moral. From the Willi Birgel character in *Zu Neuen Ufern* onwards, Sirk's most impressive characters are never up to the demands which their lives make on them, though some are sufficiently sensitive, alive and intelligent to feel and know about this inadequacy of gesture and response. It gives their pathos a tragic ring, because they take on suffering and moral anguish knowingly, as the just price for having glimpsed a better world and having failed to live it. A tragic self-awareness is called upon to compensate for lost spontaneity and energy, and in films like *All I Desire* or *There's Always Tomorrow*, where, as so often, the fundamental irony is in the titles themselves, this theme, which has haunted the European imagination at least since Nietzsche, is absorbed into an American small-town atmosphere, often revolving around the questions of dignity and responsibility, how to yield when confronted with true talent and true vitality—in short, those qualities that dignity is called upon to make up for.

In the Hollywood melodrama characters made for operettas play out the tragedies of humankind, which is how they experience the contradictions of American civilization. Small wonder they are constantly baffled and amazed, as Lana Turner is in *Imitation of Life*, about what is going on around them and within them. The discrepancy between seeming and being, of intention and result, registers as a perplexing frustration, and an ever-increasing gap opens between the emotions and the reality they seek to reach. What strikes one as the true pathos is the very mediocrity of the human beings involved, putting such high demands upon themselves, trying to live up to an exalted vision of man, but instead living out the impossible contradictions that have turned the American dream into its proverbial nightmare. It makes the best American melodramas of the fifties not only critical social documents but genuine tragedies, despite, or rather because of, the "happy ending": they record some of the agonies that have accompanied the demise of the "affirmative culture." Spawned by liberal idealism, they advocate with open, conscious irony that the remedy is to apply more of the same. But even without the national disasters that were to overtake America in the 1960s, this irony, too, almost seems to belong to a different age.

Notes

1. A. Filon, *The English Stage*, London, 1897. Filon also offers an interesting definition of melodrama: "When dealing with Irving, I asked the question, so often discussed, whether we go to the theatre to see a representation of life, or to forget life and seek relief from it. Melodrama solves this question and shows that both theories are right, by giving satisfaction to both desires, in that it offers the extreme of realism in scenery and language together with the most uncommon sentiments and events."
2. See J. Duvignaud, *Sociologie du théâtre*, Paris, 1965, IV, 3, "Théâtre sans révolution, révolution sans théâtre."
3. About the ideological function of 19th-century Victorian melodrama, see M. W. Disher: "Even in gaffs and saloons, melodrama so strongly insisted on the sure reward to be bestowed in this life upon the law-abiding that sociologists now see in this a Machiavellian plot to keep democracy servile to Church and State. . . . There is no parting the two strains, moral and political, in the imagination of the nineteenth-century masses. They are hopelessly entangled. Democracy shaped its own entertainments at a time when the vogue of Virtue Triumphant was at its height and they took their pattern from it. . . . Here are Virtue Triumphant's attendant errors: confusion between sacred and profane, between worldly and spiritual advancement, between self-interest and self-sacrifice" (*Blood and Thunder*, London, 1949, pp. 13–14). However, it ought to be remembered that there are melodramatic traditions outside the

puritan-democratic world view. Catholic countries, such as Spain, Mexico (*cf.* Buñuel's Mexican films) have a very strong line in melodramas, based on the themes of atonement and redemption. Japanese melodramas have been "highbrow" since the Monogatari stories of the 16th century and in Mizoguchi's films (*O Haru, Shinheike Monogatari*) they reach a transcendence and stylistic sublimation rivalled only by the very best Hollywood melodramas.

4. Hans Eisler, *Composing for Film*, London, 1951.
5. Lilian Ross, *Picture*, London, 1958.
6. The impact of *Madame Bovary* via Willa Cather on the American cinema and the popular imagination would deserve a closer look.
7. *Brighton Film Review*, nos. 14, 15, 21.
8. *Ibid.*, nos. 19, 20.
9. I have not seen A *Woman's Secret* (1949) or *Born to Be Bad* (1950), either of which might include Ray in this category, and the Ida Lupino character in *On Dangerous Ground* (1952)—blind, living with a homicidal brother—is distinctly reminiscent of this masochistic strain in Hollywood feminism.
10. As a principle of mise-en-scène the dramatic use of staircases recalls the famous Jessnertreppe of German theatre. The thematic conjunction of family and height/depth symbolism is nicely described by Max Tesier: "le héros ou l'héroine sont ballotés dans uns véritable scenic-railway social, où les classes sont rigoureusement compartimentées. Leur ambition est de quitter à jamais un milieu moralement dépravé, physiquement éprouvant, pour accéder au Nirvana de la grande bourgeoisie. . . . Pas de famille, pas de mélo! Pour qu'il y ait mélo, il faut avant tout quíl y ait faute, péché, transgression sociale. Or, quel est le milieu idéal pour que se développe cette gangrène, sinon cette cellule familiale, liée à une conception hiérarchique de la société?" (*Cinéma 71*, no. 161, p. 46).

Bibliography: Melodrama

This bibliography is by no means attempting to be comprehensive. It is offered by way of an outline of how the subject might be approached.

THEATRE

M. W. Disher, *Blood and Thunder*, London, 1949.
A. Filon, *The English Stage*, London, 1897.
J. Duvignaud, *Sociologie du théâtre*, Paris, 1965.

NOVEL

W. C. Phillips, *Dickens, Reade and Collins*, New York, 1919.
L. A. Fiedler, *Love and Death in the American Novel*, London, 1967.

MUSIC

Hans Eisler, *Composing for Film*, London, 1951.
T. W. Adorno, *Musiksoziologie*, Hamburg, 1968.
D. Cooke, *The Language of Music*, London, 1959.

CINEMA

H. Sachs, "Film Psychology," *Close-Up* 3, no. 5 (November 1928).
R. Durgnat, "Ways of Melodrama," *Sight and Sound*, August–September 1951.
E. Morin, *Le Cinéma ou l'homme imaginaire*, Paris, 1958.
J. Mitry, *Esthétique du cinéma*, Paris, 1962.
Cinématographie française, 7 December 1963.
B. Nichols, "Revolution and Melodrama," *Cinema* (USA) 6, no. 1 (1970).
J. L. Comolli, Sirk interview, *Cahiers du Cinéma* no. 189, April 1967.
Cinéma 71, special number on melodrama (no. 161).
Jean-Loup Bourget, *Positif*, no. 131 (October 1971).
Fernsehen und Film, special number on Sirk and melodrama, February 1971.
P. Willeman, "Distantiation and Douglas Sirk," *Screen*, Summer 1971.

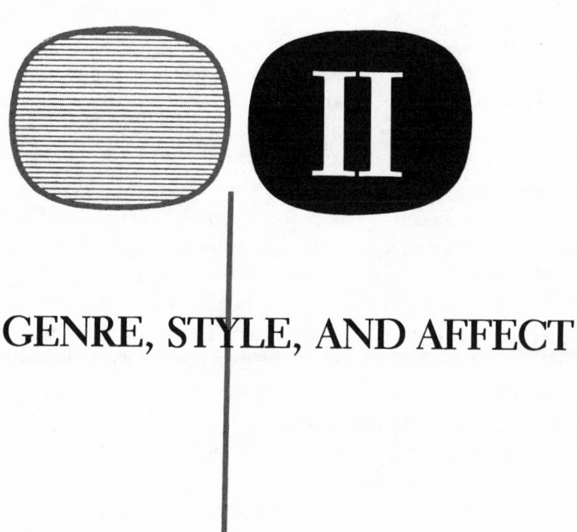

GENRE, STYLE, AND AFFECT

There is no disagreement among critics about the affective nature of the melodramatic text, though there are still those who view its strong emotionalism as an indication of aesthetic and ideological backwardness. To the serious students of melodrama, the emotive basis of melodrama constitutes a challenge. The emotional languauge conveyed through gesture, iconography, and music is not vacuous but is a register to articulate profound personal and social conflicts. Consequently, critics have sought to provide a systematic description and analysis of the specific strategies employed by melodrama. Through an examination of its formal properties, they have attempted to identify the "emotional teleology" of the form and hence to articulate its impact on the audience.

Charles Affron's discussion of the "tearjerker" addresses the negative connotations of pathos. While critics are uncomfortable in confronting works that call forth sentiment, the fact remains that pathetic fiction has been extremely popular from the earliest cinema to the present. Affron, like Peter Brooks, argues for the meaningful connection between affect and meaning in melodrama. He finds that viewers' responses are not arbitrary but are generated from experiences in their own lives which the texts call forth. The seemingly simple and transparent texts are neither simple nor transparent, and, applying methods from structuralism, narrative theory, and reception theory, Affron attempts to locate the basis of the spectator's involvement in melodrama.

By invoking the concept of identification, Affron probes the strategies involved in producing the spectator's sense of a consonance between representation and experience. Through the process of imaging and through the various ways in which the image is projected and received, spectators locate their own subjectivity. Affron applies a psychoanalytic model of the construction of the individual's subjectivity and uses Christian Metz's application of this process to spectatorship in the cinema. The viewer's experience of loss and struggle for identification is the basis for all experience. The cinema promises the spectator the illusory satisfaction of finding wholeness and is predicated on the constant interplay between possession and lack. In the viewing experience which is akin to the dream state, inducing a reduction in reality testing, the spectator is free to contemplate fiction as reality. Affron does not regard this process as one of passivity in the conventional sense. Watching a film produces a fluid state where the viewer is free to entertain a fusion of reality and dream state. The conditions of sedentary viewing in the dark are regressive, and the regression generates affect. The viewer is free to indulge in the interplay of fantasy and reality.

With the assistance of reader response theory, Affron examines how the viewer's responses to film are geared toward involvement, comprehension, and satisfaction. The experience of the film thus liberates spectators from the constraints of ideology. Following Peter Brooks, Affron regards melodrama as a challenge to the reality principle. Melodrama articulates the unsaid. However, going beyond Brooks, Affron insists on distinguishing cinematic melodrama from the novelistic and dramatic. Cinema, because it is a visual medium, requires attention to specular activity. The Italian opera offers a better analogy with film in its solo/choral emphasis, uses of ensemble, combining of action and spectacle, and hyperbolic performance. Affron finds the term *melodrama* too constraining and reductive to account for cinematic affect. For example, the typification characteristic of melodrama is subverted through the individuating qualities of the close-up. Moreover, there is for Affron a significant difference between the generality of a victimized melodramatic protagonist and the specificity of Lillian Gish as actress. In general, he finds generic considerations problematic for an understanding of the cinematic affect.

Daniel Gerould takes a more strictly generic approach to melodrama. For his discussion, he draws on the work of the Russian formalist critics who had analyzed the techniques and principles of melodrama long before other European and American critics. Formalist critics had located the basic principles of melodrama in its calling forth of intense feeling, what Gerould calls its "emotional teleology." The melodramatic plots appear to be violations of everyday experience in their use of material that produces an emotional shock for the audience, in their deployment of reversals and twists of the narrative line, alternating between success and failure, misery and good fortune. Among the technical strategies of melodrama, Gerould identifies the principle of relief, the isolation of intense narrative moment, the strategy of stark contrast in character and situation, and the creation of a dynamic whereby the characters and the spectator are constantly thrown off balance. The use of secrets is fundamental for providing tensions in melodramatic composition.

In the construction of the melodramatic narrative, Gerould identifies the importance of the prologue in containing the initial dramatic knot, open exposition by the characters, multiplicity of actions, dramatically expressive endings, indirect movement toward a denouement, a nonindividuated sense of character as well as character reversibility, the role of chance in providing new narrative twists, and the presence of a "thing" (like Hitchcock's McGuffin) which serves as a means of recognition in the final moment. Gerould's discussion of these techniques is particularly effective for an understanding of literary melodrama. To be effective for an analysis of cinema, his work would have to address the specific visual properties of the medium. Moreover, his work needs to be accommodated to the specific role of auteur, actresses, and changing historical contexts.

Raymond Durgnat's discussion of melodrama acknowledges the relationship between dramatic action and the calling forth of emotion. Drama is dependent on action and movement that are motivated, but drama becomes melodrama when emotions are invoked and when actions or threatened actions produce emotions that provide a test of character. The relationship between drama and melodrama is fluid. Melodrama may become drama, and drama may become melodrama. They are not clearly demarcated entities but often coexist. Melodrama is to drama as slapstick is to comedy. *Emotional melodrama* is the term Durgnat applies to films that subordinate action to emotion. Hollywood is most adept at this kind of melodrama. When the emotional melodrama begins to explore character, the films move toward drama. In John Huston's films, for example, there is a purposeful subduing of affect in the interests of character and action. Pure melodrama consists in the chase, in actions that involve threat and self-preservation, in minimal characterization, but these are only effective insofar as the events can be convincing. The perfect balance in melodrama consists in the film's ability to fuse dramatic episodes with emotional subtlety. Ultimately, Durgnat asserts that any formula is only as effective as the controlling vision of the creator. The problems that arise in melodrama are not related to its techniques but to the failure of the artist, to an uninteresting, banal, and conventional perception of the world.

There is by no means unanimity about the distinctive properties of melodrama as a genre, though most critics would agree that an alternating pattern of equilibrium and disequilibrium is characteristic of melodrama as it is of all genres. An emphasis on internal conflict, a heightened emotional response to events, a polarized representation of character and situation, and a tension between the personal and the social, the conventional and the deviant or marginal, may also demarcate melodrama from other genres. Beyond these general characteristics, critics would part company. The essays in this section represent different ways of considering the specific features of melodrama. It should become clear that discussions of genre are not merely descriptive but are inextricably tied to ideological issues.

Following Thomas Elsaesser's lead, Thomas Schatz's discussion of the genre privileges the family melodrama. While the 1930s and 1940s witnessed the florescence of romantic melodramas in the films of such directors as Frank Borzage and John Stahl, Schatz argues that the expressive potential of film melodrama was not fully exploited until the post–World War II era, associated particularly with the stylized techniques of the European director Max Ophuls and with the early films of Vincente Minnelli. In the 1950s, a time of ideological crisis as witnessed in the Cold War, the rise of suburban life, and the loss of faith in the "American Dream," the melodrama became a critical vehicle, exposing the underlying tensions and contradictions of American society.

Schatz focuses on the centrality of the American family in these melodramas, asserting that the family as the cornerstone of American society, upholding the values of patriarchy, upward mobility, and private property, was endangered. And the variations of the 1950s melodramas all seem to revolve around the various threats to familial stability. Schatz identifies these variations as the male intruder in a world of women of which he takes *Picnic* to be exemplary, the widow-lover variation as in *All That Heaven Allows*, the family aristocracy variation in *Giant*, the "male weepie" as exemplified in Nicholas Ray's *Bigger Than Life*. Like Elsaesser, Schatz sees the style of the films as working against the grain self-consciously to expose social, class, and sexual contradictions, and he finds that, unlike other genres of order, the oppositions to that order cannot be resolved.

Schatz's discussion reinforces the recent emphasis on the family as the subject matter and site of struggle in melodrama, thus demarcating melodrama as a genre from its expression in other film genres such as thrillers, science fiction, and horror. However, in his taxonomy of the various expressions of family melodrama, he pays scant attention to those forms of melodrama that foreground women's conflicts and women as the protagonists. The various expressions of the women's films are underrepresented and unexamined in his preoccupation with the family melodrama.

In contrast to Schatz, Noël Carroll's discussion of the "moral ecology of the melodrama" takes Sirk's *Magnificent Obsession* as an example of how the films of the 1950s as well as current expressions of the genre are a recycling of the traditional melodramas of the 1930s and 1940s. For example, he sees the 1978 films *International Velvet* and *Uncle Joe Shannon* as involving the loss and restoration of family members. Citing such elements as the presence of the orphan discovered by a relative, the family reunion, the importance of Christmas as the time of that reunion as well as its relation to the "mythic family," Carroll sees these films as resurrecting the world of D. W. Griffith. The strategies of these films are particularly problematic considering the amount of criticism that has been leveled at the nuclear family by feminist critics.

Rather than regarding Douglas Sirk's films as antidote to conformist representations of the family, as is the case with Elsaesser and Schatz, Carroll finds that *Magnificent Obsession* involves the same generic properties—loss and restitution and a narrative symmetry that reinforces a pattern of containment. Carroll identifies other aspects of Sirk's deployment of style as serving to reinforce the idea of the family plot as part of the moral order, in Sirk's portrayal of the organic unity of nature, in the nature and design of the floral arrangements, and in the color coordination of objects. Carroll's essay, therefore, calls into question the ways in which critics have read the generic and stylistic properties of melodrama as containing subversive elements.

The priority of critical attention given to the family melodrama has also been challenged by feminist critics who have called attention to another popular expression of melodrama—the women's film and, in particular, the maternal melodrama. The maternal melodrama is a staple of the Hollywood melodrama of the 1930s and 1940s when the audiences were largely female. Maternity, a familiar subject in nineteenth-century Italian and French melodrama, was also common to the pre–World War II cinema, especially in the 1930s and 1940s. Christian Viviani traces the genre through the various versions of *Madame X*. The films enact the woman's fall and her concomitant suffering as shes expiates her sin of bearing an illegitimate child. The excessive emotionality of the maternal melodrama appears on the surface to be removed from reality. An outer core of pathos and stylization, says Viviani, conceals an inner core which is intimately tied to real-life experience. Like Durgnat, Viviani sees melodrama as balancing narrative complexity and emotional simplicity.

In its earliest versions of the maternal melodrama, the Hollywood genre bore traces of its European ancestry. In the 1930s, however, with the Depression and the coming of the New Deal, Hollywood Americanized its narratives. The protagonist of the maternal melodrama was no longer the submissive and resigned mother. She became freer and more active in her own behalf. Her illicit actions are justified by her love for the father of her child and by her social, if not moral, recuperation through work. Moreover, the Hollywood mother is identified with the country rather than the city, with the earth, and hence with the traditional values of the hearth and social stability. As Viviani indicates, the Hollywood maternal melodrama is an "apologia for self-renunciation, total sacrifice, and total self-abnegation." In certain instances, as in the films George Cukor made with Constance Bennett between 1930 and 1933, the maternal melodrama is exposed through irony for what it is—namely, an illusion for overcoming the conflicts of an era that was "knowingly grounded in eroticism."

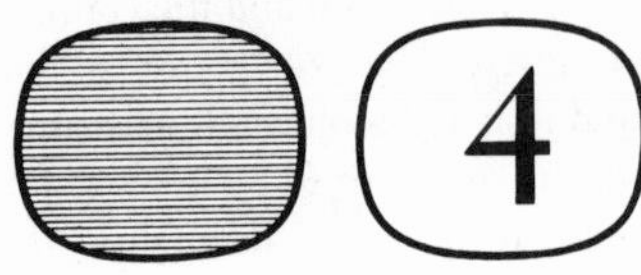

Identifications

CHARLES AFFRON

Tearjerkers

"Bathetic" and "pathetic" are phonetic siblings and semantic twins. The first, a pejorative term, euphonically qualifies the second, the designation of a type of response. The sense of low artistic worth conveyed by "bathetic" all too easily appropriates both the initial bilabial stop of "pathetic" and its capacity to provoke strong emotions in teary-eyed spectators. This unfortunate lexical confusion has given "pathetic" a decidedly negative connotation. Art works that create an overtly emotional response in a wide readership are rated inferior to those that engage and inspire the refined critical, intellectual activities of a selective readership. Much of narrative film falls into the first category, and indeed was designed to do so by its creators. The success of pathetic fiction has been continuous, ranging from the first decades of cinema and the one-reeled plights of childlike heroes to the triumph-over-adversity scenario of physically afflicted protagonists (a paraplegic, a sports hero hurt in an accident or dying of an incurable disease) of the late seventies. In the jargon of the daily press, the latter are three- and four-handkerchief films. And to many, freely flowing tears have about as much lasting value as the drenched tissues with which we wipe them away.

If we consider the movies to be a meaning-generating body of art, we cannot afford to dismiss proof that meaning has in fact been generated. Tears are that proof. Yet the affective power of narrative, responsible for so much of the cinema's popular appeal,

Charles Affron, "Identifications," from *Cinema and Sentiment* (Chicago: University of Chicago Press, 1982). Reprinted by permission of the author and the University of Chicago Press.

has made textual and evaluative criticism loath to examine some of the most *affective* film texts: the pejorative resonance of "sentimental" has deterred serious consideration of those films for which that adjective is an accurate characterization. It is argued that blatantly emotional films cheapen and banalize emotion *because* they are blatant. Their promptness to elicit feeling offends those who consider being easily moved equivalent to being manipulated, victimized, deprived of critical distance. Art works are judged *bad* when, in what are purportedly trivializing modes, they attempt to convey deep feelings about the self, the family, love, commitment, ethics. Some directors identified by their affinity for sentimental fictions (Ford, Capra) have been rescued through political, sociological, and occasionally formal exegesis; others (Cukor, Sirk) have been canonized by auteurism. Critics are not uncomfortable in treating the mythic resonance of *How Green Was My Valley*,[1] the "America" of *Mr. Smith Goes to Washington*, the self-reflexivity of *A Star Is Born*, the irony of *Imitation of Life*. But most commentators, in ignoring the fact that viewers have a strong response to "tearjerkers," also overlook how and why that response is informed with both fiction and medium. Essential aspects of these films' narrative, visual, and aural strategies, and of the nature of the cinematic experience, are reflected in those embarrassing tears.

Viewers are engaged and made to recognize their feelings in cinematic fictions, perhaps as they never recognize them in life, by the processes of representation that derive from the dynamics of films and from the specifics of their viewing. While "conventional" narrative films relish situations that seem to contain sure sentimental appeal—departure, doomed love, mother love, death—it is finally the degree to which these situations conspire with those specifics that ensures a given work's affectivity. The resulting *processes* of representation condition response perhaps more surreptitiously, but just as strongly and hypnotically as that which is represented.

Viewers respond to the medium when its conditions echo something of their feeling and their experience; viewers become involved in the image as image when that image engages them in its workings, when its constitution becomes a field as rich and inviting as those that effect involvement in life. Film provides a variety of accessibilities to its modes, beguiling viewers to enter into its processes and then using those processes to capture representations of emotional situations that are lifelike to a degree our eyes can scarcely believe.

Reading with Feeling

It is precisely the ease of such seductive beguilement that has caused some critics to be wary of affect. Affect extends the status of the work beyond what seems to be its integrity into an area that shifts with the vagaries of pluralistic readings. In a defense of textual integrity W. K. Wimsatt exposes what he calls "the Affective Fallacy . . . a confusion between the poem and its *results* (what it *is* and what it *does*)." A critical posture committed to affectivity "begins by trying to derive the standard of criticism from the psychological effects of the poem and ends in impressionism and relativism." Read as a function of the Affective Fallacy, "the poem itself, as an object of specifically critical judgment, tends to disappear."[2] I will leave it to other critics to debate Wimsatt's other, more renowned Fallacy, the Intentional. It is his dismissal of affectivity with the qualification "fallacious" that I question here. If his caution is useful in its insistence upon the reality of the text, its categorical nature prohibits the celebration of the very activity the text promotes (and in which he, of course, engages)—a sustained, concentrated, thoroughly committed reading. "Impressionism" and "relativism" are not the necessary outcomes of an analysis that considers, in addition to a text's rhetorical coherence, the mechanics of its effect upon the reader and the operations the reader performs upon the text.

With their often overlapping and mutually inspiring criteria, the methodologies of structuralism, linguistics, semiotics, psychocriticism, phenomenology, narrative theory, and reception theory hold reader and text in variable degrees of tension.[3] In doing so they release the text from the Pantheon of evaluation and from the ethical categorization of high, middle, and low culture, and have helped authorize the examination of many of the texts that interest me, films that fail to satisfy either the canons of classical coherence or those of avant-garde subversion, but that elicit, in many viewers, passionate reading activity. It is that activity that then become something like a value in the critical enterprise. Stanley Fish's definition of "Affective Stylistics," a particularly polemical statement of readership theory, expresses the character of these recent critical approaches. Fish attempts to establish the critical relevance of texts that, "because of their alleged transparency, are declared to be uninteresting as objects of analysis." An examination of the dynamics of utterance in these texts "reveals that a great deal is going on in their production and comprehension (*every linguistic experience is affecting and pressuring*, although most of it is going on so close up, at such a basic, 'preconscious' level of experience, that we tend to overlook it."[4] As soon as the activities of "production and comprehension" become relevant to criticism, textual *evaluation* seems perilous, just as our taste seems vulnerable to time and culture. Yesterday we went to the marketplace and laughed at the *Farce of Maître Pathelin*, played by amateurs and itinerant actors on a hastily erected platform; today we consider it rhetorically, generically, semiotically, psychocritically in our graduate courses on medieval theater. A popular art by definition, the farce had to be immediately legible to naive readers. But a naive reader is not an unresponsive one, and a naive reading tells us that much about art is defined by its reading-generating elements. Narrative film is a popular art and has suffered from the stigma of its transparency, the ease with which it is read. Yet, as in the case of farce, our observation that a genre or mode is of easy access should not be taken to imply that this access is easily understood or that *easy* is synonymous with *facile*. Presumably, easy fictions contain a complexity of gears whose smooth meshing conceals how they come together and how, once they are engaged, the reader is also engaged in the functioning of the mechanism. As Stanley Cavell has suggested, popular films are not necessarily disqualified from serious viewing just because they are easily read. "If film is seriously to be thought of as art at all, then it needs to be explained how it can have avoided the fate of modernism, which in practice means how it can have maintained its continuities in audiences and genres, how it can have been taken seriously without having assumed the burden of seriousness."[5] Cavell then proceeds to demonstrate, through a catholicity of illustration, the "seriousness" of Olsen and Johnson's *Hellzapoppin* and Antonioni's *L'avventura*.

"Art" Films

Even a popular form such as narrative film has not escaped its hierarchies of taste. The word "art" itself has been used to designate movies marketed as high culture (in the silent period, the "film d'art," often the filming of a "serious" or "classic" play) or perceived as such by the public (almost all foreign films released in the United States after World War II were referred to as "art films" and played at "art houses"). This implies that other movies are not art at all, or have less art than those with the designation. Yet the works of the Italian neo-realist directors, for example immediately recognized by intellectuals as challenging and by general audiences as "art," are awash with the same trappings of sentimentality—the child sorely tried by necessity (*Shoeshine, Open City, Bicycle Thief*), the faithful animal (*Umberto D.*), the pathetic death (*Shoeshine, Open City, Paisà, Bitter Rice*)—that are often considered negative in "commercial" narrative films. *Umberto D.*, one of the most stylistically austere of the neo-realist films, is the story of a dispossessed old man who spends the last hours before his attempted suicide trying to find a home for his dog. De Sica and his collaborator Zavattini may adopt a manner that creates an impression of objectivity, but they then apply it to the story of an old man and a dog! My exclamative punctuation is ironic to itself since I am not at all surprised that any narrative film, whether it be on a critic's All-Time Ten Best List or relegated to a collection of "guilty pleasures,"[6] is sustained by sentimental configurations.

No less exempt from these configurations are highly mediated cinematic fictions. Susan Sontag, in her essay on Robert Bresson, examines the function of mediation in the art work's emotional power:

> Some art aims directly at arousing the feelings; some art appeals to the feelings through the route of the intelligence. There is art that creates empathy. There is art that detaches, that provokes reflection. Great reflective art is not frigid. It can exalt the spectator, it can present images that appall, it can make him weep. But its emotional power is mediated. The pull toward emotional involvement is counterbalanced by elements in the work that promote distance, disinterestedness, impartiality. Emotional involvement is always, to a greater or lesser degree, postponed.[7]

Avoiding an overtly evaluative tone, Sontag opposes the direct, empathetic response elicited by easily accessible, presumably popular art and the deferred one of "great reflective art." She then goes on to describe how the spectator's awareness of form tends "to elongate or to retard the emotions. . . . Awareness of form does two things simultaneously: it gives a sensuous pleasure independent of the 'content,' and it invites the use of the intelligence."[8] She seems to be suggesting that the emotional response arrived at through "distance," through "the use of our intelligence," through our awareness of mediation (present of necessity in all art), is of quite a different quality than reader involvement characterized by empathy and immediacy. Yet, while Bresson's ellipses, both visual and narrative, certainly require "intelligent" reading, his fictional configurations and iconography (the "content" referred to by Sontag) are so blatantly pathetic (the country priest, victimized by his village, dying of cancer; the Christ-like donkey Balthazar;[9] the long-suffering adolescent Mouchette; the doomed lovers, Lancelot and Guenièvre, etc.) that they provide immediate affective access. For the reader who is then initiated into the mysteries of the director's style, both the story and its manner of reading become moving, and do so simultaneously. Bresson's stylistics is as familiar as Frank Capra's to those viewers for whom reseeing, an activity invited by the nature of the medium, further reduces whatever distance there may be between reading a film and responding to it emotionally. Of course, because of their unconventional editing and framing, it is tempting to think of Bresson's films in terms of mediation, and of course, Bresson's work has not had the wide-ranged popularity of Capra's films. Yet clearly Bresson is drawn to the dramatic patterns of sentimental art. The art film too, then, is subject to what Jean Mitry has described as the priority of emotion in cinema. "In cinema . . . we gain access to the idea through emotion and because of this emotion, while in verbal language we gain access to emotion by means of ideas and through them."[10] This is, in part, due to that aspect of the cinematic image (and sound) that must remain unmediated, its *non*symbolic relationship to its reference—that which was filmed—a characteristic of all cinema, from its art films to its most popular, "bathetic," tearjerkers.

What follows is a dynamic model of affective response to cinema that exploits various theories of viewer/spectator/reader identification with the art object. In the hope of accommodating the wide range of these approaches, I concentrate on identification as a function of the reader's situation vis-à-vis the text, and of the text's oscillations between versimilitudinous representations and fictive artifices. It seems to me that the passage between the reader and the text's fluctuating status locates the energy and the affect of reading.

Likeness, Sensation, and the Image of Absence

"I liked it because I identified with the characters" is a casual but insistent refrain heard in movie lobbies and classrooms. That such a remark is reductive of a complex experience in no way lessens its pertinence to the viewing of narrative film. It suggests the appeal of the surface of the fiction in its explicit semblance to the most familiar patterns and events of life, as they are conveyed by photographic images of human beings and their environments. Hugo Münsterberg describes this degree of identification in his early study of the psychological implications of silent film. "Our imitation of the emotions which we see expressed brings vividness and affective tone into our grasping of the play's action. We sympathize with the sufferer and that means that the pain which he expresses becomes our own pain."[11] This mode of identification is primarily generated by the movies' sensational aspects. Movies are able to convey sensational phenomena without recourse to codes. We perceive sensation as sensation, even though it is only a projected image on a screen. Cinematized sensation is often minimally qualified by what we call style, and therefore we distinguish its quality of presence from the deferrals of verbal and symbolic codes. In its figuring of sensation, film draws verbal and compositional articulation to a status of presence.

In Frank Capra's *It's a Wonderful Life* a complex fictional configuration is capped by an image of physical pain. The resulting dynamics transcends our sense of the image as representational, as a projection distinct from the moment and the circumstances of its creation. The young George Bailey, partially deafened as a result of saving his little brother from drowning, works at a drugstore. When he scoops up some ice cream for Mary (who becomes his wife later in the film), she whispers into his deaf ear (the locus of pain at the climax of this extended sequence), "George Bailey, I'll love you 'til the day I die." Mr. Gower, the pharmacist, drunk with liquor and grief after reading the telegram announcing his son's death, accidentally puts poison into a prescription. Aware of the error yet unable to confront the sorrowing man, George goes to his own father for advice. He interrupts a violent confrontation between Mr. Bailey, the kindly banker, and Mr. Potter, the rich, meanhearted villain. (This part of the episode is prefigurative of George's adult conflict with Potter.) Finally, in a labyrinth of planes and shadows at the back of the pharmacy, Mr. Gower slaps George in the head, bloodying his ear, before the truth finally emerges and both the guilt-ridden man and the forgiving boy are united by an embrace and a sympathy of tears. The pain of the slap and the sight of blood qualify the whole episode, shade it, give it the coherence of a literary metaphor, without betraying the immediacy of the sensation it produces. It is particularly efficient exploitation of the medium's expressivity as explicit surface and as fiction of presence.

That fiction is indubitably a powerful link between viewer and screen. It is an extension of the world of experience that, in part, identifies the viewer as a perceptive, sentient being. Yet the mere record of that experience is only the point of departure for the models of identification proposed by psychocritical discourse, a point of departure that locates the self not only in the surface of the image, but in the rhetoric of imaging and in the specific modes in which the image is received. I do not mean to undertake here an exhaustive, systematic examination of this critical literature, but only to suggest its importance in detaching the viewing experience from the norms of photographic versimilitude that have so often controlled identification theory. These approaches force us to consider the connections between who looks at the movies and how that looking occurs.

Mitry relates the dynamics of spectatorship to those of its prime factors:

> thanks to the mobility of the camera, to the multiplicity of shots, I am everywhere at once. . . . I *know* that I am in the movie theatre, but I *feel* that I am in the world offered to my gaze, a world that I experience "physically" while

> identifying myself with one or another of the characters in the drama—with all of them, alternatively. This finally means that at the movies I am both *in* this action and *outside* it, *in this space and outside of this space.* Having the gift of ubiquity, I am everywhere and nowhere.[12]

For Mitry, the viewer's rapport with the fictional character is equally ubiquitous. "It is not the situation lived by the hero that *I* suffer, it is a 'subjectivity' [*un subjectif*] that is actualized by *him*, a wish that I accomplish through his intermediary."[13] This "subjectivity," animated by the freedom of camera and of editing, affords the viewer a flux of spatial and fictional identification whose emotional appeal was already apparent to Münsterberg in 1916. "Not more than one sixteenth of a second is needed to carry us from one corner of the globe to the other, from a jubilant setting to a mourning scene. The whole keyboard of the imagination may be used to serve this emotionalizing of nature."[14] Identification is therefore liberated from the constraints of everyday experience and made part of a process suggestive of emotion itself—movement.

Movement has been located in the intersecting topologies of the work itself, the places of interchange between the work and the receiver, and in the receiver. And these topologies have been inflected by the ontological status of the screened image—its figuring of absence, its distance in time and space from what was photographed. Cinema, in its display of present (fleeting) images of an absent reality, makes the reading activity a pursuit, a desire for the fiction energized by a dialectic of possession and lack. Much of recent film theory in France and England, informed by Freudian and Lacanian thinking (to which I will return), posits the reading of cinema as a visual test of the tension between the self and intermittently mastered orders of image and symbol. For the moment I will rely on Christian Metz's work to summarize how the problematics of the viewing situation (and the viewer's identity) in front of a presence as unstable as that of cinema is made a property of the film's intelligibility. "In order to understand a film (at all), I must perceive the photographed object as absent, its photograph as present, and the presence of this absence as signifying."[15] Reading (and pleasure) are predicated on a rhythm of possession, loss, and restitution. Metz defines this rhythm in Lacanian terms, exploiting the implications of the mirror analogy:

> the durable mark of the mirror which alienates man in his own reflection and makes him the double of his double, the subterranean persistence of the exclusive relation to the mother, desire as a pure effect of lack an endless pursuit, the initial core of the unconscious (primal repression). All this is undoubtedly reactivated by the actions of that *other mirror*, the cinema screen, in this respect a veritable psychical substitute, a prosthesis for our primally dislocated limbs.[16]

Thus, the "endless pursuit" of the image is rooted in the child's initial effort at self-identification through (and in spite of) identification with the mother. Cinema's implicit mirrorness holds and withholds the promise of satisfying identifications in the activity of sight itself. Identification is therefore detached from the diegetic status of the fiction, from the pleasure of perceiving plot and circumstance, and effected by the viewer's most basic relationship to the image, a relationship made particularly crucial because of the mobility of the film image. We identify with cinema not only because of the likeness we find reflected there, but because the "reflection" forces us to acknowledge, somewhere in our apprehension of the screen image, that our looking is not predicated on the satisfaction of *finding,*: what we look at is not *there*. (Thierry Kuntzel uses the Freudian analogy of the "mystic writing pad," with its disappearing inscriptions, to suggest the paradoxically dual status of the screen image.)[17] Metz is emphatic in his characterization of absence in a medium where "everything is *recorded.*" Reading a film therefore requires the realization that "every film is a fiction film."[18]

Metz does not completely discard the notion that the viewer may derive satisfaction in finding semblance in the screen image, but he does characterize it as "a little miracle"[19] dependent on the unexpected and elusive correspondences between exterior and interior orders, the images we perceive as outside us on a cinema screen, and an experience of life composed of the constant play between sense impression and our inner beings. The fleeting, unstable nature of these inside-out links is coherent both with the nature of the medim and with a model of identification that only intermittently calls for the recognition of lifelike representations. The realm of the lifelike is extended from identities with the world as we see it to the world of dreams, fantasies, emotions, beyond the purview of wide open eyes, ours and the camera's.[20] This requires a redefinition of reality that accommodates a lowering of our ability, our desire, and our need to test reality, a lowering of our vigilance that is allowed and invited by the comfort of art and the comfort of the situation in which we receive it—the darkened theater. Edgar Morin asserts that "the passivity of the spectator, his impotence, put him in a regressive situation. Being in the theater illustrates a general anthropological law: we all become sentimental, sensitive, tearful when we are deprived of our means of action."[21] Since watching a film requires that we sit still in a dark room and that we assume an attitude of physical inactivity, it indeed exempts us from the rigors of reality. "The novelistic film, a mill of images and sounds overfeeding our zones of shadow and irresponsibility, is a machine for grinding up affectivity and inhibiting action."[22] Protecting us against the dangers of circumstance, the demands of interacativity, the spectatorial situation renders us susceptible to the meaning of reality *as* fiction, since that fiction is the only *exterior* reality we perceive.

Dispensing with but the barest mediation of temporal and spatial contingency, both viewer and film enjoy their parallel privacies and the bliss of rhythms and decors that emanate from the self and from the work of art. Metz resists the temptation to fix these activities in the dream state, but chooses instead a flux of intensities, of passages between (1) reality, (2) daydream, (3) dream. The experience of the fiction film favors a new experience, an "ongoing circulation among the three: authorizing, in sum, a sort of central and moving zone of intersection where all three can 'reencounter' each other on a singular territory, a confused territory which is common to them and yet does not abolish their distinctness." Fiction, through its particular manners of identification, contributes to this dynamics and topography:

> the diegesis has something of the real since it imitates it, something of the daydream and the dream since they imitate the real. The *novelistic* as a whole, with its cinematographic extensions, enriched and complicated by auditory and

visual perception (absent in the novel), is nothing other than the systematic exploitation of this region of reencounters and manifold passages.[23]

Working with Movies

These suggestive plays of oscillation between states of sleep and waking and between the mimetic elements of the fiction challenge a narrow application of the realist aesthetic of film. Decentered, delocated, rendered all-embracing, reality becomes a function of perception/imagination/fantasy. Identification is then found in flux between the *work* of the art and the *work* of the art perceiver, between surface and sense, between the work's motion and our emotion. This degree of identity links the real and the fictional through the patterns of their separate processes, and that linkage makes the reading of the fiction *as* fiction a reading of ourselves, of selves as free of material contingency as fiction can be.

Various exponents of readership theory have examined the dynamics of free passage between reader and text, and around reader and text, in a wide range of defining systems. This mobility requires that we reexamine those models of the film-reading situations that stress passivity, regression, and infantilism, models that need not be discarded, but rather understood as points of departure toward the specific *activities* of reading. For Wolfgang Iser, "the literary text activates our own faculties, enabling us to recreate the world it presents. The product of this creative activity is what we might call the creative dimension of the text, which endows it with its reality."[24] Iser reiterates this formulation in his more recent book, characterizing the text as event in its temporal activity:

> as we read, we react to what we ourselves have produced, and it is this mode of reaction that, in fact, enables us to experience the text as an actual event. We do not grasp it like an empirical object; nor do we comprehend it like a predicative fact; it owes its presence in our minds to our own reactions, and it is these that make us animate the meaning of the text as a reality.[25]

Iser's reader/text juncture is located in the kind of reading elicited by the written text (where images are symbolically coded), yet he has recourse to quasi-cinematic visual and spatial analogies to convey what he calls "the wandering viewpoint," the reader's shifting positions in the text:

> The switch of viewpoints brings about a spot-lighting of textual perspectives, and these in turn become reciprocally influenced backgrounds which endow each new foreground with a specific shape and form. As the viewpoint changes again, this foreground merges into the background, which it has modified and which is now to exert its influence on yet another new foreground.

This mobile viewpoint is suggestive of the camera's freedom of vantage, the altered, reversed, widened, shortened, lengthened filmic field, and of Mitry's ubiquitous subjectivity, elements that contribute to the creation of the reality effect. Iser even finds something of the *presentness* of image viewing in the reality that emerges when a written text is read:

> Every articulate reading moment entails a switch of perspective, and this constitutes an inseparable combination of differentiated perspectives, foreshortened memories, present modifications, and future expectations. Thus, in the time-flow of the reading process, past and future continually converge in the present moment, and the synthesizing operations of the wandering viewpoint enable the text to pass through the reader's mind as an ever-expanding network of connections. This also adds the dimension of space to that of time, for the accumulation of views and combinations gives us the illusion of depth and breadth, so that we have the impression that we are actually present in a real world.[26]

Claudine Eizykman provides strong counterargument to the notion of passive spectatorship at the cinema in her elaboration of an "energetics" (*énergétique*) of response. She evokes the violent effect made by film on the viewer who, after leaving the movie house, feels "extremely undone, perforated, shaken by a thousand intensities much stronger than those of television, by a thousand light beams more refractive than those of any pictorial, musical, or theatrical space." A desire for such violence runs counter to a desire for repose and passivity:

> What force moves us to shut ourselves up for two hours (minimum) in a black room where we will be inundated, invaded, bombarded, in a situation of surrender and profound discomposure without contact with the actors, the audience, that we find at the theater or a museum? No, it is not passivity that compels us. Or then, if passivity compels us, it is because it suggests something other than banal servitude, submission; it is a passivity that dilutes, that dilutes our selves, our resistances, our puny shows. Passivity, but also passion.[27]

Passion, but also dynamics, energetics. Using Freud's model of Economy, and Marx's of Circulation, Eizykman asserts that viewer response is provoked more strongly by the various functional processes of cinema than by its "references, contents, motivations, meanings."[28]

Belief

Because they consider process prior to surface, the various psychocritical and material modalities, whether they emanate from the apparatus, the screen, the story, the image, the viewer's psyche, memory, intelligence, or body, share a common redefinition of the status of fiction and our belief in it. It is no longer quite necessary to suspend disbelief if we assume that belief is engaged in the reality of the fiction's fictivity (as opposed to the reality of the fiction's illusion) and if *that* reality is to a large degree inflected by the complexity of *our* reality. When we use music as a paradigm for the art enterprise, we can see the extent of our capacity to believe in a work of art thoroughly detached from the lifelike, exempt from the need to reflect action, character, the world of things. Referring only to its own order without recourse to the register of symbol and image, music produces such strong emotional responses and identifications that we often overtly manifest them by tapping and humming. Melodies "haunt us night and day," as do fictions when we share and enjoy their fictivity.[29] Our complicity gives a different emphasis to the factors that have often been described as the *work of art* and its *content*. Do we respond primarily to the work or the content, to the activity or the schema of a fiction that urges us to hum alonng, as it were, tuning ourselves to its various tensions? Robert Scholes argues strenuously that the spectator's consciousness of the fictional is a rich source of reading satisfaction. "I should like to suggest that the proper way for narrative artists to provide for their audiences an experience richer than submissive stupefaction is not to deny them the satisfactions of story, but to generate for them stories which reward the most energetic and rigorous kinds of narrativity."[30] A fluctuating shape, an undulating texture, a mobile face caught between the medium and fiction, elements of cinematic narrativity, call attention to the art as object and invite our continued efforts at possession, activities that ultimately determine our experience of the work.

These activities force us to transcend our ideologies and our most cherished censuring mechanisms. Legions of viewers and critics proclaim their abhorrence of the politics of Ford and Capra films, to say nothing of Leni Riefenstahl's *The Triumph of the Will*, yet willingly submit, and repeatedly resubmit, to these films' emotional resonance. We reject the "cavalry" ethic, the pie-in-the-sky populism, the nazi mythology; we respond to the modes of their conveyance. These modes do not necessarily force viewers to subscribe to the values of the fictive worlds they depict. What happens is often quite the contrary precisely because films invite us to perceive them in the purity of their fictional status, and often therefore to respond to an emotional dynamics whose pressure far exceeds that of uniforms, emblems, speeches, mere signs.

Many of the meanings relevant to this emotional dynamics, this system of affect, resist thoroughly explicit articulation and thrive only in the sublimations, projections, metaphors, and allegories of fantasy and fiction. Here belief survives the menace of evidence, experience, logic; it sustains the presence of patently unreal agents and blatantly artificial formal devices. Belief can be achieved by fiction even when fictivity denies us the comfort of "real" illusions. O. Mannoni, in his analysis of theatrical illusion, *Clefs pour l'imaginaire ou l'autre scène*, traces this property of art to the Freudian notion of disavowal and the fetishist's belief in the maternal penis. The mechanics of simultaneous belief and disbelief becomes a model for other kinds of "beliefs that survive the denial of experience."[31] One of these is the viewer's belief in the baldest manifestations of theatrical (cinematic) illusionism. Mannoni locates the properties of such (dis)belief in a fluctuating movement through dream and varieties of consciousness (thereby anticipating Metz). His remarks on the mediation of belief by masks, spirits, actors are particularly helpful in explaining some of the most troublesome conventions of sentimental fiction: "If we ourselves are not victims of an illusion at the theater or in front of masks, it seems, however, that we need someone else who, for our satifaction, is prey to this illusion. Everything seems contrived to produce it, but in someone else, as if we were in collusion with the actors."[32]

Soon after the credits of *It's a Wonderful Life*, we see a Hollywood sky, replete with what seem like moving, talking light bulbs; we hear a conversation of angels, one of whom will materialize (not unlike movie stars) and conjure a fiction of the hero's absence within the fiction itself (George is made to see what life would have been like had he not been born). Capra elicits the utter incredulity of the audience through the transparency of the angelic configuration to elicit later a much deeper belief in the whole of the fiction. We witness a film mediated by an angel, and a hero who through the angel's power is made to see his life as a movielike fiction of presence and absence. So frequent is the oscillation between the levels of credence (ours, George's) that by the end of the film Capra has reminded us of the essential pertinence, in this visual medium, of the proverb "Seeing is believing." It is indeed enough to see a movie fiction, no matter how fantastic, to believe it.

Melodrama and Reality

Peter Brooks suggests that the reality principle functions as a boundary through whose traversal the melodramatic mode releases meanings that wither in less emphatic registers. "The melodramatic utterance breaks through everything that constitutes the 'reality principle,' all its censorships, accommodations, tonings-down. . . . Desire triumphs over the world of substitute-formations and detours, it achieves plenitude of meaning."[33] This extent of meaning is often masked by complex linguistic and stylistic mediations of art and the highly conventionalized discourse we use in life to avoid the pain of confrontations with others and revelations to ourselves. Brooks hears something of the speech of the psyche in melodramatic utterance as it drives toward the clearest articulation of what we prefer not to say:

> The desire to express all seems a fundamental characteristic of the melodramatic mode. Nothing is spare because nothing is left unsaid; the characters stand on stage and utter the unspeakable, give voice to their deepest feelings, dramatize through their heightened and polarized words and gestures the whole lesson of their relationship. They assume primary psychic roles, father, mother, child, and express basic psychic conditions. Life tends, in this fiction, towards ever more concentrated and totally expressive gestures and statements.[34]

It is melodrama's fullness, intolerant of the strategies of conventional expression, that is considered excessive by standard critical canons.

Brooks's psychodramatic analogy challenges the widely held prejudice against melodrama's simplicity of articulation and access. He has taken on the major task of rehabilitating what has long been considered a minor genre.[35] Many of his arguments are obviously applicable to narrative films of sentiment, works that have their sources in the melodramatic literary traditions of the nineteenth century. The affinities between narrative, cinema, and the pathetic are exemplified in the films of D. W. Griffith, whose prolific output and whose commercial success prove the viability of the melodramatic register in cinema. Griffith acted in and wrote stage melodramas before working at Biograph. Peril-rescue and evil-good scenarios (although not Griffith's *only* fictional types, as is sometimes believed) are pervasive, from his first one-reeler, *The Adventures of Dollie* (1908), through the grandiose *The Birth of a Nation* (1915) and *Intolerance* (1916), to his loving adaptation of the already "old fashioned" melodrama *Way Down East* (1920), and beyond. The pathos of these films had a formative effect on many directors, an effect evidenced in Eisenstein's theory and practice, and in the work of artists less well remembered, right to the present day. Yet, despite its obvious applicability to narrative in film, Brooks's formulation of melodrama as it is manifested in the novel and in the theater is insufficient when we consider that cinema, in its modes of production and perception, is like neither written nor "live" acted texts. Cinematic melodramas must therefore be examined in the specifics of the specular activity it elicits. Its discourse must be distinguished from the incessant symbolic codes of prose, its enactments from the presence of performers in the theater's real space and time.

A more nuanced analogy for film is probably the Italian *melodramma*, the opera, because of its amplificatory, hyperbolic registers—the utterance of singers and orchestra. I think it useful to draw a parallel between the massed effects of ensemble in the music theater and cinema's synthetic simultaneities, conveyed by long shots and montage, of decors and multitudes that would not fit on any stage. The solo/choral (emphasis on individual/emphasis on group) and the linear/harmonic (depiction of progressive action/spectacular mise-en-scène) juxtapositions of the film epic from *Intolerance* to *Close Encounters of the Third Kind* demonstrate cinema's expansion of fictional space through such syntheses. And for the sake of argument I will extend the operatic analogy of hyperbolic performance (vocal projection, extremes of range) to the close-up, a uniquely cinematic mode of theatrical presentation.

Yet, with its insistence on the uniqueness of the performer, the close-up does not belong to a melodramaturgy that, for good reason, Brooks bases upon the audience's perception of type rather than individuality. A victimized, unwed mother who baptizes her dying baby is a melodramatic configuration, but it ceases to be that when she is Lillian Gish in close-up performing that act in *Way Down East*. While the close-up sustains Brooks's notion of melodramatic plenitude, it subverts melodramatic moral typage. And further, distincxt from the modalities of both spoken and musical theater, the photographic naturalism of cinema proves to be particularly intolerant of melodrama. A stage version of *Way Down East*'s spectacular catastrophe on an icy river would undoubtedly seem both melodramatic and ludicrous; Lillian Gish's hand and hair floating in real, frigid water are not. (The sequence was shot, at peril to life and limb, at White River Junction.) When melodrama ceases to be schematic, through the cinematic particularizations of enactment and photography, it transcends that which is reductive in its mode (other aspects of performance often counteract the reductive in melodramatic live theater), pushing the specific work and the perceiver beyond type to the status of unique experience. Nor can we respond to the image as "simple" when it is read as part of a series of images whose very essence of flux violates the categorical nature of melodrama. Films cease to engage us not when they exhibit their melodramatic inflections, but when they cease to exert the lure of cinematic movement, whether that movement be defined by images of stasis or furious action. The medium has the power to rescue the surface of the fiction through its processes of movement, its illusionistic and fantastic projections, and its stagings. That surface is invested with psychological, spatial, and temporal depths into which we are invited to plunge, depths that are both distinct and inextricably mixed in their successive and renewed promises of satisfaction and fulfillment.

Genres

If melodrama is a term insufficient to cinema, and therefore to an understanding of its types of fictions, are there other designations more appropriate to cinematic affectivity? "Tearjerker," "weepy," and "sentimental" are negative and implicitly judgmental of the films to which they are applied.[36] The "woman's film" is ambiguous and inaccurate. It suggests that such a film is only about women or that it appeals only to women. Neither is true. The word "family" in family film is more indicative of the kind of audience for which the fiction is intended than it is of its type, although almost all family films have elements of sentiment. This is also true of "romantic" films, love stories. Because of their imprecise, impoverished, or evaluative semantic resonance, these terms do not accommodate the affective range of film narrative. What is the genre of *Potemkin? The Last Laugh? Mr. Smith Goes to Washington?* Tears are elicited by films about well-heeled lovers, indigent mothers, little boys, dogs, proud cavalrymen, and glamour girls, in modes that range from light comedy to the "serious." Strong emotions are often displayed in drawing-room comedies, thrillers, and action-westerns. Genre distinctions are excessively limiting even when applied to those texts that seem to define the genre. Is it not fruitful to read (as has in fact been done) Hitchcock's thrillers as love stories? The temptation is great with *Notorious* and *Rear Window,* to name two of the most obvious examples. Raymond Bellour has done a meticulous psychocritical reading of *North by Northwest* in which sexual identities and conflicts are no less perilous to the hero than a crop-dusting plane ad a narrow ledge of Mount Rushmore.[37]

Yet, faced with the omnipresence of affectivity in cinema, generic categories have helped me to identify some texts as peripheral to my argument. In mysteries, thrillers, most westerns, and *very* light comedies, affect may be pervasive, but it is only intermittently perceived on the surface of the text. The love scenes of *Notorious* and *Rear Window* punctuate what appear to be suspense films. This is not true of David Lean's *Brief Encounter* or of Frank Borzage's *History Is Made at Night.* For the purpose of examining the affective response, I have chosen a corpus of film in which, for the most part, the rendition of emotional states involving the expression of sentiment constitutes the superficial and primary fictional mode. The medium clearly displays its affectivity in films that dramatize affect itself, films in which the expression of sentiment is at the center of the narrative, films that, even after the most casual viewing, can be recognized as having as their project the dramatization of relationships of sentiment. It is precisely these films that have been judged negatively because of their sentimentality and their ability to draw strong, yet uncritical, responses from viewers. They usually image the flow of tears, and they succeed in making audiences' tears flow in sympathy.

They employ and enjoy strategies that sustain significant durations of feeling; they insistently manifest how and why emotion is manifested.

Audiences have affective responses to many films. Those treated here obviously reflect both the generalities and the particularities of *my* affective response. I have tried to remain consistent, however, in choosing films that force us to consider the workings of affect itself—in the fiction, in the medium, and in us. By doing that I do not wish to imply that a film will automatically trigger an affective response if it foregrounds affect. Some readers may be disconnected from a text because they have insufficient knowledge to read it. Others have expert knowledge of a given subject and will therefore be intolerant of distortion and fictionalization. The specifics of an individual's personal experience and situation may force the rejection of the text. A nine-year-old boy will most probably remain unmoved by the plight of the consumptive, love-struck courtesan; the historian will find ludicrous the inaccurate, falsifying "version" of Marie Antoinette's life and death; the committed feminist is likely to have a negative response to a film that idealizes a woman's sacrifice of her career to wifely subservience.

There are yet other films for which it would be difficult to identify what Stanley Fish has called an "informed reader" or an "interpretive community."[38] These are texts that fail through their own confusion, their clumsy use of conventions, their involuntary betrayal of readers' expectations. (Voluntary betrayals are often a rich source of affect.) A mother-love film will certainly not draw forth tears if its rendition is perfunctory, awkward, inappropriate, if its structure is inadvertently illogical. The death of a child and a mother's grief are affectless, fleeting episodes in *Call Her Savage*, whose plot is as hyperkinetic as the familiar gestures of the star, the post-"It" Clara Bow. Even performers and directors renowned for their work in fictions of sentiment succumb to textual incoherence. In 1938 Frank Borzage directed *Three Comrades* and *The Shining Hour*. In the first, the death scene of Pat, the character played by Margaret Sullavan, is the emotional peak of a narrative that forms a dense and consistent pattern of situations of friendship, love, and idealism. Pat sums up our feelings about these feelings in her suicide. She has just undergone surgery for tuberculosis. Warned that the slightest movement will prove fatal, she laboriously rises from her bed, goes to the terrace, and stretches out her arms to her husband in the courtyard below. Unwilling to be a burden to those who are dear to her, she sacrifices herself in a gesture that acknowledges the coherence of the fiction. Acting and direction satisfy us in their completion of an emotional trajectory, drawing us up along with performer and camera. This trajectory is denied the "interpretive community" for which *The Shining Hour* was intended. A "major studio classic narrative" film, *The Shining Hour* is meant to provide a reading perceived as coherent by a wide range of audiences. The plot itself does not prevent such a reading. A nightclub performer, Joan Crawford, unfulfilled by big-city success and sophistication, marries a rich Wisconsin farmer, Melvyn Douglas. Her arrival at the family estate provokes her husband's sister, Fay Bainter, to jealous rage, and her husband's brother, Robert Young, to adulterous desire. Bainter burns down Crawford's new house; unloved Margaret Sullavan seizes the occasion to attempt to immolate herself, thereby authorizing the love of her husband, Young, for Crawford. The audience expects a resolution whose intensity, in complementing the logic of the fiction, is a prime source of affect. The conclusion offers instead a shot whose eccentricity reflects the kind of reading that the text repeatedly generates. Margaret Sullavan, playing yet another self-sacrificing woman in love, lies in yet another bed. This time, though, she has been rescued from her suicide attempt. All we see of her face are her eyes, isolated in a cosmetically glamorous, perfect opening in the bandages around her head. A touch of the absurd, with odd echoes of *The Invisible Man* and *The Mummy,* might have been avoided if a traceable design had been established. We are even denied the satisfying outcome of the conventional "bandaged face" scene—the removal of the bandages. Emotional response to this image is short-circuited by the reading that the text's disorienting ingredients have imposed. Among the troubling configurations: the opening sequence in which Crawford, "the toast of New York," does her nightclub act, a series of "modern" turns to Chopin, partnered by MGM's resident adagio dancer, Tony De Marco; the "humorous" use of the black maid, Hattie McDaniel, who at one point is compared to a farm tractor; the strenuous shifts in tone Fay Bainter is made to display, from sarcasm to pyromaniacal fury (she has barely a hair out of place during her lunatic incendiary activities) to morning-after repentance and good sense; the shot of Crawford carrying Sullavan out of of the burning house in her strong arms (one asks why Young and Douglas were not more alert); the very premise that Young prefers Crawford to Sullavan, given the personas and abilities of these particular performers. This curiously heterogeneous mixture of textual constitutents is conveyed by a publicity still of the stars, grouped as they never are in the film, their smiles and frowns in discordant array against an ominously shadowy background. The photograph thwarts the most energetic attempt to supply it with narrative meaning. In this, as well as in style and composition, it resembles stills for films that are paragons of narrative coherence. What is remarkable, however, is how precisely it emblemizes the nearly impermeable narrative pattern of *The Shining Hour.*

There are undoubtedly viewers so attracted to some aspect of *The Shining Hour* that they are able to ignore its elisions and inconsistencies. Most of us are forced to read the film as a function of an eccentric combination of incompatible elements. How else are we to make sense of those bandage-framed eyes that stare out, perhaps in wonder at what has preceded? We stare as well and wonder, not at the film's improbability, but at the absence of the web of gestures, words, and images that sustains improbability where it belongs—within a fiction.

Angels

In his study on time and fictional coherence Frank Kermode evokes the status of angels as defined by St. Thomas. His angels are "neither matter, with its potentiality, nor pure act, but immaterial with potentiality. . . . They are therefore neither eternal nor of time."[39] So it is for the material immateriality and the eternally repeatable durations of movies and their stars, who effect the transformations once reserved for angels. The ideal medium for angels has often been the properties of the fictivity of sentimental cinema, with its constellation of ideallizing conceits. This ethos of fictivity is exemplified in the films of Frank Borzage, a director whose long career is marked by an obsessive pattern of sentimental configurations. The title of Borzage's *History Is Made at Night* is suggestive of cinema's penchant for artifice, improbability, idealization. The very notion that history, in this case a fiction film, can be "made" at night, therefore in the absence of light, suggests a distance between the medium and its requisite light. Making history at night asserts the cinema's trickery, its seductive search for what seem to be lightless photographic contexts, and its subsequent creation of purely cinematic light. This gesture is defiant of the patently documentary quality of each film frame. It posits the fictivity of a medium that for Edgar Morin projects "the world of spirits or phantoms, such as it is manifested in a great number of archaic mythologies: an aerian world in which omnipresent spirits navigate."[40]

The narrative premise of *History Is Made at Night* proclaims the force of fiction through its profusion of unlikelihoods and coincidences.[41] Paul, "the greatest head-waiter in all Europe" (Charles Boyer), saves Irene (Jean Arthur) from her estranged husband's plot to prevent their divorce. The husband (Colin Clive) frames Paul for murder and then blackmails Irene into renouncing her gallant lover. Unaware of the murder and of why Irene gives him up, Paul goes to America and transforms a dreary restaurant into the most fashionable dining place in New York in the hope that his beloved "Miss America" will appear. Meanwhile, Irene has fled from her vicious husband, but agrees to return with him to Paris when an innocent man she believes to be Paul has been apprehended. On the night of the couple's departure they just happen to dine at Paul's restaurant. Irene's joy at finding Paul out of danger is short-lived; Paul will not let the innocent man stand trial. The lovers sail for Paris on the liner owned by Irene's husband, who in a fit of mad jealousy urges the captain to reckless speed and certain disaster amid the ice fields of the North Atlantic. Paul, Irene, and the others are saved from death when the last bulkheads of the "Princess Irene" hold against the surging water.

The style of the film's narration does nothing to mitigate improbabilities that it in fact relishes. At the beginning Paul rescues Irene by masquerading as a jewel thief; they fall in love about two minutes later, in a taxicab; alone in Paul's restaurant, they dance the tango the night through, Irene barefoot, in a fur coat. They speak of love in fictions: the menu for a perfect dinner, a pair of puppets drawn on their hands. Their feelings, freed by these fictions, are replayed when Irene returns to Paul in another restaurant, in another city, and yet again, when they order that perfect meal aboard ship and dance the tango in their stateroom. They achieve a state of transcendence in the context of the final disaster, the end-of-the-world configuration of the sinking ship, the life and death enactments of couples being separted, the de rigeur, in extremis rendition of "Nearer My God to Thee" by the brave little orchestra. Awaiting what seems like certain death, enveloped in fog, the faces of Paul and Irene are suffused with the complexities of fiction and of cinematic light. The nick-of-time rescue shifts the film to yet a higher register of joy and miracle, offering the satisfaction of fiction at its purest.

This is the satisfaction too of Borzage's *Seventh Heaven*, where Diane (Janet Gaynor) and Chico (Charles Farrell) transcend harsh necessity in their Parisian garret, and transcend space, death, and blindness through their telepathic relationship, fully conveyed by the simplest of shot juxtapositions—Diane in Paris, Chico in the trenches at the front. Chico's reappearance is a miracle of faith, light, and cinema.[42] Such is the miracle of communication between the living and the dead in *Smilin' Through*, the miracle of variable photographic density in the last images of *Three Comrades*, where the survivors link arms with the dead. Myra (Catherine McLeod) and Goranoff (Philip Dorn), the protagonists of *I've Always Loved You*, "speak" through art, live as if life were the Rachmaninoff Piano Concerto no. 2, appear in sets decorated to such a high degree that they can be nothing *but* decor, and in colors so vivid that they cannot for a moment be mistaken for those we perceive in nature. At the climax of *I've Always Loved You* we perceive the extent to which cinema itself is emotion for Borzage. The last shot is not of the protagonists but *of* the means through which their feelings are conveyed—piano and surrounding decor (the source of the aural/visual image) and the camera (the recording apparatus). The invisible camera becomes the principal actor as it tracks back up the center aisle of the auditorium, away from the piano that Myra has just abandoned. The concerto thunders to its conclusion despite her absence. As music mirrors, transmits, and subsumes the emotional power of the medium, it demonstrates how for Borzage, and for so many others, there is almost no distinction between art *for* feeling and art *as* feeling.

Many sentimental narratives tend to generate improbabilities in proportion to the strength of the feelings they express. In such narratives the very activity of fiction making becomes so expressive that it reflects a measure of incompatibility between feeling and necessity, between emotion and logic. Experience tells us to reject Chico and Diane's "seventh heaven," Myra and Goranoff's audiovisual harmonies, Irene and Paul's historic night. But we succumb to these idealizations, the glamorous close-ups, the molding of faces and bodies in images whose artifices are compounded by plot, light, and the "magic" of cinema. Feeling is located in this ambiguous field of probable improbability, where real yet absent performers play out situations that both happen and do not happen. Emotional engagement is powered by the deployment of cinematic strategies that liberate actors from flesh, objects from matter, emotion from necessity.

Notes

1. The dates of films will appear only if necessary to the sense of my argument.
2. W. K. Wimsatt, Jr., *The Verbal Icon: Studies in the Meaning of Poetry* (Lexington: University Press of Kentucky, 1954), p. 21.
3. Susan R. Suleiman and Inge Crosman, eds., *The Reader in the Text: Essays on Audience and Interpretation* (Princeton: Princeton University Press, 1980), provide an excellent bibliography for reader-oriented criticism.
4. Stanley E. Fish, "Literature in the Reader: Affective Stylistics," in *Self-Consuming Artifacts: The Experience of Seventeenth-Century Literature* (Berkeley: University of California Press, 1972), p. 390.
5. Stanley Cavell, *The World Viewed: Reflections on the Ontology of Film*, enlarged ed. (Cambridge, Massachusetts and London: Harvard University Press, 1979), pp. 14–15.

6. Beginning in 1978, a series of articles has appeared under the rubric "Guilty Pleasures" in *Film Comment* in which various critics discuss the "bad" films they love most.
7. Susan Sontag, *Against Interpretation and Other Essays* (New York: Farrar, Straus & Giroux, 1966), p. 177.
8. Sontag, p. 179.
9. Nick Browne, "Narrative Point of View: The Rhetoric of *Au hasard, Balthasar*," *Film Quarterly* 31 (Fall 1977): 19–31.
10. Jean Mitry, *Esthétique et psychologie du cinéma. I. Les structures* (Paris: Editions Universitaires, 1963), p. 147. (This and all subsequent translations from cited foreign language editions are mine.) Edgar Morin is just as insistent on the function of affect in the production of cinematic meaning. "We must conceive of affective participation as cinema's *genetic stage and structural foundation*." *Le cinéma ou l'homme imaginaire* (Paris: Editions Gonthier, 1958), p. 91.
11. Hugo Münsterberg, *The Film: A Psychological Study, The Silent Photoplay in 1916* (1916; reprint New York: Dover, 1970), p. 53.
12. Mitry, p. 179. Jean-Pierre Meuneir, in *Les structures de l'expérience filmique: L'identification filmique* (Louvain: Librairie Universitaire, 1969), examines this in terms both of the notion of intersubjectivity developed by Hesnard and of the phenomenology of Merleau-Ponty and Sartre. Although he distinguishes between a viewer's sense of "being with" and "being like" the fictional character, he attaches the cinematic experience firmly to categories of lifelike recognition and resemblance.
13. Mitry, p. 188.
14. Münsterberg, pp. 51–52.
15. Christian Metz, "The Imaginary Signifier," trans. Ben Brewster, *Screen* 16 (Summer 1975): 58.
16. Metz, "Imaginary Signifier" p. 15.
17. Thierry Kuntzel, "A Note upon the Filmic Apparatus," *Quarterly Review of Film Studies* 1 (1976): 266–71.
18. Metz, "Imaginary Signifier," p. 47.
19. Christian Metz, "The Fiction Film and Its Spectator," trans. Alfred Guzzetti, *New Literary History* 8 (August 1976): 98.
20. Martha Wolfenstein and Nathan Leites, in what was probably the first book-length analysis of cinema within a Freudian discourse, *Movies: A Psychological Study* (Glencoe, Illinois: Free Press, 1950), examines film fictions almost exclusively in terms of the viewer's fantasy configurations and projections.
21. Morin, p. 81.
22. Metz, "Fiction Film," p. 79.
23. Metz, "Fiction Film," p. 102.
24. Wolfgang Iser, *The Implied Reader: Patterns of Communication in Prose Fiction from Bunyan to Beckett* (Baltimore: Johns Hopkins University Press, 1974), p. 279.
25. Wolfgang Iser, *The Act of Reading: A Theory of Aesthetic Response* (Baltimore: Johns Hopkins University Press, 1978), pp. 128–29. Stanley Fish in "Interpreting the *Variorum*," *Critical Inquiry* 2 (Spring 1976): 474, also emphasizes the temporal experience of the text in his description of reading as interpretation.
26. Iser, *Act of Reading*, p. 116.
27. Claudine Eizykman, *La jouissance-cinéma* (Paris: 10/18, 1976), pp. 7–8.
28. Eizykman, p. 13.
29. Thomas Elsaesser, in his rich and allusive "Tales of Sound and Fury: Observations on the Family Melodrama," *Monogram*, vol. 4 (1972), makes extensive use of the musical analogy. "Considered as an expressive code, melodrama might therefore be described as a particular

form of dramatic mise-en-scène, characterized by a dynamic use of spatial and musical categories, as opposed to intellectual or literary ones" (p. 6). And later, "The aesthetic qualities of this type of cinema depend on the ways 'melos' is given to 'drama' by means of lighting, montage, visual rhythm, decor, style of acting, music—that is, on the ways the mise-en-scène translates character into action" (p. 8).

30. Robert Scholes, "Narration and Narrativity in Film," *Quarterly Review of Film Studies* 1 (1976): 290.
31. O. Mannoni, *Clefs pour l'imaginaire ou l'autre scène* (Paris: Editions de Seuil, 1969), p. 12.
32. Mannoni, pp. 163–64.
33. Peter Brooks, *The Melodramatic Imagination: Balzac, Henry James, Melodrama, and the Modes of Excess* (New Haven: Yale University Press, 1976), p. 41.
34. Brooks, p. 4.
35. Robert Heilman redefines melodrama in somewhat different terms. He extends the genre to a wide range of "serious" fictions that can be characterized as belonging to "the realm of disaster." Another distinguishing feature of melodrama is its deployment of "undivided" characters. "Melodrama, in sum, includes the whole realm of conflicts undergone by characters who are presented as undivided or at least without divisions of such magnitude that they must be at the dramatic center: hence melodrama includes a range of actions that extends from disaster to success, from defeat to victory, and a range of effects from the strongest conviction of frustration and failure that serious art can dramatize, to the most frivolous assurance of triumph that a mass-circulation writer can confect." *Tragedy and Melodrama: Versions of Experience* (Seattle: University of Washington Press, 1968), p. 86.
36. Frank McConnell bravely rescues "sentimental" in his ingenious coupling of romantic art and film. "The naive perceptions of a child—or, for Schiller, of the childhood of poetry and culture, the archaic masterpieces—are forever closed to us, readers and viewers of a later day. Sentimental art, the art of the romantic imagination, recognizes both the necessity of recapturing those naive perceptions for the sake of a fully human, fully conscious life and the impossibility of recapturing that life without the aid of the sophistication, the intelligence, and the techniques of artifice which separate it from us so irrevocably." *The Spoken Seen: Film and the Romantic Imagination* (Baltimore: Johns Hopkins University Press, 1975), pp. 40–41.
37. Raymond Bellour, "Le blocage symbolique," *Communications*, no. 23 (1975), pp. 235–350.
38. Fish, "Interpreting the *Variorum*," pp. 473–85.
39. Frank Kermode, *The Sense of an Ending: Studies in the Theory of Fiction* (New York: Oxford University Press, 1967), p. 70.
40. Morin, p. 39.
41. David Thomson states, "In Borzage's best work, passion, visual eroticism, and fidelity to the ideal of love produce imagery so psychically material as to make story lines almost pretexts." *America in the Dark: Hollywood and the Gift of Unreality* (New York: William Morrow, 1977), p. 213. While in Borzage's films "the ideal of love" certainly emanates from style and enactment, it is also shaped by the idealizing fictivity of the "story lines," elements too lightly dismissed by Thomson.
42. Philip Rosen, in "Difference and Displacement in *Seventh Heaven*," *Screen* 18 (Summer 1977): 99, assesses the value of light as "signifier for all of the insubstantialities of the film," insubstantialities resumed in the film's miraculous conclusion.

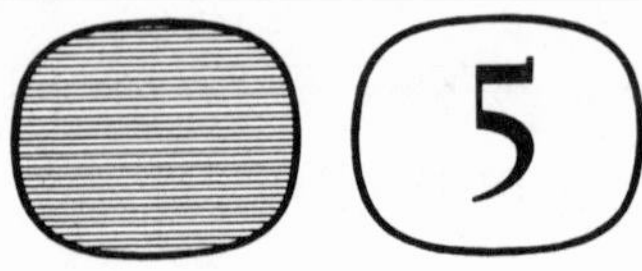

Russian Formalist Theories of Melodrama

DANIEL GEROULD

The Russian Formalist critics, who flourished in the Soviet Union in the mid-1920's, are best known for their stylistic and linguistic studies as well as their analyses of narrative and poetic techniques. In rejecting the psychological, sociological, and biographical approaches to literature and instead focusing attention on the intrinsic properties of the work of art itself, particularly its technique and structure, through rigorous scientific dissection, the Formalists anticipated by many years a number of the major principles of both the American New Criticism of the 1940's and the French Structuralism of the 1960's.[1]

For the most part, the Russian Formalists were literary and academic critics, little concerned with the performing arts, for whom the primary materials for analysis were poetic texts. It is, therefore, not surprising that in the scholarly presentation of Formalist theory in English no place is given to drama or theatre, an applied genre which would appear to lie outside the purview of the movement.[2] At first glance, melodrama especially might seem an unlikely subject for Formalist theory.

It must be understood, however, that the Russian Formalists were indeed interested in popular and oral culture and did not discriminate in favor of the printed over the spoken word. In fact, several of their celebrated analyses are of traditional oral materials, as witness Vladimir Propp's work on the fairy tale and folklore.[3] Two of the leaders of the movement, Victor Shklovsky and Boris Eichenbaum, showed a marked interest in nineteenth-century popular fiction; Shklovsky wrote of Dickens and the Mystery

Daniel Gerould's "Russian Formalist Theories of Melodrama" originally appeared in *The Journal of American Culture*, Vol. 1, no. 1 (1978), pp. 152–68. Reprinted by permission of the author and *The Journal of American Culture*.

Novel while Eichenbaum seriously investigated O. Henry and the Short Story,[4] and both dealt extensively with cinema. The Formalists were naturally attracted to genre studies, particularly to seemingly minor or marginal genres which had received virtually no critical investigation, but were clearly significant in their impact on other, better known forms.

It is in this context that Russian Formalist interest in popular theatre arose. Several Formalist critics and writers associated with the school actually did take up the study of drama, not as a purely literary form, but as a mixed theatrical mode, and the genre which called forth their most intensive scrutiny was popular melodrama, usually regarded as subliterary and ignored by the makers of poetics. For the Formalists, however, who were non-judgmentally objective in approach, and committed to exploring the essential characteristics of a genre and to tracing its evolution into "higher" types, no study of dramatic form could be more congenial and rewarding than that of melodrama.

In his seminal work, *Russian Formalism: History-Doctrine*,[5] Victor Erlich points out that the Formalists were at their best in dealing with extreme stylization; the fairy tale provided ideal material for their analytical methods because it is "one of the most thoroughly formalized literary genres" and "one of the least psychology-minded types of fiction."[6] The same thing could be said of melodrama as a subject for Formalist theoretical exploration. Of all theatrical modes, melodrama is the most conventionalized, depending for its success far less on individual talent and imagination than on the skillful manipulation of stock formulas.[7]

For all these reasons, the Russian Formalists made, I believe, an unusually valuable contribution to the theory of melodrama long before this popular genre was seriously studied as a dramatic form in England, America, or anywhere else. For the first time in the history of criticism, the Formalists analyzed the mechanism of melodrama and revealed its fundamental techniques and its aesthetic principles.

The small, but important body of Formalist writing on melodrama consists almost exclusively of three studies (all written in 1926): Sergei Balukhatyi's *Poetics of Melodrama*, Boris Tomashevsky's *French Melodrama of the Beginning of the Nineteenth Century*, and Adrian Piotrovsky's *Towards a Theory of Cinema Genres*. Although only Tomashevsky was a full-fledged member of the Formalist circle, Balukhatyi and Piotrovsky were at least temporarily associated with the school, and their essays are firstrate examples of the Formalist method and appeared as contributions to major Formalist compilations at the height of the movement in 1927, just before its rapid demise under repressive attack from reactionary Marxist quarters. Balukhatyi's essay was published in Volume III of the Leningrad Formalist periodical, *Poetika* (as was Tomashevsky's in Volume II), and Piotrovsky's study appeared in *Poetics of Cinema*, a Formalist collection, edited by Eichenbaum, that includes work by Shklovsky and Yurii Tynyanov.[8]

Melodrama was, in this period, a timely subject. Immediately after the Revolution and into the mid-1920's, there had been widespread practical interest in melodrama and spirited discussion of its place in the new Soviet theatre. Blok, Lunacharsky, and Gorky, among others, argued that the strong didactic and theatrical values inherent in melodrama made it the ideal popular theatre for mass audiences in a new revolutionary society. New Soviet melodramas as well as famous French nineteenth-century examples of the genre (such as Dumas' *Tour de Nesle*) were given magnificent stagings; Meyerhold produced Alexander Faiko's anti-capitalist melodramas, and Stanislavsky's Moscow Art Theory did a version of D'Ennery's *The Two Orphans*.[9]

Undoubtedly, the active ferment over melodrama in the theatrical life of the time finds a reflection in the Formalists' detached analytical studies, but the Formalist approach is from a diametrically opposed point of view. Whereas Gorky and Lunacharsky discovered an important utilitarian function for melodrama in Soviet society, the Formalists limited themselves to depicting the nature of the genre itself, both as an abstract form and as an evolving organism in the natural history of dramatic forms.

1. Balukhatyl and the *Poetics of Melodrama*

Sergei Balukhatyi (1892–1945) was the major theoretician of drama among the Formalists and critics associated with the movement, and he was the first to develop a coherent set of principles for Formalist analysis of drama in his book, *Problems of Dramaturgical Analysis: Chekov* (1927). Balukhatyi continued to write on Chekhov and the principles of Chekhovian dramatic construction, but after 1930 and the persecution of the Formalists as heretics, he was unable to complete his theoretical work and turned instead to the safer field of Gorky studies, particularly bibliography and text transmission, with occasional ventures into sociological analysis in order to demonstrate his renunciation of formalism.

Balukhatyi's *Poetics of Melodrama* remains to the present day the most thorough and incisive systematic analysis of the structure and technique of melodrama ever undertaken. The author's method, characteristic of the Formalists, is first to determine the functional purpose and compositional plan of melodrama and then to break it down into component parts. The following summary provides a condensed version of Balukhatyi's complete argument and retains all the headings, sections, and subsections of the original.

INTRODUCTION

The objective of the study is to establish the basic constructional principles of melodrama and to set forth the typical traits of the genre. The aim is purely theoretical, not historical; no attention is given to the varieties of national melodrama, or to the different periods in its evolution. The material analyzed consists of late melodramas in translation (primarily from the French) from the repertory of the Russian theatre, chiefly of the last quarter of the nineteenth century.

The plays, largely in manuscript, are part of the collection at the Central Library of Russian Drama in Leningrad.[10] By studying stage versions intended for performance,

Balukhatyi wishes to avoid a purely literary interpretation and establish the actual theatrical form of melodrama which has impact on a spectator, not a reader.

I. EMOTIONAL TELEOLOGY

All elements in melodrama—its themes, technical principles, construction, and style—are subordinate to one overriding aesthetic goal: the calling forth of "pure," "vivid" emotions. Plot, character, and dialogue, working in unison, serve to elicit from the spectator the greatest possible intensity of feeling.

The emotional teleology of melodrama conditions the choice of its particular poetic means—which are limited in number, but highly effective in the theatre. Melodrama is primarily characterized by its method of "playing on the emotions."

The fundamental task for the melodramatist is "baring the passions," which constitute the motive force of the characters' actions. The display of "passion" is central to the structure of melodrama as the mainspring of its plot; "passion" is revealed not for its own sake, but only to explain the dramatic action which results from it. Since action in melodrama is always extraordinary, it must be justified by a high degree of feeling, expressed as "vivdly" as possible with "maximal" intensity. Hence, the organic and mutually interactive bond between propulsive emotion and plot in melodrama, and the peculiar artistic strength of the melodramatic form.

The emotional teleology of melodrama is manifest in the following elements:

1. *In its plot themes.* Melodrama uses plots with foolproof emotional bases. Typically melodramatic are extreme violations of the normal connections among everyday phenomena; the very fact of violation and the desire on the part of the spectator to see it put right will call forth strong emotions. Usual plot themes: accusation of an innocent person in a murder or theft, the fate of a defenseless girl, a character as victim of his own passions, a person forced to commit deeds contrary to his own conscience.

2. *In the material furnished by the facts of everyday life and by the characters' actions.* Melodrama utilizes material that will invariably produce strong emotional shocks for the spectator. Usual material: murders, large-scale thefts or forgeries, confrontation with a murdered victim, trial, sentencing, preparation for the execution, hard labor, beggary, futile efforts to earn a living, a father's curse, tragic or joyous shocks connected with sudden recognitions.

3. *In the construction of a plot with unexpected twists and sharp reversals in the story line:* either incessant changes of "happy" and "unhappy" episodes for the principal characters, or an uninterruptedly "unhappy" line of development for the chief character until the denouement with its final "happy" reversal. Especially forceful is the denouement with an unexpected reversal which determines the fates of all the characters, resolves all side issues, restores to normality the violated relationships, and satisfies the spectator. The expressive quality of such a denouement is strengthened by the pathos of the closing speeches and the sententiousness of the concluding remarks.

4. *In strikingly effective situations,* which make an immediate impression on the spectator at crucial moments in the drama. Melodramatic plot construction abounds in situations susceptible to obvious "sentimental" treatment. Frequent situations: a mother parts with her daughter; a young daughter loses her mother; a father (or

mother) searches for his daughter, meets her, and fails to recognize her; a mother (or father) and daughter meet in penal servitude; a girl loves a young man, but is compelled to become the fiancee of another.

5. *In characters* involved in vivid, expressive emotional interrelationships (a loving couple, bride and bridegroom, mother or father and daughter), subsequently violated in a dramatic fashion (sudden jealousy, forced parting of lovers, loss of the child, imprisonment of the father). Melodrama expresses feelings which are comprehensible to all, universal and primitive, frequently voiced by a mother ("maternal feelings") or a loving couple ("love"—the favorite emotive theme in melodrama). The characters in melodrama are affecting by their very nature: children, adolescents, defenseless girls. A second series of feelings, such as "envy," "self-seeking," and "vengeance" creates richly effective dramatic situations.

6. *In the speeches and dialogue of the characters*, arranged dynamically and expressively. "Impassioned speech" is peculiar to the characters who are always ready to make speeches about their feelings. They have the ability to change rapidly both the themes and emotional coloration of their speeches ("joyous" tonality changing to "sorrowful" and vice versa). The character "bares" his inner emotional experiences and expresses them in pathetic speeches, using *maximally* "impassioned" words. These "deeply-felt" speeches are not only the direct expression of strong emotion, but they also contain "analysis" of the emotion being experienced, that is to say, the *character's self-appraisal* of the strength of his own feelings ("Remember with what hate my heart is overflowing!") This device reveals the intense energy of the feeling which organizes the entire expressive speech.

Expressiveness is achieved by stylistic as well as thematic qualities. Copiousness of exclamations, energetic intonations, expressive vocabulary, and rhythmic construction create the sensation of speech animated by "great feeling." The emotional speeches in melodrama are usually similar to one another, undifferentiated by the character or temperament of the speakers.

The expressive nature of the speeches is strengthened by the stage directions which accompany them; the number of these in any melodrama is immense, and the lexical variety of their specifications bears witness to the melodramatist's attempt to find striking tones of voice. Such pathos-laden speech, coming at the sharpest and most significant moments, reinforces the plot dynamics and underscores the dramatic situation.

Clear and forceful statement of emotional experiences is necessary for motivation. In melodrama we must not look for psychological justification for the actions which occur, as we would in realistic drama. Actions and deeds in melodrama are justified, not by detailed investigation of "feeling," or by its "psychology," but solely by the very *nature* and *force* of the emotion itself.

II. MORAL TELEOLOGY

Although melodramatic construction is necessarily geared to maximally calling forth the spectator's emotions, melodrama is never limited to manipulation of emotional themes alone. There is invariably a moralizing treatment of plot. Melodramatic documents are "happy" for the positive characters and "unhappy" for the negative characters. This perfect system of rewards and punishments is perceived by the spectator as a "natural" reflection of the basic "laws of morality," predetermined by the very course of events.

Melodrama teaches, consoles, punishes, and rewards; it submits the phenomena of life and human conduct to the immutable laws of justice and offers reflections upon men's actions and feelings. A favorite device for moralizing is the insertion at crucial moments in the plot of sententious speeches evaluating the ethical quality of the characters' experiences and feelings. In the denouement violated norms are righted and problems solved in a spirit of ideal morality.

III. TECHNICAL PRINCIPLES

1. *Principle of Relief.* Melodrama strives for sculptural relief within its schematization; plot situations and character traits are given in sharply-etched design. Inclined to psychological primitivism, characters are assigned the simplest and clearest function (victim, villain, insidious enemy, dedicated friend or servant). Speech or dialogue develops a single theme, in a single tone, but with vivid emotional and expressive coloration by means of intonation and gesture. The characters' deeds and gestures are absolute, devoid of nuanced transition. Everything moves forward by sharply isolating the crucial, striking moments in the dramatic action, rather than by co-ordinating them with the surrounding moments. Melodrama maintains itself on the heights of intensity, thereby obtaining the maximum force from each episode.

2. *Principle of Contrast.* Melodrama makes extensive use of juxtaposition of diverse material. A usual evice is the interweaving of the destinies of characters at different ends of the social ladder (beggar and count) or at different moral elevations (villain and victim). Contrast may exist in changes of phase for one and the same character: a character is capable of being unexpectedly transformed from vicious to virtuous (usually in the denouement), or "love" may change into "vengeance." Contrast may be found in a situation where the qualitative side of the material is antithetical to the setting in which it is placed (an innocent and defenseless victim amidst criminal vagabonds, a murder while a ball takes place in the next room).

Contrast also exists in the expressive style. Melodrama rarely maintains a single dramatic tone, but alternates the comic in situation, character, and speech with the intensely tragic. This alternation gives melodrama an "agitated" texture, imparting particular sharpness to its emotional themes through contrastive illumination.

3. *Principle of Dynamics.* In plot structure and narrative development, each phase is followed by what appears to be an entirely new phase in relation to what went before, or at least by an entirely new degree of expressiveness. In this way the spectator's emotions are constantly held at a high point of tension.

The characters are perpetually confronted with obstacles on their way to achieving their goals: temporary successes and recognitions prove inadequate or false, giving rise to new consequences leading to further struggle. Melodrama uses various devices for braking the main action: through the intrigues of a vicious character, through continual delays in the carrying out of a key action, through failure to make a crucial recognition, through unexpected circumstances. *Retardation at the denouement* has especially expressive force, putting the spectator through further trials at the concluding phases of the action when he wishes to see the resolution accomplished. Likewise, according to the same principle, the endings of the individual acts fall at moments when new plot developments are first introduced and not yet fully disclosed.

Melodrama always finds ways to introduce the *unexpected* into the action. The dynamic effect of this device lies in the fact that it violates the "course of events" as it has been outlined and already grasped by the spectator, turning it in new, unknown directions through the introduction of a new fact or deed, not stipulated by the previous action. Hence the presence in melodrama of the following: sudden arrivals, arrivals of a character at the moment when he is remembered or spoken of, sudden meetings, substitutions, kidnappings, unexpected findings, recognitions and rescues, introduction of unforeseen circumstances leading to a "happy" resolution of the plot, unexpected denouements.

Most often melodrama makes dynamic use of a *secret*. The secret is the most powerful factor in the play's dynamics, permitting the melodramatist to hold the spectator's interest uninterruptedly throughout the performance. Use of the secret is varied. There may be a *total secret*, contained in the exposition to the play, and unknown to both the characters and the spectator. The spectator can only guess as to the nature of the secret (on the basis of scattered "hints"), to which no character has the key. The gradual revelation of the secret, while the spectator attempts to guess it, gives the melodrama its compositional tension.

A second type of secret is the *secret for the characters*, but not for the spectator. In this case the play's compositional dynamics are based on the unfolding of situations which block an "easy" solution to the enigma of concealed relationships. The characters approach the solution, then move away from it again; the solution is continually braked by "fatal misunderstandings." The spectator, as though a participant in the events unfolding on stage, has a strong "will" to have the secret disclosed, but his desire must remain tense and unresolved until the denouement.

The dynamics of melodrama reside not only in the plot, but also in the language, gesture, and mime which give the stamp of forcefulness and accelerated tempo to the melodramatic style.

IV. CONSTRUCTION

The originality of melodrama lies not only in the simultaneous action of the technical principles described above, but also in the use of various constructional devices for unfolding the emotional plot, and moralizing themes inherent in the play. The actual *construction of melodrama* shows all the signs of being a fixed "model" form created by the selection of a series of expressive, effect-producing items arranged in a dramatic-scenic system. Principal among these are:

1. *The dramatic knot*. At the basis of melodrama a situation is always set up which gives rise to inevitable dramatic consequences and predetermines and favors the creation of "sharp" phases of plot development. In this initial thread of the plot, there is always some violation of the "norm" of character relationships and the habits of

everyday life, as it were a pathological situation. (A mother, wishing to hide the fruit of her first love, abandons her daughter to strangers.)

2. *The prologue.* Here the initial dramatic knot and plot thread is treated graphically, with clear stress on its role for all subsequent development of the action. The prologue stands at the beginning of the play, separated from the remaining phases of the unfolding "action" by a significant stretch of time.

3. *Exposition.* Exposition about events and the general disposition of the characters is given at the beginning of the acts (especially the first), not in masked form, but openly and distinctly, in direct speeches by the characters which stress the dramatic qualities of the basic situations. Such open exposition occurs in each of the following acts, especially if they are separated from the preceding acts by a large interval of time or contain clusters of events.

The characters are provided with *self-explanatory speeches;* in these speeches the characters themselves define their own situation, reveal the general line of their conduct, and speak of the motives of their coming actions. Thus, the spectator at any given moment is not at a loss about plot and character relationships.

4. *Multiplicity of acts.* Melodrama often has six, seven, or eight acts, sometimes as many as ten or eleven, since the action with its many themes and plot reversals passes through a long *series of phases and episodes.* Each act has its own structure and development.

5. *Epilogue, act endings.* Melodrama gives special significance to the denouement in which all the plot lines come together and the basic themes are fully articulated; sometimes the play draws to a close by means of an act which isolates the final phase in the form of an epilogue. More often, the denouement occurs in the final scene of the last act where all narrative and plot lines are exhaustively resolved—a fact which explains the special impact of the concluding act of a melodrama. The endings of each individual act are likewise dramatically expressive, since they complete the plot phase unfolded in that given act and at the same time create a new complication which will be unfolded in the following acts. The distinctive sharpness of the act endings is heightened by the pathos of the characters' speeches. Such a structuring of act endings allows for a dynamically shifting series of plot episodes, each diverting in itself, and not co-ordinated with the surrounding episodes.

6. *Movement in tiers.* Hence, what is characteristic for melodramatic composition is not a straight rise to the culminating point and then a lowering of tension until the conclusion, but rather a movement in tiers by which each new phase of the plot with its new "obstacles" and "non-resolutions" gives rise to new degrees of dramatic intensity. This new "quality" of dramatic intensity, which builds in layers, creates heightened dramatic perception on the part of the spectator, not resolved until the final moments of the denouement.

7. *Act titles.* Concerned that the spectator grasp the full dramatic weight of a given plot thread or episode contained within a given act, the melodramatist provides special designations for both the play and the separate acts, thereby directing the attention of whoever reads the poster to the intensely dramatic traits implicit in these titles. The presence of act titles—dramatic in theme and expressive in style—is a specific trait of the melodrama poster. Taken as a series, these titles offer intriguing hints as to the dramatic nature of the plot and its progressive unfolding.

8. *Play titles*. The methods of formulating play titles are various. The titles may establish the central dramatic situation, the dramatic knot, or initial dramatic event, the basic stimulus for a character, the milieu or dramatic place of action, the dramatic quality of the narrative, the designation of the thing which plays an active role in the drama. The double title with "or" is characteristic of melodrama. The complex title has a double function: for example, to name the chief character and single out the basic situation, to single out the basic situation and make a sententious comment, or to name the chief character and the chief dramatic emotion.

9. *The characters and their functions*. Melodrama unfolds before the spectator the intrigues and destinies of characters who offer occasions for baring the emotional and moralizing themes of the play. Characters in melodrama do not carry the full weight of real life; they are rather only outlined distinctly, being effective not in themselves, but as spokesmen for the emotional ideology of melodrama and as points of attachment for the springs of the plot. Above all, characters in melodrama are devoid of individuality, either personal or everyday realistic; they are interesting to the spectator, not in themselves because of their "rich" or "original" psychic substance, as are characters in realistic, psychological drama, but only because of their role in interweaving plot lines, their creation of dramatic situations, or the "pure" emotional coloration laid bare in their speeches which for melodrama is the source of dramatic intensity.

In a certain sense, melodrama is devoid of "heroes" possessing free activity who make their own destinies for themselves.[11] The dramatic spring is not the character, but the plot with its emotional bases; the characters are only its "tools" and are defined in their character traits only as much as is necessary for motivating the progression of the plot. Hence the fundamental *one-dimensionality* of melodramatic characters. They act according to principles which are predetermined by their plot roles.

Accordingly, the characters in melodrama fall easily into groups depending on their simplified dramatic functions which remain unchanged throughout the play. One-dimensional and stationary, the characters in melodrama are cast in "masks," of which there are only a limited number. The basic series—of characters who are "positive" and "virtuous"—are bearers of thematically stable and sympathetic qualities: honor, valor, selfless love, generosity. The positive ideological theme of the play is attached to the destiny of such a virtuous character and undergoes the peripeties of "suffering" experienced by him, terminated by a final "happy" ending to maintain the moralizing tendency.

The "positive" figure is juxtaposed to the "negative" character, the "villain"—a vicious, pitiless figure, whose deeds, theatrically effective in themselves, serve as stimulus for testing the positive values of the play. These primary figures are surrounded by secondary figures who are connected with the complications and share the peripeties of the "suffering" characters (as "devoted servant") or act the role of "tool" for the vicious characters (innocent or willing helper of the villain). Comic and picturesque elements are introduced into melodrama by these secondary characters who have traits lacking in the principal characters.

10. *"Reversibility" of the characters*. Characters in melodramas are subject to contrastive, polar changes. The ability of the character to become transformed into his opposite is customarily utilized in constructing the play's denouement: the rich become poor, the poor rich; the character of unknown origins invariably discovers his

distinguished parents. "Reversibility" even extends to personal qualities: the vicious figure repents and becomes virtuous, but not vice versa, since these transformations must serve the moral theme.

11. *Strikingly effective situations.* Melodrama is made up of a series of strikingly effective situations which flow from the dramatic conception and initial principle of construction. However, some particular effective situations may fall outside the basic dramatic conception, but be necessary for working out separate sections of the play. Melodrama is always on the look-out for new and untried possibilities for effective situations. The most frequently employed are: false death, unaccomplished recognition, the murdered man exposing his murderer, the villain exposing himself at the moment of triumph. The strikingly effective situation, the impending dramatic moment, is announced in the characters' speeches as the "fatal minute" or "frightful conjunction of circumstances."

12. *"Chance."* Plot development in melodrama is not "organic" and need not be psychologically or realistically motivated. The chain of events in melodrama—predetermined only by the play's emotional and technical aims and giving rise to strikingly effective situations—is an end in itself. At those moments when separate phases of plot are united, "chance" plays a key role as a cohesive element, combining and crossing lines of action and intrigue and producing sharp dramatic situations. An initial "chance" starts the dramatic action, and for the subsequent unfolding, new "chances" are required. Thus "chance" allows for new, unexpected plot twists. An illusion of organicness is created by having all the elements involved in a given situation already introduced before the chance occurrence takes place. However, melodrama also makes use of "chances" from outside simply to resolve a situation, but the automatic use of external "chance" as a deus ex machina weakens the persuasive, artistic power of melodrama.

13. *The thing.* A "thing" can be introduced into melodrama in order to complicate the "normal" course of events or to violate a harmonious series of character interactions. On the other hand, a "thing" may bring about the restoration of a violated series of relationships. By means of a "thing," the true identities and relationships of the characters may come to light. A "thing" may enter actively into the plot; its disappearance can bring about the complication by causing a false accusation. A "name" or even a "voice" can serve the same function as a "thing," as when a character uses another's name or voice with insidious purpose or to hide a "secret."

Present throughout the entire plot as a hidden sign, a "thing" can have decisive significance for the denouement when it is correctly recognized in the final moments of the play.

V. COMPOSITION FOR THE STAGE

Melodrama is written expressly for the stage and designed to be as effective as possible in the theatre. Those elements which will most affect the spectator, not the reader, are chosen; in this sense, melodrama is the most scenic of all genres. The melodramatist accordingly prepares his text so that it will have maximum effect on the spectator when transposed to theatrical conditions, as witness the presence of extensive indications of mise-en-scène, including mimed action. Setting and local color are given with maximum dramatic expressiveness, although with only as much detail as is necessary for a functional depiction of time and place.

Melodrama likes to transfer the dramatic action into the historical past, using the colorful material of a stylized epoch and giving some "versimilitude" to the strength of the emotions, which are attached to historical figures or characters of a remote era. The interweaving of tragic and comic motifs has special significance in the actual performance of melodrama, providing the spectator with alternating moments of tension and relaxation. In its search for auditory reinforcement of its expressive themes, melodrama has recourse to musical "accompaniment," especially for significant, intense, or pathetic moments. A similar "accompanying" role is played by "threatening" manifestations of nature (thunder, lightning) and by natural beauty (moonlight, sunbeams).

VI. DIFFERENTIATION OF MELODRAMA

Melodrama is not a standardized form that has remained unchanged during its one hundred years of existence; it has constantly developed variants of its basic compositional form. The earliest melodramas were richly emotional, but with only weakly developed plot. Subsequently different varieties of melodrama evolved: psychological, ideological, morals-and-manners, and pure plot. Although limited in its emotional possibilities, melodrama has always sought out new effects and developed new twists of plot; hence, judicial, criminal, adventure, and detective variants have all arisen. The growth of realistic drama has led to the creation of realistic and social melodrama.

VII. THE DRAMATIC NATURE OF MELODRAMA

With its "impression-making" plot, its "infectious" emotions, and its "exciting" themes, expressed on the stage by universal and primordial means, melodrama achieves a "staggering" impact. Melodrama operates with "pure" forms of theatrical action and is inherently dramatic to the highest degree. The laws of dramatic construction and stage effect should be studied in melodrama.

The effectiveness of the genre on the stage is demonstrated by the fact that melodrama will invariably "work" with any group of spectators whose hearts are open to such affecting emotional experiences, and such "primitive" spectators constitute an extremely broad group, even if the range of their responses is limited.

In its "pure" aspect, melodrama acts directly through its constructional and emotional forms, but melodrama can also be found in many other types of drama in which its "pure, primordial" principles are masked, weakened, and complicated by other aspects, such as realistic portrayal, psychological motivation, or ideological dialectics. It is possible to reveal the melodramatic skeleton at the basis of tragedy by reducing it to its essential elements (as happens, for example, on the provincial stage in a primitive interpretation of Shakespeare). Or, in the opposite direction, it is possible for a melodramatic skeleton to become covered with the solid flesh of realistic material and concealed beneath an elegant layer of psychology and ethical, social, or philosophical content. We thereby lose the feeling of melodramatic style and accept the play as a "higher" genre. (Elsewhere, in his analysis of Chekhov's early plays—particularly *Platanov, Ivanov,* and *The Wood Demon*—Balukhatyi shows how the great Russian dramatist, long fascinated by French melodrama, began to evolve a new, "higher" genre by covering over melodramatic skeletons.)[12]

Such is Balukhatyi's *Poetics of Melodrama*, a complete and coherent system for the formal analysis of the genre, providing a terminology and methodology for dealing not only with the verbal and literary text of a play, but also with its scenic and gestural language.

2. Tomashevsky and *French Melodrama of the Beginning of the Nineteenth Century*

Boris Tomashevsky (1890–1957), one of the major Formalist critics and scholars, wrote extensively on the theory of literature, Russian versification, and the works of Pushkin. He was also interested in drama and questions of dramatic genre,[13] and his only extended article on the subject is a masterful study of the way in which the lower genre melodrama was absorbed by the higher genre romantic drama. According to Tomashevsky, French melodrama is actually part of a popular tradition of irregular tragedy, going back to the time of Alexandre Hardy, to which Hugo and the romantics turned in their break with classicism. Attacking a problem in literary history and influence usually ignored by academic critics,[14] Tomashevsky is concerned to show the melodramatic skeleton which the romantic playwrights covered over and evolved into a new genre. And in this fashion Tomashevsky's treatment of melodrama follows the Formalist law of the "canonization of the junior branch," which Victor Shklovsky explained in the following terms: "When the 'canonized' art forms reach an impasse, the way is paved for the infiltration of the elements of non-canonized art, which by this time have managed to evolve new artistic devices."[15]

Instead of attempting to define melodrama abstractly as Balukhatyi does, Tomashevsky explores the different terrain occupied by melodrama during its early years and specifies its historical importance through an analysis of the origins of the genre. Functioning as a brilliant and incredibly learned theatre historian, Tomashevsky discloses the essential elements of melodrama as it evolved in relation to other theatrical genres of the late eighteenth and early nineteenth century. Tomashevsky uses as primary evidence what contemporaries and critics of the times said about melodrama, maintaining that they had a clear conception of the nature and significance of the new genre.

The Russian Formalist critic derives the origins of melodrama from two sources: the *drame* of Diderot, Sedaine, Mercier, and Beaumarchais and the heroic pantomime of the small Parisian theatres in the 1780's. From the *drame* melodrama took its basic method of constructing a play and from the pantomime its complex staging, each act having a different setting. According to Tomashevsky, melodrama grew up as a result of the battle between small and great theatres over regulations restricting the performance of regular plays to the licensed houses. The law was successfully evaded by heroic pantomime, a truly popular theatre using elaborate decor as well as music for emotional commentary on the action. As spoken words were gradually added, the transition from pantomime with dialogue to melodrama became imperceptible.

These early French melodramas were for the most part based on non-theatrical material, sentimental romances and adventure novels (largely English) containing mysteries to be resolved. In fact, the rapid development of action in melodrama required complicated and extended stories. Everything in these plays was geared to calling forth the spectator's emotions, an aim which melodrama shared with tragedy; what was innovative about the melodramatist's art lay in the new scenic means which he employed to produce emotional effects and in his simplification and massing of emotional motifs.

As classical modes of drama retreated into pure literature, popular theatre flourished, and melodrama for the first thirty years of the nineteenth century—like the cinema today with which it has much in common—was the most popular and highly developed form, containing many sub-genres (fantastic, exotic, historical). Often subtitled *à grand spectacle*, these plays relied on operatic staging and lavish settings; the author of melodrama had to have the imagination of a painter. Musical accompaniment, a heritage from pantomime, gradually disappeared (remaining only as an etymological vestige in the name), but pantomime itself continued as an indestructible element, revealing the origins of melodrama, prominent in the living images, or tableaux, at the end of each of the acts.

Although melodrama has its customary villains, innocent heroines, and humorous simpletons, Tomashevsky argues that the genre is essentially devoid of character types. Rather, its silhouettes are sharply drawn with only a minimum of character traits, as required by the plot. The heroes of melodrama are rigorously subordinated to the development of the action, and their characters cannot be a source of aesthetic experience in themselves, but only insofar as they contribute to the plot. Comic characters alone were free to be treated somewhat more fully and given a psychological dimension. However, in its basic formulation of character, melodrama maintains the tradition of tragedy, not comedy, by insisting on the priority of action.

Language in melodrama, like characterization, is primarily an outgrowth of plot. The melodramatists broke with tradition and abandoned verse (an exhausted medium) for prose in an attempt to create a simpler, more natural language, even though the dialogue still retained many aspects of rhetorical verse patterning. Rhythm and intonation are of crucial importance; the accelerated rhythm of short replies is characteristic of melodrama, as are stage directions stressing the role of intonation in the expression of various elementary emotions.

Comparison of melodrama with comedy on the basis of the happy ending is faulty in Tomashevsky's view; actually melodrama has taken little from the comic tradition. The happy ending is a peripheral trait, characteristic only of the first period of melodrama and not significant for the complex structure of the genre. In the second period—the 1820's—melodrama directly preceding the romantic theatre often ended in bloody disaster. Such heroic melodrama, with gloomy denouements, on historical and exotic themes, usurps the territory of tragedy.

Thus, through careful historical research, Tomashevsky is able to prove his thesis. Before the canonization, in the mid-seventeenth century, of French classical drama based on declamation, there existed another tradition—of a popular theatre of spectacle and adventure, full of exciting situations and external stage action; with the triumph of classicism, this irregular tragedy (often called tragicomedy as well) took refuge in other genres (ballet, opera, fair booth theatre, pantomime).

Melodrama belongs to this popular tradition and is, in fact, a particular kind of tragedy opposing the classical canon. Its historical role has been to penetrate the high tradition and re-assert the values of popular theatre; the battle of romantic theatre with classicism is the direct result of the gradual evolution of melodrama.

3. Piotrovsky and *Towards a Theory of Cinema Genres*

One of the most brilliant and talented young artists and writers to appear in the chaotic, yet immensely exciting world of the Soviet stage immediately after the Revolution, Adrian Piotrovsky (1898–1938) worked in almost every aspect of theatre and then went on to a distinguished career in film. Theorist, critic, playwright, and scholar, as well as practical man of the theatre, Piotrovsky was director of the Theatre Workshop of the Red Army, literary advisor of the Kirov Opera and Ballet Theatre, and artistic director of the Lenfilm Studio.

In the early 1920's Piotrovsky wrote and organized mass spectacles (such as *The Paris Commune*), which he considered as a revival of the ideals of ancient Greek drama as well as a fulfillment of Vyacheslav Ivanov's symbolist notions of a truly communal theatre in which all are participants. For Piotrovsky, Aeschylus was the model for a new post-revolutionary theatre of the masses; trained in the classics, he translated the *Oresteia* and also many works by Sophocles, Euripides, and Aristophanes.

Interested in theoretical aspects of both stage and film and their interaction, Piotrovsky made a pioneering application of Formalist principles to cinema in his essay *Towards a Theory of Cinema Genres*. Fascinated with melodrama as a genre, the young author experimented with the form himself. In 1926, the same year as his essay, Piotrovsky composed the scenario for *The Devil's Wheel*, a famous Soviet film melodrama by Kozintsev and Trauberg (about a sailor from the Aurora in the clutches of gangsters in a sinister amusement park) displaying marked Formalist leanings.[16] Thus Piotrovsky wrote both a Formalist theory of film melodrama and a Formalist film melodrama at almost the same time.

Ironically, his temporary association with Formalism in part cost him his life. Under violent attack in the late 1920's, the official and more academic Formalists were all able to survive through recantation and retreat into historical and sociological scholarship.[17] As a public figure in the arts, Piotrovsky's position was more exposed and vulnerable. In 1930 he first piously disclaimed any connection with Formalism, and finding that insufficient to satisfy his critics, he publicly confessed his Formalist errors and severely condemned them in 1932. Even this disavowal of his own past did not suffice to save his life; although he received a state prize in 1935, Piotrovsky was arrested in 1938 and died under unknown circumstances the same year.[18]

In *Towards a Theory of Cinema Genres*, Piotrovsky argues that film is a fundamentally different medium from literature and advances the thesis that cinema is rapidly evolving its own genres by abandoning the false literary genres of cinema-drama and cinema-novel (which adapt literary principles to film) and returning to its origins. In its early days when it was aware of its own technical possibilities and still not engaged in competition with the other arts, the newly discovered art of cinema reveled in its own limited means, freely using images of nature and acrobatic stunts—without any plot.

According to Piotrovsky, true cinematographic genres arise from a perfecting of cinema's own technical means. The future line of development for cinema will be essentially comic and lyrical, beyond plot and psychology. American film comedy and American adventure melodrama are the two genres which have led the way in revealing the essential nature of film. Now Soviet cinema, as represented by Sergei Eisenstein and Dziga Vertov, are continuing and carrying still further the process of freeing cinema from the influence of literature and theatre, and a new plotless genre, or poetry of the cinema, is arising, based on exclusively cinematographic means of expression.

The American comic cinema genre of Chaplin, Lloyd, and Keaton offers one model. Based on acrobatic tricks, eccentric (stunt) use of objects, and a hero with a clown's fixed mask, these films avoid plot and psychological motives and have nothing to do with theatre or literature; they rather have affinities with circus.

The second model, the American adventure cinema genre, stands in the same relation to the literary cinema-novel as the American comedy does to the salon cinema-comedy. The big city (with its detectives, policemen, and poetics of safes and armored cars) gave new life to the old masks of the cheap adventure story. The true originality and significance of the adventure genre lay in its acrobatic tricks and montage of dynamic external action; it opened up new possibilities for the composition of filmic material by its accelerating structure of serial installments, culminating in break-neck chases and racing trains.

When audiences tired of fantastic adventures (based on over-exploited tricks) and required strong emotional effects, the compositional principle "catastrophe–chase–rescue" inherent in the adventure film brought into existence a new genre, the American melodrama. The emotionally charged images of Lillian Gish and Mary Pickford replaced the pure adventure genre, represented by Pearl White.

The Griffith cinema melodrama, however, differs radically from its theatrical counterpart. In film melodrama no dramatic will directs the action. In the early portions of his melodramas, Griffith casually sketches the interrelationships and preconditions necessary for leading up to the catastrophe. Then the catastrophe itself takes place, shown through hundreds of detailed images in a complex montage. Only in cinema, due to its special means of treating "time" and "space," is such a development of the catastrophe possible. "Time" is fragmented into rapidly flashing segments, while "space" is rendered dynamic and becomes a co-ordinate of time.

The Griffith "catastrophe" is the core of film melodrama, as a creation of montage, the very model of cinematographic style. The "elemental catastrophe" in film melodrama shows the parity of human wills and natural forces; "man" and "nature" are equally important and play similar roles. Ice (*Way Down East*) can take the place of the villain; it is easier to provide motivation by natural forces and disasters than through human conduct, always so difficult to explain in film.

The principles of American film melodrama have been taken up in Soviet cinema and its emotional impact perfected, as in Pudovkin's *The Mother* and in Eisenstein's films and theory of *The Montage of Attractions* (which derives directly from Griffith). Finally, the new "lyrical" genre, which dispenses entirely with plot and even consecutive time in order to present poetic images of man–things–nature, has evolved out of the lyrical aspects of American melodrama, but has moved even further away from the old dramatic and narrative canon.

Besides offering penetrating and original insights into the nature and history of melodrama, these three Russian Formalist approaches can serve as models for the serious study of the genre. Balukhatyi, Tomashevsky, and Piotrovsky are true pioneers in the technical analysis of melodramatic form.

Notes

1. Ewa M. Thompson, *Russian Formalism and Anglo-American New Criticism* (The Hague: Mouton, 1971). In addition to a detailed comparison between the Russian Formalists and the New Critics, Thompson points out that "Another group of literary researchers that owes much to the Formalist writings is that of the French and Bulgarian structuralists of the 1960s," mentioning Todorov and Barthes as examples (p. 103).
2. Three collections of Russian Formalist writings are available in English: *Russian Formalist Criticism: Four Essays*, trans. and ed. Lee T. Lemon and Marion J. Reis (Lincoln: University of Nebraska Press, 1965); *Readings in Russian Poetics: Formalist and Structuralist Views*, ed. Ladislav Matejka and Krystyna Pomorska (Cambridge: Massachusetts Institute of Technology, 1971); and *Russian Formalism*, ed. Stephen Bann and John E. Bowlt (New York: Barnes & Noble, 1973). The French collection, *Théorie de la Littérature: Textes des Formalistes Russes*, ed. Tzvetan Todorov (Paris: Editions de Seuil, 1965), likewise contains nothing about drama or theatre.
3. In English, see Vladimir Propp, *Morphology of the Folktale*, trans. L. Scott (Bloomington: Indiana University Press, 1958).
4. The essays by Shklovsky and Eichenbaum appear in *Readings in Russian Poetics*.
5. Victor Erlich, *Russian Formalism: History-Doctrine* (The Hague: Mouton, 1965).
6. *Ibid.*, p. 249.
7. See Earl F. Bargainnier, "Melodrama as Formula," *Journal of Popular Culture* IX, No. 3 (Winter, 1975), pp. 726–733, for a discussion of the use of formula as an approach to melodrama.
8. The original Russian sources are as follows: S. Balukhatyi, "K Poetike Melodramy," *Poetika*, III, repr. Leningrad, 1927 (Wilhelm Fink: Munich, 1970), pp. 63–86; B. Tomashevsky, "Frantsuzskaya Melodrama nachala XIX veka," *Poetika*, II, *op. cit.*, pp. 55–82; A Piotrovsky, "K Teorii Kino-zhanrov," *Poetika Kino*, ed. B.M. Eichenbaum (Moscow-Leningrad: Kinopechat', 1927), pp. 143–170. I am grateful to Mel Gordon of New York University for making available to me a microfilm of the Eichenbaum collection.
9. For a discussion of the importance of melodrama in early Soviet life, see Daniel Gerould, "Gorky, Melodrama, and the Development of Early Soviet Theatre," *yale/theatre*, Vol. 7, No. 2 (Winter, 1976), pp. 33–44.

10. In the course of his essay, Balukhatyi cites some three dozen melodramas, including a number by D'Ennery and his collaborators, Dumas père, Descourcelle, Brisebarre and Nus, and many others.
11. Victor Erlich points out that "Formalist poetics assigned to the literary hero a very modest part: he is merely a by-product of the narrative structure, and as such, a compositional rather than a psychological entity." *Russian Formalism*, p. 241.
12. S. D. Balukhatyi, *Problemy Dramaturgicheskogo Analiza: Chekhov*, repr. Leningrad, 1927 (Wilhelm Fink: Munich, 1969).
13. Tomashevsky wrote an article, "On Dramatic Literature," about the difference between literature and theatre, which appears in two issues of *Zhizn' Iskusstva* in 1924, No. 13, p. 5, and No. 16, pp. 5–6.
14. Erlich comments on the Formalists' ability to chart the course of literary change and the growth of new forms: "this awareness of the fluidity of the literary process . . . made the Formalists alive to literary affinities and cross-currents undreamt of by textbook writers." *Russian Formalism*, p. 259.
15. Victor Shklovsky, quoted by Erlich, *Ibid.*, p. 260. The passage appears in *Literatura i Kinematograf* (Berlin, 1923), p. 29.
16. For information about *The Devil's Wheel*, see Jay Leyda, *Museum of Modern Art Film Notes* (October 2–November 18, 1975), p. 6; and *Istoriya Sovetskogo Kino*, Vol. I (1917–1931) (Moscow: Iskusstvo, 1969), pp. 339–342.
17. According to Erlich, at the end of the twenties "The Formalists found themselves under a savage attack. The only alternative left to them was to become silent or to acknowledge 'frankly' their errors." *Russian Formalism*, p. 135. Shklovsky recanted in 1930.
18. After the demise of Stalinism, Piotrovsky was rehabilitated. A selection of his writings, plus reminiscences (by Trauberg, Kozintsev, and Gerasimov among others) and a complete bibliography, was published in 1969: Adrian Piotrovsky, *Teatr–Kino–Zhizn* (Leningrad: Iskusstvo, 1969).

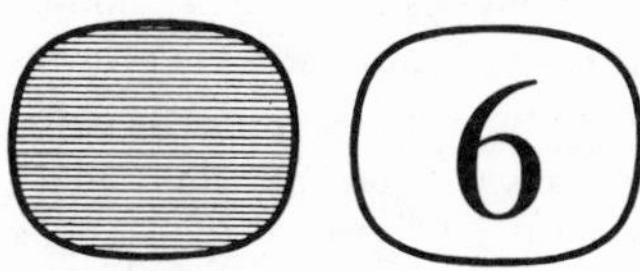

Ways of Melodrama

RAYMOND DURGNAT

I

Because violence is a leading characteristic of the postwar world, it is reflected in a good deal of contemporary art, and in consequence melodrama is no longer considered as a wholly disreputable element. A few notes on the interrelationship of melodrama and significance (in the widest sense of the word) in the cinema should be of interest.

A melodrama has been defined as a story where the characters exist to justify the action. This simple definition, on which Elizabeth Bowen's "Notes on Writing a Novel" makes interesting comment,[1] at once brings up complications. In the cinema they would arise thus:

The cinema exposes itself primarily through movement. Purposeful movement of an animate being—a man kisses a woman, or walks downstairs, or runs across the road—is generally called Action. Movement and action cannot be rigidly separated: for instance, a horserider in long shot, decorating the picture, is best classified as movement, but in close shot, or going somewhere of importance to the story, is counted as action. A stagecoach, itself inanimate but representative of people, can similarly come under both headings.

Drama demands that action and movement shall be motivated and/or express something. One director and scriptwriter will express himself largely by means of

Raymond Durgnat's "Ways of Melodrama" originally appeared in *Sight and Sound*, Vol. 21, no. 1 (1951), pp. 34–40. Reprinted by permission of the author and *Sight and Sound*.

movement—by curtains blown in the wind at significant moments, or by camera tracks into significant close-ups. David Lean uses this method almost exclusively (and somewhat monotonously). The same thing may be expressed by means of action. A man camping out on the prairie hears a coyote whine; he expresses his state of mind by firing wildly into the darkness. The man's firing at the coyote is motivated solely by his own state of mind. But if you pre-create some reason for his action—for instance, the coyote had bitten him—your action begins to become melodrama. The motivation, being obvious, no longer reveals the man's state of mind: all it tells us is that he is not a forgiving person—a negative thing. Make the motivation simpler—he was frightened that the coyote would steal his chickens, or that the whine was in fact that of an Indian spy—and his action reveals nothing about him at all. The firing just becomes reflex action following on the context.

But one notices (1) how easily action slips into melodrama, (2) that the links between melodramatic episodes are the simplest emotions unanalysed and taken for granted, and (3) that melodrama is *organised* or *consequential action*—springing from previous action, or from a state of threatened action. If you like, the melodramatic episode is to drama as slapstick is to comedy. Many comedies have slapstick climaxes, and the cheapest slapstick episode can be a framework or scaffolding for comedy. Similarly with drama and melodrama.

But if, as well as this logic of melodrama, you have a simultaneous development of feeling, you have a film which is both drama *and* melodrama. The *action* of a film may be melodramatic, but its movement and settings psychologically revealing. A gangster is betrayed to the police by his moll, and trapped in a museum: first in a room full of Reynolds and Gainsboroughs; but as the police drive him from room to room the art becomes more and more primitive, until he is finally surrounded by the ghastly deformed breasts and tortured faces of tribal totem poles. Combined with the action, this could illustrate: (1) disgust with women, (2) acute realisation of his own weakness, and (3) a reversion from a comparatively civilised veneer to a state of bestial terror. The sequence would be worthy of Welles at his wildest, but his films lack the scope and depth of context that could make his ingenious mirror and aquarium scenes significant. If a character has no real significance (which he can be given only by acute and careful observation, lacking in *The Lady from Shanghai*), then neither will any amount of extraneous symbolism or ingenuity.

Similarly melodrama must have relevance. In these notes I do not claim to deal with all its forms, but mainly with those possessing a context of some significance. It might be argued that melodrama is simply an arbitrary extension of drama: a fist fight, for instance, is a more or less arbitrary extension of hate, disagreement or competition, and adds nothing to the drama except physical intensity. Nonetheless, a melodramatic situation can often provide a searching test of character.

This idea is a basic device of John Huston's: *The Maltese Falcon*, *We Were Strangers*, *Treasure of Sierra Madre*, *Key Largo* and *The Asphalt Jungle* all put keenly observed realistic characters in highly melodramatic situations. The melodrama springs from simple emotions (greed, patriotism, self-preservation, escape) and is used to investigate not merely the quality of that emotion but the characters as a whole. Huston's films become dramas. Thus drama may be an extension of melodrama as surely as melodrama can be an extension of drama.

The reason for this lies in the nature of artistic conception. Character is often best exhibited in a special circumstance, but in order to place him convincingly in this circumstance we have to explain how his character got him there. Many artists—notably Henry James—begin by imagining a situation or a conflict, then shape the characters to fit it, then alter the emphasis of the conflict or situation as the characters evolve in their minds. Others (D. H. Lawrence) begin with a character and let him make his own situations. Lawrence said that his method of writing a novel was to invent two couples and let them work out their own affairs.

The diagram shows a circle divided into three rings. Character is generally considered as the core of a person's reaction to circumstance (actions), so I represent it as the innermost circle. Next to it is drama. Drama and melodrama together correspond to what Elizabeth Bowen called "action," but to avoid confusion I shall use this term in the sense of "purposeful movement of an animate being," emphasising the plastic rather than the narrative qualities of a film. The difference between drama and melodrama lies in whether the emphasis is on the emotion or the action. Outside comes the circle of melodrama, furthest from the centre but containing (*i.e.* necessitating) the other two, just as drama "contains" but does not necessarily reveal character, and just as character in art is investigated within a situation.

A work of art can first be conceived at any point in the circle. The first idea to come to Henry James would be that of a dramatic situation and the general characteristics of the protagonists. As the idea developed, the protagonists would take on more complex and finely developed characters. A story by D. H. Lawrence, conversely, moves outwards from the innermost circle. It is often impossible to say where a work of art was first conceived—imagination can be so flexible and so sensitive, adjusting its mechanism for suiting character to situation and vice versa, that the work seems to have been conceived at all points in the circle simultaneously.

Most fiction, drama and films incorporate some element from each part of the circle. It is misleading to speak of drama and melodrama as two distinct forms, and then try to draw distinctions between them; they are not forms but elements, and often occur side by side, and inextricably confused.

II

There is a type of film aptly called in this country "emotional melodrama." In such films emotions are like clubs which characters swing about their heads and knock each other (and often themselves) out with. The American term is "heavies"—*Deception, Stolen Life,* and so on. The rules and regulations are as clearly worked out as in any heavyweight bout: there is no real characterisation, and the films are always deliberately limited to well within the "drama" circle, with melodrama permissible as a climax (Davis shoots Rains). The keynote of the emotional melodrama is that emotions which in melodrama serve as the links between melodramatic episodes are here used to bring about not action but another emotion. The only way out is generally suicide or death in childbirth.

The Americans are the most mechanically efficient in this field; the French have produced some enjoyable examples, though in Europe generally, and Sweden above all, the passions-on-the-farm tradition is too prominent. The English insistence on good taste in emotional fodder puts them at a disadvantage with the emotional melodrama, and the *Madonna of the Seven Moons–Jassy* cycle never did justice to its own hedonistic possibilities. The latest of the series, *The Reluctant Widow,* lacked unforgiveably the courage of its own vulgarity, and devoted half its time to intentionally burlesquing itself. *The Seventh Veil* was more intelligent, but in their successor to it, *Daybreak,* the Boxes yielded to the temptation to complicate the intrigue at the expense of the drama.

The public hangman in *Daybreak* is not only a public hangman but (on the side) a barge-owner and a hairdresser. His wife knows that he is a barge-owner, but not that he's a hairdresser or a hangman. His colleague in the hairdressing business knows that he's also a hangman, but not that he's a barge-owner. A Scandinavian seaman seduces the wife and assaults the barge-owner, for whose presumed murder he is sentenced to be hanged by the hangman. Under the impression that her husband is dead, his wife shoots herself and he, having resigned his hangmanship and no longer a barge-owner, but still a hairdresser, cuts his throat. The story is told in flashback.

The same tendency toward absurd elaboration can be noted in a good many "heavies"—most of Hal Wallis's from *Sorry Wrong Number* onwards—with the result that any investigation of character, even on a superficial level, becomes impossible. For as soon as emotional melodrama begins to investigate character, it becomes—partially at least—drama. At their best, the Americans show a sensible tendency to unite the "heavy" and the thriller: the vintage Hal Wallis productions (*In This Our Life, Martha Ivers, File on Thelma Jordon, I Walk Alone, No Man of Her Own*) and films like *Double Indemnity* and *Phantom Lady* are composed equally of Chandler-style material—vicious *femmes fatales* who in most cases provide the motivation (greed and sex explode into violence), the authoritative tours of seedy, honky-tonk backgrounds—and of heavy novelette situations stemming from "The Saturday Evening Post" and elsewhere. They are successful because not weighed down with more apparatus than they can bear, and some are better than others because the talent of a superior director (Huston with *In This Our Life,* Wilder and Brackett with *Double Indemnity*) shows through.

Most of the films are constructed as thrillers with a strong emphasis on emotion, but Huston with *In This Our Life* reverses the procedure, subduing the melodrama and concentrating on the emotional drama: Ophuls did the same thing with *Caught.* These are cases of "heavies" almost turning into dramas. The converse can be seen in films like *The Passionate Friends* or the French *Pattes Blanches;* these start out as dramas, but because the drama is inadequate they turn into emotional melodramas. In the case of David Lean, one suspects that the new technique he was on the edge of has not (yet) developed further than sheer chronological complication.

Deteriorations of this sort come from a failure in conception; what begins as an investigation of character is not developed, and the characters have to be fitted improbably into melodramatic situations. Italian films like *Flesh Will Surrender* and *Tomorrow Is Too Late* show the same process. They are slow and ponderous, and great efforts are made to invest inadequate shots and actions with far more significance than they can bear. Time is not kind to this type of failure, either—one sees even what happened to the emotional melodrama in *All Quiet on the Western Front*.

III

Much the same happens to the "pure" melodrama (the thriller and run-of-the-mill western) but, for aesthetic reasons, more slowly. Sitting recently through *The 39 Steps*, a film I did not see on its original release, I was surprised to find myself totally unmoved by every excitement, except that of Hannay jumping off the train when it is stopped on the bridge, irritated by its facetious whimsicality (the Donat-Carroll exchanges), and quite unconvinced by its wildly theatrical acting.

Oddly enough, *The Lady Vanishes*, with its vivid and recognisable caricatures of English types, its catching of the Munich mood and its pleasantly well integrated script and excitements, remains enjoyable. It has a definite rapprochement with reality. But *Foreign Correspondent*, with its nominal (not organic) little people v. Germany tie-up, and its colourless characterisation of ambassadors and their daughters, fails to convince or excite. One prefers the frankly picaresque *Saboteur*, with its undisguised, authentic borrowings from earlier films.

In skilled hands the pure melodrama, the melodrama of pursuit and escape, of threat and self-preservation, can—like the emotional melodrama—be entertaining enough. The characterisation can be relatively simple and superficial but it must, like the situations, convince on its own level. How impressive the combination of emotional and "pure" melodrama can be is demonstrated by *The Third Man*, an engrossing film which yields great pleasure at each viewing. It is not only that the technique is particularly expert and sophisticated, but that the melodrama is subordinated to realism, which is closely interwoven with character—the melodrama, in fact, of significant context. The American and Italian uses of melodrama offers in this respect the most consistent interest.

IV

We have something near a perfect fusion when the melodramatic episodes are used to analyse and comment on the emotions acting as links between these episodes; when the emotions themselves are of some subtlety and complexity, and when their revelation is not overshadowed by flamboyant treatment of the melodrama itself.

It is far easier to obtain tension from a gunfight or a chase than from a mental conflict. The responsibility here lies on director and scriptwriter. The writer must invent situations that will provide powerful and expressive images; the director must realise these images on the screen. If the writer has failed to provide suitable image-situations, if he expresses mental conflict only in terms of commentary or dialogue, the director can, by visual imagination and sensitive catching of a relevant atmosphere round the dialogue, give the situation expressive images; but he is unlikely to succeed completely with this.

An excellent example of a good image-situation is this from Geoffrey Homes' screenplay for *The Dividing Line*. At the beginning of the manhunt after the terrified Spanish-American fugitive, the organiser of the hunt says: "Don't shoot unless you have to." The newspaperman also involved in the pursuit is spotted by an advance guard of the posse who, mistaking him for the fugitive, promptly blaze away. Bullets whine and ricochet about the unarmed newspaperman. The machinery of melodrama is used naturally to reveal the savagery of the posse.

A film hamstrung by weak image-situations is *Kiss of Death*. Its first point is that the hero, Nick Bianco (Mature), became a criminal through pressure of circumstances. The commentary tells us he couldn't get a job, and goes on: "This is how Nick Bianco did his Christmas shopping for his kids." And we see him with two accomplices stealing jewellery from a department store. A weak presentation of pressure of circumstances makes the episode look no more than cheaply sentimental.

Every dramatic conflict in the film is expressed through dialogue, much of it in limp scenes at the D.A.'s office. Bianco's love for his children, his repugnance at the thought of being a stool-pigeon, his grief at his wife's suicide, all these key motives are revealed in images of conversation. The image which the screenwriters impress on our minds to illustrate these emotions is simply that of two men sitting on either side of a desk.

Conversation in itself is not necessarily a weak image-situation, as Polonsky's *Force of Evil* indicates. The distinctiion is that the conversations of *Force of Evil* are intensely atmospheric, and that they make their points not in dialogue alone but by a combination of word spoken and reaction observed. Conversations in American sociological thrillers tend to be simply filmed radio dialogue, with nothing left for the camera to observe. The reactions are merely stock reactions to make the conversations look convincing.

Seeing *Call Northside 777* a second time I found it was possible to close one's eyes for long periods and yet follow perfectly situation, character, relationship, and even locale, even though I had forgotten the accompanying visual images.

Call Northside 777, *Panic in the Streets* (with the exception of a few moments), *The House on 92nd Street*, *The Naked City*, *Street With No Name*, *Union Station*, all suffer from poor image-situations invented by the writers: rather monotonously, powerful images are found for the passages of melodramatic action, but the revelation of character is restricted almost entirely to dialogue and conversation. *Boomerang*, de Rochemont's first serious drama, and Siodmak's unpretentious, under-appreciated *Cry of the City* were the only real successes of them all.

The films may be divided into two groups: those where the melodrama is intended to be incidental to the drama (*Panic in the Streets*), and those where the drama (in effect if not in intention) is incidental to the melodrama—*Kiss of Death, Union Station*. Where the melodrama is successful, as in *Street With No Name*, the film is enjoyable as such. But the more pretentious films suffer considerably from their scripts, and the inability of merely competent directors to introduce exciting filmic elements into them.

The Naked City took the form of the investigation by a police officer of a New York murder. Hellinger's intention was to use this as a pretext for examining New York life. Unfortunately the majority of the interviews took place in the detective's office, divorcing the main characters from their homes and habitual backgrounds, and the examination of New York life consisted mainly of their answers to the detective's questions. Their reactions are shown in dialogue, and in a detective's office, when they would hardly be at their most natural. Even when the younger detective investigates on the spot, the cameos through which we go are conventional and tell us little. The all-in wrestler is seen doing—guess what?—all-in wrestling exercises.

In *Call Northside 777*, James Stewart's investigation takes him into people's homes, into their contexts, as it were. But the weakness here is absurdly obvious: when a visitor calls, it is customary to stop what one is doing and to sit down opposite him and talk. The scriptwriters let this formality weaken all their image-situations, and Hathaway lacked the skill to overcome this obstacle as Polonsky might have done.

Call Northside and *Panic in the Streets* can both be resolved into a series of conversations and interviews. Wherever placed—in cafés, police stations, dives, ships, tenements, newspaper offices, prisons, council chambers—both films remain essentially a series of conversations whose point is expressed entirely in dialogue. *Call Northside* does not even show characters in action, and only Richard Conte's Weicek and Lee J. Cobb reveal any qualities (love of his wife and a tendency to fib respectively) not instantly deducible from their physiognomies. The principal characters in nearly all these films are hackneyed—the poor slaving mother, the blowsy slut, the comforting wife-girlfriend figure, the stolid fellow with a keen conscience underneath. Dana Andrews in *Boomerang* goes through exactly the same conflicts as Paul Douglas in *Panic in the Streets*, and the only characteristic of all the heroes to distinguish them from the ordinary well-disposed stock type is, simply, conscience. There is no doubt, though, that many of the secondary portraits are interesting, particularly those in *Panic in the Streets*.

Kazan's sense of atmosphere makes this one of the best of the thrillers. Hathaway conspicuously lacks any feeling for atmosphere; in *Call Northside*, for instance, no contrasting moods are evoked in the scenes in the prison governor's office, the police station or the newspaper office. The treatment is slick and perfunctory. *Panic in the Streets* is obviously superior in this respect, but even so Kazan's realism is a surface matter, more resourceful in effect than original in conception. The real renaissance in Hollywood melodrama came through some smaller and fresher films, like those associated with Dore Schary—*They Live by Night, The Window, Crossfire, The Set Up, Deadline at Dawn*—with *Force of Evil* and *Act of Violence* and the least pretentious of the Fox films, *Cry of the City*.

These films point out the difference between artistic realism and Hathaway's or

Kazan's perfunctory sense of locale. *Crossfire* was made entirely in the studio; it builds up brilliantly the mood of listlessness and boredom, of stored-up hate with nowhere to go, of dull, endless bar-crawling around cities by night and card-games by day. Dmytryk's direction has a sense of the seedy, of bare walls and low bars, dramatic use of lighting and angles. Even the minor and inferior *Deadline at Dawn*, though its attempt to catch the spirit of a big city by night failed as a whole, gave us several short and fascinating portraits of other lives—portraits as terse and vivid as those in *Panic in the Streets*. It was disappointing to find Clifford Odets' script destroying everything it had built up by false touches like the sub-Prévert crook (Joseph Calleia) and the silly twist ending. Of *They Live by Night* and *The Window* enough has been written already. In general, the flabby and conventional portraiture of the bigger films contrasts unfavourably with these smaller ones.

Similarly, the first few moments of *Intruder in the Dust* show remarkable sensitiveness. Long shot of a church steeple over the tops of trees, its bell ringing the hour: the sound of the bell is heard over the succeeding shots. The camera pans round (high elevation) the town square—the sun, the cars, the shops and the chromium signs. Cut to a man waiting at a shoeshine stand. After a moment he gets up, goes into the barber's saloon: "Where's the boy?" "Haven't you heard?" the men reply, "the niggers won't be around on the streets to-day . . . shot a white man in the back . . ." Through the windows as the barbers shave their customers, people drift by along the sidewalk: a police siren squeals—"That'll be him!"—people begin to hurry past: customers get up, one not waiting to clean the soap off his face, and rush out. A car with a flat tyre sirens and clatters its way to the kerb. Cut to a first-person viewpoint inside the car, the sheriff driving, the gazing crowd seen through the windows, and two black hands in the foreground, resting on the back of the driver's seat . . .

Intruder in the Dust is a work of brilliant observation rather than self-expression, and this makes comparison with the semi-documentary style salutary. The mechanics of its plot are far neater and better integrated than those of the sociological thrillers; there are two complex main characters (the negro and the boy), and although the rest of the characterisation is more conventional and the important psychological conflict in the boy's mind has to be expressed in commentary, the *minor* figures in *Intruder in the Dust* are as well rendered as the *major* characters in the semi-documentaries.

One is reminded here of weaknesses in *Force of Evil*, of the reasons why it remained a complex and intriguing film rather than a complete experience.

Events evolve but characters remain static in the film. Joe Morse, its hero, has two conflicting urges, the urge to make his own way and the urge to save those whom he likes. He knows that people want to be bullied into the evil of which they are afraid and he is bitterly conscious of his own inability to resist corruption. Doris is torn between her love for and disgust with Joe, and the two halves of his character; Leo distrusts his brother Joe but is too weak to withstand him. There are two interesting smaller parts—the intimidated book keeper in the small "numbers" bank, and the racketeers' wife who, half-maternally, half-sadistically, loves Joe for his humanity and weakness.

These complex characters, however, do not develop. What Doris says does not affect Joe who, drunk as he is, still lurches off to a showdown after his brother has been kidnapped; she is in danger of becoming reconciled to the evil in Joe, and of being flattened by his forcefulness, but only the second and less serious process is shown: no change, degeneration or despair is observable in Leo when he moves from a small to a big 'numbers' racket man. Action springs from intriguing characters, but it does not serve to develop character, only to bring events to a head.

Further, instead of breaking down complexity into images, Joe explains his thoughts (and nearly everyone else's), Doris hers, and Leo and Leo's wife his, and so on, in conversation. Excessive reliance on the spoken word is particularly obvious in one sequence; the cinematographic equivalent to Joe's comment, "Doris wanted me to make love to her," is Doris looking into the camera (first-person viewpoint), wanting to be made love to. The commentary is not merely superfluous but weakens, because it distracts from, the visual image. The same thing occurs twice in the last sequence.

The conversations in *Force of Evil* are, of course, unusually well written and directed by Polonsky, and the images and acting as powerful as images of conversation can be.

Cry of the City, the best of the Fox thrillers, skilfully manipulates our sympathies (alternating between pursuers and pursued): we sympathise with the escaping criminal, Rome (Richard Conte) and hope he will escape the underworld types whom he encounters; at the same time there is no sentimentality. Rome turns a gun on his mother, and then the girl who helped him, the doctor who patched up his wounds, the old convict who assisted his escape, the younger brother aping his ways, all become involved in his flight and desperation and suffer for it. This portrayal, in melodramatic terms, of criminal egotism is startling and exciting. Siodmak's direction has a fine ear for the sounds of the city, and an observant eye for the backgrounds and the snatches of action you see through windows while your characters talk.

The success of these films makes one wonder, finally, what is the justification of the "newsreel" style. Newsreels are duller than most fictional films: locational photography has by now lost its freshness as such, the urgency of the commentary of *Boomerang* has degenerated into a verbal laziness for what the writers and directors fail to present in image—and the endless procession of undercover men and women also indicates excessive exploitation of a formula.

V

At the end of the war, significant melodrama in Britain seemed on the right track, most interesting being the straightforward extension of an everyday situation into melodrama with *Waterloo Road*. Then Launder and Gilliat switched to the conventional eccentricities and situations of *London Belongs to Me*. Ealing followed the convincing, interesting *It Always Rains on Sunday* with the efficient routine of *The Blue Lamp* and *Pool of London*, and the limitations of these are reflected in almost every other British melodrama. The best of them, like *The Small Voice*, and the worst, like *Good Time Girl*, have been hamstrung not so much by any problem of image-situation, of integration of drama and melodrama, but simply by cliché characters. A few films have brought a degree of freshness into their conventions (*Once a Jolly*

Swagman, Chance of a Lifetime), but in the sphere of melodrama itself only *The Third Man*, discussed earlier, has reinvigorated a tradition. It is disappointing that British melodramas do not set themselves a higher target than imitation of American models: even when the response to locale is good, as in *Pool of London*, the characters and their relationships are second-hand. At other times, the wholesale borrowing of West End theatrical types—suburban housewife, crusty grandmother, amiable father, jovial promiscuous Hermione Baddeley type, etc.—does not produce anything fresher.

VI

One can understand the mistrust of melodrama on the part of film critics, but it is a pity this should lead to the serious depreciation of the Italian style represented by *Bitter Rice* and *Without Pity.* My intention is not to indicate that they are masterpieces (they aren't), but that their method is as worthy of serious consideration as the American crime documentaries.

De Santis uses a melodramatic story to point up the aspects of life (*Bitter Rice*) or the conflict (*Caccia Tragica*) which form the themes of his films, and the realistic element to heighten and justify the melodramatic action. The close interweaving of story and background means that every episode becomes ambivalent; it is one of a chain of melodramatic scenes, and also expresses something about theme or characters. The melodrama springs from reality, and reality informs the melodrama.

With the more florid melodramatic style of the Italian film it is less easy to appreciate social or psychological connotations. But these do exist, *pace* the critic who measured de Santis' progress from Art to Commerce by the length of leg his heroines display.

The sex element in *Bitter Rice* springs from the primitive conditions and the animalism of ricefield life as well as from box-office requirements. Similarly, the violence of this film and of *Caccia Tragica*—not exaggerated to judge from the news reports of Italy—has a perfectly legitimate place in the drama. Leaving aside for the moment the purely aesthetic pleasure derived from de Santis' understanding of the medium—which some American directors might well envy—the films show de Santis' skill at the immediate translation of relationship into situation, of problem into predicament and character into action.

Straightway *Bitter Rice* displays Sylvana's animalism (jiving), her disillusionment (exchanges with the soldiers), and her kind-heartedness (she introduces Gioi to the unofficial employment agency on the train). But her kind-heartedness is only impulse, and as soon as Gioi's interests conflict with hers, she takes the lead in opposing her. Even her kind-heartedness is mingled with her longing for excitement (Gioi was the crook's moll). We see her continual impatience with the hard way of honesty the sergeant offers her, and her naive belief and trust in the promises of the crook who manipulates her credulity for his own ends. Even at the end her weakness and inadequacy still haunt her: she is unable to fire the pistol in the slaughter-house scene.

There is a stunted, helpless goodness in her—she helps Gioi, she realises what virtue means (she wanders disconsolate in the rain), too late (after the rape), is harshly reminded of the possible consequences of her weakness and the crook's brutality (the miscarriage). Interwoven with all this is the masterly exposition of ricefield life; its misery (the rain), its despair (the fight between the regulars and the outsiders), its animalism, and, above all, the sabotage of this miserable labour by a band of self-interested men (the same idea recurs in *Caccia Tragica*).

The characterisation of Gioi, of the crook and the sergeant is equally illustrated by the action. If not searching, all these figures are adequately created and have verisimilitude. I think one would have a hard time proving any of the characters less real than the cops, floozies and bartenders in American thrillers.

Both types of film are concerned with predicament and situation. Neither attempts to go deep below the surface. Widmark in *Panic in the Streets*, for instance, has a worry about a tailor's bill, a touch generally applauded. No one could call this "going below the surface"—it was simply an interesting added predicament. In their efforts to find originality within the formula, screenwriters tend to cram in more and more of these little touches and side problems whose relevance is dubious. The predicaments in *Bitter Rice* and *Caccia Tragica* are at least an integral part of the theme. The Italian formula has, of course, its disadvantages. A script has to be extraordinarily good to integrate complicated melodrama satisfactorily with the drama, to manoeuvre the episodes into positions of significance, to prevent flamboyance from swamping revelation of character. *Caccia Tragica* was less happy in this respect than de Santis' succeeding *Bitter Rice*.

Already Lattuada failed when he essayed this style with *Senza Pieta*, dismissed by most critics as trashy melodrama with pretensions; actually it is a sincere enough film which fails not through dishonesty but through inability to deal with the complex style this method requires.

One can see the script trying to follow the accepted rules of tragedy. The more hero and heroine try to free themselves from their fate, the more entangled they become. Their eventual death comes almost as a relief, since we feel that any more struggling on their part would only have debased them further. Unfortunately the relationship between the negro and the white girl is weak (he worships her like a dog, only wants to follow her around) and never becomes more than a series of hurried meetings and conversations. Their story remains a series of melodramatic incidents, brought about by a Peter Lorre-like procurer in a white suit, by the military police and various odd, unsatisfactory characters—*not* the general circumstance of post-war chaos. Motivation is poor: we are led to believe that Angela was forced to become a prostitute because the procurer pushed her into the water and fished her out again, and then, without any perceptible change in her fortunes, she stops being one. Impossible soliloquies hold up the action at unsuitable moments, and the cutting is ragged.

But the cycle really begins to run to seed with Pietro Germi's *Lost Youth*. This illustrates nicely what happens when incompetence and a good formula combine. Though the film is a thriller, the standard of the image-situations (loving looks, family life, fathers failing to scold sons, breakfasts, pensive stares endlessly prolonged) is unexciting, and the melodrama (gangster leaves on scene of the crime cigarette lighter with his initials on it, bought because he always loses matchboxes), poor. By showing us shots of tiny tots pursuing each other with toy pistols, and giving a few statistics on the crime wave, the film tries to be socially significant. The script integrates neither its adolescent gangster's trifling characteristics nor his pathology as a whole into feeling, outlook or character (neurosis? need for excitement? Oedipus complex? degradation caused by war and familarity with violence? lack of parental discipline? bad company? love of money? or some or all of these things?).

VII

What is immediately apparent from these notes is that any formula, any style, is precisely as good as the artists it attracts. Of the many melodramas set in a contemporary reality, the failures are nearly always not the technical ones of melodrama but of a conventional or uninteresting perception of reality. This reminds one that melodrama set in spheres where realism is superseded by a poetic reality—the Western—or by fantasy, can nonetheless be significant, if there is an artist of calibre behind it.

Alexander Nevski is an interesting example of a melodrama allied to poetic reality. Its characterisation is elementary, its dramatic qualities conventional, and the fate of everyone concerned is decided in the long battle scene, which bears much of the same relation to its context as the gunfight at the end of *The Lady from Shanghai*. One's enjoyment of the film is untainted by the slightest enthusiasm for one side or the other, despite the contrast of wicked, cruel Teuton knights with vertically held lances and helmets low over their hard eyes, and the noble heroism of the gruff, bearded Russians who have no helmets and thus appear less sinister. The past which the film creates is deliberately romanticised, the melodrama has the spaciousness and simplicity of a heroic legend—not simply a Russian legend, but one common to every country and race. The film makes no comment on the legend, just recreates it; it retains a Russian flavour in the emphasis on Russian humiliation and enemy panoply. The melodrama and the beauty of the images bear relevance to an imaginary and unreal past, yet remain significant.

Perhaps the very fact that the reality and the significance would have to be poetic and not realist is what deters development in this field. We have never had a truly picaresque Western, though *Stagecoach* approached it. Because of the dearth of fantasy, these notes have been restricted to the inter-relation of melodrama and realism: one remembers Fritz Lang's fairly crude attempts at melodrama with fantasy (*Dr. Mabuse*, *Metropolis*) twenty years ago but, in more recent times, of melodrama subservient to a world of poetic reality, *Les Jeux sont Faits* is an unsuccessful, and *Orphée* a successful example.

Note

1. "What about the idea that the function of action is to express the characters? This is wrong. The characters are there to provide the action. . . . It is the indivisibility of the act from the actor, and the inevitability of *that* act on the part of *that* actor, that gives action verisimilitude."

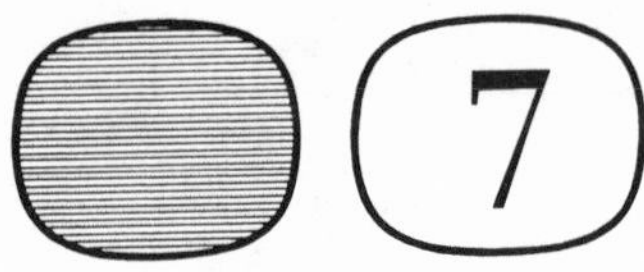

The Family Melodrama

THOMAS SCHATZ

I am not an American; indeed I came to this folklore of American melodrama from a world crazily removed from it. But I was always fascinated with the kind of picture which is called melodrama, in America. . . . Melodrama in the American sense is rather the archetype of a kind of cinema which connects with drama.
—Douglas Sirk[1]

"You're supposed to be making me fit for normal life. What's normal? Yours? If it's a question of values, your values stink. Lousy, middle-class, well-fed, smug existence. All you care about is a paycheck you didn't earn and a beautiful thing to go home to every night."
—Patient to his psychiatrist in *The Cobweb* (1955)

Melodrama as Style and as Genre

In a certain sense every Hollywood movie might be described as "melodramatic." In the strictest definition of the term, melodrama refers to those narrative forms which combine music (*melos*) with drama. Hollywood's use of background music to provide a formal aural dimension and an emotional punctuation to its dramas extends back even into the "silent" era. Live musical accompaniment (usually organ or piano) was standard from the earliest days of theatrical projection. As the

Thomas Schatz, "The Family Melodrama," in *Hollywood Genres: Formulas, Filmmaking, and the Studio System* (New York: Random House, 1981). Reprinted by permission of the author and Random House.

Hollywood cinema and its narrative forms developed, though, and borrowed elements from pulp fiction, radio serials, romantic ballads, and other forms of popular romantic fiction, the term "romantic melodrama" assumed a more specialized meaning. Generally speaking, "melodrama" was applied to popular romances that depicted a virtuous individual (usually a woman) or couple (usually lovers) victimized by repressive and inequitable social circumstances, particularly those involving marriage, occupation, and the nuclear family.

Actually, the gradual development of the movie melodrama is quite similar to that of romantic and screwball comedy. "Comedy," in the early cinema, was a narrative filmic mode that evolved into the "romantic comedy" and then, as romantic conflicts began to be treated in terms of sociosexual and familial codes, into the screwball comedy genre. Similarly, the melodramatic mode of silent filmmaking gradually was adapted to romantic narratives and because of the coincidence of certain formal and ideological factors, it emerged as a distinct formula. We can extend this analogy by considering social melodrama as the inverse of social comedy. Whereas the characters of romantic or screwball comedies scoff at social decorum and propriety, in melodrama they are at the mercy of social conventions; whereas the comedies integrated the anarchic lovers into a self-sufficient marital unit distinct from their social milieu, the melodrama traces the ultimate *resignation* of the principals to the strictures of social and familial tradition.

The master of the silent melodrama was D. W. Griffith, who established its style, tone, and substance in films like *Hearts of the World* (1918), *Broken Blossoms*, *True-Heart Suzie* (1919), *Way Down East* (1920), and *Orphans of the Storm* (1922), in which the sociosexual trials and tribulations of the sisters Gish et al. were communicated in theatrical pantomime. The narrative strategies were calculated to enhance the victims' virtuous suffering: long camera takes, ponderous narrative pacing, frequent close-ups of the anxious heroine (usually with eyes cast heavenward), somber musical accompaniment, and so on. Griffith's heir apparent was Frank Borzage, who first directed silents (most notably *Seventh Heaven* in 1927) but is best remembered for his early sound melodramas—*A Farewell to Arms* (1932), *A Man's Castle* (1933), and *No Greater Glory* (1934). John Stahl also directed both silent and sound melodramas, although he had much greater success with his sound romances, particularly *Only Yesterday* (1933), *Imitation of Life* (1934), *Magnificent Obsession* (1935), *When Tomorrow Comes* (1939), and *Leave Her to Heaven* (1945).

By the 1940s, the plight of the star-crossed couple whose love conquered all had become familiar, although the notion of melodrama still applied as much to dramatic articulation and musical punctuation as to the narrative formula that the studios were in the process of refining. Not until after the war did Hollywood filmmakers really begin to test the range and emotional power of that narrative and with films showing the anxious lovers in a suffocating, highly stylized social environment. This period was dominated by Max Ophuls, an expatriate German filmmaker who directed three intense romantic melodramas—*Letter from an Unknown Woman* (1948), *Caught* (1949), and *The Reckless Moment* (1949)—before leaving Hollywood and returning to Europe. Orphuls' fluid camerawork and elaborate sets enclosed his characters in a world where love is engulfed and overwhelmed by the material trappings of a repressive society.

Orphuls' work was complemented in the late 1940s by two novice Hollywood directors—another German expatriate, Douglas Sirk, and a set designer fresh from the Broadway musical stage, Vincente Minnelli. Minnelli's postwar melodramas (*The Clock*, 1945; *Undercurrent*, 1946; *Madame Bovary*, 1949; *The Bad and the Beautiful*, 1953), like Sirk's (*Summer Storm*, 1944; Shockproof, 1948; *Thunder on the Hill*, 1951; *All I Desire*, 1953), not only solidified the heightened visual style and somber tone of the Hollywood melodrama, but they fleshed out the narrative and thematic conventions that carried the genre into its most productive and fascinating period. It's interesting to note the concurrent development of the social melodrama and the integrated musical after the war, even though each represented radically different conceptions of contemporary social conditions—and in Minnelli's case, these different conceptions were realized by the same director.

1950s Melodrama: The Genre Comes of Age

It was in the mid-1950s that the Hollywood melodrama emerged as the kind of cinema that Sirk, Minnelli, Nicholas Ray, and other filmmakers could exploit successfully. Perhaps the most interesting aspect in the evolution of the genre is that its classical and mannerist periods are essentially indistinguishable from each other. Because of a variety of industry-based factors, as well as external cultural phenomena, the melodrama reached its equilibrium at the same time that certain filmmakers were beginning to subvert and counter the superficial prosocial thematics and clichéd romantic narratives that had previously identified the genre. No other genre films, not even the "anti-Westerns" of the same period, projected so complex and paradoxical a view of America, at once celebrating and severely questioning the basic values and attitudes of the mass audience. Among the more significant and successful of these melodramas are:

1954 *Young at Heart* (Gordon Douglas)
Magnificent Obsession (Douglas Sirk)

1955 *Cobweb* (Vincente Minnelli)
East of Eden (Elia Kazan)
Rebel Without a Cause (Nicholas Ray)

1956 *There's Always Tomorrow* (Douglas Sirk)
Picnic (Joshua Logan)
All That Heaven Allows (Douglas Sirk)
Giant (George Stevens)
Bigger Than Life (Nicholas Ray)
Tea and Sympathy (Vincente Minnelli)

1957 *Written on the Wind* (Douglas Sirk)
The Long Hot Summer (Martin Ritt)
Peyton Place (Mark Robeson)

1958	*Cat on a Hot Tin Roof* (Richard Brooks) *The Tarnished Angels* (Douglas Sirk) *Too Much, Too Soon* (Art Napolean)
1959	*A Summer Place* (Delmer Daves) *Some Came Running* (Vincente Minnelli) *Imitation of Life* (Douglas Sirk)
1960	*From the Terrace* (Mark Robson) *Home from the Hill* (Vincente Minnelli) *The Bramble Bush* (Daniel Petrie)

Movie melodramas survived in the 1960s, but the formal and ideological effects of the New Hollywood and the Kennedy administration's New Frontier affected the genre's development. By the '60s, the melodrama had been co-opted by commercial television, not only in the "daytime drama" series (i.e., soap operas) but also in prime time domestic drama. The success of *Peyton Place* (as both a bestseller and feature film) and its 1961 movie sequel *Return to Peyton Place* led to network television's first serialized prime time drama, also titled *Peyton Place*, which was on throughout the mid- to late 60's and eventually ran in three half-hour installments per week.

The melodrama's narrative formula—its interrelated family of characters, its repressive small-town milieu, and its preoccupation with America's sociosexual mores—managed to live beyond the Eisenhower years and into the era of civil rights, Vietnam, the sexual revolution, and the women's movement. Still, the distinctive spirit of the '50s melodramas was lost in the transition. One of the more interesting aspects of this period of the genre is its paradoxical critical status: the "female weepies," "women's films," and "hankie pix" which were so popular with matinee crowds in the 1950s have become in recent years the filmic darlings of modernist, feminist, and Marxist critics. The initial success of romantic tearjerkers reflected the collective capacity to stroke the emotional sensibilities of suburban housewives, but recent analysts suggest that the '50s melodramas are actually among the most socially self-conscious and covertly "anti-American" films ever produced by the Hollywood studios. Thomas Elsaesser, for example, suggested recently that Hollywood's most effective melodramas "would seem to function either subversively or as escapism—categories which are always relative to the given historical and social context."[2] His point is that Hollywood's postwar melodramas, following narrative and social conventions established in previous movies, in popular literature, on radio serials, and elsewhere, appeared on the surface to be something other than what they were. The audience was, on one level, shown formalized portrayals of virtuous, long-suffering heroines whose persistent faith in the American Dream finally was rewarded with romantic love and a house in the suburbs. Beneath this seemingly escapist fare, however, Elsaesser glimpses the genre's covert function "to formulate a devastating critique of the ideology that supports it."[3]

Thus the critical response to the movie melodrama covers a wide and contradictory range. Depending upon the source and historical perspective, it is described on one extreme as prosocial pabulum for passive, naive audiences, and on the other as subtle, self-conscious criticism of American values, attitudes, and behavior.

The widespread popularity and the surface-level naiveté of the melodrama usually discourage both viewer and critic from looking beyond its facade, its familiar technicolor community and predictable "happy ending." But in the hands of Hollywood's more perceptive filmmakers, particularly Sirk, Minnelli, and Nicholas Ray, the genre assumes an ironic, ambiguous perspective. As our previous analyses of postwar Westerns, musicals, and crime films already have indicated, the melodrama was not alone in subverting many of the ideological traditions that these genres had espoused earlier. Andrew Dowdy, in his *Films of the Fifties* (aptly subtitled "The American State of Mind"), has suggested that genre films, because of their familiarity and presumed prosocial function, could broach delicate social issues more effectively than could "serious" social dramas. He writes, "Themes that alienated a mass audience in a self-consciously *serious* movie were acceptable if discreetly employed within the familiar atmosphere of the Western or the thriller."[4]

Something does seem to be going on below the surface of '50s movies, and particularly in genre films. While current popular evocations of the '50s tend to wax nostalgic, projecting an era of stability, prosperity, and widespread optimism, those who look more closely at that period's cultural documents may see through the facile naiveté to an altogether bleaker reflection. As Dowdy observes, "If we had only movies by which to measure cultural change, those of the '50s would give us an image of an America darkly disturbed by its own cynical loss of innocence, an America prey to fears more pervasive and intense than anything admitted to during the war years."[5]

Film critic-historian Michael Wood shares Dowdy's feelings about the movies of the 1950s, and devotes considerable attention to that period in *America in the Movies*. In describing his own changing impression of Joshua Logan and William Inge's 1956 masterpiece, *Picnic*, Wood suggests that the film's "persistent, insidious hysteria," its undercurrent of alienation and loneliness, went generally unnoticed when the film was released but now seem to "haunt" the narrative. During the '50s, these qualities were "muffled by other emphases we chose to give the film, but we did see its hopelessness and frantic gestures, we did hear its angry and embittered words, and this is precisely the function I am proposing for popular movies. They permit us to look without looking at things we can neither face fully nor entirely disavow."[6] What '50s audiences were trying to avoid was a radical upheaval in the nature and structure of American ideology. HUAC and McCarthy, Alger Hiss and the Rosenbergs, Korea and the Cold War, Sputnik and the threat of nuclear destruction, changing sociosexual norms and the postwar "baby boom"—these and other events brought our fundamental values under scrutiny. America's collective dream was showing signs of becoming a nightmare.

The Family as Narrative Focus

The nuclear, middle-class family, the clearest representation of America's patriarchal and bourgeois social order, was undergoing its own transformation and became the focus of Hollywood's '50s melodramas. World War II and the "Korean Conflict" had sent men into the service and overseas and moved women out of the home and into the work force. By the mid-1950s, men had returned to increasingly alienating, bureaucratic jobs and women were caught between the labor market and the need to return home to raise families. Greater mobility, suburbanization, and improving educational opportunities uprooted families and put a strain on their nuclear coherence, which made the age-old "generation gap" a more immediate and pressing issue than it had ever been before. Among the dominant intellectual fashions of the postwar era were Freudian psychology and existential philosophy. Each stressed the alienation of the individual due to the inability of familial and societal institutions to fulfill his or her particular needs.

While these various cultural factors coalesced within the popular cinema, whose stage of narrative and technical evolution was ideally suited for the glossy, stylized world of the melodrama, the *family* melodrama began to take shape. As Geoffrey Nowell-Smith describes it, "The genre or form that has come to be known as melodrama arises from the conjunction of a formal history proper (development of tragedy, realism, etc.), a set of social determinations, which have to do with the rise of the bourgeoisie, and a set of psychic determinations, which take shape around the family."[7] Because '50s melodramas centered upon the nuclear unit, and by extension, upon the home within a familiar (usually small-town) American community, both the constellation of characters and the setting are more highly conventionalized than in other genres of integration. That these familiar social structures are at once so very real to the viewer and yet so clearly stylized within the genre's artificial framework adds a unique dimension to the iconography of the family melodrama. This might explain the sparse attention the melodrama has received from critics, as a distinct narrative-cinematic formula.

The family unit seems to provide an ideal locus for the genre's principal characters and its milieu for two fundamental reasons. First, it is a preestablished constellation whose individual roles (mother, father, son, daughter; adult, adolescent, child, infant, and so on) carry with them large social significance. Second, it is bound to its community by social class (father's occupation and income, type and location of the family home, etc.). Ideally, the family represents a "natural" as well as a social collective, a self-contained society in and of itself. But in the melodrama this ideal is undercut by the family's status within a highly structured socioeconomic milieu, and therefore, its identity as an autonomous human community is denied—the family roles are determined by the larger social community. The American small town, with its acute class-consciousness, its gossip and judgment by appearances, and its reactionary commitment to fading values and mores, represents an extended but perverted family in which human elements (love, honesty, interpersonal contact, generosity) have either solidified into repressive social conventions or disappeared altogether.

The image of the American family as it evolves through the 1940s is very interesting in that even apparently optimistic films like *How Green Was My Valley* (1941), *Shadow of a Doubt* (1943), *It's a Wonderful Life*, and *The Best Years of Our Lives* (both 1946) rely for their impact on the gradual erosion of our cultural confidence in the nuclear family. Also *noir* thrillers like *Double Indemnity* (1944) and *Mildred Pierce* (1946) developed this thematic. These films exploited the changing roles of women in wartime and postwar America, and also showed how black-widow inclinations stemmed from dissatisfaction with a suffocating middle-class lifestyle. The heroine in each film—Barbara Stanwyck in the former, Joan Crawford in the latter—is bent upon escaping a tedious husband and tacky suburban home. Little motivation is given for her dissatisfaction, but none is necessary: middle-class claustrophobia and Mom's desire to escape it are simply taken for granted. But these are *noir* thrillers and the dissatisfaction is more difficult to explain in other films whose obvious aims are to uplift the audience and reaffirm their traditional values.

Consider *Meet Me in St. Louis* (1944) and *Father of the Bride* (1950), two of Hollywood's—and director Vincente Minnelli's—more successful and saccharine celebrations of small-town family life. Each film traces the courtship and betrothal of a naive heroine (Judy Garland and Elizabeth Taylor, respectively) which is complicated by their fathers' familial-occupational confusion. This conflict is animated in both films through a dynamic "nightmare" sequence, which momentarily points up the deep-seated doubts about family and community stability that the surface stories tend to repress.

In *Meet Me in St. Louis*, Margaret O'Brien (playing Garland's younger sister) is so distraught over her family's upward mobility and Dad's having been transferred to New York that she literally goes berserk at one point, running outside in a hysterical nocturnal frenzy to demolish a "family" of snowmen. In *Father of the Bride*, Spencer Tracy's distress over his daughter's impending marriage brings on a surreal nightmare in which his role in the wedding is expressed in images of inadequacy, loneliness, and despair. This is accentuated by Minnelli's slow-motion camera, the severe visual angles, and the impressionistic set. Both of these films end happily enough. Not until the mid-1950s did Minnelli draw his cultural subversion out from under the cover of darkness and dream logic.

After the war, then, the traditional image of marriage, the home, and the family was undergoing more self-critical reflection. With the emergence of the family melodrama in the '50s, the American family moved out of its role as supporting player to achieve star billing. Films no longer simply used familial conflicts and interrelationships to enhance some external complication (a crime, the war, some social event) but focused on the social institution of the family itself as the basis for conflict. A rather interesting paradox emerged from this shift of concentration: on the one hand, the family crisis was the dominant narrative conflict; on the other hand, the resolution of that conflict had to be found within the existing social structure, i.e., the family. Unlike genres of order, the melodrama's social conflicts and contradictions could not be resolved by violently eliminating one of the opposing forces; unlike genres of integration, its social reality could not be magically transformed via music or screwball attitudes. In fact, those uninhibited types who ruled in the comedy-oriented films are often the more *angst*-ridden and oppressed members of the melodrama's community. The liberating quality of performance and individual expression of the musical and screwball comedy are simply means for establishing one's socioeconomic identity in the family melodrama.

Young at Heart and *Picnic:* The Male Intruder-Redeemer in a World of Women

The contrast is well demonstrated in the uneven and inadvertently ironic 1954 film, *Young at Heart*, a movie which shifts back and forth from a musical to a melodramatic stance. The Tuttle household is the focus of this film and contains a widowed professor of music who is raising three talented and eligible daughters (including Doris Day and Dorothy Malone—even the casting exhibits the film's generic schizophrenia). The film opens with Dad and two of his daughters playing classical music in the living room. The third daughter (Malone) enters and announces her engagement to a fellow named Bob, an overweight but available local businessman. This brings the issues of spinsterhood and marital compromise out into the open, and the remainder of the film traces the courtship and wedding of each of the daughters. Malone's home-grown fiancé is juxtaposed with a suave composer from the big city (Gig Young as Alex), who invades the Tuttle household—his father and Tuttle had once been close friends—to work on a musical. Alex's refined wit and talent initially disrupt the Tuttle milieu, although as the narrative develops it becomes obvious that he is the heir apparent to the senior Tuttle, the hard-working and responsible but somewhat aloof patriarch.

Alex and Laurie (Day) eventually become engaged, but not before Alex brings in an old friend, Barney (Frank Sinatra), to help arrange the musical score. Barney is painfully antiheroic. He derides the middle-class environment ("It's homes like these that are the backbone of the nation—where's the spinning wheel?") and agonizes that "the resident fates" are keeping him from success as a songwriter. Even though Barney does little but slouch over a piano and whine interminably through the cigarette dangling from his lips, Laurie falls in love with him and eventually stands up Alex on their wedding day to elope with her ill-matched lover. (The wedding was to have taken place in the Tuttle house, further reinforcing its value as the locus for social-familial ritual.)

The narrative moves quickly after this. Alex hangs around the household as surrogate son and "good loser"; his musical is a hit while Barney's career is stuck at the piano-bar stage. Laurie plays the domesticator, renouncing her musical talents; and she becomes pregnant. Before she can tell Barney of their impending parenthood, he attempts suicide, but when he learns he's a prospective Daddy, a miraculous transformation takes place. Dissolve to one year later: Barney's unfinished song (which we first heard the day he met Laurie) is a hit and all's right in the family household.

Ultimately, no description of a film like *Young at Heart* can begin to convey the emotional and intellectual reversals that would have been necessary to sustain the narrative. The film's own internal schema—its inherent value system, characterization and *mise-en-scène*—is so inconsistent, so filled with ruptures, and so illogical that the narrative is an amalgam of confused, self-contradictory impulses. The resolution is especially illogical: we have seen the central characters as either victimized by or utterly hostile to the existing social-familial-marital system, but somehow romantic love and parenthood magically transform familial anxiety and despair into domestic bliss. The unevenness is intensified by the casting—Doris Day's vibrant, naive enthusiast and Sinatra's emaciated, withdrawn sulker seem utterly incompatible. Their individual values and attitudes (as well as their established screen personalities) are so diametrically opposed that marriage, a hit tune, and kids in the house scarcely seem adequate to reconcile their differences. Director Gordon Douglas might have turned these drawbacks into assets by assuming a more ironic, distanced perspective, but he develops a straightforward, unselfconscious narrative that treats its material as "realistically" as possible.

Nevertheless, a number of generic elements converge in *Young at Heart*. They anticipate the more effective films that would turn logical inconsistencies into assets. The aging patriarch in a female-dominated household, the search for the father/lover/husband by the anxious offspring, the male intruder-redeemer who regenerates and stabilizes the family, the household itself as locus of social interaction, and the ambiguous function of the marital embrace as both sexually liberating and socially restricting—these qualities were refined through repeated usage and incorporated into melodramas that were at the same time coherent, consistent, and complex.

A direct narrative descendent of Douglas's film is *Picnic*, a 1956 adaptation of William Inge's Pulitzer Prize–winning drama which director Joseph Logan took from stage to screen with enormous success. Like its predecessor, *Picnic* involves a community of women whose preoccupations with marriage, spinsterhood, and morality are disrupted and intensified by a male intruder-redeemer. The plot traces a small Kansas town on Labor Day as it celebrates the harvest. The film follows the nomadic Hal (William Holden), who jumps the freight train on which he rode into town in search of an old college schoolmate, Alan (Cliff Robertson). Hal's search begins on "the wrong side of the tracks," where he happens upon and completely disarms a female collective. This group includes Madge (Kim Novak, who we later learn is Alan's girl), her widowed mother and younger sister, an old maid schoolmarm (Rosalind Russell as Rosemary) who boards with them, and a wise old neighbor, Mrs. Potts (Verna Felton), whose invalid mother lives upstairs.

These four generations of unmarried women form a complex and fascinating configuration of characters and attitudes. Madge, the beauty queen, and her little sister (Susan Strasberg), the bookish tomboy, envy each other's distinct talents. While Madge repeatedly decries her reputation as "the pretty one," her mother encourages her to exploit her sexuality to snare Alan (a member of the local aristocracy), even if it means compromising her "virtue." Mrs. Potts, the stable matriarch who is too old and seasoned to let society's opinions dictate her judgment, continually calms the discord within the female collective. Peripheral to the group is Rosemary, the shrill neurotic spinster bent on snagging her long-standing beau, Howard (Arthur O'Connell). Rosemary's endless denials of her own sexual frustration and fear of spinsterhood affect the entire group, providing an almost hysterical subcurrent that touches each woman.

Madge is the central figure in this constellation. Each of the older women projects a different conception of sexuality and marriage to her: her mother (whose husband had deserted her years before) considers sex a commodity that can be exchanged for an improved social standing; Rosemary understands the spinster's social outcast status but seems even more concerned with marriage as a refuge against loneliness and an opportunity for natural human contact; Mrs. Potts, the one woman willing to admit she's pleased to have Hal ("a *real* man") around the house, is the most overtly romantic of the lot, suggesting that true love is—or should be—oblivious to social circumstances.

Madge's anticipated coronation as harvest queen at the Labor Day picnic is complemented by Alan's anticipated proposal of marriage—the holiday festival represents an initiation rite for the heroine in both a communal and a marital sense. Hal's arrival on the morning of the picnic, his obvious sexual rapport with Madge, and the fact that he's come to ask Alan for a job create a network of social and sexual tensions that intensify throughout the film. Both Hal and Madge are in a position to use Alan and thereby improve their social class, although their own "natural" attraction to one another keeps them from becoming manipulative and self-serving.

At one point in the film, Hal leaves the women to see Alan at his family estate, and Alan takes him on a tour of the family's grain mills which are the economic and agricultural lifeblood of the community. Overlooking the Kansas wheatfields from the top of a huge grain elevator, an appropriate image of his father's domination of the milieu, Alan promises Hal a job, but makes clear his intentions regarding Madge. Alan also is planning to attend the Labor Day festivities, and thus is willing to cross the socioeconomic barrier in order to woo Madge and impress Hal.

The various narrative subcurrents surface at the picnic: Madge is crowned Queen of Neewollah (Halloween spelled backwards) and celebrates that rite of passage in a sensuous, moonlit dance with Hal. A drunken, panicky Rosemary interrupts their embrace as she tries to establish her own sexual and feminine identity, but she only causes an ugly scene that attracts the attention of the other picnickers. Hal is accused of disrupting the community's tranquility—he has clarified the myriad sociosexual tensions beneath the surreal glaze of fireworks, Japanese lanterns and the full moon. At this point, director Logan and cinematographer James Wong Howe depart from naturalistic style and begin to use camera angles, movement, and lighting to create an artificial, stylized narrative-visual tone. The closing sequences take place in daylight on the following morning, once the community neuroses return to their subliminal realm, and this day/night break further stresses the importance of the picnic itself as the narrative and thematic core of the film.

Picnic is resolved with the promise of two weddings—one between Rosemary and Howard and the other between Madge and Hal. After the picnic, each couple had consummated their love in true Midwestern small-town fashion, driving into the Kansas night to the music of locusts and locomotive whistles. By now Rosemary's and Howard's relationship takes up roughly the same amount of screen time as Madge and Hal's, and the viewer is able to contrast the two couples' radically different views of marriage, with the older pair sharing none of the romantic naiveté or sexual exhilaration of the initiate-lovers.

The film's closing sequences focus upon Madge, though, and upon the reactions of her mother and Mrs. Potts to the news of her impending marriage. Madge's mother warns her not to repeat the same mistake she and Madge's father had made, whereas Mrs. Potts accepts the irrationality of romantic love. The film's closing image, in which the lovers are moving in the same direction but by different means (Hal has hopped a freight, and Madge promises to follow by bus), reinforces the ambiguity of their embrace. It represents an idealized sexual union, but it is also an impulsive flight into the same social traps which had ensnared their parents. Still, the possibility of escape from the repressive community and the obvious chemistry between Holden's and Novak's characters tend to enhance the "happy end" nature of this resolution, even though we cannot logically project that ending into the "ever after."

The Widow-Lover Variation

Because the lovers in *Picnic* have managed to escape their milieu, it is possible for us to believe that their marriage might be a natural and human coupling as well as a social institution. This belief is reinforced by the intruder-redeemer Hal, a genuinely "natural man" whose character developed outside the community, seemingly in some timeless dimension. This is essentially the basis for his personal and sexual attraction. The prospect of a liberating marriage is actually quite rare in the '50s family melodrama, which usually depicts that social ritual as solidifying the couple's position within the community rather than providing them with an escape from it.

A more familiar narrative strategy traces the courtship of a widowed mother as well as—or perhaps in lieu of—that of the postadolescent daughter. *Magnificent Obsession, All That Heaven Allows, Peyton Place, Return to Peyton Place,* A *Summer Place, Imitation of Life,* and many other '50s films involve the courtship of an older woman, invariably a widow or divorcée, whose adult status and established familial role minimize the possibility for flight from her repressive environment. In *Picnic,* Madge, as yet unburdened by children, family home, or any significant community position, had a certain freedom denied to the women in these other films. In the family melodrama's puritanical moral climate, that freedom is closely related to the woman's virginity: Once she is literally and figuratively "taken" by a man, the heroine surrenders her initiative, her self-reliance, and in effect, her individual identity.

Her life is determined thereafter by the male—and by extension the male-oriented, patriarchal society—she commits herself to. The strategy of these films, generally speaking, is to counter the heroine's role as mother-domesticator with that of sexual partner. This opposition itself is intensified by the role of her daughter who is just reaching womanhood and whose romantic delusions are propelling her toward the same marital and social traps as her mother. Of the "weepies" just listed, only *Magnificent Obsession* lacks a mother-daughter opposition, although this film, like the others, does portray a woman in early middle age caught between her socially prescribed role as mother and her reawakened individual and sexual identity. As numerous critics have pointed out, the heroine's choice is scarcely viable: regardless of her ultimate commitment, which usually is to her lover-redeemer, the heroine merely exchanges one trap for another, allowing her individual destiny to be determined by the values of her new lover rather than her previous one.

The previous lover's ghost still haunts the heroine and impedes her romance, usually in the guise of her children and their class-bound family home. *All That Heaven Allows*, for example, shows a recently-widowed mother-domesticator, Cary (Jane Wyman), whose postadolescent children, her friends from the club, and her middle-class home urge her to remain a carbon copy of her dead husband (Conrad Nagel). Much to the community's consternation, she falls in love with her gardener, Ron (Rock Hudson), a younger man of somewhat lower social class. To intensify the conflict between true love and social conventions, director Douglas Sirk constructs an elaborate pattern of visual and thematic oppositions that contrast the lifestyles of her lover and her dead husband. But ultimately the heroine merely makes a choice between her stoic, Emersonian gardener and her dead bourgeois husband—one of these men will govern her life. Wyman makes the "right" choice, of course, opting for love and Rock Hudson, but only after a virtual act of God brings her to his aid when he is injured in an accident. Thus Sirk undermines the film's happy end on two levels. Only an arbitrary event within the logic of the narrative (Ron's accident) enables the heroine to break out of her assigned role; and on a broader thematic level, she manages to escape one dominating patriarch only to accept another.

We would have to assume that Cary's marriage to Ron would be less repressive and dehumanizing than her earlier, class-bound marriage had been, and so the resolution seems more positive than not. Like Hal in *Picnic*, Ron personifies the intruder-redeemer who somehow has fashioned his own value system outside the small-town community which has entrapped the heroine. But this does not alter his role as "breadwinner" and patriarch, nor is he any less "socialized" within his own community than was Cary's first husband.

The redeemer's ambiguous status, particularly in Sirk's films, is finally a function of the filmmaker's penchant for irony, as well as his capacity to depict the repressive middle-class environment so effectively. Like Vincente Minnelli, Sirk was a master of formal artifice and expressive decor. His filmic world—at once familiar and yet lavishly artificial and visually stylized—is inhabited by characters who are always emotionally at arm's length, operating in a social reality that clearly is once removed from our own. As Sirk and the other principal melodrama directors understood, any "realistic" narrative strategy in these glossy romances would be both aesthetically and ideologically counterproductive, and would undercut the films' obvious idealization of the viewer's social reality. Sirk's success is closely related to his use of music, camerawork, casting (Rock Hudson is ultimately nothing more than a evocative cardboard cut-out in Sirk's films), set design and costuming (especially the use of color to "codify" the characters and their milieu), and other formal filmic devices.

Other directors chose the path of realism over stylization, and their films, straightforward paeans to the American middle class, generally have suffered critically in the long run. Mark Robson's *Peyton Place*, for example, relates much the same story as *All That Heaven Allows* but has not worn well over the years, mostly due to the fact that the viewer is supposed to take the subject matter seriously. Sirk never stooped to this level of insult—as Andrew Sarris has observed: "Even in his most dubious projects, Sirk never shrinks away from the ridiculous, but by a full-bodied formal development, his art transcends the ridiculous, as form comments on content."[8] *Peyton Place* traces the romantic events in the lives of an unmarried woman and her daughter after an intruder-redeemer enters the community and courts the mother. Whereas *All That*

Heaven Allows dealt primarily with America's socioeconomic and materialistic values, this film focuses upon its marital and sexual taboos. Whereas Ron's character was a synthesis of Thoreau and Marx, here the redeemer is an amalgam of Drs. Freud and Spock—in fact, the community crisis in the film results from the new high-school principal's efforts to initiate sex education classes. Cary's attempts to shed her materialistic value system are not similar to those of this heroine (Lana Turner as Constance McKenzie), a woman who is attempting to resolve the sexual hangups that resulted from her sordid past—adultery with a married man in the big city.

Constance has paid dearly (true to the melodrama's moral demand of absolute retribution), not only through a lifetime of guilt and sociosexual pathology, but through the very existence of her illegitimate daughter, Allison. Just as Sirk's film established a network of oppositions involving enlightened versus unenlightened capitalism. *Peyton Place* counters sexual inhibition with a more liberal (at least by '50s standards) attitude. The film suggests that the community can learn the error of its repressive ways and achieve the American Dream.

The film's utopian vision and neat happily-ever-after resolution are its undoing, however, since they create a rupture in narrative logic which cannot possibly be rationalized. While Sirk avoided this by resolving the plot with an arbitrary event (Ron's accident), in *Peyton Place,* Robson resorts to a ritual sequence—a sensationalized small-town trial—in which the community comes to its collective senses and renegotiates its system of values and beliefs. The climactic trial brings into the open the various acts of adultery, rape, incest, and other iniquities committed throughout the story. But the essentially benevolent citizenry is encouraged to appreciate the value of truth and understanding over retribution—that, in the local doctor's words, "we've all been prisoners of each other's gossip." The community realizes that in the past, "appearances counted more than feelings," but through honest human interaction they reach what Allison terms "the season of love." If the forced, arbitrary nature of its resolution is not obvious in the original, one need only look to the sequel, *Return to Peyton Place,* to realize how easily this utopian community and the pat happy end could be undone.

The Family Aristocratic Variation

At the narrative-thematic core of family melodramas is a metaphoric search for the ideal husband/lover/father who, as American mythology would have it, will stabilize the family and integrate it into the larger community. Hollywood mythology tends to portray the husband and the lover in essentially contradictory terms: the woman's dilemma is that she must opt for either socioeconomic security *or* emotional and sexual fulfillment. Her dilemma is intensified in what might be termed the family aristocracy variation of the '50s melodrama, which includes films like *Written on the Wind, The Long Hot Summer, Giant, Cat on a Hot Tin Roof, From the Terrace,* and *Home from the Hill.* These melodramas trace the behavioral and attitudinal traits of succeeding generations. The dramatic conflict is based on a contradictory view of marriage: it is a means of liberation from unreasonable familial demands and also the only way of perpetuating the family aristocracy.

The family's status is enhanced by its role within the community, whose economy and social climate it controls either directly or through benign neglect. This motif surfaces in *Picnic*—Alan will inherit the "family business" and thus the socioeconomic lifeblood of the community generates much of the tension surrounding his character. But the lovers' flight from Alan and from his father's wealth offers an option that is unavailable to the class-bound lovers in the family aristocracy melodramas. The Varner family in *The Long Hot Summer*, the Hadley family in *Written on the Wind*, and the Benedict family in *Giant* are established as inescapable ideological givens; they create the socioeconomic climate that is around them. Significantly, these films usually are based in the South, where the conception of the landed gentry has survived into the twentieth century. The dramatic action may be confined exclusively to the family's mansion and estate, as in *Cat on a Hot Tin Roof*, or it may extend to the larger social community, as in *Written on the Wind*, *Giant*, and *The Long Hot Summer*, where the community is an extension of the family estate. In *Written on the Wind*, the town and the estate share the Hadley name, and the family insignia is everywhere—on automobiles, oil rigs, street signs—giving considerable weight to the actions and attitudes of the family members themselves.

The constellation of characters in this variation revolves around an aging patriarch (sometimes close to death), whose wife is either dead or else functions only as a peripheral character who has produced inadequate male heirs and sexually frustrated daughters. The patriarch's search for an heir to his feudal monarchy usually sets up the conflict between his own spoiled, ineffectual son and an intruder-redeemer figure who is equal to the patriarch in strength, intellect, and self-reliance. The son's inability to negotiate the wealth and power of his legacy mirrors the daughter's sexual confusion, although the idealized intruder inevitably enables the daughter to clarify her sexuality and develop an individual identity beyond familial context. (An interesting twist on this convention occurs in *Cat on a Hot Tin Roof*, in which Paul Newman and Jack Carson are cast as the tormented, inadequate offspring of patriarch Burl Ives, with Elizabeth Taylor assuming the role of the intruder-redeemer, whose "true love" stabilizes Newman's sexual confusion and reaffirms his role as heir apparent to "Big Daddy.")

Thus these films stress the patriarch's search for an heir and everything implied by the handing down of power from one generation to the next. Operating in a way similar to many of the screwball comedies, the redeemer figure often helps the wealthy aristocrat to recover whatever values and attitudes had enabled him to attain his wealth. His son's inadequacy demonstrates that these attributes have been lost, and often the son, as well as the patriarch and the daughter, profits from the intruder's redemptive powers. The role of the spoiled, whining offspring is one of the more interesting in the aristocracy melodramas, and provided actors like Jack Carson (*Cat on a Hot Tin Roof*), Tony Franciosa (*The Long Hot Summer*), and Robert Stack (*Written on the Wind*) with some of the most intense and rewarding roles in their film careers. As such, these melodramas are actually as much male "weepies" as they are female ones.

Although the son's inadequacies are a function of his father's wealth, most of these films stop short of an outright condemnation of wealth and the corrupting influence of unchecked socioeconomic power. As in the screwball comedies, the patriarch generally is reeducated and thus humanized by the redeemer figure. Ultimately, this progressive enlightenment resolves the various conflicts within the family and returns the tormented son to the patriarch's favor. In *The Long Hot Summer,* for example, the aging and decadent Will Varner (Orson Welles) consistently bemoans the lack of male heirs and "the establishment of my immortality." His only son, Jody (Franciosa), is woefully insecure and inept, and at one point asks his father, "Where do you go looking for it, Poppa, if you ain't got it in you?" Intruder-redeemer Ben Quick (Paul Newman) eventually weds Varner's renegade daughter (Joanne Woodward), promising Will many grandsons (i.e., real heirs with more potential), and he also helps Jody discover his own worth, prompting the patriarch's closing pronouncement, "Maybe I'll live forever."

The strain on internal narrative logic with such a pat ending is severe. The existing social and familial structures act as both the problem and its eventual solution, and the only significant motivation for the resolution is the influence of the redeemer figure. But the problems themselves are so immediate, familiar, and intense, they scarcely can be resolved as easily as their narratives suggest. Generally speaking, then, family melodramas might be seen as critical of American ideology at the level of narrative exposition and complication, but their resolution invariably reaffirms, however implausibly, the cultural status quo.

Occasionally a film like *Written on the Wind* surfaces, however, where the subversion of familial and socioeconomic conventions is sustained throughout. In Sirk's 1957 melodrama, the patriarch dies upon learning of his daughter's scandalous sexual activities, she in turn loses the only man she ever loved, and the tormented son commits suicide. Sirk provides us with a moderately happy ending, though. The redeemer (Rock Hudson) is finally cleared of the accusation that he murdered the son (Stack), and he leaves the Hadleys' world with the dead son's widow (Lauren Bacall). This arbitrary, ambiguous closure does little to resolve the social and familial tensions that had destroyed the entire Hadley family, although it provides the protagonists with a fortuitous escape hatch.

Nicholas Ray, Vincente Minnelli, and the Male Weepie

The aging patriarch and tormented, inadequate son appear most frequently in the aristocracy variation, although they occasionally are part of middle-class families as well. In films like *Rebel Without a Cause, Bigger Than Life, Tea and Sympathy, East of Eden,* and *The Cobweb,* the central conflict involves passing the role of middle-American "Dad" from one generation to the next. Here, the patriarch's anxieties and the son's tormented insecurities cannot be attributed to family wealth or a decadent aristocratic view of life. As a result, these films tend to be more directly critical of American middle-class ideology which both the characters and the majority of the audience know so well. The master of the tormented-son portrayal was James Dean. Whether encouraging his emasculated father (Jim Backus) to stand on his own in *Rebel Without a Cause* or simply trying to win his insensitive father's (Raymond Massey) love in *East of Eden*, Dean's soulful stare and agonized gestures projected the image of a son either unwilling or unable to accommodate society's expectations of male adulthood.

While Dean's films focus on the son, others like *The Cobweb* and *Bigger Than Life* are straightforward male "weepies," examining the plight of the middle-class husband/lover/father. Each of these melodramas is a sustained indictment of the social pressures which have reduced the well-meaning patriarch to a confused, helpless victim of his own good intentions. The heroes in Nicholas Ray's *Bigger Than Life* (James Mason as Ed Avery) and Vincente Minnelli's *The Cobweb* (Richard Widmark as Stewart McIver) are both professional bureaucrats and community serrvants: Avery is a grade-school teacher, and McIver is the head of a psychiatric clinic. These films, like those of Douglas Sirk, develop artificial conflicts that are intensified and finally overwhelmed by the family conflicts they touch off.

In *Bigger Than Life*, we are introduced to the victimized hero as he is finishing his work day at school and slipping off to put in a few extra hours as a taxi dispatcher to "make ends meet." Ed is overworked and having dizzy spells but is too proud to tell his wife of his moonlighting or his illness. She, in turn, suspects that Ed's unccounted extra hours mean that he's having an affair to escape the boring routine of their static life. Ed eventually collapses, and his physical illness is treated with a '50s wonder drug, cortisone. Ed abuses the drug because it gives him a sense of power, mission, and self-esteem that his familial and social roles do not. As the narrative develops, Ed becomes increasingly monomaniacal, loudly criticizing his family, his colleagues, and his social environment. Director Ray does not focus on cortisone as the cause of Ed's antisocial behavior and psychotic outbursts, and so, ultimately, we are interested in his character as a bizarre critique of American middle-class values and attitudes. Ed's tirade at a PTA meeting ("we're breeding a race of moral midgets") and his refusal to let his son eat until he catches a football properly are neuroses that any frustrated parent might exhibit under duress. They emphasize not only Dad's own past failures and lingering anxieties but also the social basis for those anxieties, as well as one man's impotence in effecting a change in the status quo.

While Ed's own family senses something is wrong—at one point his son whispers to Mom, "Isn't Daddy acting a little foolish?"—his lip service to social conventions prevents anyone else from recognizing the severity of his mental condition. This central apathy reinforces the film's subversive tone, in that those around Ed may look askance at his outbursts, but they accept his behavior as his way of "letting off a little steam." Ed's criticism of the American family, educational system, and class structure becomes more vocal and more intense, until he finally decides upon an Abraham/Isaac-style "sacrifice" to atone for his own failures and to save his son from the same class-bound fate. Over the protestations of his wife—"But God stopped Abraham," she pleads, to which Ed replies, "God was wrong!"—and with the television turned up to full volume in the background, Ed prepares for the ritual execution. A spectacular fistfight with the grade-school gym teacher (Walter Mathau), which devastates Ed's bourgeois home, prevents disaster as well as precipitating his return to the hospital and eventual recovery. In the film's ironic epilogue, the family is tearfully reunited in Ed's hospital room. The family doctor prescribes the same cortisone treatment but closer regulation of the dosage. Consider the narrative sleight-of-hand involved in this resolution: the real issue in the film is not the danger of wonder drugs but rather the kind of social-familial climate that Ed's drugged state permitted him to condemn. At the end, Ed's aberrant behavior is resolved but not the social conditions that motivated his behavior.

Ray's film recalls Sirk's in that it exploits a superficial plot device to camouflage its social criticism. Vincente Minnelli's male "weepies"—particularly *The Cobweb*, *Tea and Sympathy*, *Home from the Hill*, and *Two Weeks in Another Town*—also follow this narrative strategy. Whether Minnelli is examining the *angst*-ridden familial relationship in a mental hospital (*The Cobweb*), on a college campus (*Tea and Sympathy*), or even within a foreign-based Hollywood film unit (*Two Weeks in Another Town*), his melodramas trace the search for the ideal family. Usually, he contrasts the protagonist's "natural" family with an artificial group from his professional environment. In *The Cobweb*, for example, Richard Widmark portrays a clinical psychiatrist (Stewart McIver) torn between his domestic family (Gloria Grahame as his wife Karen and their two children) and the surrogate family that he cultivates in his psychiatric clinic with a staff worker, Meg (Lauren Bacall), and a disturbed adolescent artist, Stevie (John Kerr), Meg and McIver ask Stevie to design new drapes for the clinic's library as a therapeutic exercise, not realizing that Karen and a matronly bureaucrat at the clinic (Lillian Gish) already have assumed responsibility for doing it. This banal plot device generates an intricate network of familial, social, and professional conflicts, none of which is resolved satisfactorily—and at film's end the library is still without drapes.

The emphasis on family interaction is highlighted by the fact that McIver is a Freudian psychoanalyst. "Why don't you analyze my Oedipus complex or my lousy father?" Stevie asks McIver early in the film, to which the psychiatrist later responds, "I'm not your father, and I won't run out on you like your father did." As good a surrogate father as McIver is on the job, though, his domestic feelings are sorely lacking. He does not communicate with his wife either verbally or sexually and is a virtual stranger to his own children. We learn that when his daughter was asked at school what she wanted to be, she replied, "One of Daddy's patients."

McIver's role as a professional father to the clinic's children clearly is more rewarding. He and Meg develop a cameraderie that is eventually consummated sexually—or at least Minnelli's well-timed fades imply as much within the limits of the Production Code. Their relationship is based on their shared devotion to Stevie. McIver eventually tells Meg: "If we make this work we may be able to show him we're different—good parents." Stevie does show signs of recovery at film's end, but these are not entirely due to the couple's ministrations.

Stevie, as Minnelli's spokesman against the "unbalanced" nature of contemporary society, assumes the role as principal social critic in the film. He has impeccable credentials for this job as both frustrated artist and deserted son. (Not only had his own father deserted him, but he confides in Meg midway through the film that his mother died the previous year, an event that triggered his breakdown.) Stevie's role as critic is established even before we learn that he's a patient at the clinic. When McIver's wife offers him a ride in the film's opening sequence, the two strike up a conversation about art and artists. With Leonard Rosenman's ominous, pulsating music in the background, Stevie laments: "Artists are better off dead—they're not so troublesome. . . . They said Van Gogh was crazy because he killed himself. He couldn't sell a painting when he was alive, and now they're worth thirty million dollars. They weren't that bad then and they're not that good now—so who's crazy?" As they pull onto the clinic grounds later, Stevie suggests that "everybody's tilted around here. That's why you didn't know who I was. You can't tell the patients from the doctors." "Yes, I can," replies Karen, "the patients get well."

This remark ultimately governs the narrative. Stevie's ability to "get well" and come to terms with himself is juxtaposed throughout with the essentially negative view of the community into which Stevie might hope to integrate himself. Although Stevie does emerge as a relatively "stable" individual, his insightful outbursts against McIver early in the film cast real doubts on the value of his "cure." In a psychiatric session early in the film, Stevie pours out a devastating critique of McIver and his lifestyle: "You're supposed to be making me fit for normal life. What's normal? Yours? If it's a question of values, your values stink. Lousy, middle-class, well-fed, smug existence. All you care about is a paycheck you didn't earn and a beautiful thing to go home to every night."

These are not the hysterical ravings of an unbalanced adolescent, since we can see that McIver's own deteriorating personal and professional competence lend credibility to these criticisms. We can also see that Stevie will be able to "recover" because he seems to understand that society itself is not well—an understanding that none of the "normal" characters exhibits.

McIver and Meg finaly bow to the social impediments to their union, and he returns to his wife with the half-hearted pledge that he will work harder at their relationship. Minnelli himself accepted the arbitrary nature of his resolution, admitting, "It seemed dishonest, since we'd established extraordinary bonds between the doctor and the staff member, but the conclusion was very much within the existing movie code."[9] Which, of course, is a reflection of America's implicit moral code, and Minnelli clearly was sensitive to the need to resolve the issues raised in the film within an acceptable framework. McIver's decision to remain with the jealous, whining Karen rather than the stoic, supportive Meg scarcely represents a positive resolution, however, and *The Cobweb*'s end is more an act of resignation—for both McIver and Minnelli—than of integration.

Stylization, Social Reality, and Critical Values

The Cobweb is a typical Hollywood melodrama in that it traces the identity crisis of an individual whose divided domestic and occupational commitments provide a rational basis for confusion and anxiety. The more adept filmmakers learned to exploit these contradictions and ambiguities via plot and characterization and through heavy stylization as well. Although we have devoted most of our attention in this chapter to conventions of setting, plot, and character in the melodrama, ultimately their formal orchestration may well be the most significant quality in these films. In a 1959 review of Sirk's most successful and most overtly stylized melodrama, *Imitation of Life,* critic Moira Walsh described the film as a "pretentious, expensive, overstuffed Technicolor example of Hollywood at its worst," and she went on to condemn the film as "a perfect example of the tendency to confuse fantasy with reality which serious students of our mass culture are inclined to regard as most destructive of the human personality."[10] This was written about the same film which German critic-filmmaker Rainer Werner Fassbinder, who himself has remade several of Sirk's films, recently termed "a great, crazy movie about life and about death. And about America." It is a film, argues Fassbinder, in which "nothing is natural. Ever. Not in the whole film."[11]

In retrospect, the reviewers' highbrow myopia is not surprising—contemporary critics of Flaubert, Dickens, and D. W. Griffith often misunderstood what their melodramatists were doing. The huge success of *Imitation of Life,* and the renewed interest critics and scholars have in it, suggest that this and other film melodramas work on substantially different levels of viewer engagement. They range from transparent romantic fantasy to a severe indictment of the culture that perpetuates that fantasy. Moira Walsh was accurate about the confusion of fantasy with reality, but it is the characters within the melodrama, not the filmmaker, who are confused. In fact, Sirk's popularity seems closely related to his capacity to flesh out the *un*natural aspects of America's social reality, to articulate cinematically how that reality is itself a collective cultural fantasy.

In discussing *Imitation of Life* more than a decade after its release, Sirk compared his narrative strategy to classical Greek drama in which "there is no real solution of the predicament the people in the play are in, just the *deus ex machina,* which is now called 'the happy end.' "[12] Sirk's capacity to articulate the nature of these social conditions that fashion our individual, familial, and social identities. He offers an ambiguous resolution, so we in the audience can take it in a variety of ways.

One of the more fascinating aspects of the '50s melodramas is the breadth of emotional and intellectual response they elicit from viewers. Whether we regard the genre as a formula for prosocial pap or as a genuine critique of American ideology, however, depends upon our own attitudes, prejudices, and expectations. Unquestionably, the vast majority of Hollywood movie melodramas have been designed as transparent celebrations of the cultural status quo. But the family melodramas of the 1950s, particularly Sirk's, Minnelli's, and Ray's—with a nod toward Joshua Logan and Mark Robson—do seem to extend the genre into a stage of formal cinematic artistry and thematic sophistication not characteristic of other melodramas. The more effective of these films stand not only as works of considerable artistic merit, but also as cultural documents of Cold War America and, perhaps even more importantly, of Hollywood in its death throes. The repressive ideological climate, the false sense of sociopolitical security, and Hollywood's advanced stage of narrative and cinematic expression all coalesce in the family melodrama to produce a stylized and disturbing portrait of '50s America that, with each passing year, comes more clearly into focus.

Notes

1. John Halliday, *Sirk on Sirk* (New York: The Viking Press, 1972), p. 93.
2. Thomas Elsaesser, "Tales of Sound and Fury: Observations on the Family Melodrama," *Monogram* #4 (1972), p. 4.
3. *Ibid.*, p. 13.
4. Andrew Dowdy, *Films of the Fifties* (New York: William Morrow and Co., 1973), p. 72.
5. *Ibid.*, pp. 62–63.
6. Michael Wood, *America in the Movies* (New York: Basic Books, 1975), p. 163.
7. Geoffrey Nowell-Smith, "Minnelli and Melodrama," *Screen* (Summer 1977), p. 113.
8. Andrew Sarris, *The American Cinema* (New York: E. P. Dutton, 1968), p. 110.
9. Vincente Minnelli, *I Remember It Well* (Garden City, N.Y.: Doubleday and Co., 1974), p. 295.
10. Moira Walsh, review of *Imitation of Life*, *America* (May 9, 1959), p. 314.
11. Rainer Werner Fassbinder, "Fassbinder on Sirk," *Film Comment* (November–December 1975), p. 24.
12. Halliday, *op. cit.*, p. 132.

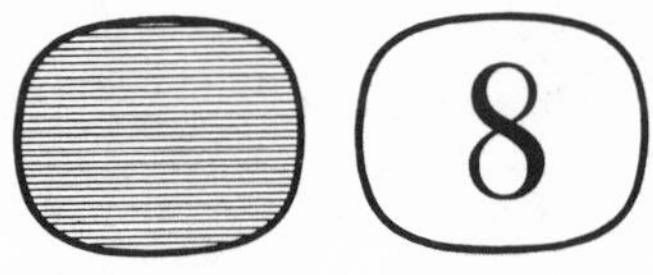

Who Is Without Sin: The Maternal Melodrama in American Film, 1930–1939

CHRISTIAN VIVIANI
(Translated by Dolores Burdick)

Melo must be moving, and thus it has recourse—not to the grotesque, as many believe—but to situations, feelings and emotions which everyone has experienced at one time or another. These elements are juxtaposed, telescoped, multiplied, in order to maintain the pathos at an intense level, simultaneously creating both an outer layer, which seems unreal by virtue of its excessiveness, and an inner core, which calls upon a collective experience of real life. Successful melo maintains the difficult equilibrium between its narrative form—often of a baroque complexity—and its emotional content of disarming simplicity.

In this perspective, it is only natural to grant a privileged place to maternal sentiment. Disconsolate, unworthy or admirable mothers were already populating the plays of the nineteenth century, touching the spectator by appealing to the "Oedipus" in him which/who asked nothing better than to rise to the surface. Let us recall the incest theme in Hugo's *Lucrèce Borgia* or—in an entirely different key—the *Parfum de la dame en noir* by Gaston Leroux, to pick two works at random.

In cinema, the entire edifice of Italian melo finds one of its sturdiest foundations in

Christian Viviani's "Who Is Without Sin: The Maternal Melodrama in American Film, 1930–1939 originally appeared as "Qui est sans péché: Le mélo maternel dans le cinéma américain, 1930–39" in *Pour une histoire du mélodrame au cinema*, *Les Cahiers de la Cinémathèque*, no. 28, edited by Maurice Roelens. Translated by Dolores Burdick and published in *Wide Angle*, Vol. 4, no. 2 (1980), pp. 4–17. Reprinted by permission of the translator and Johns Hopkins University Press.

the mother theme, as one can clearly see in the films of Rafaello Matarazzo, or in evocative titles such as *Le Fils de personne* [*Nobody's Son*] (Matarazzo), *Le Péché d'une mère* [A *Mother's Sin*] (Guido Brignone), *Les Enfants ne sont pas à vendre* [*Children Are Not for Sale*] (Mario Bonnard). [These titles are kept in French, as Viviani gives them. The English translations in square brackets are my own—Translator.]

French cinema, always lukewarm and somewhat soberly elegant (and a touch boring) in its treatment of melodrama, found in the mother theme a rare occasion to give free rein to the emotions: either by honoring tested literary classics, like *La Porteuse de pain* or *La Porchade*,[1] or by featuring an actress of magnitude. Gaby Morlay was the veritable queen of these films, rivalled for a while by Francoise Rosay, who did not last as long, but who had the distinction of starring in Jacques Feyder's French masterpiece of the genre, the near-perfect *Pension Mimosas*.[2]

The theme developed just as richly in Hollywood where any star worth her salt gave in at least once in her career to the ritual of maternal suffering; either totally, in a film conceived entirely around this idea, or episodically, in a film where the idea is introduced as a side issue. (One thinks of Greta Garbo in Edmund Goulding's *Love* [1928] and Clarence Brown's *Anna Karenina* [1935] or Marie Walewska in Clarence Brown's *Conquest* [1938].) A smooth lovely face, still untouched by age but where imploring eyes are ringed with pain and greasepaint furrows, the hair streaked with appropriate silver threads delicately traced by a master hairdresser—it was a kind of rite of passage, an ordeal whereby the actress proved she was a True Actress. And then the Oscars would rain down, and the moviegoers would line up at the box office.

This type of role was also a kind of guarantee for the actress's future; it assured her that the public was ready to accept her aging. Starting with the silents, maturing actresses used this type of film as a bridge between playing the seductress and playing "the heavy." There were some rather sensitive psychological analyses (*Smoldering Fires* [1924] and *The Goose Woman* [1925]—both by Clarence Brown) or attempts at serious social analysis (Henry King's *Stella Dallas* [1925]). But much earlier Griffith had already made the mother one of the central figures of his universe and had dedicated to her the first, and perhaps the finest, classic of the genre: *Way Down East* (1921), to which he gave a unique and quasi-epic breadth (three hours of running time).

During the Forties, the theme flourished exceptionally well because of the high preponderance of female viewers during the war. Only slightly hidden under "realist" wraps, the maternal melo was in its full glory in a filmic world where femininity was organized between two poles: the pin-up (Betty Grable, Rita Hayworth) and the mother (Greer Garson). The end of the war and the progressive evolution of social mores gradually weakened the importance of something which had already been constituted as a subgenre. The 1966 version of *Madame X* (by David Lowell Rich) tolled its death knell. Things had come full circle since one could date the birth of the genre with the first version of *Madame X*, Frank Lloyd's film of 1920. Certainly the origins of the maternal melo lie deeper and tracing its cinematic prehistory would make an exciting narrative; but let us simply say that the first version of *Madame X* fixes a certain set of elements and influences which already existed in a somewhat disparate state, fixes them into a strongly structured scenario which will serve as thematic matrix to the films that follow.

I. *Madame* X: Eve Expelled from the Bourgeois Eden

The different versions of *Madame* X mark off the various stages of the history of Hollywood's maternal melo. In 1920, Frank Lloyd directed Pauline Frederick. In 1929, Lionel Barrymore directed Ruth Chatterton. In 1937, Sam Wood directed Gladys George. In 1966, David Lowell Rich directed Lana Turner in a production lengthily prepared by Douglas Sirk.

Madame X is an adaptation of a French play by Alexandre Bisson who seems to have left scarcely any trace in [the French] theater, but who became a veritable war horse on Anglo-Saxon stages. Until 1966, the theatricality and "Europeanness" of the work will be fully assumed: stage actresses play the lead,[3] and the Parisian setting of the original is maintained. We must wait until 1966 to see *Madame* X played by a movie star—Lana Turner—who had no previous stage experience. In addition, this last version transposed the story to the U.S. and—adding the character of a Machiavellian mother-in-law (Constance Bennett)—brought the archetypal melo into a typically American social context for the first time.

The commercial failure of the 1937 version, the only failure of the four, can be explained by the refusal of its creators to make their *Madame* X either "cinematic" or "American." The two earlier versions had been smash hits, addressed to a public not yet caught in the double trauma of the Wall Street crash and the coming of talkies. Theater stars still possessed a dignity and prestige which were denied to movie stars and which predisposed them to the playing of admirable-mother roles. One can only explain the immense popularity which the already mature Ruth Chatterton met in films at the beginning of the second era on the basis of the almost mystical reverence which then surrounded actors coming from the stage already loaded with fame.[4] The moral code of old Europe still exercised a profound influence on Americans. Audiences were able to accept the fact that Madam X's fall was traceable to her adultery, committed in a moment of frenzy and expiated in lifelong maternal suffering.

One could also wink at the nobly theatrical and studied character of her suffering which, in a way, seemed to set the pose for posterity. But 1929 jostled the mind-set. Under the pressures of necessity America strengthened its nationalism and isolationism: internal problems needed attention and the time was no longer right for an admiring tenderness toward Old Europe. Cinema reflected this changing politics.

A careful study of dates shows the American cinema progressively eliminating Europe from the majority of its films after 1930; Europe is only tolerated when described with the irony of comedy or when fixed in an historic past envisaged as a simple romantic setting. This Americanization of Hollywood cinema, which had been cosmopolitan in the silent era and would go back to cosmopolitanism in the Forties, was particularly clear in the melo; we witness the close of Garbo's career and the end of Dietrich's "serious" period. In this context, the *Madame* X of 1937, faithful to tradition, and played "as though on stage" by Gladys George, seemed a prehistoric fossil.

The critics took note of the old-fashioned nature of the film and the public stayed away. Moreover, so many maternal melos had bloomed beteen 1929 and 1937 which had created strong and valid causes for the mother's "fall" other than her breaking of a rigoristic moral code that the plight of Gladys George's Madame X must have seemed totally disproportionate to her initial fault.

The influence of *Madame X* on the whole sub-genre it more or less launched is not of an ideological order; the failure of the 1937 version proves that much. This influence was rather of a structural and dramaturgical nature. A woman is separated from her child, falls from her social class and founders in disgrace. The child grows up in respectability and enters established society where he stands for progress (in *Madame X* he becomes a lawyer). The mother watches the social rise of her child from afar; she cannot risk jeopardizing his fortunes by contamination with her own bad repute. Chance draws them together again and the partial or total rehabilitation of the mother is accomplished, often through a cathartic trial scene. Let us note that if the American films of the golden age often showed the story of a success and a rise to fame, *Madame X* and the maternal melos tended to show the reverse: the story of a failure and a descent to anonymity or oblivion. Happy endings in this genre are as common as unhappy endings, but the former often have a false or tacked-on quality, do not really affect the basic pessimism of the maternal melo and may be used by talented filmmakers as an unconscious prolongation of the characters' desire. Think of the oneiric aspect of the ending of von Sternberg's *Blonde Venus* (1932), for example: a gleaming Dietrich, swathed in furs, repeating the fairy tale she had been reciting to her child at the opening of the film.[5]

Madame X had two lines of progeny. Its legitimate offspring constitute a small, clearly delimited group of films in which we see the "European" vein of Hollywood's maternal melo. The bastard offspring are much more numerous and varied and make up what we can call an "American" line of the sub-genre.

II. The Children of *Madame X*

The impact of the first two versions of *Madame* X was such that a good number of maternal melos went on to borrow from Bisson's play, even copied it outright, blurring the original's outlines with more or less skill. These films, direct descendants of the model, were generally characterized by a European setting, sometimes situated in a recent past (turn-of-the-century, early twentieth); the mother's fall from grace was symbolized by a tormented odyssey which marked an opposition to the permanence of the bourgeois household, veritable ideal of this thematic, totally impregnated by Victorian morality. This European vein of maternal melo developed before Roosevelt's coming to power, except for the *Madame* X of 1937, whose failure we discussed above, and certain films with Kay Francis made when her career was already declining[6] (Joe May's *Confession* [1937] was a remake of a German film starring Pola Negri.) In addition to the films of Kay Francis, which were already marked by a certain theatricality and Europeanness, this whole vein can practically be defined in five specific films. In *Sarah and Son* (Dorothy Arzner, 1930) Ruth Chatterton easily repeated her success of the previous year in Barrymore's *Madame X*. *East Lynne* (Frank Lloyd, 1931) was the nth version of an old British classic, treated in films since 1912. *The Sin of Madelon Claudet* (Edgar Selwyn, 1931) brought to Helen Hayes, great lady of the stage, the cinematic consecration of the Oscar. The *Blonde Venus* of the next year trafficked in traditional structures tinged with a certain intellectual perversity. *The Secret of Madame Blanche* (Charles Brabin, 1933) went back to the same materials with conscientious application.

At the outset of the story, one finds the bourgeois Eden: the home. Before the Fall, Ann Harding (*East Lynne*), Kay Francis (*House on 56th Street*, *Confession*) or Gladys George (*Madame X*) know a semblance of happiness in the lovingly preserved comfort of a great house dominated by an immense staircase,[7] filled with discreet and faithful servants and lit up by the presence of a child. *East Lynne* is the name of a house and *The House on 56th Street* (Robert Florey, 1933) tells the story of a house. *Blonde Venus* is quite different, since it starts out by isolating the married couple in a crowded, uncomfortable little apartment, thus operating a critique on the pettiness of this domestic ideal and the irony that lay in making it an ideal at the very moment when the economic crisis had made this kind of home truly mythic. This statement of frustration was further underscored by the recital of a fairy tale, mentioned earlier, which simultaneously betrayed both the need for an ideal and its lack. This petit-bourgeois couple tells a fairy tale which is in fact only an episode of their own past, prettified by nostalgia.

At the exact opposite of this idealization, we find the dance hall and the furnished room at the opening of *Sarah and Son*, the music hall of *The Secret of Madame Blanche* and the painter's studio of *The Sin of Madelon Claudet* which establish a more realistic, more tawdry or desperate ambiance. In contrast, the music hall of *The House on 56th Street* is painted with affection and brilliancy, like some carefree paradise. But it is a derisory paradise, ready to crumble. The man, authoritarian and rigid, unquestioned master of the place, is assimilated to a wrathful, Biblical God-the-Father (Conrad Nagel in *East Lynne*, Warren Willian in *Madame X*): Eve commits the sin (adultery) in thought (*East Lynne*) or deed (*Madame X*) and what follows is nothing but a modern transformation of the myth of Eve's Fall. But the man can also be emotionally weak (Philip Holmes in *The Secret of Madame Blanche*, Neil Hamilton in *The Sin of Madelon Claudet*), physically weak (Herbert Marshall in *Blonde Venus*) or both (Ruth Chatterton's husband in *Sarah and Son*); then it is he, as a vulnerable Adam, who drags Eve down into the Fall. However, he often pays for his weakness with his life (Philip Holmes in *The Secret of Madame Blanche* and *Sarah and Son*, Gene Raymond in *The House on 56th Street*) and leaves the woman alone to bear a burden for which he is at least partly responsible.

There remains the child, whose mother is separated from him (*East Lynne*, *Madame X*) or who is quickly doomed to separation (*The Sin of Madelon Claudet*, *The Secret of Madame Blanche*, *Sarah and Son*, *The House on 56th Street*). Thus punished in her motherhood, the woman begins a downward trajectory which is often paralleled by a geographic odyssey "toward the bottom." Ann Harding, driven out of England, makes a long journey through Europe which will lead to her lover's death in Paris and an illness which will leave her blind (*East Lynne*). In the same way, Irene Dunne leaves England for France where she ends up running a bar for soldiers (*The Secret of Madame Blanche*). Gladys George leaves Paris for the Côte d'Azur where she finds momentary peace as a governess, then goes all the way to New Orleans where she becomes a prostitute (*Madame X*). New Orleans is also the scene of Marlene Dietrich's degradation; she becomes a streetwalker there and loses her child (*Blonde Venus*). But this latter film (like *Sarah and Son*, like *Comet over Broadway* [Busby Berkeley, 1939] and *I Found Stella Parrish* [Mervyn LeRoy, 1935] both with Kay Francis) shows the woman's fall followed by her rise to success. Actress or singer, the woman pulls herself up by means of her talent to the pinnacle of money and fame, gaining weaponry with which to do equal battle against the society which has dispossessed her of her role as mother. Thus Ruth Chatterton rises from shady cabarets to the stage of the opera to finally be worthy of winning back her child (*Sarah and Son*). Marlene Dietrich goes by way of Paris and becomes a great music hall star, coming back in an extravagantly stylish outfit to take up her role as mother and bring back to Herbert Marshall part of the dream of which their marriage had been deprived (*Blonde Venus*). Kay Francis leaves second-rate night clubs to find fame and dignity as a dramatic artist on the English stage (*Comet over Broadway*). These latter films, because of the personalities of their directors or their screenwriters, show—with a certain bitterness—that money alone can put a woman on an equal footing with the society that rejects her. Instead of showing us mothers burrowing into anonymity, undergoing their punishment and sacrificing themselves for the sake of their child, these films set up an opposite model of women who reconquer their dignity by coming *out* of anonymity.

One can isolate the case of Kay Francis, in whom one finds the insistent motif of the stage (*I Found Stella Parrish*, *Confession*, *Comet over Broadway*), nostalgia for the bourgeois ideal of house and home (*The House on 56th Street* which parallels the moral decline of the woman with the physical decay of the house where she lived) and sacrifice for the daughter (Sybil Jason plays the daughter in both *Stella Parrish* and *Comet*). This last theme, the most clearly drawn, is exploited in a particularly troubling manner in *The House on 56th Street* and *Confession* where Kay Francis kills, or takes responsibility for a crime, in order to protect her daughter from falling into her own "sin" (gambling in *House*, love of the same man in *Confession*). This treatment of the theme of motherhood corroborates the idea of a Christian vision of Eve's Fall as operating in the maternal melo, the daughter seeming ready to follow exactly the same degrading itinerary as her mother.

If Kay Francis was able to incarnate such a reactionary ideology as late as 1939,[8] it was because the outdated aspect of the plot was fortunately balanced by the cleansing speed and irony of the Warners professionals. But we must recognize that with a few exceptions here and there, the European vein of the maternal melo is eminently reactionary in the ideological perspective of the New Deal. Heroines who are submissive, resigned, sickly, even naive (Helen Hayes in *Madelon Claudet*), defenseless, lacking in energy or decisiveness were hardly good examples for the moviegoing public of 1932 and 1933 who needed to be mobilized to face the economic crisis. The direct lineage of *Madame X* was an uncomfortable reminder of an earlier state of mind which had *led* to the Wall Street crash. If dramatic structures were efficient as models, it was imperative to people them with more stimulating, combative heroines, a type already implicit as the ideal of the New Deal. Already the slightly feminist coloration of *Sarah and Son*[9] and the devastating arrogance of Dietrich in *Blonde Venus* had shown the way. In 1932, with the elections coming up and with men like Darryl F. Zanuck and Philip Dunne—both rather close to Roosevelt—occupying key posts in the big studios, the American vein of the maternal melo was beginning to take form.

III. The Bastards of *Madame X*

From Griffith on, the American cinema had been exploring an essentially American domain of film melodrama: *True Heart Susie* (1919) and *Way Down East* (1920) already contained a great number of elements which would be used again in the Thirties.

In addition to traditional elements such as the secret, the illegitimate child, the rejected woman, the seduction, the silent love, Griffith introduces the city/country dichotomy, the critique of prejudices no longer aristocratic but petit-bourgeois, even rural, the permanence of the earth, the counterpoint of the elements of nature unleashed—these are new motifs grafted onto an already constituted corpus of melodrama.

Of all these elements, the most important is doubtless the displacement of the action's social milieu. In order to become truly American, the melo had to be adapted to a society without a true aristocracy, where the moral ideal was represented by the petit-bourgeoisie.[10] One cay say that it was Griffith who accomplished this decisive transposition in 1918 when he made *True Heart Susie*, a rural American melodrama, and *Broken Blossoms*, a traditional melo of British origins.[11] *True Heart Susie* takes place in a context both rural and petit-bourgeois, but contains no critique of the social milieu. We must wait for *Way Down East*; here the social milieu no longer serves as a mere setting, but takes on its own meaning by way of the filmmaker's critical glance. Significantly, in this latter film it is an unwed mother who is in conflict with the society in power. By symbolically underscoring the struggle of Lillian Gish against the prejudices that overwhelm her, by creating the spectacular finale on the thawing river, Griffith brought out the tragic composition that maternal melo was to take in its American vein: a rejected and solitary individual who bravely tries to go against the current. All-powerful destiny has been replaced by all-powerful society.

Griffith did not have to wait long for followers. The combined influence of *Way Down East* and the first *Madame X*, both of 1920, engendered the American vein of maternal melo. Films like *So Big* (Charles Brabin, 1923) *The Goose Woman* (Clarence Brown) or *My Son* (Edward Sloman, 1925) quickly mined this lode with considerable public response. For convenience, we shall take as our initial milestone Henry King's *Stella Dallas* (1925).[12] Adapted from a popular novel by Olive Higgins Prouty, the great American specialist (along with Fanny Hurst) in lachrymose literature, *Stella Dallas* still remains a classic of the genre, thanks to the sincerity and honesty of King's treatment. He depicted the rural, petit-bourgeois milieu he had already shown in the admirable *Tol'able David* (1920), a film already bearing that aftertaste of bitterness and disillusionment which was going to give such a particular tone to the great epic frescoes he was to make his domain (*Stanley and Livingstone* [1940], *Captain from Castile* [1947]). We can set *Stella Dallas* as a parallel to *Madame* X because of the presence of certain themes—maternal sacrifice, the descent into anonymity, the reinsertion of the child in the mother's life. In contrast, there are the new themes of prejudice, education, female understanding, the "good marriage" of the children. Capital innovation: the moral sin of *Madame* X is replaced by the social error that Stella undergoes, but for which she is scarcely responsible. This new position will be quickly absorbed by the maternal melo and will be impressively fruitful after 1932, as soon as the ideals of the Roosevelt period are in the air.

To the precursor role of *Stella Dallas*, we must add the catalytic function played by *Back Street* (John M. Stahl, 1932). It is not a maternal melo, but this film started the rage for the story of "the other woman." This success seems almost a sociological phenomenon and is hardly surprising in a period where rejects and marginals, gangsters and fallen women, seemed to conquer instant public sympathy. Irene Dunne, playing Rae Smith, "the woman in the back street," surely felt this when she said, in a 1977 interview with John Kobal, "*Back Street* was very popular with women. The number of letters I received from women who were living in the 'back street' of a man's life, and who thought I could give them answers to their problems! Sometimes they signed their letters, but most often they didn't. They simply wanted someone to talk to."[13]

After 1932, Frank Capra made *Forbidden*, really another version of *Back Street* with an illegitimate child added. The same remark holds true for *The Life of Vergie Winters* (Alfred Santell, 1934). In fact, if children were missing from *Back Street* (except for John Boles' legitimate children who caused many torments for poor Irene Dunne), the theme of frustrated motherhood was there: Rae, the woman condemned to the shadows, looked with envy and emotion at the children of others, legitimate children she could never hope to bear. It was easy to superimpose the figure of "the other woman" on that of the unwed mother and even reinforce the sympathy of the (mainly female) audience for the heroine. From all these influences was born the American vein of the maternal melo. Unlike the European vein, it is rich and diverse; born a little before Roosevelt's rise to power, it would stay in favor for a very long time, up until a film like *My Foolish Heart* (Mark Robson, 1951). All the great female stars, from Bette Davis to Susan Hayward, would succumb to it.

In contrast with the weakly, pathetic heroine of the European cycle, symbolized by the little Helen Hayes of *The Sin of Madelon Claudet*, the American cycle of maternal melo proposed a decisive and energetic heroine, more liberated and autonomous, a type of which Barbara Stanwyck remains the archetype (in *Stella Dallas* [King Vidor, 1937] and especially in *Forbidden*, Frank Capra's great film). The new heroine was born around 1932, during Hollywood's period of relative freedom from censorship, which can explain the fact that in 1933 Margaret Sullavan, in her first film, gave the character its freest and most perfect expression in the fine work of John M. Stahl, *Only Yesterday*, a film unfortunately eclipsed by the popularity of *Back Street*. *In Only Yesterday*, everything combines to exculpate the unwed mother, justifying her behavior by her deep love for a man. She chooses anonymity of her own free will, refusing to marry a man who has forgotten her, preferring to keep a marvelous memory rather than chain him artificially through duty. She chooses to remain single, but is not abandoned. She finds honorable work and is not forced to degrade herself to support her son. When the time comes, she will even give herself once to the man she loves and who has forgotten her, accepting with a poignant vitality this chance to live only in the present moment.

Unlike what happened in the European vein, in the American vein the mother is generally *not* socially outcast, but accepted by way of her work life. Menial jobs are rather rare and usually occur only in pre-1932 samples of the genre: Constance Bennett in *Common Clay* (Victor Fleming, 1930) and Loretta Young in the remake of *Private Number* (Roy del Ruth, 1936) flee a troubled past by becoming chambermaids, but love will soon raise them from this lowly condition. Sylvia Sidney in *Jennie Gerhardt* (Mario Gering, 1935) is, on the other hand, exploited because of her status as a domestic even if the critical plot, based on Dreiser, has been somewhat softened in the adaptation. Finally, poor Winifred Westover goes through a veritable calvary of the struggling, uneducated woman in *Lummox* (Herbert Brenon, 1930). In general the woman has an honorable job which makes use either of her aptitudes for devotion (a journalist in *Forbidden*, a nurse in *Born to Love* [Paul Stein, 1931], a secretary in *That Certain Woman* [Edmund Goulding, 1937]) or of her artistic gifts (a milliner in *The Life of Vergie Winters*, a decorator in *Only Yesterday* and in Gregory La Cava's *Gallant Lady* [1933] and Sidney Lanfield's remake, *Always Goodbye* [1938], a music teacher in *Wayward* [Edward Sloman, 1932]).

Socially accepted through her work, it is very rare that she becomes a prostitute like poor Clara Bow in *Call Her Savage* (John Francis Dillon, 1933) or that she doesn't work at all like Barbara Stanwyck in *Stella Dallas*. Integrated into the world of work, she unconsciously participates in the general effort to bring America out of the crisis; she is set up as an antagonist to a hoarding, speculating society, repository of false and outworn values. Often described acerbically, this society is rich but idle, thus sterile, and it is the sacrifice of "the other woman" and the presence of her bastard child which, in a certain sense, end up placing society in the perspective of hope for social progress.[14]

If the woman is accepted in her environment through her work, morally she is still more or less rejected. We have here the residue of an outworn morality, dictated by the rich and idle society, stigmatized and swept away by the morality of these films. No film is clearer on this point than the fine *Stella Dallas*. Stella, to whom Barbara Stanwyck lends a moving mixture of strident vulgarity and overflowing sentiment, acts throughout the film as though she were guilty of something. The cowardice of John Boles has managed to convince her that she is guilty of having been born into a lower social class and for lacking either the means or the will to rise. Vidor, who seems never to have finished settling his accounts with a certain petit-bourgeois American mentality,[15] makes the subject far more than a simple anecdote, and confers on it a burgeoning complexity found in few melodramas (except perhaps in Capra's *Forbidden*). He gives us the portrait of an uncultivated, generous woman, all emotion and impulse, who does not realize that the "good society" she admires so much is injuring her, and who, in a tragic and absurd sacrifice, ends up stripping herself of everything in the name of that society which has cast her as an inferior. If Vidor's version lacks the padded softness of Henry King's (cf. Ronald Coleman's courting of Belle Bennett at the opening of the silent version), it has, on the other hand, added a stifled rage which makes the ending seesaw toward veritable tragic-grandeur: the wedding of Stella's daughter offered as a spectacle to anonymous passersby, whom a policeman disperses.[16]

In *Stella Dallas*, misfortune comes from the city. John Boles, ruined by bankruptcy, and then by his father's suicide, comes to work in a small town. With the promise of social betterment, he abandons Stella and their daughter, who are in his way, and returns to the rich heiress who incarnates his own easy and symbolically sterile idea. Boles represents the false values of the city and is bearer of destruction (suicide, bankruptcy, sterility). Stanwyck represents the true values of the country—generosity, abnegation, fertility. She finds an unexpected ally in Barbara O'Neil, the rich heiress, who offers Stella's daughter the values of culture and civilization which, added to the simple and basic values inculcated by the mother, will permit city and country to join in an ideal of progress of which Stella's daughter will be the heir and repository. In a philosophy one could compare with that of Joan Crawford's films of this era, the ideal of the New Deal is incarnated halfway between city and country at the cost of heavy sacrifice from each, and thanks to female solidarity.[17]

This idealization of the country is already found in Griffith's *Way Down East*. *The Sin of Madelon Claudet* also suggested it through its idyllic depiction of Madelon's youth on a farm. But it is perhaps *So Big* (1932), William Wellman's fine remake of Charles Brabin's 1923 silent, which really puts the issue at the center of the maternal melo. Made a year before Roosevelt's coming to power, *So Big*—like many Hollywood films of that crucial year—bears an ideal rather close to Roosevelt's (cf. Wellman's western epic *The Conquerors*) which would tend to confirm the theory of connections uniting Roosevelt to certain Hollywood personalities (mainly at Warners or Fox, like Darryl F. Zanuck, producer of *So Big*). In this Wellman film, a social itinerary doubled by a moral and philosophical one (Thoreau and Whitman are not far away) make Barbara Stanwyck move from the role of city woman to that of country woman through a series of losses (two widowings, a financial failure, the moral loss of her son who denies the "heritage" of his mother), losses which lead her toward happiness and wisdom, close to the earth and happy in the success of a young man to whom she has become attached. Here Stanwyck incarnates an archetype of the eternal mother (which the script drives home by depriving her of a male companion) linked, naturally, to the earth envisaged as an inexhaustible and permanent source of riches. In this adjusting of the pantheistic philosophies of Thoreau and Whitman to the needs of the crisis, women, once again, play a central role. They are the keepers of true values, shown by the complicity linking Stanwyck to Bette Davis, fiancée of Stanwyck's son, a girl who is a double for the Stanwyck of the film's opening, and who gives us a gleam of hope for the young man's future. Finally, success is represented once more by a character "between country and city," who, because he is an artist, has a privileged, quasi-mystical rapport with nature.

Perhaps *Call Her Savage* carries to its ultimate expression this theme of the return to the earth: Clara Bow, more "American" than "natural" in behavior, after going through frightful vicissitudes worthy of Madame X, returns to the country of her Indian forebears and finds happiness with an attractive half-breed (Gilbert Roland); the half-breed motif is symbolic, of course, since Clara herself is depicted as the daughter of an upper middle-class woman and an Indian chief.

The symbolic child who carries within him the salvation and progress of a society which has just undergone a real-life setback—the mother often gives him up of her own free will, while in the European cycle, the child was *taken away* from her. The mother gives up her child to insure him an education, a moral training that only a well-placed family can provide him. The mother's first reaction to the birth of her child is to reject him (Helen Hayes in *Madelon Claudet*, Barbara Stanwyck in *Forbidden*, Ann Harding in *Gallant Lady*); she then accepts him briefly, then realizes that her single state can only lead the upbringing process to failure. She allows herself to be convinced to give the child to a childless family which is often that of the natural father (*Forbidden*, *Vergie Winters*, *Give Me Your Heart*). In sum, the maternal melo plays—sometimes with a certain cunning—on two levels. It seems outwardly attached to the old moral code by making the mother pay for her "sin." But it implicitly condemns the old system of values represented by a sterile or unhappy couple, which is obliged to adopt the bastard child in order to offer up the image of a traditional family. The only notable exception: *Only Yesterday*, where Margaret Sullavan rears her child by herself. In general, the ruse comes out, as in *Vergie Winters;* or the death of the "legitimate" wife ends it by permitting the constitution of another family, united by both love and blood (*Gallant Lady*, *Always Goodbye*, *That Certain Woman*).

Give Me Your Heart (Archie Mayo) pushes to the absurd the creation of a new family around the child: the illegitimate son of Patric Knowles and Kay Francis, adopted by the married couple Patric Knowles/Frieda Inescourt, unites, thanks to the plotting of the two women, two couples around him: Kay Francis/George Brent, the American couple, and Knowles/Inescourt, the English couple. The bastard is a carrier of life, destined to regenerate a paralyzed society. This role is particularly obvious in *Only Yesterday* where, on learning of his paternity, John Boles—ruined in the Wall Street crash—decides against suicide and takes care of the child Margaret Sullavan leaves him upon her death.

These films recount the tale of a woman's loss due to a man's lack of conscience and show her reconquering her dignity while helping her child re-enter society thanks to her sacrifices. It is a clear metaphor for an attitude America could adopt in facing its national crisis. *Only Yesterday* is a case in point; the sentimental errors of John Boles are clearly associated with his financial errors, for his stock market speculations ruin him. The entire American vein of maternal melo reflects the era and describes a society in transition, coming close to tragedy in this twilight preoccupation (the end of a world), for melodrama is only the illegitimate child of tragedy.

Between the respectable family, which represents the dying world, and the mother, who represents hope for the future, we find the man. In these films, he is usually a strange and weak-willed character, rarely played by a great star, a person who hasn't the courage to make up his own mind and who relies on the family to make decisions. This sometimes turns into an Oedipal conflict between mother and son, as in *Wayward* which indeed treats the struggle between two women for the affection of a man—Nancy Carroll his sweetheart, and Pauline Frederick, his mother.[18] The weapon of the decadent family being hypocrisy (*Wayward*, *Common Clay*, *Private Number*, *Give Me Your Heart*, *That Certain Woman*), it is often through a ruse that the "real" mother regains her rights (*Gallant Lady*, *Wayward*, *Always Goodbye*), or else by accident (*That Certain Woman*, *The Life of Vergie Winters*). Indisputably, the entire genre tends to establish the recognition of the rights of the natural mother. A refusal of such recognition is rare and resounds in a particularly poignant manner. The pessimism of *Forbidden* is almost unique: the final action of Barbara Stanwyck tearing up the will that recognizes her as the mother of Adolphe Menjou's daughter, and which leaves her the fortune, is not an ultimate sacrifice, but an act of revolt and refusal. Compare this attitude with the serenely assumed independence of Margaret Sullavan in *Only Yesterday* and the tragic absurdity of the ending of *Stella Dallas*.

One can find a separate fate for *The Old Maid* (Edmund Goulding, 1939), one of Bette Davis's greatest successes. Set in nineteenth century America (George Brent dies in the Civil War, leaving Bette Davis pregnant), it explores an era and a society where the unwed mother cannot for a moment contemplate rearing her own child. In order to remain near her daughter, she is forced to undergo all the torments and humiliations caused by the sick jealousy of her horrible cousin (Miriam Hopkins, more viperous than ever) and to become an object of fear and ridicule in the eyes of her own child. It is significant that in order to show such a subject in 1939, one must have recourse to a rather considerable temporal distance. *The Old Maid* is different from the other American maternal melos because the heroine comes from "good family," is not cast out of her social class because of her child, but rather chooses silence and anonymity. This very sentimental film is not however without tragic resonances in its depiction of a society tearing itself apart and has a crespuscular atmosphere that can lead us to consider it the final point of the maternal cycle as developed in the Thirties in Hollywood. In many points (female jealousy, sentimentality, the personality of Bette Davis) *The Old Maid* already announces the forms that maternal melo will take in the Forties with films like *The Great Lie* (Edmund Goulding, 1941) or *To Each His Own* (Mitchell Leisen, 1946).

The Old Maid, unlike the other maternal melos of the Thirties, is isolated in a sort of "placeless timelessness." In becoming Americanized, the maternal melo had become more and more inflected toward the social, except in this film. For proof we have only to look at *Jennie Gerhardt*, a rather mediocre film despite a still vibrant Sylvia Sidney, but which clearly presents the sorrows of the unwed mother in a perspective of class prejudice.[19] The moral sin of the "European-style" melos is replaced by a social error, vestige of a bad system stigmatized by the film: Sylvia Sidney in *Jennie Gerhardt*, Constance Bennett in *Common Clay* or Loretta Young in *Private Number* are all more or less victims of a form of *droit de cussiage* ("groper's rights") because of their position as servants. On the other hand, women who do "noble" work (decorators, journalists, secretaries) find in their work the strength to bear the ordeals and problems of their lives: a sort of independence, a way of balancing the unstable nature of their condition as unwed mothers. This stability is reinforced by the presence of a man, product of the world of work, who sustains the heroine and loves her in silence (Ian Hunter in a number of Kay Francis's films).

In short, work, a social value, redeems the moral fault by permitting the mother to hide both her guilty liaison and her child. The reactionary nature of these works seems scarcely dented by the switching of accent to the social, for the mother now pays for her fault no longer through a veritable degradation, but by being condemned to anonymity, the true curse in the Hollywood thematics of the Thirties, totally geared to the success story and the rise to fame. In this regard there is hardly any difference between films after Roosevelt's accession, and a film like *Lummox* (1930) where the heroine, a cleaning woman, pays for her motherhood with a life of humiliation and anonymity.

The maternal melo in its American vein is an apologia for total renunciation, total sacrifice, total self-abnegation. Melodramatic exaggeration, of course, but still transparent enough in a period when America really needed to mobilize good will and dedication without promise of immediate recompense; witness the numerous "unhappy endings" one finds in the sub-genre. While scrupulously respecting established dramatic structures, conscientious craftsmen and talented filmmakers made movies of high quality which it would be interesting to study anew and subject to critical reappraisal: *Common Clay, So Big, Gallant Lady, Vergie Winters, That Certain Woman.* Others created masterpieces whose scope makes them transcend the simple limits of a genre: *Forbidden, Blonde Venus, Only Yesterday, Stella Dallas, The Old Maid.* These filmmakers and stars worked in a strict form whose rules they respected. The case of George Cukor and Constance Bennett is somewhat different.

Between 1930 and 1933, Constance Bennett was extremely popular, and was thus able to command very high salaries. In addition, she was the only major star of the time who was not attached to a given studio and who negotiated her own contracts with a legendary shrewdness. She specialized in the wildest melodrama, which seems strange if we consider her aristocratic bearing, sophistication and witty cynicism, so out of keeping with her roles of simple shopgirls, and so much more in tune with comedy, in which she also excelled. Her personality seemed to allow her to act her way through the most extravagant situations with a sort of ironic detachment that resembled a wink of complicity at the audience; basically, it was a way of getting the viewer's sympathy as valid perhaps as the pure and simple "identification" that happened with a Barbara Stanwyck, for example. Constance Bennett often worked with directors intelligent enough to make use of the very ambiguity of her persona: Gregory La Cava and George Cukor were among the decade's best comic directors and Victor Fleming had a great sense of humor. But there was a privileged relationship between Bennett and Cukor; she found in him her ideal director. For his part, Cukor was floundering a bit at the beginning of his film career, having difficulty getting rid of the influence of theater. He was stimulated by his association with Bennett, and out of their meeting came his first major film, *What Price Hollywood* (1932), a first version of *A Star Is Born*, far from the polished work of 1954, to be sure, but certainly far more than a simple sketch. Cukor's approach differs radically from that of other directors in that he managed when necessary to suppress the ironic distancing in Bennett and to weld her very artificiality into the character he gave her to play. Thus, in the role of a movie actress, she is credible and moving from start to finish in *What Price Hollywood*, or in *Our Betters*, where she plays cruel and bitter social comedy like a virtuoso.

Cukor and Bennett made their contribution to the maternal cycle (in which the actress had already participated with films like *Common Clay* or *Born to Love*) in a strange work which curiously mingles melo and comedy—*Rockabye* (1933). For an actress who had already played the suffering mother, *Rockabye* was a subtle, almost Machiavellian exposé of the workings of maternal melo. A successful actress and a frustrated mother, she is separated from her adopted child and then from the man in her life, because his wife is expecting a child. With nothing more than this, Cukor was able to ironize the traditional structures: instead of bearing an unwanted child, Bennett here takes the trouble to go out and adopt! *She* is sterile, while the "legal wife" gives birth. In addition, the Bennett character acts in a play called *Rockabye*, written by the man she loves and which seems a veritable parody of numerous contemporary melos like *Call Her Savage* or *Blonde Venus*: the abandoned mother finds herself walking the streets in order to earn her living and support her child! In this film the clichés are given as clichés: everything is false and the melodrama is nothing but a show, an indirect way of denouncing the illusionism of the genre. The miracle is that in spite of everything, *Rockabye* contains natural and moving scenes, and that the artificial calvary of this actress manages to be touching through attention to detail and truth of emotion.

The point of *Rockabye* was that the maternal melo was only convention and illusion. But that is exactly what melo had to be—an illusion destined to mobilize the public in a certain direction, an illusion that transposed the anguish of an era, an illusion—who can deny it?—knowingly grounded in eroticism. The attractiveness of the actress was important, of course, but also the Oedipal theme which runs like filigree throughout Hollywood cinema from 1930 to 1945, and which a film like *Random Harvest* (Mervyn LeRoy, 1942) would set forth in nearly Freudian terms. And besides, what male viewer has never dreamed of being fondled by a desolate and arousing mother with the face of a Constance Bennett, a Kay Francis, a Marlene Dietrich, an Ann Harding? What female viewer has not dreamed of herself looking like an Irene Dunne, a Barbara Stanwyck, a Sylvia Sidney? The melodramatic mythology of Hollywood is doubtless false, but it is nonetheless seductive for being illusory.

Notes

1. One can compare more recent versions of these classics: *La Porteuse de pain* (Maurice Cloche, 1963) and *La Pocharde* (Georges Combret, 1954).
2. One can wonder at the large number of paternal melos in French cinema, many more than one finds in Italy or in Hollywood, but comparable to certain German productions: *Nostalgie* (Tourjanski, 1937), *Le Coupable* (Raymond Bernard, 1937), or *Nuit de décembre* (Kurt Bernhardt, 1939) and even—why not?—Pagnol's trilogy, where César is certainly the central figure.
3. Pauline Frederick and Ruth Chatterton won movie stardom in their respective versions. Gladys George was less lucky, and found herself quickly relegated to secondary roles, despite the "name" she had made on the stage.
4. This may be the only way, for example, to explain the astonishing success of the already old George Arliss at the beginning of the talkies.
5. This fairy tale, in fact, transposed into legendary terms Herbert Marshall's meeting with Marlene Dietrich: a stalwart knight, he saves her from a terrible dragon. The final reprise of this interrupted legend is thus all the more oneiric.
6. Even if her melos were often set in the U.S., Kay Francis was marked by the European influence. Perhaps it was her slightly formal appearance? She was hired at Warners at the same time as Ruth Chatterton and in a certain way she prologues the universe of Chatterton.

7. The staircase, symbol of power, is one of the traditional motifs of melo; for example in *Written on the Wind* (Doublas Sirk, 1956).
8. Kay Francis began to lose her popularity around 1934–35. If she hung on after that, it was thanks to an ironclad contract that made her the highest paid star of the moment, even if her films had only middling success of if they were sometimes not much better than B pictures.
9. If Dorothy Arzner is interesting because she was the only woman director then working in Hollywood, her feminist hagiographers have based too much of their admiration on the ideas in her work, without really taking into account the rarity of fine films in her output. *Sarah and Son*, for example, is rather heavy handed. One exception: the excellent *Craig's Wife* (1936), well served by Sidney Buchman's brilliant script.
10. This was already the case in Josef von Sternberg's *Blonde Venus*, not without irony. The petit-bourgeois setting was already in place in the shorts of Griffith, like *The New York Hat* (1912).
11. Although it was made before *Broken Blossoms*, *True Heart Susie* was released immediately after. But Griffith remained faithful to traditional melo; for example in *Orphans of the Storm* (1922) or *Lady of the Pavements* (1929).
12. King Vidor's film follows quite faithfully the plot of Henry King's first version. Only their very different approaches help distinguish between the two films. [The issue of *Les Cahiers de la Cinémathèque* (No. 28) in which this article was originally published contains an appendix featuring plot outlines of all the melodramas discussed in the issue, which is entirely devoted to materials on melodrama in cinema.]
13. In *Focus on Film No. 28:* "Irene Dunne: A Conversation with John Kobal."
14. This antagonism is emphasized by racial difference in *Madam Butterfly* (Marion Gering, 1932), a film one could easily include in the category of Hollywood maternal melo.
15. *Stella Dallas* is certainly a work marked by the personality of this very great director; its heroine has more than one point in common with those of *Beyond the Forest* (1949) and *Ruby Gentry* (1951).
16. The framing of the scene, its lighting, even the form of the bay window where the wedding ceremony is enacted, evoke in a troubling way a cinematic spectacle.
17. This solidarity is obvious in *The Shining Hour* (Frank Borzage, 1938), where Joan Crawford and Margaret Sullavan are bound together in a series of reciprocal sacrifices. Let us also mention *Give Me Your Heart* (Archie Mayo, 1936), where Kay Francis is united with her son, thanks to the sterile wife who has adopted him.
18. This theme is luminously treated in John Cromwell's remarkable film *The Silver Cord* (1933), where Irene Dunne violently denounces the abnormal character of Laura Hope Crews' love for her son Joel McCrea.
19. It is curious to note that the work of Theodore Dreiser, a socially committed novelist, can easily be reduced to a melodramatic structure—for example, in *Carrie* (William Wyler, 1951), a fine film, strangely neglected and underrated.

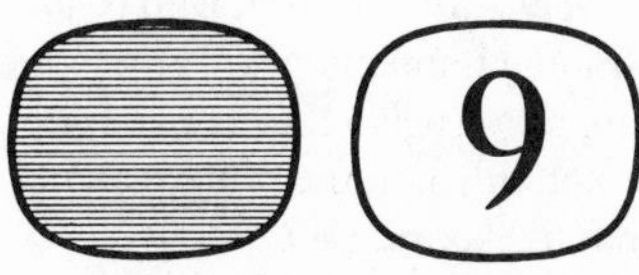

The Moral Ecology of Melodrama: The Family Plot and *Magnificent Obsession*

NOËL CARROLL

In the late 1970s, Hollywood film production is increasingly reliant on traditional genres. The exhumation of old formulas—from the 1950s especially but also from the 1930s and 1940s—is becoming more and more pronounced. Programmatic, albeit often high-budget, horror, sci-fi, war, and sports films dominate the current fare of domestic releases. To a certain extent this is a result of Hollywood's innate business conservatism: Nothing succeeds like something that succeeded before; old genres never die, they merely await rebirth in another decade. But Hollywood had been more daring in the range and types of films it experimented with from the late 1960s to the mid-1970s. The retreat to genres is not completely an industry initiative; it is also a response to the growing conservatism of the period, which, in turn, is reflected in the films.

Melodrama is among the genres presently being recycled. Two 1978 releases—*International Velvet* and *Uncle Joe Shannon*—are particularly interesting because of the similarities of their structures. Both concern the symbolic reconstitutions of families; lost parents are replaced by loving parental figures who, concomitantly, gain surrogate children. In certain respects, these films can be seen as in the lineage of the melodramas of kidnap and restoration that are so important in Griffith's Biograph work. They also recall the Dickensesque ploy of an orphan who is rediscovered by a relative. Of course, in Griffith and Dickens, a family is literally reunited, whereas in *International Velvet* and *Uncle Joe Shannon* the reconstitution is symbolic. Neverthe-

Noël Carroll, "The Family Plot and *Magnificent Obsession*," originally printed in *Melodrama* (New York: New York Literary Forum, 1980), pp. 197–206. Reprinted by permission of the author and the New York Literary Forum.

less, the narrative structures in all these examples are predicated on the "rightness" of the nuclear family. Indeed, that "rightness" underlies the esthetic "fitness" of the plot; i.e., narrative closure is achieved through the restoration of nuclear family relations.

International Velvet is a belated sequel to *National Velvet*. In it, Velvet, who is now in her forties, has a niece whose parents have died in some unmentionably gruesome accident. The resentful orphan is shipped from Arizona to England to stay with her aunt who has a writer boyfriend. The child is sullen not only because of her parents' death and her abrupt resettlement, but, more importantly, because she has never felt loved. We ruefully note that the only reason the child did not die with her parents was that, because they always ignored her, they did not take her on their last, fateful trip. The child is described in the film as lacking an identity, as living a cardboard, cut-out existence with no depth of feeling. And this is associated with the lack of parental affection.

The child's lack of a real family (in both a literal and psychological sense) is paralleled by a similar lack on Velvet's part. We learn that Velvet tragically lost her own child as the result of a miscarriage during a riding accident. Both Velvet and her niece are depicted as psychologically "incomplete"; they both need families to make them "whole."

The niece's alienation first begins to ease when riding and caring for Velvet's legendary stallion, Pie. Her eyes glow while she watches the birth of Pie's last foal. As the colt gambols with its mother, the editing connects the maternal scene with the niece, symbolically defining the child's yearning as not just for the horse but, more broadly, for a family. When Velvet buys the niece the horse, the girl rides it day in and day out, becoming even more obsessive about riding than Velvet had been in the earlier film. Years pass as the child, now a teenager, evolves into Velvet Junior. However, she is so preoccupied with the perfection of her equestrian art that she forgoes boyfriends and a social life. Thus, though somewhat fuller, the character is not yet complete. For that we wait until the final reel when as a member of the British Olympic riding team she "miraculously" wins a Gold Medal while also learning the meaning of teamwork. With the medal comes the sense of personal identity she lacked all along and this is connected with her marriage to the captain of the American riding team. Returning to England, the niece introduces her new husband to "her parents," finally acknowledging the family bond whose denial has caused all the emotional tensions in the film. The act is further commemorated when the niece gives Velvet her Gold Medal; this compensates for the award that Velvet didn't receive, for technical reasons, in the earlier film. Thus, from one horse race, we get two generations of families whose constitution neatly solves all the emotional problems presupposed by the rest of the plot.

The melodramatic elements of *International Velvet*—including the emotional extremes, coincidences, and improbable complementary plot symmetries—are even more exaggerated in *Uncle Joe Shannon*. Released as a "Christmas" film, it underscores its use of the "family plot" with all the imagery of the Yuletide season. Christmas is the day on which our culture celebrates the completion of its mythic first family. Because Christmas exists in large measure as a mass fantasy—inextricably bound up with childhood associations of the warmth, generosity, and security of the family—the holiday is one of the most potent symbols in Hollywood's arsenal. In the hands of a master propagandist like Frank Capra, a Christmas carol at the right moment becomes a veritable national anthem, instilling a wave of irrational fellow-feeling that makes Capra's nebulous populism seem almost plausible. The mechanics of this effect are simple—Christmas imagery induces regression, rekindling childlike beliefs in social stability and community that grow out of idealizations of the family. In *Uncle Joe Shannon*, the ideological use to which Christmas is put is not in the service of a broad political stance like populism but as a reaffirmation of the family and its role as the central and natural form of human relation.

The film opens with the eponymous Joe playing his trumpet at a recording studio. The camera pans around him, the circular movement suggesting that he is complete as well as at the center of his harmonious universe. It is his son's birthday and Joe gives the boy a trumpet like his, only smaller. Joe is at the height of his career, but the film makes it clear that fame is less important to him than family. Joe is unremittingly uxorious, touching and kissing his wife at every turn. He ignores triumphant curtain calls after his concert at the Hollywood Bowl in order to be home in time for his son's birthday party. But disaster strikes; his home is aflame as he pulls into his neighborhood. The film dissolves, and seven years later we see Joe—a skid row wino desperately clutching his horn. He has lost both his family and his art. These are the two losses the plot must recuperate.

Joe visits a prostitute, but she is out. Her son, Robbie, who calls all her clients "uncle," demands that Joe tell him a story. Joe and Robbie fall asleep. Next morning, the police awaken them at gunpoint. Robbie's mother has run away and the boy must go to an orphanage. He revolts and hides in Joe's car, convinced he can make something (namely, a father) out of this bum.

In the tradition of Chaplin's *The Kid* (a particularly interesting film in terms of the family plot), Robbie comes to idolize Joe. Christmas is approaching so Robbie steals a Santa Claus outfit from a department store, and the duo plays street-corner renditions of "Jingle Bells" to earn their keep. At this point Joe does not yet understand that Robbie is his salvation. He slaps the boy for playing with his own dead son's trumpet, tries to send Robbie away, and finally puts the boy in the orphanage. Joe's inability or, perhaps more aptly, his refusal to acknowledge Robbie as his symbolic son is an example of a key device of melodrama for engendering suspense. We know the boy is exactly what Joe wants; when will he realize it?

Joe attempts to commit suicide after he puts Robbie in the orphanage. This is the symbolic turning point in the film. Director Joseph Hanwright floods the scene with metaphors. As Joe sinks to the bottom of the bay, he looks up and sees a ball of light shimmering on the surface. Having "seen the light," he struggles upward, no longer "drowning in self-pity." He kidnaps Robbie from the orphanage. In subsequent scenes, his music begins to improve. The opening symbol of "harmony" continues; each station in Joe's progress is reflected in his playing. Insofar as the etymology of "melodrama" is drama plus music, *Uncle Joe Shannon* is at least notable for making Joe's solos an explicit index of each phase of his moral growth.

Though Joe acknowledges his paternal affection for Robbie, a catastrophe (the favorite type of plot complication in melodrama) erupts. Robbie has cancer. Joe convinces him to undergo surgery. But when Robbie's leg is amputated, the boy feels Joe has betrayed him. He refuses to talk to his surrogate father. He won't practice using his wheelchair or his crutches. The doctors fear that he has lost the will to live.

The plot becomes perfectly symmetrical. Now Joe must redeem Robbie. He gives Robbie his son's trumpet, a gesture whose phallic significance is no harder to decipher than the horse symbolism in *International Velvet*. But Robbie still won't budge. Joe tries to infuriate him back to life. Joe plays his horn at a Christmas party for the other hospitalized children. He has never played better. Hearing the music, Robbie struggles downstairs to reclaim his "father." Unsteady on his crutches, he glowers at Joe; but hatred and pride give way to love. The boy hangs on Joe's neck while Joe plays mellifluously with one hand. The camera circles them, echoing the opening shot. Both have become complete again. The father has a son, and the son, a father. The music, the camera movement, and the Christmas iconography heighten the effect of this "family reunion." The esthetic "unity" and integration of elements here not only correspond to but mirror the theme of emotional symbiosis between father and son.

Coming on the heels of a decade of radical and/or feminist criticism of the nuclear family, melodramas like *International Velvet* and *Uncle Joe Shannon* are somewhat surprising. In their particular use of the family plot, they project and unquestioningly endorse the family as the right structure for human relations. Parent-children relations are posed as inevitable—something characters are irresistibly drawn toward (for their own good). Emotion is engendered in the audience by means of characters who, for a given period of time, fail to see or refuse to acknowledge the rightness of the symbolically reconstituted family proposed by the plot. The idea of the family, as it is shared with the audience, makes these stories possible. But, at the same time, the existence of these stories reinforces prevailing beliefs in the idea by symbolically rehearsing a faith in the family through fictions that train, or, at least, further inculcate audiences in this particular way of ordering everyday human events.

A sense of *déjà vu* accompanied my encounters with *International Velvet* and *Uncle Joe Shannon*. I knew I had seen their basic plot structures in operation before, and I set about trying to remember where. The answer came quickly; it was *Magnificent Obsession*, a 1953 adaptation of a Lloyd Douglas novel of the same title, directed by Douglas Sirk. Sirk was, among other things, a highly successful director of film melodrama whose critical currency shot sky-high in the early 1970s. Part of the reason behind this reevaluation is the fact that new German directors, like Rainer Werner Fassbinder, who are interested in parodying or extending the melodramatic form, honor Sirk as a major forebear, including, for example, homages to his style in their films. Sirk is now considered a central exemplar of film melodrama. In some cases, especially with reference to *All That Heaven Allows* and *Written on the Wind*, favorably disposed critics argue that Sirk uses melodramatic formats in order to subvert regnant values and preconceptions. Historically, melodrama has at times provided a vehicle for social criticism. Yet, though I am not sure whether *All That Heaven Allows* and *Written on the Wind* merely appear subversive, I am certain that *Magnificent Obession* is conformist in terms of form and content, and form as content.

Whereas in previous examples, the symbolic transformations of the family plot involve the replacement of parents and children with surrogates, in *Magnificent Obsession* the plot works to substitute a lost husband with a new one. Like many melodramas, the film begins with a tragic accident. Millionaire playboy Bob Merrick overturns his speedboat; an ambulance rushes to the scene with Dr. Wayne Phillip's resuscitator. At the same time, the venerable Doctor Phillips has had a stroke, but without his resuscitator, he dies. His young wife, Helen, is informed. Several characters pointedly remark on the irony of the situation. A great humanitarian and surgeon has been lost so that a wastrel like Merrick can live. They presuppose an injustice or imbalance in the way Wayne Phillips died, something that will in fact be rectified in the way the plot unravels.

Merrick is introduced as reckless, arrogant, brash, discourteous and selfish—the very opposite of the saintly, always thoughtful-to-others Helen Phillips. Merrick, hospitalized in Wayne Phillips's clinic, barks at the doctors, diagnoses himself, and lectures on medicine; he announces that he once was a medical student—a fact that will become important shortly. The clinic staff treats Merrick aloofly and he sneaks out of the hospital. In the tradition of melodramatic coincidences, he hitchhikes a ride with none other than Helen Phillips. He tries to make a pass at her until he learns that she is Mrs. Phillips and that he is connected with her husband's death. He gets out of the car but faints. She returns him to the hospital, learns who he is, and vows to avoid him. Yet their fates have already been intertwined. His desire for her continually grows while she resists each of his advances.

Another story line develops parallel to the romantic interplay between Merrick and Helen. Just as these two characters "discover" each other's identities, so Helen gradually "discovers" who her husband, Wayne Phillips, really was. People write to, and visit, her with stories of mysterious debts owed to Dr. Phillips. At crucial points in their lives, Phillips helped them with money, advice, and influence. In each case, he swore them to secrecy. When they attempted to repay him, he said it was already "all used up." We learn, primarily through a painter named Randolph, that Phillips practiced a bizarre, quasi-religious faith. He believed that helping others gives the benefactor access to "power." One could achieve whatever one wanted through his cosmic power. Strained analogies with electricity are offered to explain how this moral-metaphysical mechanism works. For example, the secrecy is like insulation. Great men "ground" themselves in this power. In fact, their greatness "flows" from this power. Christ is cited as one of the founders of this system of self-interested altruism. Randolph's career as a painter floundered until he mastered the method under Phillips's tutelage.

Randolph explains Phillips's religion, his "magnificent obsession," to Merrick who, despite warnings against trying to "feather one's own nest" with it, attempts to apply the power in his pursuit of Helen. He helps a parking attendant whose family is in trouble and suddenly he sees Helen. He rushes to tell her about this "miracle" and about his allegiance to her husband's faith. She grows increasingly annoyed and, in her efforts to escape from him, is hit by an oncoming car. As a result of the accident, she is blinded. Along with her widowhood, this is another tragedy the plot will commutate.

Merrick, moved by the consequences of his actions, begins to practice Phillips's doctrines in earnest. He secretly helps the Phillips family by buying their house at an exorbitant price. He also enrolls in medical school again as the best means to help others, and predictably he specializes in surgery. Quite clearly, he is becoming Wayne Phillips. Helen refuses to allow him to see her, but he takes advantage of her blindness and visits her at the beach daily. He tells her that his name is Robbie Robinson. His whole manner is changed. He is no longer brash but humble, self-effacing, other-directed, and reassuring. He emotes all the cultural cues of being a "concerned" person—a visible altruism has supplanted his earlier selfishness. He secretly pays for Helen to travel to Switzerland where she is examined by a battery of the world's most renowned specialists. When they tell her that a cure is impossible, he flies to her side to lend support. He takes her to a peasant festival to distract her, and after they dance all evening he confessses his love as well as his real name. She says that she knew he was Merrick (the theme of identity again) and that she loves him. But the obvious denouement is blocked, enhancing melodramatic suspense. She runs away; she is afraid that he will marry her out of pity. He goes on to become an internationally famous doctor. His sideburns turn grey. He repairs patients' private lives, demanding secrecy and refusing future repayment on the grounds that by that time "it [the power] will be all used up." As he rushes about the hospital corridors, we assume that this is what Wayne Phillips must have looked like. In short, during this interlude, both Merrick and Helen prove they are "good," which, in this context, means "self-sacrificing." They are ready to reap their rewards.

Randolph tells Merrick that Helen is ill in New Mexico. He arrives and the local surgeon asks Merrick to perform the operation. Merrick is afraid he is not skilled enough, though we realize he has stored up a surfeit of "power." After some reluctance he operates, hoping to restore Helen's eyesight. He spends an all-night vigil at her bedside. She awakens; she can see; they will marry. The injustices and imbalances, the disequilibriums in Helen's life, introduced earlier in the plot, are adjusted by means of the practice of Wayne Phillips's "magnificent obsession," and homeostasis returns. Helen regains her husband in the form of Merrick who has been molded according to the Phillips prototype. The original family has been reconstituted with a kind of narrative symmetry that portends "destiny."

Sirk's *Magnificent Obsession* differs from Lloyd Douglas's novel in many respects; a large number of plot details have been changed, dropped, or added including Randolph's occupation, Merrick's age, Helen's blindness, etc. Also, Sirk's film avoids Douglas's banking metaphors for the power, relying only on the electrical one, while also deleting Douglas's notion that religion is a science. According to Sirk, his script, which was prepared by Robert Blees, was primarily based on the screenplay for the 1935 adaptation of *Magnificent Obsession*, directed by John Stahl. Nevertheless, the Sirk film remains true to the essential tenets of Douglas's mysticism. As in Douglas's *Disputed Passage* and *Green Light* (also films directed by Frank Borzage in 1939 and 1937 respectively), *Magnificent Obsession* promotes an ethic of service and sacrifice, devoted to systematic selflessness which is connected to impersonal, moral powers that have causal efficacy in the world of everyday events. That is, Douglas and Sirk present a viewpoint where morality is treated as part of the basic structure of the universe. Facts and values are not strongly demarcated; moral disequilibriums are reflected in events.

In the film, Merrick's wasteful existence and arrogant manner "cause" Phillips's death and, later, Helen's blindness. His melodramatic regeneration, through a hodgepodge of metaphysics and popular mechanics, results in redressing these tragedies. In this sense, what I call a moral ecology is presupposed by the plot. That is, the plot is structured as if there were a strong causal interdependency between a fundamental moral order (which is geared toward producing self-sacrifice) and everyday events. A violation of the moral order, an imbalance like Merrick's selfishness, causes a repercussion which, in turn, causes further events until the imbalance in the system is adjusted and equilibrium again obtains in the relationship between the moral order and human affairs. Melodrama, in general, emphasizes strong dichotomies of good and evil as well as exact correspondences between moral conflicts and dramatic ones. In *Magnificent Obsession*, the metaphor of "the power" is a device that conflates the moral order and everyday events into one synchronised (ecological) structure.

The values and virtues in all variants of *Magnificent Obsession* are "other-regarding." They include some elements that are not normally thought of as "moral," but more as matters of etiquette. In Sirk's film Merrick is initially marked as "bad" because he is rude, impatient, and domineering. Politeness and courtesy-to-all rather than the proverbial white hat is the most important sign of the good guy in American film. Merrick is the villain until he learns the power—a form of cosmic sensitivity (and good manners) to others—at which point he is virtually a demigod.

Stoicism, both in terms of physical and emotional sufferance, is also lauded. Both Helen (vis-à-vis her blindness) and Merrick (in his love of Helen) evince it and are duly rewarded. This stoicism, especially in Helen's case, is other-regarding; she does not want to burden her friends and companions. Humility and generosity, of course, are the prime ingredients of "the power." Thus, the film projects a seductive fantasy, catechizing receptive audiences in courtesy, stoicism, humility, and charity. A constellation of values is ideologically reinforced by promising that that precise ethos is connected with, is even constitutive of, "the source of infinite power."

The moral order, or at least the moral order being valorized, is presented as part and parcel of the nature of things as a causal force or as a regulatory force with causal efficacy. In this respect, the particular moral order is represented as natural, namely, as part of the nature of things. The nuclear family—the favored form of human relationship in this ethos—is also part of the cosmic order. If damaged, it restores itself. This process is given as natural in a context where to be natural is right and vice versa. The family plot in melodramatic fiction structures human events in a way that exemplifies and endorses the ideology or ethos it presents as natural.

In *Magnificent Obsession*, the family is not only associated with the structure of the universe (unfolding itself), but also it has connotations of being curative, both psychologically and physically. By the end of the film, Helen is no longer alone and she is no longer blind. Both the sicknesses of the heart and those of the body have been cured by Bob Merrick's becoming Dr. Phillips. This notion of the curvature power of the family is implicit in the family plot. Though *International Velvet* and *Uncle Joe Shannon* lack the metaphysical trappings of *Magnificent Obsession*, they too rely on the idea that the (figurative) restoration of the family is "restorative" in a broad sense, namely, a remedy for existential maladies. The family plot is a narrative structure with strident ideological implications; it portrays the family as part of some underlying order and as having naturally revivifying powers.

Sirk develops the theme of order in *Magnificent Obsession* visually in a way that buttresses the family plot with consistent metaphorical imagery. Throughout the film, there is a recurring motif of nature. Large windows look out over landscapes; one of the many examples is the forestry outside Randolph's house which we see when he opens the blinds. The Phillips's home is surrounded by compositionally emphatic, well-kept lawns and trees. We see many tranquil, picture-postcard vistas around the lake. Nature is presented as quiet, serene, and harmonious. That these specific connotations are the relevant ones for the imagery in *Magnificent Obsession* is established in the opening shots. Merrick's white speedboat with its red stripe plows through the placid lake. Sirk stresses its speed and its intrusiveness as it cuts a high, vertical wave through the water. Merrick's recklessness, symbolized by the boat crash (and later the car crash outside Randolph's house), is set against the order and calm of nature. When nature reappears, as it does often, it stands not only for beauty but for organic unity. Though the idea that the natural order is providential or divinely appointed is never made explicit, it hovers in the background. The "harmony" of the landscapes functions as a visual correlative to the moral ecology of the plot.

Another major motif is that of floral arrangements. These are flowers of all kinds everywhere in the film. Sometimes these flowers satisfy a simple compositional need, drawing the audience's attention to what will be a dramatically pertinent sector of the screen. Sometimes the flowers play a symbolic role; when a despairing Helen, who believes she is incurably blind, accidentally knocks a pot with a rose in it off her Swiss balcony, we remember an earlier rose, associated with Dr. Phillips's death, and the pathos of the scene is magnified by correlating her blindness with her other major tragedy. But over and above the local effects of flowers in a given shot or scene, the sheer statistical volume of floral arrangements in the film as a whole is expressive. They connote beauty, nature and design, a cluster of attributes that summarize the sentimental order of the family plot.

Of course, the use of color throughout the film serves a similar end. Image after image can only be described as color coordinated. The compositions resemble those of a department store catalogue. Everything is new and matches everything else in the most balanced and symmetrical way. For example, in the first beach scene there is a green and white striped tent in the background and a matching chair in the foreground. As the camera pulls back when Helen arrives in her pink dress we see two matching low symmetrically disposed, red beach chairs. Later she has a green beach blanket to go with her green swimsuit. These color coincidences can be quite insistent. Helen hands a lilac bouquet with a white spray to a companion wearing a lilac-colored suit with a white collar. We see a close-up of Helen's farewell letter to Merrick; it is written in lilac-colored ink and it is held in front of a floral arrangement with lilacs visible in the background. Not all of the color coordination is as aggressive as some of these examples but it is never understated either. We feel that both the manmade and natural environments are incredibly designed. That sense of design is educed through visual clichés of harmony and order that associatively bolster the concept of design and destiny (the inevitability of the family) in the narrative.

The concurrence of the style of composition and choice of iconography with the narrative theme in *Magnificent Obsession* is an example of a variation of the pathetic fallacy, though the technique is really more of a donnée than a fallacy when it comes to film melodrama. Sirk began his artistic career (in theater and film) in Germany in the 1920s. In certain respects, the stylization of *Magnificent Obsession* recalls some tendencies of the expressionist-neoromantic films of the Weimar period. His color symmetries, for example, are reminiscent of the black and white, architectural symmetries of Fritz Lang's *Siegfried's Death*, where the composition also has connotations of "design" and "destiny." Another expressionist device—the use of height to signal authority—comes into play in one of the key scenes in the film. Just before Merrick operates on Helen, he has a crisis of nerve. He looks up; there is a cut to a low-angle shot of Randolph standing behind a plate of glass and observing Merrick from the gallery of the operating theater. The soundtrack blares the "Ode to Joy" theme from Beethoven's *Ninth Symphony* (which has been the leitmotif of the "magnificent obsession" throughout the film). The low camera angulation plus the "celestial choir" render Randolph as a fatherly, godlike figure suddenly come to earth to dispense courage, strength, and assurance. This notion of (secret) providential intervention inflects the significance of the stylization throughout the film—all the various visual orders and designs are ciphers of a supranatural system which works through characters, casting them in terms of a specific ensemble of "other-regarding" virtues and quite literally "sanctifying" the family. Stylization functions as a virtual hierophany in *Magnificent Obsession,* expressing a religious faith in the subservience of the visible world to deeper principles.

Neither *International Velvet* nor *Uncle Joe Shannon* traffic in theology as overtly or as systematically as *Magnificent Obsession*. Their idiom or rhetoric is psychology rather than religion. Both assume an extremely broad notion of a psychological economy that has the capacity to adjust to the loss of beloved objects through processes of symbolic replacement. This somewhat general principle is then put in the service of the nuclear family. The psychologically wounded characters find replacements for lost relatives who actually play the social (not merely the psychological) role of their lost family. The films begin with a valid enough (though vague) psychological principle but employ it to construct plots that celebrate the inevitability of the nuclear family. Undoubtedly, the use of psychology is more palatable to audiences of the 1970s than the theology of *Magnificent Obsession*. But the effect is the same.

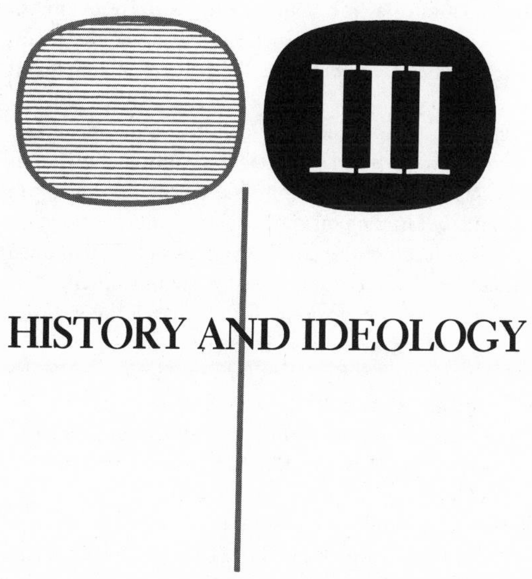

III

HISTORY AND IDEOLOGY

While there is consensus among critics of melodrama about its connection to social and economic conditions, there is decided disagreement about the various forms it takes, its modes of address, its impact on the audience, and its subversive potential. For critics like Brooks, the primary impetus of melodrama is moral and spiritual, a representation of the striving to transcend ambiguity and conflict. Carroll finds the tendency in the genre to reinforce traditional values, in particular the preservation of the nuclear family, while Elsaesser and Schatz find subversive elements at work in the style which undermine prevailing values and attitudes. The essays in this section explore how the production of melodrama converges with particular historical moments and how its mode of representation reveals the operations of ideology. The aim of the essays is not so much to identify the "reactionary" or "progressive" tendencies of the works so much as to expose contradictions in the works and in the society.

Chuck Kleinhans's "Notes on Melodrama and the Family under Capitalism" examines the evolution of the family in the bourgeois era, noting how it comes to assume central importance in the private sphere as a place of retreat. This separation is endemic to life under capitalism which thrives on divisions between the work and family, between leisure and productivity. The family is expected to provide the emotional gratification denied in the productive sphere, but the demands placed on it are more than the family can satisfy. Kleinhans argues that this provides the stuff of melodrama, and for this reason melodrama and social experiences coincide. Melodrama provides conflicts and situations which parallel the conflicts experienced by the audience, and the audience, rather than being passive, is actively involved in comparing its situation to those presented in the melodramas. Here Kleinhans echoes Gramsci in regarding mass forms as containing strategies for dealing with everyday reality. In reading the melodrama a certain amount of translation is necessary, since the melodrama often utilizes a language that displaces the social onto the political, the material onto the spiritual.

In his analysis of *Marked Woman*, Charles Eckert explores the structure of this Warner's film which appears to balance two forms of expression: a controlled melodramatic plot and a series of scenes that erupt with uncontrolled emotion. The film's center does not reside in the melodrama but in the portrayal of class conflict. Capitalizing on the Lucky Luciano trial, the film develops the familiar plot of women exploited and brutalized by a villainous gangster and his eventual capture and punishment. The decor of the film, the disjunctive acting styles, and the particular role of the gangster invite speculation about the film's social motives. The intensely emotional scenes seem to be raising questions about the women's suffering that are not answered by the melodramatic plot with its reductive form of explanation. By reading the film in terms of its deeply embedded oppositions which are disguised through a number of displacements, Eckert seeks to expose how the clues in the film lead to a narrative that unsuccessfully masks the issue of the Depression and of class conflict.

The forms of displacement that are successfully concealed in other films surface in Eckert's analysis of this film. For example, in his discussion of the gangster, Eckert notes Vanning's difference from pre-Depression gangsters who were played by Anglo-Saxon actors and associated with the upper classes. In *Marked Woman*, Vanning is the locus of a number of contradictions which mask his entrepreneurial origins in his lower-class and ethnic persona and threaten to turn him into the undifferentiated melodramatic villain. The transformation is not effected, however, and Vanning cannot be sentimentalized. Neither can the women's suffering. Melodrama does not successfully mitigate the harsher aspects of class conflict embedded in the film. Since melodrama is often a strategy of sentimentalizing and deflecting from social issues, Eckert's essay seeks to reclaim what melodrama seeks to conceal.

Michael Renov's essay on *Leave Her to Heaven* examines the film in the context of immediate post–World War II melodramas. Renov adopts the psychological terminology of the double bind in order to account for the appearance of the pathological female in films of that era. At that time, servicemen were returning to their families. There was a concerted effort to change women's orientation, a process in which women were themselves complicit. As the focal point of double-bind communication, women were confronted by conflicting messages, forced to reconcile conflicting demands. In this no-win situation, no matter how the individual responds, the response is dissonant with the message being sent because the messages are contradictory. During World War II, women were told that if they did not work, the war would be lost and their men would die.

On the other hand, the message from the Depression was communicated that working women were a reproach to unemployed men. Guilt was generated, too, around the working mother's presumed neglect of children. In the postwar era, women were also enjoined to heal the traumas of the returning servicemen. Moreover, the necessity of reproduction was also enjoined on women with the corresponding injunction to enjoy the pleasures of motherhood. The woman was to answer all these demands, contradictory though they might be.

The homicidal actions of Gene Tierney in *Leave Her to Heaven* appear on the surface to be the consequence of jealousy, but the source of her conflicts is actually something else more akin to the family melodrama than to one of individual pathology. Her Oedipal drama seems ostensibly to arise from the desire to please and possess the love object, her reincarnated father in the person of her husband. This love assumes a totally destructive direction. Placed as she is between a father whose affection for his daughter was countered by the hostility of the mother, she is, in Renov's terms, already situated at the heart of the double bind. And this double bind is reproduced in her relations with others which Renov situates at the heart of the society. Renov's essay is an attempt to bring together the insights of psychiatry with those of social history.

David N. Rodowick's "Madness, Authority, and Ideology in the Domestic Melodrama of the 1950s" addresses melodrama as a mode of experience more than as a genre, and as the locus of aesthetic, social, psychic, and formal determinations which are carriers of history and ideology. Like Elsaesser and Kleinhans, he finds that the family is a dominant, though not sole, institutional determinant in the melodramatic text, a surrogate for other aspects of power within the society. While the focus in the domestic melodrama appears to be restricted to private issues—inheritance, the creation of social and sexual identities—the family does in fact participate in the reproduction of the social relations of production under patriarchy and in the formation of sexed and gendered identities that can participate in the social order. The arena of the domestic melodrama is the crisis of identification. Violence and sexuality are equated, and the texts alternate between paralysis and surplus energy, dramatizing the irreconcilability of desire and the law.

Not all melodramas are bearers of criticism and resistance to the status quo, but these domestic melodramas of the 1950s are, in their formal qualities, characterized by stylistic excess which allows for the appearance of contradictions that were rampant within the culture and part of the historical conditions of the 1950s in the postwar disillusionment, the Cold War, and the failure of traditional familial and institutional structures. Melodrama is thus, for Rodowick, not the reflection of that reality but intrinsic to it in recognizable ways.

Pam Cook's discussion of melodrama focuses on the women's pictures produced by the British Gainsborough Studios in the 1940s. She notes the auteurist emphasis of critical works that, following Elsaesser, seek "cinematic countercurrents." She contrasts this with the feminist work of Laura Mulvey, who regards the analysis of melodrama less as a quest for the progressive text and more as a matter of identifying contradictions specifically around women's position under patriarchy. Mulvey identifies the difference between tragic melodrama and the women's picture. The former is concerned with the Oedipal conflict, male domination, and a male point of view, the latter with the traditional female values of nurture, sentiment, and a female point of view.

The question of point of view is tricky, Cook argues, since the distinction is not always clear-cut. But the importance of pursuing this difference is crucial to an understanding of both the ways in which the women's picture participates in the dominant male discourse and the ways it diverges from it. For example, the tragic melodrama is linear, based as it is on the central conflict of the challenge to the father's power, while in women's melodrama the challenge is presented in the heroine's desire to take the mother's place. Her position is one of uncertainty, lack of knowledge, hence the emphasis in these films on the investigative mode. The narrative is circular rather than linear, closed rather than open, returning often to the point of inception. The hero's conflicts involve escape from society, while the heroine's conflicts involve confrontation with society often in terms of failure resulting in her accommodation to the status quo or punishment for transgression.

Cook discusses the visual codes of melodrama which, in tragic melodrama, function to intensify the male protagonist's suffering and serve often as ironic commentary. In the women's picture, objects, particularly domestic objects, can serve as correlatives for the female protagonist's feelings and point of view. Unlike the tragic melodrama, the meaning of these objects is inaccessible to the characters though accessible to the spectator, endowing the spectator with knowledge superior to that of the characters. The protagonist's limited knowledge marks her world as one of fantasy. The women's picture is problematic in the context of classical cinema insofar as female discourse can only be communicated through the language of hysteria or paranoia. The female body becomes a map on which to read female desire, but the ubiquitous physician, psychoanalyst, or lawyer cannot decipher the signs.

Cook's analysis of the Gainsborough women's films situates them at a specific moment in British history: World War II and the immediate postwar era. Much like Renov's discussion of the Hollywood postwar melodrama, Cook's essay insists that the films can be best understood by exploring the conjunction between the wartime ideology and the female audiences that many films addressed. British women of the time would have been subjected to dual attitudes. On the one hand, the women voluntarily and through conscription swelled the work force. Child care was available to free them from the home. With men away in the service, casual sex was not uncommon. At the same time that these real changes in women's position were evident and often reinforced, concerns were also expressed about the traditional position of women and the future of the family. The films of the era display a similar sense of contradiction relating to women's position. Continuing into the immediate postwar years, the women's melodramas present females as struggling, in varying degrees, between traditional femininity and the imperatives of social change.

Notes on Melodrama and the Family under Capitalism

CHUCK KLEINHANS

Caught between the longing for love
And the struggle for the legal tender

—Jackson Browne[1]

First, some statistics. About one-half of the marriages that take place in the large urban areas of the United States this year will end in legal failure—separation, divorce, desertion, etc. This rate is about the same as the state average for California, which is widely taken to be the vanguard state in lifestyle. Nationally, one-third of all marriages end in divorce.[2]

A conclusion: the traditional, white, "middle class," two generation nuclear family and marriage, its legal form, no longer function as viable institutions. Today we are at a point in the U.S. where the traditional family and marriage are the exception rather than the norm.

Second, a popular song lyric.

Little One, whatcha going to do?
Little One, honey, it's all up to you.
Now your daddy's in the den
Shooting up the evening news
Mamma's with a friend
Lately she's been so confused[3]

Chuck Kleinhans's "Notes on Melodrama and the Family under Capitalism" originally appeared in *Film Reader* 3 (February 1978), pp. 40–47. Reprinted by permission of the author and *Film Reader.*

Another conclusion: the situation of the family, which has been a core social unit in the bourgeois epoch, is represented in popular culture, from songs like the Rolling Stones' "Mother's Little Helper" to Hollywood's *Looking for Mr. Goodbar.* But we expect that. This representation appears acutely in the stage and film domestic melodrama during the capitalist era. Of course I will acknowledge that as a general dramatic form melodrama can be found in many periods, as in Euripides' Athenian dramas. Yet the tragedy—or melodrama—of Ancient Greece is clearly of a different order than the situation of Lessing's *Miss Sara Sampson*, Dumas' *Camille*, Ibsen's *Doll's House*, or O'Neill's *Mourning Becomes Electra*.

When we look at the emergence of the modern melodrama about 250 years ago (the bourgeois domestic melodrama, to be more precise), today everyone can clearly understand its class nature as drama of and for a specific class, poised against another class: a cultural-ideological weapon in a political and economic struggle that changed history forever. Standard theatre histories and national literary histories acknowledge it. And we can remember that this class interpretation of melodrama emerging as a bourgeois genre was first fully advanced by Lenin's teacher, Plekhanov, and developed with finesse in Arnold Hauser's *The Social History of Art.*[4] Yet today it seems much harder for people to see the class nature of melodrama, for what are, I suspect, a few good reasons (such as its diffusion across class lines by the mass media), and some bad ones (such as a deliberate refusal to acknowledge class politics).

Since bourgeois domestic melodrama emerges with the ascension of capitalism, and since it deals with the family, it makes sense to look at the family under capitalism to better understand melodrama. In his preface to *The Origin of the Family*, Engels observes that,

> According to the materialist conception the determining factor in history is, in the final instance, the production and reproduction of the immediate essentials of life. This again is of a two fold character. On the one side, the production of the means of existence, articles of food and clothing, dwellings and of the tools necessary for that production; on the other side, the production of human beings themselves, the propagation of the species. The social organization under which the people of a particular historical epoch and a particular country live is determined by both kinds of production; by the stage of development of labour on the one hand and of the family on the other.[5]

In the bourgeois era, as contrasted with all earlier historical epochs, the family becomes the central area of personal life, a place of respite from productive life, from the alienated labor that most workers must face. This split between productive relations and personal relations, between work and family, between production and reproduction, is unique to capitalist social organization. Whereas in precapitalist social formations laborers (including slaves) operated within a unified life situation while working and not working, under capitalism the proletarian has one life at work and another life at leisure. Meaning and purpose are not in one's work, which consists of alienated labor, but in whatever can be defined outside of work. Given that one's sense of identity and social worth could not be achieved in productive labor under capitalism, the division of social from economic life meant that the family and the area of interpersonal relations took on a huge burden.

In a feudal society the family as a whole was occupied in the area of production, most commonly in agriculture. This pattern persists in the artisan and petit bourgeois family until relatively recently. It is sustained in the U.S. by the long persistence of the family farm and the arrival of immigrants who brought older family patterns—often peasant patterns as in the case of Irish, Polish, southern Italian, and Greek immigrants—into the urban industrial life of American capitalism. But, if the U.S. in some ways has held onto an older pattern of the family for a longer time—especially in nostalgic forms such as we see in the Western, as in *Shane*—America has also moved fast and far into the social problems of advanced capitalism.[6] In twentieth-century America the family completed the transformation from being a productive unit based on private property (the farm, the artisanal tools of production, the small business) to being the center of personal life, the primary institution for the acquisition of personal happiness, love, and fulfillment. From a central place in production under feudalism and early capitalism, women and children were moved to a marginal place as a new division emerged. The home becomes the realm of women and children, and the industrial workplace emerges as the area of proletarian men. Women are responsible for the remaining material production within the home and also for the personal or human values. At the same time, domestic material production has been increasingly socialized (that is, turned over to other institutions of education, health, welfare, etc.) and commodified, as seen on a large scale in the increase in the service sector of the economy and more immediately in the shift to packaged and prepared food. In this context, housework and childcare are divorced from their productive base. Women are assigned domestic tasks that seem increasingly trivial and emotional responsibility for personal problems that have their origin outside the home. These two aspects of women's lives overlap at the point of consumption. Thus a Pillsbury jingle for prepared dough products claims,

> Nothing says you love 'em
> Like something from the oven
> And Pillsbury says it best.[7]

The more the family loses its possibilities for material production, the more it becomes a prime site of consumption. Mass consumption, the domestic side of imperialist market expansion, contains an ideology of pleasure and self-gratification which is defined largely in individual rather than social terms. With consumption detached from production (the fetishism of commodities Marx describes in the first chapter of Capital), a full life is thwarted. Rather than life, one has a succession of lifestyles.

The family becomes a center of subjectivity, cut off from the world of action and decisions. Home is for passion, suffering, sympathy, sacrifice, self-attainment. Work is for action, doing, for the money which pays for the home. Yet home is also shaped by the ideology of individualism, especially as shaped by the Puritan-Protestant heritage of U.S. life. The family is supposed to achieve the personal fulfillment denied in the workplace for adults and denied in school for children. At home everyone becomes a consumer trying to get a bigger slice of the emotional pie.

From this perspective we can see why so much of the early resurgent women's movement was involved with a critique of the role of the housewife and mother, both by older women rejecting the social mold they were a part of and by younger women rejecting the future that was held out to them. Nor is it mysterious why the emergent feminist movement has often had deep contradictions in defending subjectivity as women's special social quality while also trying to advance the position of women in the male-dominated productive sphere. The personal *is* political, but that awareness can produce a strategy for change only if we see that capitalism has produced the split between the personal and the productive and that capitalism must be overcome to transcend that dichotomy.

In short, "personal life," the contemporary family, and the special role of women in a social sphere separated from the production sphere can and must be seen as a historically specific form. It is as much a part of the development and transformation of capitalism as Taylorized work and the state operation of education. Under capitalism people's personal needs are restricted to the sphere of the family, of personal life, and yet the family cannot meet the demands of being all that the rest of society is not. This basic contradiction forms the raw material of melodrama.

In this context it is no surprise that melodrama and life coincide. Perhaps more than any other genre, melodrama deals directly with one side of the capitalist dichotomy, with the personal sphere, home, family, and women's problems.[8] When I visit my parents, my mother and I often sit over coffee while she tells me all the family news, which consists of a series of new changes of personal relations in the clan—deaths, divorces, children rejecting parents and vice versa, people losing jobs and lovers and finding new ones, etc., etc. And my mother often closes the updating of these family stories with the spontaneous observation that they are melodramatic, or "like a soap opera." And they are. In fact, knowing that melodramas are like family situations, we can rather easily find a number of schemes or frameworks with which to analyze both of them, such as the Freudian family romance (which some of the *Screen* critics have now discovered about 20 years after American critics pointed it out), or R. D. Laing's description of the structure of schizophrenic families, or Eric Berne's transactional analysis, or Gregory Bateson's interactional systems theory.[9] Clearly, they all "work" in the sense of providing a structural framework with which to approach melodrama. For example, Bateson's double bind fits the situation of Cary (Jane Wyman) in *All That Heaven Allows* (Sirk, 1955) perfectly.

More directly than other genres, melodrama helps us understand, relate to, or deal with the same kind of situations that we emotionally experience in personal life. I do not want to say it is cathartic and get caught in an Aristotelean framework, but clearly we relate to melodrama largely because it does present situations which are structurally similar to those we emotionally experience in life. It represents to us the contradictions of capitalism as evidenced in the personal sphere.

Melodramatic situations are sometimes directly parallel to the audience's experience. For example, I'm sure some of my readers have direct experience from their own family with the central question in *All That Heaven Allows*: should a widow remarry, and if so, outside her class and to a younger man? For others the same situation may have an indirect relation to our experience—should a divorced mother remarry, and on what basis with regard to her children's feelings? Or, what are the sexual options of a woman who has reached menopause in our society? Yet others may relate to these portrayed situations only in the more abstract form of seeing a generation conflict which is analogous to the pattern of one's own upbringing.

One of the most persistent structures in bourgeois domestic melodrama is the pattern of a woman sacrificing her own goals—which may be defined as personal achievement, a career, happiness, independence—for the happiness of another person. Without being aware of it when I selected the films, I taught a course in melodrama which showed a series of films all of which have a woman's sacrifice as a major theme: Lois Weber's *The Blot* (1921), Curtiz's *Mildred Pierce*, Cukor's *Camille*, Arzner's *Christopher Strong*, Preminger's *Daisy Kenyon* and *Fallen Angel*, Stahl's *Back Street*, the Stahl and Sirk versions of *Imitation of Life*, and Sirk's *All That Heaven Allows* and *Written on the Wind*. It is not very difficult to see that the constant reoccurence of the pattern of a woman's self-sacrifice in melodrama bears some relation to the actual lived emotional experience of women in our culture. As the guardians of the home, as the family member given virtually total responsibility for the emotional life and well-being of the family, women are constantly called upon to sacrifice for the greater good of keeping the man ready for the world of production and raising the children.

Melodramas provide the audience with situations which are analogous to those commonly experienced in family and personal life. Much of melodrama's recurring appeal lies here, in the artistic representation of situations such as a woman's sacrifice that the audience has experienced as well. Understanding melodrama in this way helps explain why "high culture" techniques of analysis and evaluation do not obtain in understanding the genre. For example, plots often unfold with coincidence an essential component of narration. This is easily judged a fault. But if melodrama is appreciated for its situations, rather than for its overall development, then weak transitions are not significant. In other words, the parts may be more important than the whole, and thus the concept and value of organic unity may be irrelevant if applied to a melodrama. Understanding the key role of dramatic situations in melodrama can also help us understand why we so often find totally truncated explanations of character motivation in the genre. In melodrama our interest is not in the gradual exposition and development of a character's personality and decision making, but rather in the direct portrayal of the social psychological situation itself in its artistically disguised, but relatively "raw" form.[10]

Considering melodrama in this light throws doubt on the assumption that because a melodrama typically demands close identification of audience with narrative, it necessarily follows that the spectators are also passive. It seems possible that the audience is (or could be) actually rather active—selecting, using, judging what it sees. Clearly, at this point I am offering a speculation, but it is one worth following up with further analysis. Although I am approaching it from a different perspective, my argument here intersects with one made by Laura Mulvey in a paper on *All That Heaven Allows* because we both argue that melodrama gains its strength from evoking contradictions in the sphere of personal life.[11]

Since I've begun to speculate, I will offer four additional hypotheses. First, melodrama depicts the return of the repressed, in the Freudian sense. Sometimes this may be seen directly by showing conversion hysteria symptoms in characters as is rather obvious in *All That Heaven Allows* when Cary is diagnosed for psychosomatic headaches. Or hysteria can erupt in the narrative pattern itself, as Geoffrey Nowell-Smith has recently argued with regard to Minnelli's melodramas.[12] In addition, and perhaps more importantly, melodrama may act in terms of much deeper psychological structures in an attempt to reconcile the irreconcilable. Specifically, we find the oedipal structure reappearing repeatedly in terms of the home/career division in many melodramas. Some of the strange resonances in *Mildred Pierce* can be attributed to the working out of a set of oedipal structures.[13] Similarly, Gretchen Bisplinghoff has suggested that Stahl's *Imitation of Life* resolves the reproductive/productive, home/career dichotomy by having the white mother take on the father function while the black mother serves the mother function.[14] Close examination of specific films is needed to confirm, deny, or qualify the function of such oedipal structures.

Second, while it may seem that the great age of film melodrama is over, I think it is not dead but rather going through further changes, and we should not be looking for its current health in *The Other Side of Midnight* but elsewhere. All three versions of *The Godfather* offer an interesting juxtaposition of the gangster and melodramatic genres with the former genre carrying the realm of production and the latter the realm of personal life. Especially curious: women disappear—the melodrama of interpersonal relations goes on between the men of the family. The result, as John Hess points out, provides an acid critique of the middle class American family.[15] Also we can regard a film such as *Looking for Mr. Goodbar* as a melodrama dealing with the social-sexual position of young women today. Through a deeply sexist misunderstanding of the objective and subjective situation of women, the film shows not only the split of productive life and personal life in the day and night transformations of Terry, the Diane Keaton character, but also the impossibility of a reconciliation, underlined by an inverted *Liebestod* ending.

Third, I want to add a footnote to one of the best recent articles discussing melodrama, Charles Eckert's analysis of *Marked Woman*.[16] Eckert says that by studying structural oppositions in the film we can see the transformation of class issues into other oppositions: male/female, urban/rural, and so forth. The class nature of the film's central conflict is disguised by these changes. I would add that in domestic melodrama we find the oppositions contained within the family, in the personal sphere, in a way that is at once dense and illusive. Repeatedly we discover very deliberately structured ambiguities in family melodrama. For example, in *All That Heaven Allows* the specific reasons that keep Cary and Ron (Rock Hudson) apart are multiple and vague. Some of it is a difference in class: petit bourgeois property owner and small businessman vs. haut bourgeois widow. Some of it is age (30ish vs. 40ish); some of it is lifestyle. The oppositions can be expressed and interpreted in various ways: within society vs. outside society, small town vs. rural, children vs. no children, sexual fulfillment vs. fear of sexuality, sacrifice vs. happiness, and so forth. But the effect of this multiplicity is not richness and complexity, a presentation of overdetermination, but rather a poverty and ambiguity. The film allows, even encourages, multiple readings. One spectator can interpret the conflict as one of age; another can see class as the central issue, and so forth. No particular reading of the film is correct, except as it is completed by a specific viewer.

Finally, I would point out that melodrama, the genre made earlier by men for women, is now taken over and changed by women filmmakers. Several experimentalists illustrate the use and reinterpretation of melodrama: Yvonne Rainer (especially *Film about a Woman Who . . .*), Joyce Wieland (*The Far Shore*), Chantal Akerman (*Jeanne Deilman*), Laura Mulvey (*Riddles of the Sphinx*, made with Peter Wollen), and Marguerite Duras.

The flexibility and malleability of melodrama presented here should indicate the importance of studying the genre. Melodrama appeals to the mass audience (and to film critics) because it offers artistic presentations of genuine problems. At the same time bourgeois melodrama locates those problems in the area of the family, precisely where many of the issues raised cannot ever be solved. In this it reproduces capitalist social relations by assuming that the family can and should resolve contradictions arising in productive life. Thus alcoholism can be appropriate subject matter, as in *Days of Wine and Roses*. But bourgeois melodrama rather carefully avoids topics that expose the dialectical relation of production and reproduction. The psychological dynamics arising in families and personal relations during periods of lay-offs, unemployment, and underemployment are seldom portrayed.[17] Only when society can reconcile production and reproduction will melodrama be robbed of its animating contradictions. Until that time we can expect the genre to echo the endless transformations of personal life in the capitalist era. In a utopian future, when class history comes to an end, melodrama may well be seen as one of the most poignant expressions of the bourgeois epoch.

Notes

I presented an earlier version in a Film Division seminar, Northwestern University, November, 1977. Many participants there influenced my revisions, especially Val Almendarez and William Horrigan who also gave papers and Thomas Elsaesser who lectured at length on film melodrama. These ideas took initial shape through interaction with students in a course I taught at Northwestern, fall, 1977. I want to stress that this essay is tentative in the sense that specific case studies are needed to elaborate and qualify my argument.

1. "The Pretender," on his album of the same name (Asylum 7E-1079).
2. I have been unable to find the precise documentation of these figures which I read in the summer of 1977 in two sources, one of which I believe was *Time* or *Newsweek*. However I have checked the data for individuals divorced and married in two standard reference works: U.S. Bureau of the Census, *Statistical Abstract of the U.S., 1976* (97th ed., Washington: Dept. of Commerce, 1976), and Department of Health, Education and Welfare, *Vital Statistics of the U.S. 1973*, vol. 3, *Marriage and Divorce* (Washington: HEW, 1977). I am sure the statistics are reliable. Nationally, there are now half as many divorces as marriages each year. The national divorce rate remained about the same from 1920–1960. It increased every year from 1960–1973, doubling in that time. If marriage is no longer a viable social institution, it may be that divorce increasingly is. The growth of related services (special lawyers, counselling and therapy, self-help books, etc.) supports this observation.
3. Jackson Browne, "Red Neck Friend," on his album *For Everyman* (Asylum SD-5067).

4. Georgi V. Plekhanov, "French Drama and Painting in the 18th Century," in his *Art and Society and Other Papers in Historical Materialism* (NY: Oriole, 1974). This edition appears to reprint from a variety of unacknowledged sources: perhaps from *Art and Social Life*, tr. E. Fox and E. Hartley (London, 1953). Arnold Hauser, "The Origins of Domestic Drama," in his *The Social History of Art*, vol. 3, *Rococo, Classicism, Romanticism*, tr. Hauser and Stanley Godman (NY: Vintage, n.d.), pp. 84–99.
5. Fredrich Engels, 1884, quoted in Sheila Rowbotham, *Woman's Consciousness, Man's World* (Baltimore: Penguin, 1973), p. 47. I am greatly indebted to Rowbotham for my analysis and to Eli Zaretsky, *Capitalism, the Family & Personal Life* (NY: Harper, 1976). I have also been influenced by the work of and discussions with Serafina Kent Bathrick who is completing a dissertation on women and the family in Hollywood films of the Forties at Wisconsin, Madison.
6. It's worth pointing out as an aside that most people reading this essay have, or hope to have, a life which combines production and reproduction, economic life and social life. Such unification is the great appeal of being a professional—one's work and life can be one. Yet such unity is achieved for the individual professional and not by the family unit. Increasingly, many professionals—especially those working within state institutions—understand they are not free professionals but rather privileged wage laborers, as is evidenced in the wave of teacher unionization, health sector organizing, etc. An excellent exposition of the proletarianization of traditional white collar work: Harry Braverman, *Labor and Monopoly Capital* (NY: Monthly Review, 1976).
7. From memory. Carol Lopate, "Daytime Television," *Radical America* 11:1 (Jan.–Feb. 77), 33–51, provides a fine explanation of the relation between the housewife's daily situation and television's soap operas, quiz shows, and commercials.
8. Conversely, the "male" genres such as the Western and the action film provide a fantasy of power, control, and autonomous activity in the "outside" world of production: precisely where workers do not have power, control, and autonomy.
9. A particularly interesting application of Bateson's work is Chapter 5 of Paul Watzlawick, Janet Helmick Beavin, and Don D. Jackson, *Pragmatics of Human Communication: A Study of Interactional Patterns, Pathologies, and Paradoxes* (NY: Norton, 1967), which examines the Edward Albee play *Who's Afraid of Virginia Woolf?* as a model of confused communication.
10. From this point of view, attempts to assign a psychological pathology to characters are misguided. Characters are inconsistent, but not because they are "crazy" (with the obvious exception of when this is explicit in the narrative).
11. "Douglas Sirk and Melodrama," mimeo, presented at the Society for Education in Film and Television weekend school, March, 1977, in London.
12. "Minnelli and Melodrama," *Screen* 18:2 (Summer, 1977), 113–119.
14. More accurately they are electra structures (female rivalry for the same man or thing which is initially linked to one of the women): Mildred vs. Veda for Bert, Mildred vs. Mrs. Beiderhoff for Bert, Mildred vs. Veda for Wally, Mildred vs. Veda for Monte, and Mildred vs. Veda for the business. *Mildred Pierce* provides a good example of my previous point about situation being more important than character consistency. It is virtually impossible to answer the Aristotelean question, "what is Mildred's flaw or mistake?" without obvious reductionism. My understanding of the film is indebted to Joyce Nelson, "*Mildred Pierce* Reconsidered," *Film Reader* 2 (1977), pp. 65–70.
14. In classroom discussion.
15. "*Godfather II*: A Deal Coppola Couldn't Refuse," *Jump Cut* 6–7 (May–July 75), 1, 10–11.
16. *Film Quarterly* 27:2 (Winter, 73–74), 11–24.
17. Fassbinder's *Fear Eats the Soul: Ali*, an exception to the rule, gains depth by dealing with relations of production *and* reproduction.

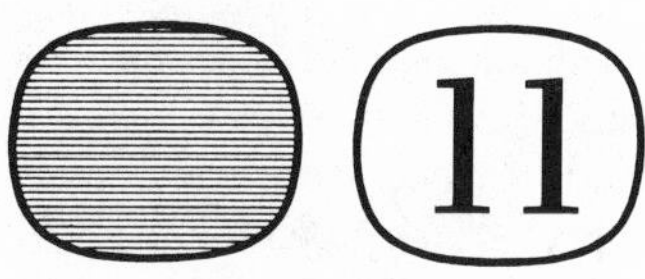

The Anatomy of a Proletarian Film: Warner's *Marked Woman*

CHARLES ECKERT

Marked Woman was produced by Warner Brothers–First National in 1937, based on an original script by Robert Rossen and Abem Finkel, and directed by Lloyd Bacon. It is, to give its fullest definition, a topical, proletariat-oriented gangster film. As such, it must be understood within a complex tradition of films, and against a backdrop of Depression issues. The analysis I shall attempt respects the context of the film and centers upon three crucial problems.

The first concerns a striking contrast between the cool, rigidly controlled emotions typical of the scenes that develop the melodramatic plot and a different order of emotions spanning a spectrum from despair to rage that appear in a series of interspersed scenes (and in the crucial final scene). The affective center of the film seems displaced into another dimension than the melodramatic, a dimension that the latter scenes define.[1] The second problem concerns the way in which the moral and social dilemmas are developed. And the third concerns the significance of the prime-mover of the plot, the gangster-racketeer: since he is a heavily stereotyped figure bringing with him not simply the swagger and jargon of dozens of previous incarnations but a specific aura of significances and values, understanding him requires what we might call a "theory of the gangster," the development of which will take us beyond *Marked Woman*.

 Charles Eckert, "Anatomy of a Proletarian Film: Warner's *Marked Woman*," originally appeared in *Film Quarterly* 27, no. 2 (Winter 1973–74), pp. 10–24, and was reprinted in Bill Nichols, *Movies and Methods* (Berkeley: University of California Press, 1985), pp. 407–28. Reprinted by permission of the University of California Press.

However disconnected these analytical concerns may seem, they are, I believe, aspects of a single unified intellectual operation that affects almost every detail of the film. It may be helpful to define this operation and to sketch in the conclusions I will be moving towards before entering upon an extended analysis. My major contention is that the ultimate sources of *Marked Woman* and its tradition are in class conflict; but the level at which the film-makers perceive this conflict, and the level at which it is lived by the fictional characters and perceived by the audience, is existential rather than political or economic. It is in the lived experience of the Depression, in the resentment directed at those who "caused" the Depression, and in the sense of disparity between being poor and being rich, that this popular notion of class conflict originates.

The expression of the conflict in the films, however, is almost never overt. It is instead converted into conflicts of a surrogate nature—some ethical, some regional, some concerned with life-style, some symbolized by tonal or aesthetic overlays created by the makers of the films. The analysis of this elaborate secondary structure requires close attention to the processes of condensation and displacement by which latent content is converted into manifest content. I would like to avoid jargon for its own sake, but Freud's terms and their strict definitions are essential for an understanding of the processes involved (I shall give definitions at the appropriate point in the analysis). I hope to show that the effect of these operations is to attenuate conflicts at the level of real conditions and to amplify and resolve them at the surrogate levels of the melodrama. This solution is not always successful, however; it can lead to dialectical play between the real and disguised conflicts, the effect of which is to make the usually opaque operations transparent. I believe that this is what happens in *Marked Woman* and that it is the chief source of the atypical feel of the film and of the forceful and unsettling character of a number of its scenes.

But all of this can only be clarified after we have recalled the film and its topical basis. *Marked Woman* capitalized upon a sensational trial reported almost daily in the *New York Times* between May 14 and June 22, 1936. Because the details of this trial strongly influenced Rossen and Finkle, and because the trial provides a body of real analogues to the fiction of the film, I shall review it first. I will then give a summary of the film designed to make the disjuncture between the melodramatic and the strongly affective scenes apparent, while giving enough detail to familiarize the reader with the whole film and to provide material for the subsequent analysis.

The Trial

Charles "Lucky Luciano" Lucania won his place in the pantheon of Depression Mafiosi by cornering a market more durable than liquor—the brothels of New York. His method was that of the simple "take-over," with promises of protection from the law and fair treatment for all concerned. The reasons why the state of New York decided to get Luciano were as politically and socially complex as those that drove Capone out of Chicago—and fortunately need not concern us here. The state's instrument was a task force set up under as ambitious a prosecutor-cum-politician as the country contained, Thomas E. Dewey.

Dewey began by raiding the brothels and arresting almost one hundred women as material witnesses. In its early stages the trial was high-spirited, with an absurdly Runyonesque cast: "Jo-Jo" Weintraub, Crazy Moe, "Little David" Betillo, Cokey Flo. But as the trial centered more and more upon the women, whose testimony would make or break the prosecution's case, the proceedings became a bleak window upon a world of exploitation, drab servitude and occasional terror.

Nancy Presser said that one of Luciano's men drove her into prostitution by threatening to "cut me up so that my own mother wouldn't know me."[2] And Thelma Jordan said, "I knew what happened to girls who had talked about the combination. The soles of their feet and their stomachs were burned with cigar butts for talking too much. . . . I heard Ralph [Liguori] say that their tongues were cut when girls talked."[3] Liguori also threatened that if any of the women testified against the combination "their pictures would be sent to their home town papers with stories of what they were doing for a living."[4]

Another of the women, Helen Kelley, testified to the economics of prostitution. She had quit an underpaid job to become a prostitute and in her first week made $314. After a friendly booker persuaded her to quit and go straight she took a job as a waitress averaging twelve dollars per week. After a year of this she went back to the booker "to solve an economic problem."[5]

The conditions of the prostitutes' lives influenced Rossen and Finkle, as we shall see, but the real issue of the trial was the conviction of Luciano. To this end Dewey faced two obstacles—convincing the women that they would be protected from retaliation, and convincing the jury, and the public at large, that prostitutes were "worthy of belief" in a court of law. When he found that his star witness's life had been threatened, he spent hours persuading her to testify, and then fatuously described to the court the sense of "responsibility" that the experience had aroused in him. And when he had finally gotten his conviction, he assured the court that it was in no sense a personal victory; credit rather belonged to "the men who prepared the case through months of grueling, hard work. . . ."[6]

And where were the "confessed prostitutes" who had been barely "worthy of belief" at this moment of sharing the spoils? They left the House of Detention and "were sent to Special Prosecutor Thomas E. Dewey's offices in the Woolworth Building, where they received, as fees, sums ranging between $150 and $175"—barely a half week's earnings for a working prostitute. "Many said that they planned to return to their home town," or so the *Times* sentimentalized.[7]

From the trial Luciano went on to organize the prison at Dannemora, then the New York dock workers, then the international drug trade. Dewey became governor of the state of New York and candidate for the presidency in 1944 and 1948. The women, who had served both men equally well, disappeared, as they do in the film, into the fog.

The Film

Now let us summarize the film that Warner's made to capitalize upon this trial, with particular attention to the affective split referred to earlier. In the first sequence Johnny Vanning (Eduardo Cianelli) enters the Club Intime, a dinner-club that he had just taken over and intends to convert into a "classy" nightclub and gambling room. He informs the women who work there, among them Mary Dwight (Bette Davis), that he has all the clubs in town and the women who work in them "sewed up." He intends to "organize" the place and to give the women protection from the law. In the course of the sequence he fires one of the women who looks too old to be a hostess, is asked by Mary to let her stay on, relents, shows an interest in the outspoken Mary, and is repulsed by her. Emotionally, all of the dialogue is muted: Vanning is a study in icy cynicism; the women are apprehensive and morose. The tonalities established in this initial sequence are those that dominate the melodrama throughout.

The next scene shows us five of the women in an apartment they rent together: homey curtains, department-store art, an air of proletarian domesticity. They enter depressed, discussing whether they should continue to work for Vanning. One of them suggests that working in a factory or as a waitress would be preferable. Mary suddenly interrupts with the first strongly felt language in the film: "We've all tried this twelve-and-a-half-a-week stuff. It's no good. Living in furnished rooms. Walking to work. Going hungry a couple of days a week so you can have some clothes to put on your back. I've had enough of that for the rest of my life. So have you." And as for Vanning and his hoods, "I know all the angles. And I think I'm smart enough to keep one step ahead of them until I get enough to pack it all in and live on easy street the rest of my life. I know how to beat this racket." This insight into the real conditions of the women's lives is so strongly assertive that it momentarily diverts our attention from the melodrama. The dilemma is as real, and as compelling, as it was for the Helen Kelley of the trial.

In the third sequence, we are back at the Club. The women introduce themselves to the "chumps" who have come to be bilked of their money, then two of them sing songs compounded equally of cynicism and sentiment. Mary picks a man named Crawford who pays for his gambling losses with a bad check, leaves with Mary and is tailed to his hotel by Vanning's men. Mary returns to her room and is surprised by the visit of her innocent kid sister, Betty, in town for a football game. As the girls help Mary in her explanation that she is a fashion-model, the police enter with the news that Crawford has been killed and that Mary is implicated. All of the women are taken in, including Betty.

Enter David Graham (Humphrey Bogart), a jejune, dedicated prosecuting attorney who tells his chief that he thinks he can get Vanning with the aid of the women implicated in the murder. He takes Mary to his office and threatens to indict her if she does not testify against Vanning. Then, in the middle of the scene, Graham becomes pontifical and infuriates Mary:

Graham:	Now, Mary, we're trying to help you.
Mary:	I'm doing all right.
Graham:	For how long? Until Vanning gets as much as he can out of you and then throws you in the ash can? Now, we're trying to put a stop to that—help people like you. But there's nothing we can do unless you're willing to help yourself. Now, why don't you give us a break?
Mary:	(passionately) What kind of break have you ever given us? Outside of kicking us around every chance you get. There's only one kind of a break we want from you, and that's to leave us alone. (Voice rising) And let us make a living in our own way! Or is that asking too much? (Long pause) Anything else you want to know?

The outburst is over quickly, and the scene ends with Mary sullenly uncooperative. But we have been given another insight into the conditions and psychology of the women that diverts our attention back to the realities of the Luciano trial—and the Depression itself.

In a series of rapid scenes Vanning's lawyer Gordon (John Litel) develops a plan to ruin Graham: Mary will be told to "cooperate" but a bought witness will destroy Graham's case. When Mary is called into see Graham again, she pretends to be terrified of Vanning, but otherwise willing to cooperate. The characterization of Graham in this scene seems intentionally self-righteous. He tells Mary, "You're not the only one in the world who was born with two strikes against them. I probably got kicked around just as much as you did. I didn't like it any better than you do. The only difference between us is that—well, I did something about it, you won't."

Pretending to be challenged by Graham, Mary agrees to testify. The emotions of the courtroom scene are largely played out in the faces of Mary and Betty. Mary allows herself to be accused of "entertaining" men after hours and grimly accepts the shame; Betty cannot look at her sister. The exchange between Graham and Mary at the end of the scene is cold: "Thanks for the ride." "So long chump, I'll be seeing you."

Back in the apartment the contained emotions of the courtroom explode. Betty is convinced that her friends will have read their story in the newspapers and that she cannot go back to school. In a scene of mercurial emotions she and Mary bicker, then collapse weeping in each other's arms; again it is the women's exploitation and despair that is forced on our attention.

In the next scene we discover Betty sitting alone in the apartment, obviously unhappy. Emmy Lou enters and invites her to a party at Vanning's where, under the spell of liquor and gaiety, Betty accepts the advances of an experienced lecher. When she returns to the apartment with a one-hundred-dollar bill, Mary knows where she has been and is furious. Betty says that she is no different from Mary, that she has the right to lead the same sort of life. Then she goes back to the party.

On a balcony, against a background of drunken high life, she is again cornered by her would-be seducer. As she struggles to escape him, Vanning comes out and strikes her for "putting on an act." Betty falls, hits her head and is killed. Emmy Lou, the only sympathetic witness, is warned to keep her mouth shut. Mary learns of Betty's disappearance from the party and confronts Vanning, with a threat to "get" him if anything has happened to Betty. She then goes to Graham—now reluctant to trust her—and says she will provide evidence against Vanning. While they talk Graham receives a report that Betty's body has been fished from the river.

Graham comes to the women's apartment and pleads with them to help him and Mary proscute Vanning. But the women feel that the law isn't for them; besides, another gangster will take Vanning's place. Shortly after Graham leaves, defeated, Vanning enters. In the film's most powerful scene Mary accuses Vanning of Betty's death and swears she will tell the DA. Vanning calmly orders the other women into the next room, nods significantly to his strong-arm man, Charlie, and follows the women out.

It would seem that the melodrama can no longer be played out in terms of glacial confrontation. And yet it is. The camera stays in the room with Vanning and Mary's friends. First, in a long shot, we see a picture jump on the wall from the violence of the beating in the next room. As the beating continues, then is followed by a silence cut by an anguished scream, we move from one woman's face to another—each an ambiguous study in fear, rage and acceptance. Quite forcefully we are reminded that the women have no strength of their own, no recourse for help, and no choice but to accept his denigration by the men who exploit them. But it is their condition, not the cruelty of Vanning, that the visual treatment underlines.

Graham then sets out on a search for the only witness he can hope to shake, Emmy Lou. Vanning learns of Graham's search and sends his men to get her first. In a melodramatic chase scene, Emmy Lou escapes from her pursuers. In the following sequence we are in a hospital room with Mary and her three remaining friends. Mary is wrapped in bandages, her face swollen and her eyes bruised. Her friends assure her that she will be all right and that her scars can be disguised. Her reply is one of the most telling lines in the film: "I got things wrong with me that all the doctors in the world can't fix."

As Mary tells her friends that she can't pretend the beating didn't happen, Emmy Lou enters. Both she and Mary weep as they recall Betty, and Emmy Lou agrees to talk to the DA. One of the women argues against provoking Vanning: "You want to keep on living, don't you?" Mary, her voice partly muffled by her bandages, says, "If this is what you call living, I don't want any part of it. Always being afraid. . . . There must be some other way for me to live. If there isn't, I—well, I'd just as soon put a bullet in my head right now and end it." A powerful *Angst* penetrates this scene, for which the physical metaphors are Mary's battered face and listless voice. At this point Graham enters the room and is told that all of the women are ready to testify.

We are next in Vanning's jail cell. Gordon tells him he must make a deal, but Vanning says that he doesn't make deals. Then he launches into a speech that indicates to us that madness and the blindness of the gods have descended upon him—that he is now marked for destruction.

Vanning:	You think I care for money? All I care about is to make people do what I tell them.
Gordon:	You're crazy, Johnny.
Vanning:	Yes, maybe I am. Maybe I ain't. I just know one thing. I ain't gonna let no five crummy dames put the skids under me now. Get

> word to those dames. If they talk, sure as my name's Johnny Vanning, I'll get 'em.

In a brief scene, the women, who have been imprisoned for their own protection, look out the window and see one of Vanning's hoods staked out in the street. Then we are in the courtroom again. One by one the women take the stand and deliver damning evidence against Vanning and his men. Mary is the last, and as she recounts the details of her beating, she turns the right side of her face toward the camera. We see why she had screamed so desperately in the earlier scene: Charlie has cut an X in her cheek—Vanning's mark for those who double-cross him.

The verdict is assured, but Graham's summation and appeal to the jury remain to be heard. The speech obviously transcends its function in the trial and is directed at the audience as a kind of thinking through of all of the issues presented in the film.

> You should consider not only Vanning the murderer, but also Vanning the Vice Czar, who at this very moment is exacting his staggering tribute from a supine and cowardly city. . . . Out of all the teeming millions of this great city only five girls had the courage to take their very lives in their hands and accuse Johnny Vanning. In spite of all the threats of reprisal . . . they were ready to appear before you to testify. And let me be the first to admit the truth of the accusations that were brought against these girls in a desperate effort to discredit them. Frankly they're . . . they're everything the defense has said they are. Their characters are questionable, their profession unsavory and distasteful. Oh, it's not been difficult to crucify them. But it has been difficult to crucify the truth. And that truth is that these girls in the face of sheer, stark terrorism did appear in court, expose themselves to the public gaze, told the truth about themselves, told the world what they really are. Well, then, surely you must believe that they were telling the truth when they testified that Johnny Vanning was responsible for the death of Betty Strauber.

In two short scenes the jury returns a verdict of guilty and the judge pronounces a sentence of 30 to 50 years, with the warning that if anything happens to the women the full sentence will be served. As reporters rush toward Graham, the five women rise slowly from their seats. "Well, that's that," Mary says. "Come on kids. Let's go." Then they walk unnoticed from the courtroom. As the women descend the steps, Graham appears at the door. He calls Mary back.

Graham:	You're the one who should be getting the congratulations, not me.
Mary:	Um um. I don't want them.
Graham:	But where will you go?
Mary:	Places.
Graham:	But what will you do?
Mary:	Oh, I'll get along, I always have.
Graham:	Mary, I'd like to help you.
Mary:	(curious . . . and interested) Why?
Graham:	Why . . . because I . . . because I think you've got a break comin' to you.
Mary:	(still curious) And?
Graham:	And I'd like to see that you get it.

Mary: (suddenly dejected) What's the use of stalling? We both live in different worlds, and that's the way we've got to leave it.

Graham: I don't want to leave it that way. I once said to you that if you ever started helping yourself I'd be the first one to go to bat for you, and that still goes. No matter what you do or where you go, we'll meet again.

Mary: Goodbye, Graham. I'll be seeing you.

Mary descends the steps to join her friends as a melancholy blues theme swells on the sound track. As they walk into the engulfing fog, the camera picks them out in a series of close-ups. The women stare straight ahead, their faces erased of all emotion, almost of life—walking deliberately toward the fog as if they accepted it as their natural element. Behind them, in the bright doorway, there are voices: "How about a couple of pictures of our next DA?" "what do you mean, DA? If he isn't our next governor, he ought to have his head examined."

Structure

Marked Woman is vintage Warner's *cinéma brut*—aesthetically spare, almost devoid of metaphoric effects achieved with the camera or lighting. Any veneer of meaning upon that projected by the faces and words of the actors most likely originates in our empathy for the women's conditions and the sense that these are mirrored in the barren *mise-en-scène*. Because of this aesthetic minimalism, the structural split that I have outlined in the previous summary is all the more forcefully experienced. One set of scenes develops a standard melodrama concerned with the outrages and the eventual destruction of a stereotyped villain. Another set, composed of Mary's outbursts to her friends and to Graham, her quarrels with Betty, the study of the women's faces while Mary is being beaten, Mary's thoughts of suicide, and the striking conclusion (all of them strongly affective), comprises a separate order of experience. And yet there seems to be some necessitous link between the two orders, as if one gave rise to the other or was a precondition of its existing: how else could they maintain so dialectical a relationship throughout the film?

Perhaps we can begin to understand the reasons for the split by looking closely at the scenes concerned with the real conditions of the women's lives. Each of these scenes is characterized by forceful emotion and some attempt to conceptualize the dilemmas that the women face. These attempts, as I shall show in detail later, are frustratingly confused: there is no clear analysis of their situation or the causes of their misery, but rather a muddled pointing at this, that, or maybe that—an obfuscation that paralyzes the mind. At this level the exploited have no exploiter—or, at best, a faceless one called "life" or "the way things are." The true exploiters—the capitalist system, sexism, pernicious ideologies—are vaguely immanent in some of Mary's outbursts, but recede like ghosts as quickly as they are glimpsed. The degree of emotion in these scenes seems directly related to their dead-endedness. There are no answers to the women's questions; the intense confrontation with reality leads only to a stifling semantic cul-de-sac from which they—and we—must escape. And the escape is exhilaratingly easy: we merely leap into the alternative reality of the melodrama.

This leap is typical of what are usually called "proletarian" or "socially conscious" films of the thirties and very early forties. One can specify the exact moment at which they occur in such films as *Public Enemy, Crime School, Dead End, Angels with Dirty Faces, Invisible Stripes, The Big Shot, They Drive by Night* and others. The leap is by its nature dialectical (from one order of experience to an opposite order); and we therefore encounter a series of inversions. To return to our immediate example, *Marked Woman*, we find, first of all, an inversion of emotions: from scenes of weeping, depression, and apathy we move to melodramatic scenes in which the characters project the sort of controlled affect epitomized in the terms "tough," "smart," and "smooth." Spontaneity has no place in this world; if the face breaks at all, it is into a smirk or a leer; and the expression is as calculated as a grammarian's comma. There is also an inversion of activities: from circular, frustrated behavior we move to highly motivated actions, saturated with purpose. One is out to serve one's interests, to rid society of corruption, to "get" somebody.

Obviously, all activities and emotions at this level are surrogate. And any return to the depiction of real conditions may bring this fact home to the audience and destroy the illusion, and the function, of the melodrama. In *Public Enemy, Crime School*, and similar films the depiction of real conditions is limited to the first third or half of the film. These depictions often function as explanations, and partial exonerations, for criminality. Once the melodrama asserts itself strongly, however, there is no break while it runs its course.

But it is precisely this clear function of the melodrama that is lacking in *Marked Woman*. Not only do the real conditions assert themselves in scenes throughout the film, they dominate the crucial final scene. The dialectic comes close to being a contradiction as we realize that the expected denouement of the melodrama has been frustrated. There is also, as a close viewing of the film would demonstrate, occasional penetration of the attitudes typical of the real conditions into the melodrama—alienation, apathy, and confusion. As I will show in the next section, the whole ethos of the melodrama is affected—the women are not altering their conditions, and the destruction of Vanning does not accomplish anything.

Certainly the massive dose of reality infused into the film by its topical sources could be responsible for these effects. But there are other and more proximate causes. Through analysis of passages in which the ethos is developed we can perhaps come closer to them.

Ethos

Since every ethos presents itself as a unified body of polarized conceptions we need for our analysis a methodology attuned to polarity. The form of structural analysis developed by Lévi-Strauss, although idealist and limited in vision, can help us here. Two of Lévi-Strauss's insights are specially provocative: that a dilemma (or contradiction) stands at the heart of every living myth, and that this dilemma is expressed through layered pairs of opposites which are transformations of a primary pair. The impulse to construct the myth arises from the desire to resolve the dilemma; but the impossibility of resolving it leads to a crystal-like growth of the myth through which the dilemma is repeated, or conceived in new terms, or inverted—in short, subjected to intellectual operations that might resolve it or attenuate its force. We can best locate the important ethical dilemmas in *Marked Woman* by close inspection of individual scenes.

In preparation for what follows, an extensive structural analysis of *Marked Woman* was made, the recounting of which would demand more interest and patience than I can presume in a general audience. The method, however, is illustrated here. My selection of only a few passages for analysis is motivated by an additional consideration: the fact that *Marked Woman*, like most works of popular art, relies upon a few dilemmas and a limited number of transformations of them. It is initially difficult to grasp the relationships between transformations and to find one's way to the crucial dilemmas. Only concrete examples will illustrate what I mean. Let us begin with a very simple but typical transformational set found in a song sung by one of the women in an early nightclub scene (the two songs in the film, by Harry Warren and Al Dubin, seem expressly written to reflect the women's attitudes, or chosen because of their content).

City people pity people
Who don't know a lot
About the night life,
But they are wrong.
Though they may be witty people,
They don't know that folks
Who lead the right life
Still get along.

To a plain old fashioned couple
Let me dedicate my song.

They're not sophisticated people,
And though they're only common folk,
You don't know how I envy people
Like Mr. and Mrs. Doe.

They don't know much about swing music,
They wouldn't care for risqué jokes,
But every morning birds sing music
For Mr. and Mrs. Doe.

The lyric continues, developing variations on the basic oppositions found in these stanzas, so that we wind up with the following essential pairs (in the following analysis a colon means "is opposed to" and brackets indicate an implied term):

witty people	:	people who lead the right life
[modern people]	:	old fashioned people
sophisticated people	:	common people
swing music, risqué jokes	:	the music of birds
wreath of holly	:	garden
[nightclub life]	:	home life

All of these are rather obviously transformations of a simple, more basic pair, city life:small town life (with agrarian overtones). This opposition is amplified in the film through the use of many codes of dress, speech and taste. Working-class apartment decor clashes with penthouse decor, Mary's plain dresses with her silver lamé hostess gown, Emmy Lou's curled blond hair with Betty's plain brunet, Graham's law-school English with Mary's terse vernacular. The city:small town opposition, which has a long history in the Hollywood film, turns up frequently, and somewhat unexpectedly, in many gangster films. For instance, it utterly polarizes such films as *The Roaring Twenties, King of the Underworld, High Sierra,* and *It All Came True;* and it has crucial functions in *Little Caesar, The Big Shot, Public Enemy* and others. We can return to this opposition later; for the moment I merely want to define the primary opposition that the song transforms into many pairs. As we look over these oppositions we note that all of them are simple transformations, with one striking exception—the opposition "witty people":"people who lead the right life." We can reduce this to the crucial terms "witty" and "right." The opposition is at first sight illogical. "Witty" demands as its antonym a term that implies witlessness: the common adjective "dumb" (dumb cop, dumb blonde) is perhaps the proper one. "Right," of course, demands "wrong." As we read the opposition, then, we take "witty" as a metonym for "wrong" and "right" as a metonym for "dumb." Because the opposition demands interpretation, it is the most foregrounded and active in the song; and because of its doubled metonymic character it comes across as a pair of dilemmas: why, we ask, is wittiness wrong? Why is dumbness right? These simple dilemmas are, by context of the song, related to the primary opposition of city life and small town life. Before analyzing this relation let us note the appearance of these dilemmas in other parts of the film.

Mary Dwight's first outburst directed at Vanning contains these lines directed both at Vanning and at her conditions: "I know all the angles. And I think I'm smart enough to keep one step ahead of them until I get enough to pack it all in and live on easy street the rest of my life. . . . I know how to beat this racket." Mary's concerns, seen in the larger context of American puritanism, are self-centered and hedonistic, and therefore "wrong." If we miss the point here, we cannot miss it in Graham's remarks to Mary just before they receive news of Betty's death (a kind of moral punishment for Mary): "You know what's right and you know what's wrong. You know better but you just won't do anything about it. You choose to think that you can get through the world by outsmarting it. Well, I've learned that those kind of people generally end up by outsmarting themselves." And, finally, there is an almost syllogistic example in the argument between Mary and Betty:

Betty:	If I can't live one way I can live another. Why not? I'm young and pretty and . . .
Mary:	And dumb!
Betty:	But you're smart! You can teach me the rest.

There are other examples which show the dilemma bound up in the use or disuse of one's wits. But how is it related to the regional opposition represented by city:small town? More specifically, is either opposition seminal for the other and therefore the "crucial" dilemma we are seeking? We should first recall some key references: Mary and Betty came from a small town; Betty feared returning because of a scandal; and the women in the Luciano trial were threatened with exposure in their home-town newspapers. Mary's wrong use of her wits should probably be seen, then, as a city-oriented trait, something she has learned through contact with men like Vanning. But there is something recessive about the city:small town opposition, and it seems more in keeping with the emphasis in the film to see the right:wrong opposition as seminal. If we did, we would arrive at a familiar characterization of the film: we would see it as a kind of exemplum or moral fable. And yet such a definition would have to ignore the scenes that seem most striking—those in which the women are depicted as disconsolate, angry or apathetic. These are not morally toned attitudes as are those of hedonistic ambition and egotism. If there were a primary pair to which all the oppositions we have so far mentioned were related, as well as the opposition between real conditions and melodrama, one would feel that the analysis was more true to the whole film and that it respected the complex interaction between ideas and emotions that the film maintains.

For a fresh start, let us look at a quite different set of oppositions, one found in a song sung immediately before the one already analyzed:

Ain't it funny that paper money
Don't seem like genuine jack?
And every check has the knack
Of jumpin' and bumpin' and bouncin' back?
I like nothin' but silver dollars
And I've collected a few.
When silver starts in ringin',
It rings so true.

My silver dollar man,
He ain't a tie-and-collar man.
A rough and ready man,
But he's a mighty steady man.
And though he can't supply
A lot of luxuries that I demand,
he never leaves me till he leaves
A bit of silver in my hand . . .

Obviously the major function of the song is to valorize the poor: the poor man is the true man; she would love him even if he had no money (his poverty and his class valorize him). But there is more at work in the song. The principle oppositions are:

rough and ready man	:	tie-and-collar man
silver dollars	:	paper money
[sufficiency]	:	luxury

Class consciousness (and class prejudice) figures strongly in this complex, however tritely conceived. And we are suddenly made aware of the absence of class oppositions of this sort in the song previously cited, and in the film as a whole. Prostitutes, the song reminds us, follow their trade, like the Helen Kelley of the trial, "to solve an economic problem." Only Mary's early allusions to making "twelve and a half a week" and going hungry two days out of seven strikes at the heart of her dilemma—and the force of this passage is vitiated by the immediate characterization of Mary as greedy for "easy street" luxuries to be won by the (wrong) use of her wits. Or at least it apparently is, since our attention is shifted to the ethical (and implicit regional) dilemmas defined earlier. This movement from incipient class or economic protest to ethical dilemma can be found elsewhere, and in crucial scenes: in Mary's encounters with Graham in his office, in Graham's visit to the apartment, in the hospital scene, and in the obtuse summary for the prosecution. But all of this only compounds our problem: what do we have here—merely obfuscation as the result of censorship, or another form of transformation?

Deduction has probably taken us as far as it can, so let us proceed inductively. If we posited that the roots of *Marked Woman* are in class opposition and that its ethos is the product of "displacement" as Freud defines this term (the substitution of an acceptable object of love, hate, etc., for a forbidden one), we would be able to see the relation between class opposition and ethical dilemma as both the product of censorship and as transformational. The irresolvability of crucial dilemmas in myths leads to their transformation into other dilemmas. The intent is to resolve the dilemma at another level, or to somehow attenuate its force. If class opposition is regarded as seminal, its displacement into ethical, regional and other oppositions can be seen as both the result of conscious censorship and a myth-like transposition of the conflict into new terms. The latter is an unconscious or less conscious procedure whereby the *force* of the opposition is diminished while its form and some of its substance are retained.

The effect in the film is for the ethical and regional dilemmas to function as displaced, and partly defused, class oppositions. They can still *feel* like class oppositions and be treated as such by the writers and director; the city with its penthouses and limousines can function as reified capitalism; wittiness can be allied to the manipulations of financiers; all of this can be given high resolution by the use of visual coding—skyscrapers, tuxedos, one-hundred-dollar bills; but every thrust of class or economic protest is sufficiently blunted to avoid breaking the skin.

But all of the relations I have examined need a more exact formulation, one that must include a major figure that I have so far only mentioned—the gangster. As the autarch of the universe the women inhabit, his class affiliations, his goals and his psychology need close examination.

The Gangster

Unquestionably *Marked Woman*, like many films of its genre, transmits a sense of compassion for the poor and the exploited. But at the level of real conditions we cannot tell why the poor are poor nor who their exploiters are. Instead of real opposition and conflict we encounter substitute formations—principally dialectical movements between such feeling states as anger and apathy or despair and sentimentalism. Sentimentalism seems to function as the most retrograde of the many possible states. As a tendency toward passive compassion, toward meditative solipsism, it contains nothing insurrectionary, no components of hostility or criticism. It cannot be a coincidence that so many proletarian films head unerringly toward sentiment in their final reels. When, in *The Roaring Twenties*, Eddie (James Cagney) lies dying on the steps of a church while "Melancholy Baby" is heard on the sound track and his motherly friend Panama weeps over him, a lumpen *pietà* mitigates whatever social criticism the film has made.

Opposition is only fully manifested when we make the leap into melodrama. This leap is subjectively fulfilling and clarifying: the exploited now have an exploiter in the gangster—a figure subjected to an almost cosmic overdetermination. If displacement is the principal Freudian mechanism at work in the ethos, it is largely condensation that produces the gangster. Condensation, to give it its simplest definition, is a process whereby a number of discrete traits or ideas are fused in a single symbol. Each component is usually an abbreviated reference to something larger than itself, a sort of metonym that must be interpreted properly if we are to understand its discrete significance as well as its relation to other components in the symbol. By 1937 the figure of the gangster had acquired a remarkable symbolic richness. Every personal mannerism and every artifact of his world resonated with meaning. And he had also become a *vade mecum* for anyone in search of a scapegoat. The judge, in his presentence speech to Johnny Vanning, pronounces him "a low and brutal character, an unprincipled and aggressive egotist." Vanning is guilty of "every vicious and reprehensible crime."

Such attempts to blame the gangster for all important civic ills were, of course, abetted by the tabloid exposés of criminals like Luciano. But it would be shortsighted, and ultimately confusing, to look to real criminals for the prototypes of Johnny Vanning. We must start with the gangsters found in the films themselves and note their most common traits. Although the discussion will initially take us afield, it should lead us to a more exact understanding of Vanning, his relation to the women he exploits, and his function in the structure I have outlined. In a film made up of many specificities, he is the most generalized, and traditional, object.

We must distinguish, first of all, between two almost antithetical images of the gangster. The first obtained between 1927 and 1931 and was projected by such actors as John Gilbert, Conrad Nagel, Walter Huston, William Boyd, Lowell Sherman, Richard Dix and Monte Blue. The type is basically Anglo-Saxon, aristocratic, polished in speech and bearing, and dressed in the formal clothing of the wealthy (often white tie and tails or morning suits). The same actors could, and did, readily play the roles of artistocrats and pillars of the community. Walter Huston, for instance, appeared as a bank president in *American Madness* (1932) and as the President of the United States in *Gabriel Over the White House* (1933).

The class image of this species of gangster was frequently commented on by reviewers. Speaking of John Gilbert in *Four Walls* (1928) the *New York Times* reviewer said, "Mr. Horowitz is so careful regarding the cut of his clothes, the selection of his necktie, the spotlessness of his linen and the combing of his hair that one could never imagine him as a killer living on Manhattan's east side, but rather a broker with an apartment on Park Avenue."[8] And of Monte Blue in *Skin Deep* (1929), "The gangster chief is always to be seen attired in excellent taste. . . . Curiously enough, the master mind's henchmen are usually the lowest underworld types, presenting a ludicrous contrast."[9] Curious indeed, but not inexplicable. So much did the gangster resemble a blue-blood financier that he needed crude, proletarian sidekicks to make his criminality manifest.

The physical image, demeanor and speech were most important, but, in addition, the early gangster was often an explicit capitalist in his methods. Huston, in *The Ruling Class* (1931), headed what he called a "board of directors" who received checks according to what they had accomplished. And this whole group of gangsters frequently dealt in "gilt-edged securities," diversified their interests, and invested in businesses. Their principal occupation, of course, was bootlegging, an activity that required organization, the careful division of "territories," and legal and political manipulation.

Class conflict and implicit criticism of the world of business and finance are unmistakable in these films, lying so near the surface that they frequently shoulder their way free. It is interesting that films of this era dealing directly with capitalists and "millionaires," of which there were a great many, took the uncontroversial form of love romances, fantasies (inheriting a fortune) or comedies. The mask of the gangster film, fragile as it was, seems to have provided the right degree of displacement needed at this time for class criticism.

While this first generation of gangsters still dominated the screen, the second had made its appearance in the person of George Bancroft, the star of *Underworld* (1927), *Tenderloin* (1928), *Thunderbolt* (1929), and *The Mighty* (1929). Bancroft's lower-class origins were egregiously conveyed by his simpleton grin, his oversize hands and nose, his rough vitality and illiteracy. He is the most important progenitor of the type elaborated by Cagney, Robinson, Gable, Raft (in his early films), Carillo, Muni, McLaglen, and Eduardo Cianelli (Vanning). The shift in type must be the result of many forces. Before the stock-market crash the aristocratic gangster may have absorbed some of the resentment normally directed at the wealthy; but public attitudes were suddenly less mild; they were, indeed, sour and embittered. Instinct and a sense of the audience's mood must have played their parts, along with the rise of proletarian sympathies, the clamor against glorifying the criminal, "Latinizing" as a method of rendering the criminal comic (Raft, Carillo) or of making him an acceptable scapegoat (Cianelli), and other factors.

The end result, however, was to invert the class image in terms of physical appearance and life-style and to bring the forces of displacement and condensation into full, compensatory action. In general, the gangster retains his taste for formal dress, silk scarves and spats, but he usually looks *arriviste* or anthropoidal when wearing them. His capitalist affinities are more covertly projected by his language, his philosophy and his methods.

The advent of sound, of course, makes displacement into language possible and somewhat lessens the need for forceful visual coding. The gangster's speech, however, is not simply a substitute code—it is a partial disguise. The accent and vocabulary tell us that he is lower-class, and yet a lexicon of business terms surrounds him like an afflatus: "I got a *job* for you," "I *own* city hall," "This is a *business*," "Let's give him the *business*," "The *business* end of a gun." When, in *The Roaring Twenties*, a young lawyer tells Cagney, "This isn't my kind of law. I started out to be a corporation lawyer," Cagney, who has invested his bootlegging profits in a fleet of 2,000 cabs, says, "This is a corporation. We're making money." In the opening scene of *Marked Woman* Vanning strolls about the Club Intime giving orders in his broken Italianate English that demonstrate his organizational astuteness even as they reveal his illiteracy. But there is no need to elaborate this all too familiar element. What is important is its function as one trait in the condensed figure of the gangster.

Equally active are the conceptions that the gangster is egotistic, ruthlessly acquisitive, and ambitious to control or torment other people. The formation is, of course, the classic Freudian anal-sadistic. These two traits, when they appear in adults, are usually fused. It is important, therefore, to note that they are frequently presented as separate poles of the gangster's character, between which a contradiction may arise. A clear statement of the contradiction is Vanning's "You think I care for money? All I care about is to make people do what I tell them." The formulation is at least as old as *Little Caesar:* "Yeh, money's all right, but it ain't everything. Naaa, *be* somebody. Look hard at a buncha guys and know that they'll do anything ya tell'em. Have your own way or nothin'. *Be* somebody!"

The anal-sadistic formation is, of course, appropriate to the real capitalist character, but the emphasis upon sadism to the exclusion of acquisitiveness has an obscuring effect upon the gangster's identity, since it tells us that the formal clothes, limousines and penthouses are not his goals in life. Capitalists, in popular mythology, may be predominantly interested in controlling people, too, but they are always interested in wealth, and their sadism is not self-destructive or insane. Their cruelty reflects their alienation and loneliness—they are men who can possess Xanadu but not Rosebud. This pernicious conception, designed to placate the dispossessed, is also latent in those scenes in which the gangster finds himself alone; but it is not central. The sadism of the gangster functions more as a device than a trait: when it asserts itself we know that he is marked for destruction and that the melodrama will shortly complete its course.

Robert Warshow's well-known analysis of the tragic arc of the gangster's life is germane here.[10] The definition is, however, almost exclusively formal and generic; although it accounts well for the gangster's function in the melodrama, it misses an important function of the melodrama itself. The class criticism displaced upon the gangster's methods, tastes and acquisitiveness is obscured by his transformation into a sadistic villain who deserves his death solely for his cruelty. His exploitative methods, unlike those of the wealthy, are ultimately crude and palpable, and he can be brought to the bar of justice or shot like a mad dog without guilt.

Clearly, many more forces impinge upon the portrait of a gangster like Vanning than upon his aristocratic predecessors. The total effect is to almost obscure his significance behind a semantic welter, making him both exploiter and one of the exploited, indeterminate in class, after money but contemptuous of it, deserving of his death but somehow pitiable. His most important function, however, is to be the exploiter, to cause civic corruption, and to create the existential hell that Mary Dwight and her friends awaken to every morning. Vanning's penthouse is the reified suffering of his enslaved "girls," and his white silk scarf is the badge of his class. But lest we smell out his precise identity, we are faced with his illiteracy, his disinterest in money, and his madness. The Charles Foster Kanes of Hollywood have their flaws, but they die in beds reeking of mystified capital, reverentially pitied by those they have exploited, awesome to the end. Only obfuscated capitalists like Vanning are sent to prison—or die, like Little Caesar, in the litter behind a billboard.

Conclusion

Throughout the analysis I have attempted to stick to the task of applied criticism. I have deliberately slighted discussions of methodology because the prospect of validating the several methods I employ and then pushing all of that abstract lumber ahead of me through so lengthy an analysis was, frankly, overwhelming (it would also make a monograph of what was intended to be an article). I trusted, I hope correctly, that the many methodological articles now appearing in film magazines would provide a rear-projection against which my analysis would seem to move. My essential ingredients are Marxist, Freudian, and structuralist; but I would argue that the mixture is not heretically eclectic: structures and their permutations are central to each form of analysis, making them complementary and intrinsically suited to the task of illuminating a work rooted in class conflict. The idealist tendency of structuralism does not, I believe, invalidate it for a specific role in an ongoing materialist criticism: the description of transformational operations. The *substance, causes,* and *significance* of these operations must, of course, be sought for in the material realms of history and psychology—and I have, at least, begun this search.

But I have not yet sorted out the relations between the levels of opposition that were defined in the discussion of the ethos. The analysis of the figure of the gangster serves, I believe, to support the contention that *Marked Woman* is rooted in class conflict. It would be absurd to argue that this insight exhausts the film; but it does satisfy the requirement for an *optimal* criticism: one that illuminates the aesthetics, form and content of a work, as well as its relation to its era and to its creators. Class opposition, as we have seen, is displaced into a number of surrogate conflicts, most of which obtain at the level of the melodrama where the exploited face an unequivocal exploiter. Ethical dilemmas appear first. The intensity with which they are expressed seems proportionate to the intensity of the real-life dilemmas they displace; and their muddled logic reflects, in part, a struggle between desires to articulate and to repress class conflicts. As we move up the chain of displacement to the regional oppositions, class conflict is more covertly represented; as a result, there is less need for obfuscations and the oppositions are clearly and richly developed through the use of many codes. There are, in addition, tonal overlays (toughness, sentimentality), which cover the film like a skin, masking the real and substitute conflicts alike, and enticing the audience into solipsism and false emotion.

Marked Woman was produced toward the end of a rather bone-weary tradition. It is often mindlessly trite and perfunctory. But its makers had read their way through a depressing court record of real exploitation and suffering, and they approached the task of making the film somewhat as adversaries. If, limited by ability, temperament, and studio realities, they could only produce another melodrama, they could at least deny it a full life. By centering their attention upon the women, they mitigated some of the worst effects of the melodramatic form—and most certainly lessened their personal sense of venality.

As the women descend from the courthouse steps we know that they face a world without Vanning, but one in which they will still be exploited. If their exploitation is not analyzed, it is at least acknowledged and located in the real world. And yet—and yet—the melancholy blues theme rises on the sound track. Sentimentalism beckons: after all they are only women and their lot is suffering. Suddenly everything that has been gained seems perilously compromised. But against the music the camera pits the faces of the women. Bette Davis and the other actresses, who must have understood it all better than the men they worked for, cut through the swelling mystification with tough, implacable expressions. Let the Warner's music weep; the women are as alienated as the street, and they will not be sentimentalized.

Notes

1. Readers familiar with Althusser's "The 'Piccolo Teatro': Bertolazzi and Brecht" reprinted in *For Marx*, trans. Ben Brewster (New York: Random House, 1969), will recognize both my indebtedness to this essay and the many ways in which I deviate from it. I have also benefited from Karyn Kay's study of *Marked Woman*, "Sisters of the Night," *The Velvet Light Trap*, Fall 1972, pp. 20–25.
2. *The New York Times*, May 26, 1936, p. 2. I follow the *Times* account throughout because of its immediacy. There are more elaborate reports in Hickman Powell, *Ninety Times Guilty* (New York: Harcourt, Brace and Co., 1939), and in issues of *Liberty* magazine published soon after the trial. Warner's acquired the rights to the *Liberty* material (which was based on interviews with only two informants, "Cokey Flo" Brown and Mildred Harris) and used it as the ostensible basis for the film.
3. *Ibid.*, p. 2.
4. *Ibid.*, p. 2.
5. *Ibid.*, May 21, p. 4.
6. *Ibid.*, June 8, p. 8.
7. *Ibid.*, June 13, p. 6.
8. *The New York Times Film Reviews*, I (New York Times and Arno Press: New York, 1970), p. 465.
9. *Ibid.*, p. 558.
10. "The Gangster as Hero" in *The Immediate Experience* (New York: Doubleday and Co., 1962), pp. 127–33.

Addendum: Shall We Deport Lévi-Strauss?

In a recent article, "The English Cine-Structuralists" (*Film Comment*, May–June 1973), I reviewed the work of a group of English critics whom I designated "auteur-structuralists," faulting some of them for what I considered an improper and unproductive application of the structural method of Lévi-Strauss to the study of directors. I also described Lévi-Strauss's method and discussed its application to other areas of film study (really my principal interest). My article was intended to be an informative survey of what had been done and a suggestive prolegomenon to what might be attempted. The article has now received attacks (considerate, but damaging) from Geoffrey Nowell-Smith and Brian Henderson, both of whom point up what can only be called the assiduous naiveté of portions of my article.[1] Perhaps I shouldn't bother to respond, but I fear that if I don't, my article will continue to stand in opposition to their criticisms; and I would like to rise in my pew and acknowledge this Rosemary's Baby—after all, acceptance brought Mia Farrow some measure of peace.

My article was written at a moment when I was only half-emerged from a fetishistic attachment of Lévi-Strauss's method. My infatuation had no grounds in theory; it was merely idolatry, deriving from a long-standing interest in myth and ritual and my sense that Lévi-Strauss had provided the logico-mathematical tools by which they were henceforth and forever to be comprehended. Films were like myths, I reasoned, since they were communal in origin (Hollywood, or a given studio, could constitute a community—why not?); and directors might function as creators of myths (I adduced Renoir and others on the subject of the artist as myth-maker). But soon after the article was sent off I encountered Marvin Harris's destructive exposé of Lévi-Strauss's idealist premises in his *The Rise of Anthropological Theory.* Harris, a Marxist anthropologist, meets Lévi-Strauss on his own grounds and demonstrates that his almost exclusive concern with mental structures arose from his early grounding of kinship structure in the theory of reciprocal gift-giving. Lévi-Strauss reasoned that men exchange gifts (the most important being women) because of a universal psychological need arising from "certain fundamental structures of the human mind." But, Harris asks, Candide-like, "if reciprocity is so fundamental to the human psyche why do we have the ancient and contemporary condition of the opulent and powerful haves (possessing, among their valuables, more than their share of women) and the miserable have-nots?" In general, Harris argues, "Lévi-Strauss's picture of the human psychological landscape is . . . noteworthy for its disregard for the biopsychological, emotional, and affective drives and instincts. Hunger, sex, fear, love, are present, but they seem to be peripheral. More important for the French structuralist program is the basic propensity of the human mind to build logical categories by means of binary contrasts. For Lévi-Strauss such oppositions or dualities lie at the bottom of large portions if not the totality of sociocultural phenomena."[2] Harris's entire discussion, which surveys the history of idealism in French anthropology, should disabuse anyone of Lévi-Straussian hero-worship.

I still felt, however, that my article had value as a survey of a group of English auteur critics united by their use of structural method. But my unambitious history-of-ideas approach (Nowell-Smith begat Wollen begat Lovell) turns out to be inadequate because it is, as Nowell-Smith patiently demonstrates, "empiricist idealist"; because I was ignorant as to *why* this group of critics was attracted to structural method; and because my provincial Indiana situation led me to presume that English critics contacted each other's ideas (as I do) by reading criticism. But, Nowell-Smith informs us (in a passage as full of surprises as a piñata), the critics concerned were not attracted to structuralism because they wanted to import Lévi-Strauss into film study, but rather because they were seeking in the notion of structuralism "a materialist (or if you prefer objective) basis for the concept of authorship" redefined "as to take account both of the specifics of film production, which seem at first sight to deny the concept of the author/artist entirely, and of the equally specific authorial presence in the movie text." Equally surprising is Nowell-Smith's statement that some of the critics actually knew and talked to each other, apparently meeting at a sort of bar and grill called "London W.1." This is enough to send historians of ideas begging in the streets. And it has, of course, the deeper implications that a history of ideas is a helpless and false endeavor in the face of so diffuse a critical development. I only hope that my blind assumption that Lévi-Strauss was the "source" of their structuralist interests (which I based on Wollen's allusion) will stand corrected; it has already influenced Brian Henderson and exposed him to the same criticism I received. So, once and for all, there is no formal history of auteur-structuralism; and Nowell-Smith, Wollen, *et al.* were not attempting to employ Lévi-Strauss's method or to meet his standards.

This leaves standing the question of whether they should have been more demanding if they intended their structural analysis to be productive as well as corrective. I would still contend that the *Mythologiques* sets a standard for intelligence, subtlety, and conformity to its critical object (within its limited apprehension of its object) that bears comparison with the best of Barthes and Metz. It is because Lovell rather dabbles in structural analysis, for instance, that he is so exposed to Murray's disparagement of structuralist results.

But I may seem to be dragging Lévi-Strauss back through the transom after dismissing him through the door. Actually I am only attempting to bridge my way to the larger question of whether Lévi-Strauss's method has any future in film criticism. Brian Henderson masses a body of critics against structuralism itself in a long passage that cannot be easily summarized. I now substantially agree with what he says, having been educated by Harris and Julia Kristeva in particular,[3] but I would like to add my penny's worth on the kind of structuralism in which I am notoriously expert—Lévi-Strauss's.

The most fundamental question that one should ask, perhaps, is. "Are films Lévi-Straussian myths?" I think that Harris has indirectly answered this. The idea that any social group, even a tightly knit production team, could constitute a single entity bent upon "thinking" through a social dilemma, or projecting its universal mental structures into a film, or however one wants to put it, is a patent denial of the way men truly think, relate, and create. The gain to the critic of this idealist gambit is very real: it severs films from their existential roots, obviates the need for an abundance of facts, and makes the refining of concepts both easy and seemingly important.

A less simple issue is the status of Lévi-Straussian "dilemmas" of the sort that I isolated and discussed in my recent article on *Marked Woman* (*Film Quarterly*, Winter 1973–74). In the conclusion I stated that "The idealist tendency of structuralism does not, I believe, invalidate it for a specific role in an ongoing materialist criticism: the description of transformational operations." I was forced into this pragmatism by an awareness of a methodological split that had developed in the process of writing the article. Beginning with an idealist structural analysis of *Marked Woman* I found that the transformations I was dealing with could only be *comprehended* through the Freudian operation of displacement, and *accounted for* by a recourse to the Marxist notion of class conflict and its censorship in ideology. Since both Freud and Marx are structuralist in the broadest sense of the term (they deal in polarities and their structured relationships), I reasoned that I was merely being eclectic in wedding them to Lévi-Strauss. Specifically, I argued that such shifts as that from class conflict to ethical dilemma could be described as both transformational *and* the results of repression or censorship. I thought of these operations as occurring in the minds of the writers and director (and, for what they add in interpretation, the actors) with the censoring influences of the studio and class ideology ranked behind them. But clearly these operations cannot be idealist and materialist at the same time: minds cannot operate simultaneously divorced from their own history and psychology and engaged in them. Lévi-Strauss's description of the mental act whereby one attempts to resolve a dilemma by "transforming" it into another dilemma connotes a pure mental activity—the activity of what Husserl calls a "transcendental ego" exalted above, severed from, the contingencies of psychology, biology, and society (except in so far as one is *thinking* about a *social* dilemma).[4] The transformations I described, if the term is to retain its Lévi-Straussian connotations, are no such things. They *are* displacements produced by censoring influences. They occur because of complex personal and socially responsive acts of inhibition, assertion, obfuscation, and so forth. This amounts to more than a confession of methodological incest, however. It also, as Brian Henderson makes clear, argues a different theory for what a film text is, since it views it as a product rather than a "found object" analogous to a Lévi-Straussian myth.

All of this does not lead me to repudiate the insights of *Marked Woman;* one of them, that ethical dilemmas displace class conflicts, is, I discover, an independent corroboration of the *Cahiers* contention in its analysis of *Young Mr. Lincoln* that morality represses politics. But if one is to do more than penetrate the deeply symptomatic surface of *Marked Woman*, one must know more—all that there is to know—about the film's several creators, their working conditions and social situations.

Henderson ends by citing the *Cahiers* analysis as probably the best thing going in terms of an exemplary combination of film theory and analytic method. Adopting it, or a close variant of it, means that we will not only have to forgo the welfare-state comforts of idealist analysis, but also perhaps the more recently purchased luxuries of structures, codes, sign-systems, Nowell-Smith's authorial "structure in dominance," and the rest, and chart a retrograde course back into the dense, existential humus in which films, like all cultural events, reside. It's a little like coming out of a theater and discovering that the messy, contingent world is still there.

But whether or not one adopts *Cahiers'* specific proto-type—which is, of course, a custom job for *Young Mr. Lincoln* and will have to be modified for every use—film study is becoming increasingly demanding, just in terms of the organization of one's work, since everything needs to be pursued at once, presented at once, theoretically validated as it is presented, and subjected to scrutiny in terms of one's motivations for establishing categories and arriving at solutions (which, in turn, in the interest of truth, must be converted into problems of a new order). But maybe this is where film study is, since we are increasingly intolerant of self-serving narrowings of the field of inquiry ("I want to write about Delbert Mann") and expedient defenses for methods of study which "get results." In a sense this is less a choice between critical monism and holism than it is a growing conviction that monism won't work—a demand for a "totalizing" criticism, to use Frederic Jameson's term,[5] which has arisen with the disintegration of the whole formalist-idealist endeavor. At any rate, as my experience—and that of Graham Petrie at the hands of John Hess in the last issue of *Film Quarterly*—demonstrates, there is a stiff, cold wind blowing against partial, outmoded, or theoretically unsound forms of film criticism—and it just might blow many of them away.

Notes

1. Nowell-Smith, "I Was a Star-Struck Structuralist," *Screen* 14, no. 3 (Autumn 1973): 92–99; Henderson, "Critique of Cine-Structuralism I and II," *Film Quarterly* 17, no. 1 (Autumn 1973): 25–34; 17, no. 2 (Winter 1973–1974): 37–46.
2. Harris, *Rise* (New York, 1968), pp. 492–93.
3. Kristeva, "The System and the Speaking Subject," *Times Literary Supplement* (October 12, 1973), pp. 1249–50.
4. I am indebted here to Kristeva, *ibid.*
5. One should read the entirety of the final chapter of Jameson's *Marxism and Form* (Princeton, 1971), pp. 306–416.

Leave Her to Heaven: The Double Bind of the Post-War Woman

MICHAEL RENOV

The period of Hollywood film production in the immediate post–World War II years is a rich and varied moment of cultural production, due in large part to the prevalence of that fascinating object we call the "film noir." These were the years of elation and despair, the years of the industry's greatest box office success juxtaposed with that descent into fear and self-loathing we associate with the resurrection of HUAC, the inception of the blacklist and the curbing of Hollywood's power as an untouchable social institution.

But the roller coaster of the film industry's fortunes was but one manifestation of the volatility of the time; throughout America, at many levels of social life, rapid and disconcerting changes were the common fare of the 1940s. With the war, families had been up-rooted and divided; men went off to battle while women were implored to support the war effort in multiple, often contradictory ways. It is here, in the realm of social address to women, that I shall look for the historical antecedents for the development of a representational figure well-known to us—the evil woman of the film noir tradition.

In the early and mid-forties, the potentially culpable female, often shrouded in mystery and inscrutability, remained a candidate for vindication. Bad women were often counterweighted by good women placed in markedly parallel positions of narrative structure or within a clearly defined family arrangement (*Son of Fury, Orchestra Wives, In This Our Life*—all released in 1942), but by war's end this moral/ethical split

---

Michael Renov's "*Leave Her to Heaven:* The Double Bind of the Post-War Woman" originally appeared in *The Journal of Film and Video,* Vol. 35, no. 1 (Winter 1983), pp. 13–36. Reprinted by permission of the author and *The Journal of Film and Video.*

was likely to be condensed into a twin-sister structure as in *The Dark Mirror* or *A Stolen Life* (both 1946). From the twin structure, it is but a short step to the figure of the self-contained split, a persona of great pathological potential. I don't mean to imply here a rigidly historicist or deterministic pattern; certainly, representations of evil women have been prevalent since the beginnings of literature. Yet, it is hard to resist asking why a particular female representation, ranging from dangerously seductive to incorrigibly wicked, appears so vividly and so repeatedly by 1945 and 1946. Here I am thinking of *Scarlet Street, The Postman Always Rings Twice, The Razor's Edge, The Killers, Shock* and the object of my deepest consideration—*Leave Her to Heaven*.

It is my assumption that this outpouring represents neither a foisting of misogyny upon a viewing audience nor a backlash of popular resentment after years of valorization of the self-sacrificing female. Such notions are incapable of coming to grips with the disturbing sense of the partial complicity of women as spectators to this guilt-placing game. I would argue that, at some deep cultural level which I shall attempt to specify, a process of double binding had occurred by 1946 by which a profusion of contradictory cultural messages had produced a confusion, a self-distortion rich with the possibilities of schizophrenia. Although the women of America may not have killed their crippled brothers-in-law or destroyed their unborn children or themselves as the Gene Tierney character does in *Leave Her to Heaven*, the shifting, ultimately irreconcilable injunctions of government appeal, advertising and popular culture undermined the stability of the female self-image, thus enabling a degree of identification with the panic and rage of the pathological Tierney types.

I shall pursue this line of inquiry both historically and by textual analysis—first by examining public utterances of the mid- and late forties, then by looking at *Leave Her to Heaven* as a particularly dramatic instance of the double bind dynamic. For it is my claim that this dynamic constitutes both the hidden motor of female wrongdoing in the film and is the basis for the degree of receptivity and identification by the female audience of that time.

First, however, I would like to clarify the term "double bind," since it long ago entered the vernacular, simultaneously losing a great deal of its conceptual specificity. The double bind was initially theorized in a paper entitled "Toward a Theory of Schizophrenia" published jointly in 1956 by Gregory Bateson, Don D. Jackson, Jay Haley and John H. Weakland after some four years of research at Stanford University.[1] Originally conceived as an exploration of the etiology of schizophrenia, the double bind model came to provide a way of tracing the foundations of psychopathological and, to an extent, everyday behavior to the tangles of epistemological contradiction. The founding nexus of contradiction, according to the theory, is the family system; the original research theorizes the family relations which are schizophrenogenic—likely to produce schizophrenic behavior in the child. The double bind hypothesis posits a patient who had been reared in a particulr learning context in which the child is forced to respond to messages which generate paradox.[2]

The prototypical and recurrent formal sequence of the double bind environment occurs in the following way: The child receives a primary negative injunction—"Do not do so and so, or I will punish you" or "If you do not do so and so, I will punish you." The punishment to be avoided is either the withdrawal of love or the expression of hate or anger or, most devastating, the abandonment of parental attention.[3] A secondary injunction is thereafter introduced, conflicting with the first at a more abstract level, enforced in a similar manner. This secondary injunction is often communicated by non-verbal means such as posture, gesture, tone of voice or verbal implication. These conflicting messages may issue from one or both parents. For a concrete example of this pattern, consider the case of the hostile or withdrawn parent and normal affection-seeking child. When the child approaches, the parent exhibits withdrawn or hostile behavior, yet when the child responds to the original hostility through retreat, the parent exhibits signs of affection as a way of denying the original withdrawal. If the child approaches the parent in response to these latter signs of affection, the hostility is resumed, thus renewing the cycle.

Such is the force of this dynamic that, once the victim-child has learned to perceive his/her universe in double bind patterns, almost any part of a double bind sequence may be sufficient to precipitate panic or rage. Furthermore, the bound party suffers an impairment of the ability to read communicative and metacommunicative signals, so that violent, otherwise unexpected responses may be invoked by a social cue recognized as an element of the double bind process.

The family setting is the environment par excellence for theorizing this schema because escape is not feasible while response is demanded. That is, "one cannot *not* communicate."[4] Instances of this paradigm tend to occur within families in which overt parental agreement conceals covert disagreement. But although the deception may be realized and/or internalized by the child, he/she is unable to address the conflict directly, due in large measure to the degree of concealment, denial and inhibition inherent in the contradictory messages of the parents.[5] The double bind victim may in fact develop along more or less "normal" lines until an escalated level of anxiety exceeds a critical threshold. At this point, the patient switches into an alternate tension-releasing but potentially pathological response mode some of whose symptoms include "increased tension or confusion," "heightened preoccupation with suicide," "delusional accusations," "overt aggression," and "evidence of dissociation."[6]

John H. Weakland, a member of the original research group which generated the initial study of the double bind, subsequently suggested the possibility of "moving further toward a social psychiatry [by which] one could investigate the existence, handling and effects of incongruent messages in wider spheres of social and cultural organization."[7] It is with this premise in mind that I refer to the World War II years and their immediate aftermath as a moment of profound contradiction in the realm of public address to the American woman. Although I am convinced that the double bind dynamic during this period was pervasive and multiple, I shall single out two specific areas. In both instances, the self-contradictory injunctions are historically rooted, publicly communicated, yet privately experienced, in keeping with the character of ideological address.

The first double prohibition revolves around work and can be stated in the following manner: "If you women don't take jobs in the factories, schools, hospitals and offices across America, your husbands and sons will die and we will lose the war." In the words of Margaret Hickey, chairperson of the Women's Advisory Committee to the War Manpower Commission: "The day of the lady loafer is almost over." The most direct expression of the injunction can be found in the title of a War Manpower Commission booklet, *This Soldier May Die—Unless You Man This Idle Machine.*

Ironically, the object of this call to "man" the machines was the American woman. The woman-power appeals, using slogans such as "the more women at work, the sooner we'll win," were often preceded on radio broadcasts by the announcement of dead, wounded and missing in action from that community. One Office of War Information ad came right to the point in its attention-getting headline: "Woman of [fill in the town], are you making these casualty lists longer?"[8]

At a deeper level of consciousness, a set of contradictory injunctions fused, which enumerated the social horrors to ensue if the first injunction were obeyed. In the first place, a certain residue of the Depression remained, to wit: "If you women work, bread-earning men will be humiliated and unemployed." Although vigorously countermanded after Pearl Harbor, this message had been legally enforced by the Economy Act of 1932 which stipulated that government jobs could not be held by two family members; wives were fired. Memories of such Depression directives lingered in the popular consciousness. For example, childcare facilities, woefully inadequate to begin with, were utilized by less than 10% of those in need. After years of conditioning the necessity of self-improvement and prideful independence, working women felt the taint of the dole in public childcare. Even in the aftermath of the war experience and the elevation of status and pay scale for the woman worker, a 1946 *Fortune* magazine poll indicated that a mere one-quarter of the women surveyed agreed that all women deserved an equal chance for a job regardless of their economic need to work. Less than one-half of the sample felt that even those women forced to support themselves were entitled to equal opportunity.[9]

But the effects of Depression thinking were but one component of the anti-work injunction, the second half of this double bind mechanism. Another ingredient involves the "latch-key child" syndrome and the rising public awareness of juvenile delinquency. The common cry was against women who opted for the challenge and exhilaration found outside the home in addition to the necessities of child-rearing. The message here: "If you women don't stay home and remain full-time mothers, our children will become riotous, our society will decay." There was little official attention given to the double duties inherent in the female worker's lot. If, as eventually happened, she needed to take off entire days to shop, clean and care for the sick in her family, she was reminded of the dramatically higher absentee rate of women. The statistics offered proof of female unreliability and provided negative reinforcement when the opposite was vitally needed.

An awareness of the difficulties of contradictory message-sending is evidenced in many government documents, including a folder entitled "Womanpower Campaigns" issued as a confidential directive of the Office of War Information to its community offices ("This is confidential and must not be circulated except to government agencies"). Among its suggested strategies is a curious even insidious form of positive reinforcement—insidious for its neglect of the other half of the double bind. "By an overwhelming recognition of the woman *on the job*," says the OWI, "we hope to make all women who are not working wonder why they are not." Or a bit later, ". . . any strong, able-bodied woman who is not *completely occupied* with a job and a home is going to be considered a 'slacker' just as much as the man who avoids the draft." Here, the double duty is directly alluded to, but with the sense that the tasks of home and workplace are complementary rather than contradictory. These governmental opinion-makers were absolutely prepared to stand a conventional value on its head if it furthered a war aim; to consider the psychic fall-out from destabilizing self-definition was a luxury unthinkable during wartime. Hence, the exemplary rhetoric of the Womanpower pamphlet: "What kind of *hands* have you? Pretty, peacetime palms? Or slightly work-roughened ones—broadened and strengthened and made far more beautiful by physical effort? Are the hands *capable*, can they accept *responsibility*, are they proud of honest dirt?"[10]

The second double bind set is based in the immediate post-war female experience and is related to the contradictory requirements of the wife and mother. The first term suggests, "If you are not an absolutely dedicated nurse, helpmate and love partner, our men will never recover from their wartime traumas." Films such as *Pride of the Marines* and *The Best Years of Our Lives* provide direct dramatizations of the injunction while a similar, more mediated pattern of rehabilitation is undertaken by Jane Wyman in *Lost Weekend*. A part of the recovery phase for the returning vet was the security of an old job, which meant that many women workers were summarily dismissed. In fact, the female had from the first been considered a temporary worker by government and industry leaders, although never acknowledged as such publicly. Within one month of the war's end, 600,000 women were laid off; more than two million by November 1946.[11] Not surprisingly, the "Blue Ribbon Citizen," according to a pamphlet prepared by the War Advertising Council entitled *How Your Advertising Can help the Veteran Readjust to Civilian Life*, is pictured as a smiling, bright-eyed, carefully coiffed woman whose virtues are stated in the intransitive. This valorized passivity provides a dramatic contrast to the heavily promoted action verbs of "doing" and "becoming" addressed to the female in her immediate past. Now the active position is male; wordless support is female. The "Blue Ribbon Citizen":

> Like all good people, she asks no questions, weeps no tears, doesn't stare at disabilities. To her, a returned veteran is an abler, more aggressive and resourceful citizen than the boy who went away. She's proud of him, proud to know him. Anxious to be of real help. She's the kind of person we should all be.[12]

The second and contradictory injunction reminds the woman: "If you do not bear children, especially sons, dutifully and in large number, the American way of life for which so many suffered and died will be seriously threatened." The childbearing priority was noticeable throughout the war in various forms. In such melodramas as *Journey for Margaret*, *Penny Serenade*, *Tender Comrade* and *To Each His Own*, the child is portrayed as the suture for the family and the hope for civilization. Advertising images throughout the war heralded the reproductive female for her role as the bearer of the future. Ads underscored the bond between mother and newborn son, who were capable of surviving the absence of the adult male as father and husband. In the copy of an ad which appeared in the Christmas 1942 issue of *Life* magazine, the mother tells her son: "Now we two are about to celebrate our first family Christmas though your father will not be here. We have loaned him to America." The romantic couple so familiar to us from Hollywood cinema is replaced by the new, forward-looking couple—mother and son.

A particularly applicable advertising image selling an innovative, high tech baby carriage in a *Mademoiselle* magazine in January 1945 makes tangible the split of the wife/mother roles. While one woman hangs onto her man in seeming adulation, the concentration and handhold of the other woman are firmly placed on the baby-carrying device. For the woman so recently initiated into the machine secrets of the industrial workplace, this baby carriage appears to offer precision and mobility. The image also maps out the bifurcation of female attentiveness, particularly in a post-war context when men demanded the nurturing attention of their women. The infant is constituted by demand as a biological necessity—for the breast, for physical protection, for the maternal touch. The affection and focus of concentration tendered in this image is directed *either* to the man *or* to the child. And this bifurcation speaks the split I am indicating.

But the mobility promised by this baby carriage was less and less available to the American mother as the birthrate climbed to all-time highs; the population increased by some 18.5% during the fifties. The book *Modern Woman: The Lost Sex*, a much-quoted volume appearing in 1947 written by female psychiatrist Marynia Farnham and social scientist Ferdinand Lundberg, went so far as to suggest that female sexual pleasure and childbirth were inseparable. "We are saying that for the sexual act to be fully satisfactory to a woman she must, in the depths of her mind, desire deeply and utterly to be a mother. . . . If she does not so desire . . . it will be sensually unsatisfactory in many ways and will often fail to result in orgasm." Although the wife/mother contradiction has been with us from the first and has been managed well enough, the historical pressure on women to pursue both wifely and motherly functions—vigorously and therapeutically—engendered an inescapable sense of inadequacy in the post-war era. Wife and mother were the traditional roles; surely the woman proved so competent in so many new social roles could excel at the two most familiar to her. Yet it is crucial to recall that this high-pressured set of contradiction-producing messages, never perceived as such, provided a convenient displacement of the arena of conflict. The psychic energy required for the struggle to maintain a presence in the workplace was certainly undermined by the domestic push whose twofold nature, I would argue, were themselves devilishly irreconcilable.

It is here that I return to the film text, *Leave Her to Heaven*, for it is my claim that the evil-doing of the Tierney character is traceable to a double bind dynamic which is virtually invisible at the level of narrative exposition. It is crucial to note at this stage that this extrapolative reading does not attempt to complete the puzzle of female iniquity, fragmented and left incomplete by the play of narrative, but rather goes beyond the 1946 historical consciousness to suggest the epistemological conditions which can produce both a representational pathology and a basis for identification with that pathology. At the outset, it is worthwhile noting the clues to Ellen Berent's pathological behavior offered by the film. An attorney friend of the Berent family, Glenn Robey, is the nominal source of the flashback which is the body of the film. As narrator, Robey's words bear a certain weight as he observes to his companion, as if in explanation of Ellen Berent's crimes, ". . . of all the seven deadly sins, jealously is the most deadly" and, one might add, the most stereotypically feminine. Ellen's triad of homicides—of the crippled Danny Harland, her unborn son and herself—are meant to be the actions of a jealous woman. In fact, the roots of her disturbance must be looked for elsewhere.

The moment of Ellen's first meeting with author Richard Harland (Cornell Wilde) offers visual evidence of a crucial transference on Ellen's part and an intensity of psychic investment which this transference calls forth. Ellen is shown reading Harland's book whose dust jacket—Harland's face—replaces her own face. This blocking of her visage is a startling sign of her emotional truncation, her desire to replace a portion of her identity and selfhood with that of another person, a male person. Her first lines of dialogue provide a connection to a preexistent family dynamic. "I didn't mean to stare at you," says Ellen to Richard, "but you looked so like my father . . . when he was younger . . . a most remarkable resemblance." And still later, as she takes Dick to meet her mother and cousin, she remarks further on the resemblance: "His face, his voice, his manner—it's uncanny." We learn from Ellen of the unusual bond between her recently deceased father and herself: "We were inseparable . . . from the time I was able to walk, we were both happiest when we were together."

Soon after Dick and Ellen's meeting, the Berent family gathers at the Robey's ranch in New Mexico where Dick observes an unsettling ritual; Ellen, dashing on horseback along the mountain ridges like a goddess possessed, scatters Professor Berent's ashes from an urn. This in accordance with a prior agreement between father and daughter. That night, Ellen confides a particularly significant thought to Dick: ". . . I know now, people you love don't really die." For Ellen, this thought is incontrovertible; she has displaced her arguably preternatural attachment for her father onto Harland. Instead of exorcising the hold of the primal father by the ash-scattering, Ellen has in fact celebrated the successful transfer of her obsessional attachment. At the moment of their betrothal which she instigates, Ellen whispers to Dick: "I'll never let you go . . . never, never, never." Ellen's imprecation, uttered once again at the moment of her death, is the sign of a transmutation formed within the double bind system—affection turned to violence.

What appears to be a strongly marked female Oedipal attachment yields much more on closer analysis. First, the words of Mrs. Berent in answer to Dick's inquiry on the causes of Ellen's increasingly disturbed behavior: "There's nothing wrong with Ellen . . . it's just that she loves too much . . . perhaps that isn't good . . . it makes an outsider of everyone else . . . you must be patient with her . . . she loved her father too much." Still later, Ellen's cousin Ruth offers a reading of the Berent family system in an angry flurry aimed at Ellen: "With your love you wrecked mother's life, with your love you pressed father to death, with your love you've made a shadow of Richard." In this manner, Ellen is constructed as the source of the family's troubles rather than as a participant in a structure into which she was born. Thus Ellen's violent acts are presented as the inevitable results of her over-cathected, destructive affections. We are here offered a pseudo-explanatory model of the "evil woman" of post-war fame—filled with a corrosive, all-consuming passion which preys particularly on men, a creature better left to heaven than to rational explanation.

Although an analysis of the representational family, the Berents, is difficult due to its contradictory and enigmatic character—which, one need add, it is the work of the narrative to produce—it is possible to reconstruct a family scene indicated by the fictional representation which is redolent of the double bind dynamic. In much the same way that the double bind dynamic remains a concealed component in the destabilizing of the American female self-image in the post-war period, the double bind scenario constitutes the generative conditions for Ellen Berent's pathology. Ellen, the only child, receives the greatest affection from her father from whom she is inseparable. The mother, on the other hand, remains an outsider from what would seem to be the most highly charged family circuit. Mrs. Berent has adopted her own child Ruth, approximately the same age as Ellen. (We are told in Ruth's encounter with Harland: "I'm a cousin . . . I've lived with them since I was a child . . . *Mrs. Berent* adopted me.") Ellen, in the meantime, could only have encountered emotional responses of the most contradictory kinds from her mother and father: deep affection from the latter, inattention if not hostility from the former. The more affection shared with the father, the more antipathy from the mother—a classic schizophrenogenic arrangement. A clue to the mother's feelings is offered early on when, the hour being late, Harland questions Mrs. Berent as to Ellen's whereabouts: "Suppose something happened to her?" says Dick. The reply: "Nothing ever happens to Ellen."

One scene midway through the film stands out as proof of Ellen's unease with her mother and cousin—the "other half" of the Berent family. Ellen has begun to show signs of unhappiness at the remote cottage, Back O' the Moon, when her perfect isolation with Harland is disturbed by the crippled brother Danny and handy man Thorn. Misreading the source of her displeasure, Dick summons the other Berents to the cottage, a move which intensifies Ellen's discomfiture more than Harland could know. It is predictable that the expression of intra-familial hostilities of this sort would be blocked and inhibited, never directly communicated. Another instance of Harland's unintentional blundering occurs during Ellen's first meeting with Danny in a Warm Springs, Georgia, sanitarium. "I hope you like her, Danny, 'cause if you don't we'll send her back." Such an off-handed remark could only produce profound disturbance in a person who has perceived a similar desire in her own mother—that is, "to send her back."

At the level of the narrative, the young Ellen's response to the systematically contradictory universe which she comes to inhabit would be to invest more and more into the one source of emotional sustenence—the father. Harland is made to replace the now-absent love-object, but under quite different conditions. Ellen had occupied a wifely position vis-à-vis Professor Berent, but as a wife free to concentrate exclusively on the mate rather than on childbearing, here effectively removed as an option. But with Harland, she is soon forced to share her love object with a crippled brother who receives Harland's warmest attention. Somewhat later she becomes pregnant as a lure to Harland's flagging affections, only to self-abort in a moment of panic and self-loathing (she sends herself hurtling down a flight of stairs). At each moment of irrational expression, Ellen has reached that critical threshold referred to by the Bateson group resulting in a tension-releasing, but pathological response. The schizophrenic's ability to read and offer metacommunicative signs is severely impaired; Ellen is incapable of expressing her accelerating sense of suffocation resulting from the withdrawal of the love-object already once lost through her father's death.

Ironically, Ellen originally presents the image of an ideal and dedicated wife. In a scene just after their marriage, Ellen serves a perfect luncheon to Dick. Dressed in a pink peasant blouse with flounced sleeves, accompanied by soft, domestic music, Ellen expresses her obsessive desires in a speech which apotheosizes the post-war idea of wifely devotion, here rendered ominous in its excess.

> I have no intention of hiring a cook, a housekeeper or any other servant—ever. I don't want anyone else but me to do anything for you. I'm going to keep your house and wash your clothes and cook your food . . . besides, I don't want anyone else in the house besides us.

"Ever?" asks Dick. "Ever," replies Ellen.

The final element of the pathological pattern concerns the effects of introducing a child into the Ellen-Richard relationship. Recall that the appearance of the child in the original Berent family scheme, Ellen herself, was the occasion of the full materialization of the rift between husband and wife. With the introduction of Danny, Ellen perceives a duplication of the previous, crippling family dynamic. Responding in what looks to be cold premeditation, Ellen lets Danny drown in the lake as she looks on from behind dark glasses. Here are the signs of a radical dissociation, an act of violence motivated by the demands of self-protection as perceived by the double bind victim. The second murder, that of the biological child, is even more dramatically dissociative; Ellen's tumble down the stairs is, in a literal sense, aimed at a part of herself which she wishes to deny and destroy. For it is Ellen herself who is the original interloping child; the objects of her pathological gestures have been mere substitutes for herself. The violent act functions as a relief of guilt for the original family dysfunction for which she blames herself. The previous murders were but vain efforts at enacting the final gesture of her pathology—self-annihilation.

I have sketched out the play of the double bind dynamic at two quite distinct levels, both of which require a certain expansion from the original theory. In the first instance, the notion of contradictory injunctions and their effects was applied to the level of mass society. Various forms of public address aimed at the female audience, particularly government promotion and advertising imagery, were examined for their destabilizing of the self-image of the post-war woman. Here I suggested that this confusion of self-image fostered a degree of identification with the proliferation of "evil woman" representations of the day. The second application of double bind theory was to a specific filmic text in which an acute and recognizably female pathology is represented. Here too—at the level of narrative and image-making, the level of representation which was earlier termed instrumental in the disruption of the self-esteem of real women—I have located a debilitating double bind system. Despite its fictional grounding, the misrecognition of the etiology of the Tierney character's violent behavior offers a valuable and somewhat analogous model for the social analysis which precedes it. Certainly, much remains to be done by way of theorizing the linkage between the historical and representational levels of analysis. Yet, it seems to me that such concrete hypotheses as double bind theory offer a fertile avenue of research for those of us who seek to understand the relationship between cultural expression and human experience in an historical frame.

Notes

1. Gregory Bateson, Don D. Jackson, Jay Haley, and John H. Weakland, "Toward a Theory of Schizophrenia," *Double Bind: The Foundation of the Communicational Approach to the Family* (New York: Grune & Stratton, 1976), pp. 3–22.
2. Gregory Bateson, Don D. Jackson, Jay Haley, and John H. Weakland, "A Note on the Double Bind," *Double Bind* (New York: Grune & Stratton, 1976), p. 39.
3. Bateson et al., "Toward a Theory of Schizophrenia," pp. 6–7.
4. Carlos E. Sluzki and Donald C. Ranson, "Comment on Part One," *Double Bind* (New York: Grune & Stratton, 1976), p. 47.
5. John H. Weakland, "The 'Double Bind' Hypothesis of Schizophrenia and Three-Party Interaction," *Double Bind* (New York: Grune & Stratton, 1976), p. 27.
6. *Ibid.*, p. 34.
7. *Ibid.*, p. 37.
8. Eleanor F. Straub, "Government Policy Toward Civilian Women During World War II," PhD dissertation, Emory University, 1973, p. 137.
9. *Ibid.*, p. 322.
10. Office of War Information, "Womanpower Campaigns," p. 3, Box 156, Record Group 208, Washington National Records Center, Suitland, Maryland.
11. J. E. Trey, "Women in the War Economy—World War II," *The Review of Radical Political Economics*, Vol. 4, No. 3, Summer 1972, p. 48.
12. War Advertising Council, "How Your Advertising Can Help the Veteran Readjust," p. 6, Box 167, RG 208, WNRC.

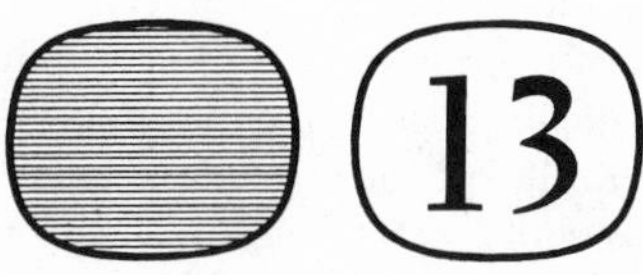

Madness, Authority, and Ideology in the Domestic Melodrama of the 1950s

DAVID N. RODOWICK

The difficulty with submitting the term melodrama to a conclusive, critical definition is that it is such a historically complex phenomenon. Moreover, this problem is complicated by the apparent ease with which it is possible to point out melodramatic situations and conventions in a wide variety of dramatic and literary media of different historical and cultural situations.

The development of a melodramatic tradition would seem to coincide, in fact, with the evolution of many popular narrative forms, including that of the cinema. Without doubt, the early development of the American narrative film was determined in part by its internalization of a melodramatic tradition, inherited from the 19th century novel and theater, which was already characterized by considerable formal and stylistic diversity. The problem of melodramatic "specificity" was then further complicated through its incorporation by a new narrative form which, in its turn, blossomed into a variety of styles and genres; Warner's social melodramas, Capra's "populist" melodramas, and so on were themselves engaged in patterns of cross-fertilization. Thus, even well-defined genres like the western and gangster film[1] were heavily determined by their melodramatic content.

In this manner, Thomas Elsaesser discusses melodrama not as a distinct genre, but

David N. Rodowick's "Madness, Authority, and Ideology in the Domestic Melodrama of the 1950s" originally appeared in *The Velvet Light Trap*, no. 19 (1982), pp. 40–45. Reprinted by permission of the author and *The Velvet Light Trap*.

"as a form which carried its own significant content: it served as the literary equivalent of a particular, historically and socially conditioned *mode of experience*,"[2] which, as he points out, was endemic to the history of the bourgeoisie as a social class. He then continues by saying that "even if the situations and sentiments defied all categories of verisimilitude and were totally unlike anything in real life, the structure had a truth and a life of its own." In this respect, melodrama might best be understood as an aesthetic ideology which, in accordance with a historically specific complex of social, cultural, and economic determinations, "enables a series of possible forms and disables others."[3] As such, it is a structure of signification which may reproduce itself within a variety of narrative forms (or indeed, create new forms) by organizing the historically available series of discourses, representations, concepts, values, etc., which constitute the dominant ideology, into a system of conflict, which, in its turn, produces the fictive logic of particular texts.

Perhaps this can be clarified by addressing a historically specific form of melodrama—the domestic or family melodrama of the 1950's. According to Geoffrey Nowell-Smith[4] the domestic melodrama may be understood as the conjunction of three sets of determinations, which I would like to revise and expand in the course of this article. They are: (1) a set of social determinations (which restricts the representation of the social relations of production to the sphere of influence of the bourgeois family); (2) a set of psychic determinations (which concerns the problem of individual identity within the represented set of social relations); and (3) a formal history. It is necessary to understand that these determinations are themselves the products of more general ideological formulations whose internalization by the melodramatic text may promote varying degrees of difficulty in its narrative structure. In this manner, a particular aesthetic ideology (in this case the domestic melodrama) is produced which confronts the organization and enunciation of its principal sets of determinations as a problematic to which it must find an aesthetic "solution." As Terry Eagleton notes,

> It is important to grasp here the closeness of relation between the "ideological" and the "aesthetic." The text does not merely "take" ideological conflicts in order to resolve them aesthetically, for the character of those conflicts is itself overdetermined by the textual modes in which they are produced. The text's mode of resolving a particular ideological conflict may then produce textual conflicts elsewhere—at other levels of the text for example—which need in turn to be "processed." (*Criticism and Ideology*, p. 88).

Thus, it is also essential to recognize that the relationships formed among the sets of determinations are not necessarily symmetrical. In any given text, they each have their own internal complexity and "a series of internally and mutually conflictual relations may exist between them" (Eagleton, p. 61). As critic Pierre Macherey has noted,[5] such relations may introduce elements of structural dissonance within the text which are visible in its failures of signification. These dissonances are not, however, the reflection of ideology (which, in any case, will admit no contradictions to itself), but they can be read in the structure of its effects in the text: its discontinuities, abjurations, equivocations; in sum, its "eloquent silences." Thus, between ideology and the textual modes in which it is worked, there is an uneven quality, an incompleteness, a distance between the aesthetic "solution" and the determinate condition which ideology has placed on the articulation of the "problem." Therefore, what ideology cannot admit appears as contradiction within the work of the text, and what the text cannot resolve it must displace and attempt to work out at another level or within another problematic. It is precisely the structure of these displacements within the melodramatic text, and the system of textual silences in which they are dispatched, which interest this analysis.

1.1 Social Determinations

In the domestic melodrama, this set of determinations concerns itself with a representation of the social relations of production, in which the institutions of family and marriage, as well as the iconography of the middle class home, are privileged "contents." This does not mean that other institutions (for example, the law, medicine, education, etc.) are excluded from representation; however, it is significant that the structure of institutional authority, and its function in the represented social formation, is only understood to the degree that it receives and reproduces the structure of familial politics. But notice the curious paradox which takes form here: although the family tries to substitute itself, *pars pro toto*, for the global network of authority in which it is implicated, it also imagines itself as a world divested of significant social power addressing itself to an audience which does not believe itself to be possessed of social power.[6] The domestic melodrama is attentive only to problems which concern the family's internal security and economy, and therefore considers its authority to be restricted to issues of private power and patriarchal right. The power it reserves for itself is limited to rights of inheritance and the legitimation of the social and sexual identities in which it reproduces its own network of authority. The right of inheritance, then, may be enlarged to describe the social values and norms valorized by a given system of conflict in which a more global set of ideological determinations produce the family as "a microcosm containing within itself all of the patterns of dominance and submission that are characteristic of the larger society" or "a legitimizing metaphor for a hierarchical and authoritarian society."[7]

1.2 Psychic Determinations

"In all institutions, something of the individual gets lost." This line of dialogue from *The Cobweb* perfectly expresses the central crisis of the domestic melodrama where individual identity is defined as a problem to the extent that it is out of sync with the relations of authority which are required to legitimate it. As Geoffrey Nowell-Smith explains:

> What is at stake (also for social-ideological reasons) is the survival of the family unit and the possibility of individuals acquiring an identity which is also a place within the system, a place in which they can both be "themselves" and "at home," in which they can simultaneously enter, without contradiction, the symbolic order and bourgeois society. It is a condition of the drama that the attainment of such a place is not easy and does not happen without sacrifice, but it is very rare for it to be seen as radically impossible. ("Minnelli and Melodrama," p. 116)

It is in this process that the sets of social and psychic determinations are crucially linked.

In this intersection of the two sets of determinations, the social and the psychic, the figuration of patriarchal authority plays a central role. The figuration of patriarchal authority need not be characterized by a single character (although this is often the case); rather it defines the center of a complex network of social relations whose symbolization is undertaken by the domestic melodrama. Thus, in a film like *Magnificent Obsession*, it can be a purely imaginary figure (the saintly Dr. Phillips, whose death causes a deep structural wound in the social-ideological fabric of the text which can only be repaired by gradually molding the character of Bob Merrick to fill his place in the social economy of the narrative), or indeed this function can be split, distributed across a number of characters as in *The Cobweb*. It is through this symbolization that the condensation of institutional and familial authority takes place with the overdetermination of the latter as a kind of knot in which all representations of authority are given form. As the linch-pin on which the structure of conflict will turn, it is a system of power against which the logic and the order of the representations of social relations are measured. Thus, the figuration of patriarchal authority in a given text will formulate the terms of conflict through the perpetuation of a series of symbolic divisions and oppositions which organize the narrative around the problem of individual identity, both social and sexual. Moreover, it is interesting to note that the domestic melodrama demands that, in the last instance, sexual identity be determined by social identity. In this manner, the family both legitimizes and conceals sexuality by restricting it to a social economy defined by marriage—men assume the place of their fathers in the network of authority, and women are mirrored in this network by their relationship to men as wives, mothers, daughters, etc.

The form which the problematic of identity takes is one of the crucial determinants of the domestic melodrama. The forward thrust of narrative is not accomplished through external conflict and the accumulation of significant actions, but rather through the internalization of conflict in a crisis of identification: the difficulty which individual characters find in their attempts to accept or conform to the set of symbolic positions around which the network of social relations adhere and where they can both "be 'themselves' and 'at home.' " And here I must emphasize the word "difficulty," for although the domestic melodrama rarely acknowledges the *impossibility* of this identification (as Nowell-Smith points out), it may readily concede its *failure*. The signs of this failure are given form in the dissatisfaction and sexual *angst* so common in the melodramatic protagonist as well as the unpredictable outbreaks of violence which are given an expressly psychological tone: from impotence to hysteria and from alcoholic depression to full-blown psychoses, the domestic melodrama runs the full gamut of psychological disorders. The conditions of this failure are already present in the terms which consider desire to be a fundamental danger to successful socialization and thus require the division of sexuality from sociality. This problem is especially crucial in the representation of women who, split between the passive, suffering heroine and the turbulent sexual rebels, are identified in the relations of patriarchal authority only by their systematic exclusion. In this manner, feminine sexuality is always in excess of the social system which seeks to contain it. One need only think of the scene in *Written on the Wind* where Dorothy Malone's wild dance is cross-cut with her father's death to comprehend that the domestic melodrama can only understand sexuality as a kind of violence and a threat to narrative stability.

It is significant here that the melodramatic text forces the equation of sexuality with violence, for the greater the repression of desire in the narrative system, the greater the energy of its displacement as violence against the system. Unlike more action-oriented, outward-directed genres, whose narrative structures may contain and evenly distribute excesses of violence and sexuality across a closely regulated system of conflict, the melodrama is better characterized as a centripetal system which directs these forces inward. Or more precisely, the expression of violence would seem to be regulated only by an economy of masochism which often gives the narratives a suicidal thrust, channelling the disruptive forces back into the system. In this manner, the melodramatic text is balanced on the edge of two extremes, one of which is inertial (the paralysis of the system, its resistance to change or any form of external development) and the other of which is entropic (where action is expressed only as an irrational and undirected surplus energy).

The inability of the system of conflict to resolve these two extremes—that is, to find a way to compromise the inertia of the law (the social system defined by patriarchal authority) and the restlessness of desire within the individual characters—constituted a real crisis of representation for the domestic melodrama. In other words, the domestic melodrama was required to build concrete, cinematic narrative structures out of a highly internalized and introverted system of conflict which would also rationally account for the *failing* of this system. The solution of the genre was the incorporation of the discourse of popular Freudianism[8] and the tendency to organize its patterns of conflict in rather self-conscious oedipal terms. Thus, even melodramas which did not explicitly refer to psychological subjects seemed to demand this interpretation by several criteria: (1) the refusal to understand the economy of the social formation in anything but familial, personal, and sexual terms; (2) the definition of conflict as a struggle with patriarchal authority; (3) the tendency to describe in psychological terms the difficulty of identifying oneself in the social network founded in patriarchal authority. This solution had two distinct advantages. First, it provided a means for naturalizing the often irrational and unpredictable behaviors of the melodramatic protagonists. But secondly, and most importantly, it produced a form of narrative which could satisfy the contradictory demands of this genre in which the tension between sociality and sexuality was both the product and the subject matter of a system of conflict which played out this drama of "demand, refusal, and wounded desire,"[9] but only in an ambiguous way. Thus, on one hand, the adoption of a self-conscious oedipal structure established a pre-determined symbolic path in which the resolution of the conflict was measured against a successful identification with authority. In this scenario, patriarchal authority could automatically represent itself in the network of social relations as a self-producing, and thus ahistorical category. That this path was mined with contradictions, I have already explained. However, even in those moments when the narrative systems produced by this scenario of identification were on the point of collapse, the oedipal structure was ready to consider itself reflexively as a hermeneutic system which could produce a rational explanation for the objective signs of its own failure.

In summary, even though the incorporation of the oedipal scenario enabled the domestic melodrama to establish a concrete form of narrative organization, this scenario still reproduced, within its own structural relations, the central contradiction of the genre—the impossibility of an individual reconciliation of the law and desire. This structure could thus resolve itself either on the symbolic level (acceptance of authority) or on the hermeneutic level (which accepted madness and usually self-destruction), but not both. In a moment, I will attempt to explain the historical conditions which led to this stalemate.

1.3 Formal Determinations

It is necessary to understand that structurally and stylistically the domestic melodrama is a product of a history of forms—a confluence of narrative codes and conventions—some of which are cinematically specific, some non-specific. As I have already pointed out, the narrative structure of the domestic melodrama was at least partially determined by a number of non-specific conventions (with which, one might add, it was also historically non-synchronous) through its internalization of a 19th century narrative tradition.[10] At the same time, of course, the development of the domestic melodrama was determined more directly by a history of cinematically specific forms and styles in which the film melodrama had already concretized a network of influences drawn from diverse styles of composition, lighting, and editing, etc., as well as conventionalized forms of cinematic narrative structure.

Briefly, I would like to examine some points of form which characterized (more or less specifically) the domestic melodrama of the 1950's. As Thomas Elsaesser explains, the domestic melodrama was

> at its best perhaps the most highly elaborated, complex mode of cinematic signification that the American cinema has ever produced, because of the restricted scope for external action determined by the subject, and because everything, as Sirk said, happens "inside." To the "sublimation" of the action picture and the . . . musical into the domestic and family melodrama there corresponded a sublimation of dramatic values into decor, colour, gesture and composition of frame, which in the best melodramas is perfectly thematised in

> terms of the characters' emotional and psychological predicaments. ("Tales of Sound and Fury," p. 7)

It should be understood here that the highly expressive mise-en-scène of the domestic melodrama did not so much *re*produce as *produce* the inner turmoil of the characters; or in other words, the dynamic relations of the mise-en-scène took over the objective signification of the social network which entrapped the characters and strictly determined their range of physical and emotional mobility. "This is emphasized," Elsaesser continues,

> by the function of the decor and the symbolization of objects: the setting of the family melodrama almost by definition is the middle-class home, filled with objects, which . . . surround the heroine [or hero] in a hierarchy of apparent order that becomes increasingly suffocating. . . . [It] also brings out the characteristic attempt of the bourgeois household to make time stand still, immobilise life and fix forever domestic property relations as the model of social life and a bulwark against the more disturbing sides of human nature. (pp. 12–13)

Here, one might also point out the extreme compartmentalization of the frame common to the domestic melodrama in which the decor of the home (via window and door frames, mirrors, partitions, grille-work, etc.) is used to isolate the characters architecturally and emphasize the lack of human contact in their home environment.

The isolation of the characters is also expressed in the organization of point of view and in the more global orchestrations of narrative structure. It is in this manner that the domestic melodrama thrives on the multiplication of silences, alibis, and misunderstandings generated in the characters' incomplete comprehension of the melodramatic situations in which they are implicated, or the degrees to which their actions (or lack of action) tend to further complicate those situations. Thus, narrative devices such as alternating montage (as in *The Cobweb*) or flashback structures (as in *Written on the Wind*) tended to introduce an ironic distance between character point of view and the narrative voice of the film which underlined not only the power and complexity of the represented social network, but also the absence of any possibility of self-determination within that network.

It should be clear, then, that the domestic melodrama tended to reproduce in its formal economy the drama of inertia and entropy in which the social and psychic determinations collided. Thus, on one hand the reification of the bourgeois universe was reproduced in the compositional space through the compartmentalized frame and the proliferation of a world of objects which defined the characters only in their isolation. On the other hand, the mobility of the syntagmatic relations, and the ironic point of view they provided, were able to cumulatively give form to the progressive disorder which individual characters could unknowingly introduce into the narrative system.

2 History and Ideology: The Ambiguity of Domestic Melodrama

In "Tales of Sound and Fury," Thomas Elsaesser points out that the popularity of melodrama often coincides with periods of intense social or ideological crises, and that relative to the given historical context, melodrama could function either subversively or as escapist entertainment according to ideological necessity. Thus, in the period where the bourgeoisie was still a revolutionary class, the melodrama served a subversive function, but later,

> with the bourgeoisie triumphant, this function of drama lost its subversive charge and functioned more as a means of consolidating an as yet weak and incoherent ideological position. Whereas the prerevolutionary dramas had often ended tragically, those of the Restoration had happy endings, they reconciled the suffering individual to his social position by affirming an "open" society where everything was possible. (p. 4)

In either case, an extreme polarization of values remained constant (e.g., good vs. evil, virtue vs. corruption, heroism vs. villainy, etc.), and despite a variety of situations and predicaments, the structure of conflict was essentially the same, preserving the moral order from a largely external threat. Both cases were also concerned with the representation of the bourgeois family as the means through which the structure of patriarchal authority could be reproduced and reconfirmed. In this manner, the nature of the conflict and the conditions of its resolution relied on either the enforced separation of families or the resistance to their formation as prompted by an immoral force; but in either instance, the natural "right" of bourgeois authority and values ultimately went unchallenged. Thus, when the melodrama functioned "subversively" it was because its class interests were being challenged by an enemy (the aristocracy) which resisted its historical destiny.[11]

What isolates the domestic melodrama of the 1950's from this historical tradition is its inability to fully internalize either of these two functions. In other words, it contained within itself two contradictory demands—one determined by a history of conventions which required an "affirmative" resolution, the other the product of more contemporary ideological demands on the text—which, paradoxically, existed as counter currents within the same structure. Thus, on one hand the affirmative tendency seems to have been restricted to the conventional "happy end," though as Douglas Sirk described, it could often be only an ironic appurtenance included at the demands of the studio heads.[12] On the other hand, the structure of conflict common to the domestic melodrama was produced *internally* by contradictory forces which challenged the bourgeois family and patriarchal authority from within. Therefore, the domestic melodrama could only lapse into an ironic form because it lacked several traditional criteria for arriving at the narrative "solution" demanded of it: faith in the power of self-determination and the ability to transform society through individual action, a structure of conflict built on a system of black and white values, and a transcendental faith that identification with the law (patriarchal authority) predetermined the outcome of conflict through a moral destiny.

Here I can only suggest a highly schematic outline of the historical conditions which produced this phenomenon: though risking oversimplification, I would tend to characterize it as the failure of the ideological system produced in the post-war period to insure social normalization and the orderly transition to a peace-time economy. In this context, the necessity of redefining and reestablishing the place of the individual in the social formation became crucial.[13] This was initially confined to the reintegration of men into the labor force, and thus the restoration of women to the home. This reestablishment of social identities was effected in the promise that, through the sacrifice of the war effort, the restoration of "democratic capitalism" and a free enterprise system would reinstate the possibilities of economic and social mobility. However, the ideals that one's future could be self-determined and that prosperity was assured through individual labor and adherence to the system were largely contradicted by the aggressive expansion of corporate capitalism along with a burgeoning system of bureaucracy. It soon became clear that social identity was not determined through individual effort, but by one's place in a monolithic and hierarchic network of authority in which the range and power of individual action were highly restricted.

A second area involved a changing perception of the nature of potential threats to a political and ideological stability. The threat of nuclear annihilation had tempered somewhat the possibility of direct, armed confrontation, and therefore the Cold War was conceived mostly as a conflict of ideologies with "domestic" stability at stake. Moreover, there was an increasing paranoid fear that the next threat to society would come from within through the internal subversion of democratic ideologies (witness, for example, the power of the Red Scare and the scale of its effects on the entertainment industry). In addition, the relative affluence of the Eisenhower era, and the steady growth of a commodity culture, paradoxically contradicted this vision of internal instability—one began to wonder if economic stability really did guarantee social stability.

Thus, what characterizes the aesthetic ideology (that is, the domestic melodrama) is the absence of any reflection on the terms of the general ideology which has placed a determinate condition on its production. Of course, this is perfectly consistent with the demands of the melodramatic imagination which, as Althusser points out, can only be dialectical as long as it ignores the real conditions which subtend it by barricading itself within its own myth.[14] However, it is precisely in the absence of such a reflection that we can read the structure of its effects: the "eloquent silences" of the domestic melodrama which map out the network of resistances in which its narratives fail. At the very center of this network, giving form to the contradictions of the general ideology while ignoring its historical filiation to it, is the figuration of patriarchal authority. Thus, where the melodramatic Father formerly functioned to legitimate the system of conflict and guarantee its resolution by successfully identifying its heroes on the side of the law, morality, and authority, in the 1950's he functioned solely to throw the system into turmoil by his absences through death or desertion, his weaknesses, his neglects, etc. In this manner, the failures of identification so characteristic of the domestic melodrama, and the self-conscious "oedipal" solutions they demanded, can be directly linked to the figure of the Father as representing either the very sign of madness (the transgression of the law he represents) or as an empty center where the authority of the law fails. As a film like *Bigger Than Life* demonstrates so well, the relationship between madness and authority was in a sense two expressions of the same term. Either pathetically castrated or monstrously castrating, the figurations of patriarchal authority completely failed the social and sexual economies of the melodramatic narrative and the structure of conflict in which they found form.

The failure of the domestic melodrama, then, would seen to take place in the form of a historical displacement in which the contemporary demands of ideology had become partially disjunct with the set of formal conventions which were required to articulate it. Thus caught between the suspended resolutions which marked the stalemate between its social and psychic determinations, and the demands for a "happy ending" which would "reconcile the suffering individual to his social position," the domestic melodrama could only

> produce ideological discourses as to display variable degrees of internal conflict and disorder—a disorder produced by those displacements and mutations of ideology forced upon the text by the necessity to arrive, in accordance with the laws of its aesthetic production, at a "solution" to its problems. In such a text, the relative coherence of ideological categories is revealed under the form of a concealment—revealed by the very *incoherence* of the text, by the significant disarray into which it is thrown in its efforts to operate its materials in the interest of a solution. (Eagleton, p. 86)

3 Conclusion

The domestic melodrama of the 1950's might best be understood as an aesthetic ideology whose means of expression were organized by three sets of determinations—social, psychic, and formal. In this manner, the kinds of narratives produced by this aesthetic ideology were characterized by three factors: (a) the systematic refusal to understand the social economy of the text, and the historical conditions which gave it form, in anything but familial and personal terms; (b) a highly internalized narrative structure taking form in a drama of identification which often understood itself in self-consciously oedipal terms; and (c) a system of conflict determined by the figuration of patriarchal authority which in turn mediated the relationship between the social and psychic determinations in the text. However, the internal economy of the aesthetic ideology was disrupted by the contradictory demands of the general ideology which promised, through an acceptance of its authority, a world of economic mobility, self-determination, and social stability, but delivered in its stead a hierarchic and authoritarian society plagued by fears of the internal subversion of its ideologies. This contradiction was structurally reproduced in the inability of the melodramatic text to evolve as either a fully affirmative or fully subversive form. Split between madness and authority, it could either adopt an arbitrary and purely formal resolution (in which case its social and psychological dilemmas would remain unresolved), or else it could let its crises of identification follow their self-destructive course (in which case the power of authority came into question). In reality, the domestic melodrama usually opted for a partial solution—articulated through one or two of the sets of determinations—which fell between these two extremes. In this manner, the melodramatic Father, failing the symbolic order of which he was the center, still functioned as a sort of "destiny" in the narratives, but one which introduced a structural disorder in the organization of the three sets of determinations into a system of conflict.

Notes

1. See, for example, Charles Eckert's "The Anatomy of a Proletarian Film: Warner's *Marked Woman*," *Film Quarterly*, 27, No. 2 (Winter 1973–74), 10–24.
2. "Tales of Sound and Fury: Observations on the Family Melodrama," *Monogram*, No. 4 (1973), p. 5.
3. Terry Eagleton, *Criticism and Ideology* (London: Verso Editions, 1978), p. 4.
4. See his "Minnelli and Melodrama," *Screen*, 18, No. 2 (Summer 1977), 113–19.
5. See his "Lenin, Critic of Tolstoy" in *A Theory of Literary Production*, tr. Geoffrey Wall (London: Routledge and Kegan Paul, 1978), pp. 105–35.
6. See, for example, Nowell-Smith, pp. 114–15.
7. Sylvia Harvey, "Woman's Place: The Absent Family of Film Noir," in *Women in Film Noir*, ed. E. Ann Kaplan (London: British Film Institute, 1978), p. 24.
8. See, for example, Elsaesser, pp. 11–15.
9. Paul Ricoeur, *Freud and Philosophy: An Essay on Interpretation*, tr. Denis Savage (New Haven and London: Yale University Press, 1970), p. 372.
10. For an interesting discussion of the relationship between 19th century narrative and film, see Janet Bergstrom, "Alternation, Segmentation, Hyponosis: Interview with Raymond Bellour," *Camera Obscura*, No. 3/4 (Summer 1979), especially pp. 87–103.
11. Elsaesser notes, "The same pattern is to be found in the bourgeois tragedies of Lessing (*Emilia Galotti*, 1768) and the early Schiller (*Kabale and Liebe*, 1776), both deriving their dramatic force from the conflict between an extreme and highly individualized form of moral idealism in the heroes and a thoroughly corrupt yet seemingly omnipotent social class (made up of feudal princes and petty state functionaries)" (p. 11).
12. See Jon Halliday, *Sirk on Sirk* (New York: Viking Press, 1972), especially pp. 82–135.
13. While writing this section, I was fortunate to see, for the first time, *The Best Years of Our Lives* (1946), a film which not only addresses this problematic with surprising directness, but which in the end also adopts a purely melodramatic solution for its series of conflicts.
14. See his "Le 'Piccolo' Bertolazzi et Brecht (Notes sur un théâtre materialiste)" in *Pour Marx* (Paris: François Maspero, 1977), pp. 130–52.

Melodrama and the Women's Picture

PAM COOK

Melodrama has been more hotly debated than any other genre in cinema. Its potential to move the audience deeply while laying bare the impossible, painful contradictions of social and personal relationships appeals strongly to radical film critics, and recent feminist interest has focused on the way in which it deals with aspects of women's experience marginalised by other genres. Feminist criticism has shifted the terms of the debate and enlivened it. In particular, it has brought forward the women's picture, a sub-category of melodrama and one of the most despised and neglected genres, as an important object of critical investigation. The women's picture is differentiated from the rest of cinema by virtue of its construction of a "female point-of-view" which motivates and dominates the narrative, and its specific address to a female audience.

At the beginning of the melodrama debates in the early 1970s, attention focused on the most sophisticated, "accomplished" examples in Hollywood cinema of the 1940s and 50s, authored by great directors like Douglas Sirk, Vincente Minnelli, Fritz Lang. Hollywood's women's pictures, the "weepies," were either subsumed within this category, or, in the case of those which were unauthored, blatantly generic and identified by their female stars rather than by directors, were mentioned in an aside, or not at all. Subsequently, the relationship between melodrama and the women's picture has been assumed rather than argued, although feminist criticism has begun to draw some distinguishing boundaries. The Gainsborough melodramas provide an opportunity to

Pam Cook, "Melodrama and the Women's Picture," in *Gainsborough Melodrama*, BFI Dossier 18 (1983). Reprinted by permission of the author and the British Film Institute.

look at these critical debates in terms of a particular historical manifestation of the women's picture, and to suggest some directions in which future discussion might move.

Cinema Melodrama: Roots and Definitions

It is notoriously difficult to define melodrama. Everyone has their own idea of where its roots lie, and attempts to trace its history often take on the complexity characteristic of melodramatic plots themselves. Thomas Elsaesser made one of the earliest and most influential attempts to trace a line through its multiple traditions in literature and drama to the highpoint of Hollywood melodrama of the 1950s. He separates out "the melodramatic" as an expressive code which uses drama and music to heighten and intensify emotional effects, and which can be found in widely different cultural forms. He identifies its origins and generic development in the medieval morality plays, oral narratives and folk songs, through eighteenth-century romantic drama and sentimental novels to the nineteenth-century historical epics of Charles Dickens and Victor Hugo, pointing to a radical ambiguity at the heart of melodrama: its moral emphasis (stories of innocence persecuted and virtue rewarded) was countered by the ironic use of music and voice to comment critically on the moral tale. Moreover, the focus on individuals as the site of sexualised class conflict allowed it to present social struggle and change explicitly, and, depending on historical and social context, criticise the *status quo*. The complex narratives of melodrama, deriving from its focus on social transition, the twists and turns of "outrageous fortune," provided another level on which the simplistic moral content was complexified, and often undermined or contradicted. Extending this to Hollywood cinema melodrama of the 1940s and 50s, Elsaesser describes the use of "cinematic counterpoint" in the most "sophisticated" melodramas to work against the current of ideology: the most gifted directors used all the potential of *mise-en-scène* (colour, lighting, wide-screen) and narrative structure (compression, displacement, ellipsis) to create a closed, hysterical world bursting apart at the seams in which the protagonists, unable to act upon their social environment, suffered severe psychological and emotional symptoms (paranoia, masochism, hysteria) which were displaced onto the expressive codes of the films themselves. For Elsaesser, the power and importance of melodrama lies in its ability to produce a criticism of the oppressive domestic property relations of the middle-class bourgeois family, and it is this argument that sets the terms of the debate: under certain historical conditions, and depending on the presence of a gifted director who can use the ironic potential of *mise-en-scène* and narrative, melodrama can be mobilised in the interests of social criticism.

Elsaesser's argument was taken up and explored by a number of critics; its auteurist bias meant that it was developed in a certain direction, interest focusing on a small number of 'sophisticated' melodramas which could be defended as "progressive," rather than on a historical appraisal of the genre in cinema as a whole. The historical approach emerged subsequently, after feminist critics intervened to shift the terms of the debate towards the general question of the representation of women in Hollywood cinema.

Feminist Approaches to Melodrama

Laura Mulvey's discussion of Douglas Sirk's melodramas, while retaining an auteurist approach, shifts the emphasis away from the search for the "progressive text" towards the function performed by melodrama in working through the contradictions of women's position in society. Reconstituted as an object of feminist study, melodrama is useful in helping us to understand how women are positioned under patriarchy so that we can formulate strategies for change.

Mulvey finds the roots of melodrama in Greek drama, and distinguishes two traditions: the tragic melodrama, in which male oedipal problems dominate the scenario, and melodrama "proper," which is dominated by the female protagonist's point-of-view as a source of identification. In the former, the feminine domestic sphere acts as a critical corrective to the overvaluation of virility by the male social order, whereas in the latter the male perspective is displaced by the point-of-view of a female protagonist whose desires structure and order the narrative. This distinction opens the way to discussion of the women's picture as a separate strand of melodrama, and Mulvey takes up Elsaesser's description of the ironic function of the expressive visual code: in women's melodrama, she argues, the protagonists are unaware of the forces which shape their destiny; the visual code on the one hand provides the audience with an indication of the characters' emotional state, and on the other with privileged knowledge of their situation, offering the spectator a position of moral superiority from which to judge the characters. Using *All That Heaven Allows* as an example, Mulvey describes how, in the women's melodrama, the woman transgresses socially accepted class and sex barriers, only to find her transgression turned against her by society: family and friends punish her, and her final happiness is marred by a bitter twist of fate. The woman who acts on her desires, challenging conformity, suffers, and it is this conservative moral emphasis in the women's picture that feminist critics object to. Mulvey hints that the women's picture is potentially more contradictory than this. The positing of a female point-of-view at the centre produces a problem, an excess which the Hollywood narrative cannot contain and which troubles its resolution. These "troubled narratives" mark the woman's desire to escape her fate as pure fantasy, ultimately unrealisable. In Mulvey's example, *All That Heaven Allows*, the heroine's desire to return to a lost pastoral ideal is both marked as a dream in the overblown romanticism of the *mise-en-scène*, and rendered unobtainable by a final cruel twist of fate. More recently, Charlotte Brunsdon has explored this question of the self-consciously fictive element in the romantic happy endings of women's melodrama in relation to 1970s Hollywood women's pictures, arguing that their lack of plausibility works both to recognise and accentuate the impossibility of the fulfillment of women's romantic fantasies. I would argue that the marked ambiguities inherent in the narrative structure and ironic *mise-en-scène* of the women's picture are the cinematic equivalent of the discourses of fantasy and romance in women's romantic fiction, which, as Janet Batsleer has pointed out, relies on an overt and excessive use of cliché, superlatives and purple prose to create a utopian dream world. The women's picture is similarly marked as "fiction," or daydream, locating women's desires in the imaginary, where they have always traditionally been placed.

For Barbara Creed, "the woman's melodrama is a moral tale." She emphasises that the trajectory of the films is along an "axis of female transgression, desire, sexuality, temporary happiness, opposition, separation, atonement, capitulation. It is one of mutually contradictory states: possession and loss, desire and frustration, presence and absence, power and impotence, fulfilment and lack." For Creed, whatever the contradictions worked through, the narrative emphasis is on replacing women within patriarchal ideology, within the confines of marriage and the family, where they are ultimately unable to act on male society to change it.

The feminist emphasis on the conservative bias of melodrama stems from a wider critique of classic narrative cinema. Feminist film criticism has constructed this cinema as the site of the working through of male oedipal problems, and the retrenchment of male/female power relations in favour of male domination. The resolution of the drama may not be unproblematic: in melodrama in particular the feminine is frequently valued as a corrective to masculine values. But the feminine corrective is defined in traditional terms: "feminine" virtues of caring, compassion and sensitivity are set against "masculine" aggression, violence, destruction. The feminine corrective is mobilised to redress the moral balance; it can modify, mediate, but it can never act to destroy, or to radically change society. (The powerful, destructive heroines of melodrama rarely survive; if they do, they lose whatever they most wanted.) Moreover, it is a feminity defined exclusively as maternal.

In my view, feminist scepticism about melodrama is totally justified. But there is a pessimism about many of the arguments which tends to close down discussion by emphasising the ways in which melodrama forecloses on female desire. It is important, I think, not to lose sight of the basic contradiction Mulvey points to: in order to appeal to a female spectator, melodrama must first posit the possibility of female desire, and a female point-of-view, thus posing problems for itself which it can scarcely contain. Furthermore, if, as Elsaesser suggests, melodrama characteristically comes to the fore at times of social and economic upheaval, which inevitably produce repercussions in the film industry too, then melodrama emerges from, and must negotiate, a matrix of contradictory determining factors: economic, social, historical, ideological and industrial. At different moments different elements predominate, allowing for a wide variety of different emphases on the basic problematic.

Molly Haskell has attempted to define the many different varieties of women's picture, and the different patterns of female experience they articulate. She identifies three kinds of heroine: the extraordinary, upper middle-class woman who aspires to an independent existence; the ordinary middle-class woman who is a victim of her society; and the ordinary working-class woman who aspires to be mistress of her fate, but whose aspirations are defeated by the primacy of passion, love and emotion. One or more of these heroines are set in the context of four thematic categories which can co-exist or overlap: Sacrifice (the woman must give up whatever is most important to her for the sake of moral order); Affliction (the woman is struck down by illness/misfortune as atonement for transgression—her own or another's); Choice (the woman is faced with a choice between two suitors, representing two different ways of life); and Competition (women compete for the attention/love of the hero, often discovering in confrontation that they prefer one another to him). Haskell also points to the "middle-classness" of the women's picture, the way in which middle-class values and aspirations are set up as ideals, or are used as the standard by which actions are to be judged.

Feminist film criticism has been enormously productive in opening up the women's picture and in indicating the strategies it uses to position women. One question insists: why does the women's picture exist? There is no such thing as "the men's picture," specifically addressed to men; there is only "cinema," and "the women's picture," a sub-group or category specially for women, excluding men; a separate, private space designed for more than half the population, relegating them to the margins of cinema proper. The existence of the women's picture both recognises the importance of women, and marginalises them. By constructing this different space for women (Haskell's "wet, wasted afternoons") it performs a vital function in society's ordering of sexual difference.

In trying to understand what is at stake in the construction of a sub-genre called the women's picture, it is important to look at the ways in which it differs from other "male" genres, and also how it is related to the genre of melodrama itself, since this relationship is not always self-evident. Laura Mulvey has argued that cinema melodrama deals with the private world of sexual relationships and the family, and represents the "other side" of the stoical heroism of genres such as the western, which marginalise women. Within this general distinction, Mulvey distinguishes further between tragic melodrama, in which the male point-of-view predominates, and women's melodrama, in which events are seen from the female protagonists' point-of-view. I should like to take Mulvey's distinction as a starting point, elaborating on some of her observations in the interests of a more general approach to the women's picture. I will also draw on some of the other arguments about melodrama and women's pictures outlined above, and my remarks are, at this stage, essentially speculative.

Tragic Melodrama and the Women's Picture

Mulvey's distinction is useful on several levels: by focusing on the different construction of "masculine" and "feminine" points-of-view, it shifts emphasis away from the representation of women in melodrama to a more complex notion of the ways in which the genre orders and contains sexual difference; it draws attention to the problematic status of the woman's point-of-view placed at the centre of the Hollywood narrative; and it enables us to look at the women's picture as a separate but related strand of melodrama, to begin to understand why it has suffered from wholesale critical neglect, while maintaining mass popular appeal.

The distinction between masculine and feminine points-of-view is not always easy to maintain, particularly in melodrama where there is often a softening of sexual difference, and a merging of masculinity and femininity. Also, the construction of point-of-view in cinema is a complex process which is not simply reducible to identification with characters. Here, in talking about the construction of a female point-of-view, I am referring to the ways in which, in the women's picture, the female protagonist's perspective is presented through a combination of first-person (subjective) and third-person (objective) strategies roughly equivalent to those used in novels. In practice, the distinction between tragic melodrama and women's melodrama is not clear-cut; to imply that a masculine point-of-view predominates in tragic melodrama is not to suggest that it does not also offer feminine points-of-view, and vice versa in the women's melodrama, or that real spectators simply identify with one or the other according to their sex. But if, as feminist film theory has argued, classic narrative cinema is marked by the predominance of a masculine perspective to which the feminine is subordinated, then it is important to ask what the consequences are of the apparent reversal of this state of affairs in the women's picture. Women's melodrama shares many of the basic characteristics of tragic melodrama, but it also reverses some of them.

OEDIPAL CRISIS

It has been argued that male oedipal problems are the mainspring of the action in tragic melodrama. The hero's incestuous desire to challenge the power of the father and take his place drives the narrative forward along a linear trajectory, though ironic twists of Fate can complicate the narrative. The tragic hero is brought low, redeeming himself through a new-found humility. He becomes aware of his guilt, and the reasons for his suffering (e.g. *Tarnished Angels*, *Written on the Wind*).

In the women's melodrama the heroine's oedipal desire to take the place of the mother predominates, but in contrast to the tragic hero her position as subject of desire is presented as a problem of lack of knowledge and understanding of the forces which control her destiny (e.g. *All That Heaven Allows*). She frequently finds herself in a world she does not fully understand, and which she must investigate (e.g. the 1940s Hollywood women's pictures, *Rebecca*, *Suspicion*, *Secret Beyond the Door*). Her perspective is often distinguished as paranoid, and the status of her perceptions (are her intuitions right or wrong?) is always in question. Her access to knowledge is blocked, and her desires are presented through narrative and *mise-en-scène* explicitly as fantasy. The construction of the woman's point-of-view privileges intuition, emotion, accident, questioning the validity of female desire in that very construction. The narrative structure is often circular rather than linear, circles within circles, delaying final resolution (as in *All That Heaven Allows*, where the heroine is returned, ironically, to the position of mother in the very act of trying to escape it).

SOCIETY

In tragic melodrama, society is kept at a distance, subsumed into Fate or Destiny. The hero is alienated from society, unable to act to change it, trapped in a closed world of domestic property relations where power rests in kinship structures and patterns of inheritance. This world is oppressive and inward-looking, leading to violent emotional excess (e.g. *Home from the Hill*, *Two Weeks in Another Town*, *Written on the Wind*).

The women's melodrama reverses this situation. The heroine's transgression resides in her desire to act against socially accepted definitions of femininity, bringing her face to face with society. Work or a career is set against maternity and the family, and the heroine often gives up both for the sake of love, the "grand passion" (e.g. John Stahl's 1930s women's pictures *Back Street* and *When Tomorrow Comes*). The heroine suffers for her transgression, sometimes with death, but her humiliations are small-scale and domestic compared with the tragic hero's epic downfall.

THE VISUAL CODE

In tragic melodrama, the expressive visual codes of *mise-en-scène* are used to heighten the intense emotional suffering of the protagonists, and so can act as an ironic visual commentary on the simplistic moralism of the plot, or can undercut middle-class values by showing that they lead to repression and violence. In women's melodrama, the visual code can also be used to express the feelings of the heroine, and to offer her point-of-view as a focus for identification. Household objects, furnishings, clothes are all important as indications not only of her social status, but of her state of mind. But as Mulvey points out, codes of lighting and colour cannot be perceived by the characters, and are used to provide privileged information to the spectator about them. As outlined above, the women's melodrama uses the visual code to mark the woman's world as fantasy, and to show that the woman's point-of-view is limited in comparison with the spectator's. So female desire is problematised, located outside knowledge in the realms of the imagination.

From these preliminary remarks I should like to offer some general speculations about the women's picture, which would clearly need to be tested against specific historical examples. The construction of a genre specifically addressed to women, demanding a central female protagonist who is the active subject of desire rather than the object of male desire, presents a problem for the classic narrative which it can only contain by in turn problematising the woman's point-of-view, by representing it as paranoia, hysteria, or by overtly fictionalising it. The woman's ability to see is frequently questioned; she may be literally blind (*Magnificent Obsession*) or blinded by desire (*Spellbound*), or lost in a world of shadows and uncertainty (*Rebecca*, *Suspicion*). Her desire is often presented as a symptom, resulting in mental and physical illness (Joan Crawford in *Possessed*, Bette Davis in *Dark Victory*) so that her body becomes an enigma, a riddle to be read for its symptoms rather than an object of erotic contemplation. This hysterical body is inaccessible to the male protagonists, often a doctor or psychiatrist who fails to understand it adequately, to explain it, or to cure it (e.g. *Three Comrades*). Thus it threatens to slip out of male control, and the only solution is frequently the heroine's death. The male body, by contrast, *is* presented as an object of erotic contemplation for the heroine, who actively desires the romantic hero, but the problematisation of female desire in the women's picture means that her choice of the romantic hero as love object is usually masochistic, against her own best interests, and she suffers for her desire.

The Women's Picture as Commodity

"The women's picture" does not only evoke a specific and exclusive mode of address; it also suggests an object of exchange, designed to be consumed by a particular group. Its existence is an indication of the film industry's recognition of the importance of women as an audience, and in a wider economic context, of women as consumers of commodity products. One element in the women's picture's address to a female audience is to women as consumers, whether mothers, housewives or working women, although the emphasis on consumption depends on the period. Charles Eckert has analysed the way in which the Hollywood studios of the 1930s set up a system of "tie-ins" with other consumer industries, arguing that films became showcases for product display. Stories were set in "fashion salons, department stores, beauty parlours, upper and middle-class homes with modern kitchens and bathrooms, large living rooms and so forth" (Eckert, 1978, p. 20). Female stars reached an unprecedented zenith during this period, endorsing consumer goods such as cosmetics, fashion, jewellery, kitchen and other household equipment, while Hollywood produced a steady output of women's pictures dealing with contemporary women's experience from the heroine's perspective, featuring female stars whose faces and bodies appeared everywhere in advertisements for consumer products. Eckert's analysis is useful for demonstrating that audience address does not simply reside in the textual strategies of films themselves; but the strength of his closing remarks on the women's picture lies in his recognition that in order to capture its target female audience, the film industry had to mobilise desire in that audience. Eckert's account leaves off precisely at the point where feminists begin: the specific ways in which women's pictures activate feminine desire. As he suggests, a combination of his historical approach and detailed analysis of particular films could throw light on the powerful appeal of the women's picture to female audiences at different historical moments.

History and the Women's Picture

On one level, then, the women's picture emerges from a historical economic imperative: the attempt to capture and exploit a female audience in the interests of consumerism, which vary according to the given moment. In this sense, it is explicitly tied to history: it must deal with the images of women in circulation in society (even if set in another period) in order to gain recognition from its audience. It has to stimulate desire, then channel it through identification into the required paths. It negotiates this contradiction between female desire and its containment with difficulty, often producing an excess which threatens to deviate from the intended route. Eckert's analysis cannot account for this excess: it implies a complex, but rather neat process. Feminists, on the other hand, look for excess as a sign of the system threatening to break down.

Both Eckert and Haskell suggest that the Hollywood women's picture emerged in the 1930s, when the American economy grew wise to the potential of cinema as a vehicle for product display, and to women's purchasing power, coinciding with changes in the film industry which led to an influx of women script-writers and stars. It continued into the 1940s, when various kinds of women's pictures proliferated in Hollywood (Higham and Greenberg, 1968), and were shown on British cinema screens, a period which is of particular interest to the Gainsborough melodramas produced at this time.

I have argued that any attempt to theorise the women's picture must be sensitive to historical change. No genre evades history: although basic patterns and concerns may remain constant, their particular configurations shift, emphases change, certain elements are excluded, and so on. A brief look at the Hollywood women's pictures of different periods reveals enormous differences between, for instance, John Stahl's 1930s films, the Joan Crawford/Bette Davis/Barbara Stanwyck 1940s "weepies," and Douglas Sirk's 1950s Universal melodramas, to mention but a few.

The Gainsborough 1940s melodramas, while retaining some of the characteristics of Hollywood's melodramas, are different again, differences which can be traced to their circumstances of production in war-time and post-war Britain and its film industry. Although the links between history, production conditions and films are not straightforward, I would argue that any discussion of the Gainsborough women's pictures in terms of the way they construct femininity in order to appeal to a female audience should recognise the historical specificity of this female audience as British and wartime, or immediately post-war.

As feminist historians have indicated (Riley, 1981; Wilson, 1980), the period of the war and the years immediately following was contradictory and confusing in its attitude towards women. Women's labour was important (albeit temporarily) to the war-effort, and married women were encouraged to work by the provision of child-care facilities. At the same time, there was a prevailing anxiety about the falling birth-rate and the disintegration of the family under pressure of war-time sexual mores, leading to planned population control and the growth of contraceptive education which could potentially free women's sexuality from reproduction. During the war, short-term sexual relationships, adultery and illegitimate births flourished; sex, passion and the drama of emotional life were brought to the fore, breaking up family unity (Minns, 1980). After the war, although the temporary concessions to working mothers were withdrawn, and married women were once more predominantly thought of as mothers rather than workers, there was still a need for female labour in certain areas. It was not entirely a question of pulling women back into the family, rather of placing them differently in relation to post-war social democratic ideals, to which a healthy family life and the "good mother" were indeed vital. I haven't space to develop this history here, but I want to emphasise the unstable nature of this transitional period, characterised by a prevailing climate of opinion which gave rise to a number of different, often contradictory representations of femininity. Moreover, although the actual economic and sexual emancipation of women which the war years encouraged was more or less submerged by the post-war emphasis on motherhood and family, I would argue that the *idea* of the emancipated "free" woman, monogamous, but active, dedicated to self-help and capable of fighting for what she wanted, was important to post-war social democratic ideals of a better world for everyone.

In their attempt to capture the female audience, then, the Gainsborough women's pictures had to negotiate this complex network of shifting influences, to dramatise the contemporary sexual and emotional conflicts of women's lives. The films work through these conflicts, bringing contradictions to the surface. They present their heroines' lives as in transition, undergoing radical changes as the result of choices wisely or unwisely made. Women are presented as active, able to affect the progress of history, but the choices they make must be the right ones if a healthy British society is to be built. A number of ideals of social health are set up (e.g. in *They Were Sisters*), among them the ideal family (no more than four children), the ideal mother (active) and father (tolerant), the ideal house (large enough to contain an array of attractive consumer goods and a maid), and the ideal relationship (heterosexual monogamy). Each film gives a different emphasis to these ideals, depending on its specific context. For example, middle-class ideals of wealth and consumption can be posed as less important than stable family values (*They Were Sisters*), or, in the context of post-war economic hardship and restraint, openly criticised (*Root of All Evil*). And though the films do, on one level, most particularly in their narrative resolutions, confirm prevailing social ideals of women as faithful wives and mothers, the contradictions inherent in those ideals, and the emphasis of the women's pictures on fantasy and romance, work to seriously undermine their value as social propaganda.

The Gainsborough women's pictures' address to a British female audience is also coloured by conditions prevailing in the British film industry at that time. Briefly, for my argument: after the war the industry made a number of attempts to expand, seeing its major task as providing effective competition for Hollywood cinema, both at home and abroad. John Ellis has described the aim of British cinema in the 1940s as that of producing a national "quality" product which would both educate the British public and promote British culture abroad. Popular medium-budget melodramas like *The Wicked Lady* were blatantly escapist and hardly fitted prevailing critical notions of "quality" (aesthetic coherence, psychological realism, humanist values). They went far beyond the bounds of "good taste" in their emphasis on sex, sadism, violence and brutality. But they succeeded in differentiating themselves from, and competing effectively with, Hollywood, maintaining good production values on small budgets, and drawing large female audiences (Murphy, 1981). But while these films were clearly dedicated to criteria of mass entertainment and profit, particularly under Maurice Ostrer's control, it is possible to argue that the film-makers were also to a certain extent caught up in prevailing ideals of British cultural merit, even though the films were seen by critics to fall far short of those ideals. They were often adapted from respected British novels (Margery Lawrence's *Madonna of the Seven Moons*, L. A. G. Strong's *The Brothers*), and the music was conducted and played by eminent musicians (Muir Matheson and the London Symphony or the Royal Philharmonic). *Madonna of the Seven Moons* was publicised as part of the industry's move to produce a new kind of British picture, showing British ideas and ideals to the public at home and abroad, combining entertainment with fine techniques and originality in story design. In 1947 Sydney Box defended *The Brothers* in the columns of *The Evening News* (Friday, 16 May) against charges of gratuitous sadism in terms of its serious *literary* merits, and announced a forthcoming series of productions "based on the work of this country's best writers."

These claims may seem extravagant in the face of the films themselves but, I would argue, an understanding of the Gainsborough women's pictures in terms of a *double* impetus to provide entertainment without losing "artistic quality," to exploit controversial subject matter without sacrificing British ideals, is necessary to an understanding of the way in which they construct femininity very specifically in terms of class and nationalist ideals. The "feminine point-of-view" constructed by these films is explicitly British and middle-class, tied to a specific historical period, and this partly accounts for their popularity, the success of their attempt to compete with Hollywood.

I would argue, then, that the Gainsborough melodramas of this period emerge from a complex network of determining factors: industrial imperatives to compete with Hollywood while maintaining British cultural standards; the desire to maintain post-war audiences of war-time capacity by addressing a female audience, and dramatising women's contemporary experience; an increasing understanding of the propaganda function of fiction films; and the consequent attempt to negotiate a number of conflicting images of women circulating in society.

Gainsborough Women's Pictures in the 1940s

As a result of their specific location in British history, the Gainsborough films, for the most part, appear very different from Hollywood melodrama, although it can be argued that they reveal similar patterns and preoccupations. Gainsborough melodramas have no great *auteurs*, for instance, and though *mise-en-scène* can sometimes be seen to be important, it has nothing like the force of 1940s Hollywood. At the same time, they do have their own cinematic vocabulary, a repertory of female stars, and, in the case of the "contemporary" women's pictures, a concern with women's lives: their hairstyles, fashions, houses and furniture. They were also overwhelmingly British, set in British locations, projecting a British middle-class way of life. I believe the films would benefit from a close reading in terms of their relationship to British social history, though as I have argued, this relationship is contradictory. However, I only have space here to look briefly at the way some of the women's pictures which deal with contemporary women's issues attempt to negotiate those contradictions.

Schematically, it is possible to trace a shift in the women's pictures' address to its audience between the war-time and post-war films. *Love Story* (1944), like many women's pictures, ostensibly deals with the tragedy of its central heroine, a London concert pianist played by Margaret Lockwood, who tries to join the WRAF, only to find that she is fatally ill. Previously dedicated to her work, she decides to spend her remaining time becoming involved in life, taking more risks. On holiday in Cornwall, where she stands out in the closed, moralistic world of the community because of her glamour, youth, and open-minded attitudes (Lockwood's appearance, her clothes, underwrite her "independence of spirit" and are important in giving positive value to her social transgression), she falls passionately in love with a local Lothario (Stewart Granger) whose own tragedy is his impending blindness, which prevents him from going back to war. He is also loved by a faithful woman friend (Patricia Roc), a successful theatre director, who, it becomes clear, sees his blindness as a way of keeping him dependent upon her, the only way she can get him to marry her.

The narrative is extremely convoluted, concentrating on the point-of-view of Margaret Lockwood, whose status as a 'good woman' is gradually established by the playing off of the desires of its two strong heroines against one another. Lockwood sacrifices her desire so that Granger can regain his sight and Roc can marry him, undertaking a gruelling concert tour for the benefit of British soldiers which brings her close to death. Her self-denial is rewarded by fame as a pianist, and she is released from her promise by Roc, who realises that a marriage based on friendship rather than desire would be hopeless. Lockwood and Granger agree to marry, grasping the happiness of the moment rather than looking for permanence.

Love Story is striking for the way in which it dramatises sexual and emotional conflicts without resolving the contradictions it throws up. Female desire is first mobilised, then channelled by the presentation of two paths: sacrifice or self-interest. Ironically, it is only through sacrifice that Lockwood achieves her desires, but that sacrifice is negated in the film's resolution, which affirms the value of short-term passion rather than long-term fidelity. The film manages to present at one and the same time an ideal of femininity based on sacrifice and denial, a validation of women's desires outside home and family, and an endorsement of monogamy based on ephemeral passion.

Madonna of the Seven Moons (1945), while dealing with a similar problem of the mobilisation and channelling of female sexual desire, and mounting a critique of marriage based on love without passion, shifts the emphasis of its resolution towards the need for a new kind of independent woman, resourceful and courageous, capable of forming egalitarian relationships with men. This "new woman" is seen to be important to the founding of a new social order based on honesty and democracy, allowing for the woman's freedom of action, unlike the "old" order based on a religious suppression of women's sexuality. This aspect of the film is interesting in the light of British attitudes to women's freedom of choice in family planning towards the end of the war (see Riley, 1981).

Set in Italy, the film tells the story of a young convent girl who is raped by a peasant, then married off against her wishes to a wealthy merchant, whereupon she leads an apparently saintly life, protected from the outside world by her patient and loving husband. The smooth surface of her existence is, however, troubled by her strange hysterical symptoms, inexplicable to both husband and family doctor, and a crisis is precipitated by the arrival of their daughter, fresh from her education in England (representing the "new democratic order"), who tries to bring her mother round to her own modern ideas (involving much play with fashionable clothes). The mother's "other self" takes over, and she runs away to live as a peasant with her jewel-thief lover. The sexual freedom and passionate fulfillment offered by this "other world" is powerfully presented, and acts as a criticism of her married life on one level. However, it is also presented as a transgression, in class and sex terms, and as a symptom of repression, of the failure of a certain social order to cope with female sexuality. It is this repressive order which must be changed. The film sets up the daughter as the new, independent resourceful heroine who can bring about this change by becoming the investigator who will solve her mother's secret where her father and the doctor have failed.

Madonna of the Seven Moons addresses itself to a British female spectator who is active, capable of contributing to changing society. Crucially, heterosexual monogamy, albeit more egalitarian, is at the centre of this new order, which is projected in middle-class terms. Maddalena/Rosanna is a victim of the old order: she dies with the two signs of her impossible existence on her body, the red rose (passion) and the cross (saintly love). Unity, rather than contradiction, is the hallmark of the new order. But it is one of the contradictions characteristic of the women's picture that while Maddalena/Rosanna is clearly a sacrificial victim, her symptoms, her retreat into illness, also perform a positive function. Her symptoms represent one way in which her body manages to elude the control of her husband and family doctor by becoming a text to be read for its symptoms, rather than an object of erotic contemplation. Moreover, the male protagonists' inability to interpret, explain or cure those symptoms indicates the limits of male control of the female body. In *Madonna of the Seven Moons* the incomprehension of the male characters in the face of the mother's symptoms makes space for the daughter, the "new woman" to act.

The question of the limits of male control can provide the mainspring of the narrative in melodreama, as it does in *The Upturned Glass* (1947). James Mason plays a paranoid doctor who is initially unaware of his psychosis. He plans the perfect murder as just revenge for the death of the woman he loves. The film is tragic melodrama rather than a women's picture, because it presents events through the eyes of its male hero (using his voice-over and occasional subjective shots to do so), who gradually comes to realise his guilt, and the limits of his power to act in society. Mason is a brilliant doctor with a strong sense of social responsibility who becomes the victim of his compulsions, so that his ability to distinguish between right and wrong, to understand the limits of his power, is severely impaired. The hero's tragic flaw necessitates his death if a healthy social order is to be maintained. Mason comes to understand his guilt after a confrontation with another doctor, detached, objective, cynically aware of the limits of his ability to achieve good in society. He kills himself when he realises that his actions were the result of overweening pride, or tragic "hubris."

They Were Sisters (1945) is a women's picture which deals with the problem of the constitution of the ideal family, posing its problem in terms of making the right choice of love object. It opens with a montage of images from fashion magazines, clearly setting up its address to a female audience. The emphasis on fashion in women's pictures functions to establish women as both subjects and objects of desire. Women adopt the accoutrements of femininity in order to attract men in the stories: fashion is an integral element of desire. But it can also function as a focus of identification for women in the audience (see Eckert, 1978) and as a means of offering the audience information about the characters. Often in the women's picture, to be 'well-dressed' suggests order, stability, and balance, whereas excess or lack of taste in clothes indicates transgression, or inability to negotiate social codes (e.g. Vidor's *Stella Dallas*).

Of the three sisters, one (Phyllis Calvert, the stable, "good" woman) dresses with restrained good taste; another (Anne Crawford, the selfish woman) goes for a rather calculated elegance; while the third (Dulcie Gray, the masochistic victim) is hopelessly badly dressed. Calvert chooses her husband well: a middle-class professional man, tolerant and willing to allow her considerable freedom, as befits her independent spirit; she has a happy, but childless marriage. Her two sisters choose unwisely: Crawford marries without loving her wealthy husband, a weak man who cannot control her and whom she despises; Dulcie Gray, blinded by desire, chooses a husband from a lower social class (James Mason) who turns out to be a sadistic brute of whom she's in constant fear. Both these unsatisfactory marriages produce unhappy neglected children, and it's up to Calvert to act to redress the moral balance. She is mobilised as the agent of the narrative, acting to save her weaker sister from destruction by Mason. Although she fails, and her sister commits suicide, Calvert exposes Mason in court and so defeats him, finally ending up with all her sisters' children and the family she always wanted. In a final idyllic scene which is almost conscious of its own utopian, fictional quality, the ideal middle-class mother and father assert euphorically, "God's in his heaven and all's right with the world," and "There are millions of families like us. . . ."

Complicated, unbelievable narratives with blatantly fictional resolutions are one of the hallmarks of the women's picture, and one of the reasons, perhaps, that critics condemn them as trivial and escapist. *Root of All Evil* (1947) takes this fictional aspect of women's desires as one of its main problems. They story opens with a discussion between the heroine (Phyllis Calvert) and her fiancé about what she hopes for from love and marriage, set in idyllic rural surroundings. Before long, she is brutally disenchanted, and her loss of her romantic illusions about love motivates her to renounce romance in favour of revenge and power. She is enormously successful as a business-woman, though family and friends criticise her hardness, and becomes a partner in an oil business with a man she falls in love with. She buys and furnishes a luxury house for them both, only to discover he is already married. Betrayed again by love, she takes over his share of the business as revenge, but the refinery burns down, and only when she has lost everything does she discover her true love: a farmer she's known since childhood.

Once again the women's picture negotiates an impossible contradiction between the mobilisation and validation of female desire, and the need to channel it in the required direction. In this case, romantic illusions about love and marriage are set up, questioned and relocated in order to mount a criticism of materialism, speculation and consumerism. But in the process, and even in its resolution, the film seems to ironise its own moral trajectory.

Through these very schematic readings, I've tried to indicate some of the ways in which, as I see it, the Gainsborough women's pictures, while retaining some of the characteristics of Hollywood's women's pictures, are necessarily transformed by the historical context of 1940s Britain and its film industry. I think my discussion of the difference between tragic melodrama and women's melodrama might be extended to an examination of the differences between, say, *The Upturned Glass* and *Root of All Evil* in terms of the way each deals with the downfall of its central protagonist, in order to throw light on the way each film constructs sexual difference. But I think it's important to stress the tentative nature of my attempt to theorise the women's picture, and the fact that I do not see it as having a direct or necessary application to the very different context of Gainsborough melodrama. It is intended rather as a filter through which to view the Gainsborough films, and I hold the differences between those films and Hollywood melodrama to be as important as any similarities. Throughout this discussion I have tried to make space for historical difference and contradiction as a vital part of theory, and would like to suggest that this approach might prove fruitful for future discussion of the women's picture and its construction of femininity.

References

Thomas Elsaesser, "Tales of Sound and Fury," *Monogram* 4, 1972.

Laura Mulvey, "Notes on Sirk and Melodrama," *Movie* 25, 1977.

Charlotte Brunsdon, "A Subject for the Seventies," *Screen*, vol. 23, no. 3/4, September/October 1982.

Janet Batsleer, "Pulp in the Pink," *Spare Rib*, no. 109, August 1981.

Barbara Creed, "The Position of Women in Hollywood Melodramas," *Australian Journal of Screen Theory*, no. 4, 1977.

Molly Haskell, *From Reverence to Rape*, Penguin, 1979.

Charles Eckert, "The Carole Lombard in Macy's Window," *Quarterly Review of Film Studies*, Winter 1978.

Charles Higham and Joel Greenberg, *Hollywood in the 40s*, Tantivy Press, 1968.

Denise Riley, "The Free Mothers: Pro-natalism and Working Mothers in Industry at the End of the Last War in Britain," *History Workshop Journal*, no. 11, Spring 1981.

Elizabeth Wilson, *Only Halfway to Paradise*, Tavistock, 1980.

Raynes Minns, *Bombers and Mash*, Virago, 1980.

John Ellis, "Art Culture and Quality," *Screen*, Autumn 1978.

Robert Murphy, "Gainsborough Pictures: A Popular Commercial Studio," Polytechnic of Central London MA Thesis, 1981.

Daily Mail Film Award Annual, 1947.

British Film Annual, 1949.

British Film Institute Information Library microfiches on individual film titles.

Appendix: British Melodrama Debates: Selected Bibliography

Screen, Summer 1971. Special issue on Douglas Sirk.

Jon Halliday, *Sirk on Sirk*, Secker and Warburg/BFI, 1971.

Laura Mulvey and Jon Halliday (eds.), *Douglas Sirk*, Edinburgh Film Festival, 1972.

Laura Mulvey, "Fear Eats the Soul," *Spare Rib*, no. 30, 1974.

Griselda Pollock, Geoffrey Nowell-Smith, Stephen Heath, "Dossier on Melodrama," *Screen*, vol. 18, no. 2, Summer 1977.

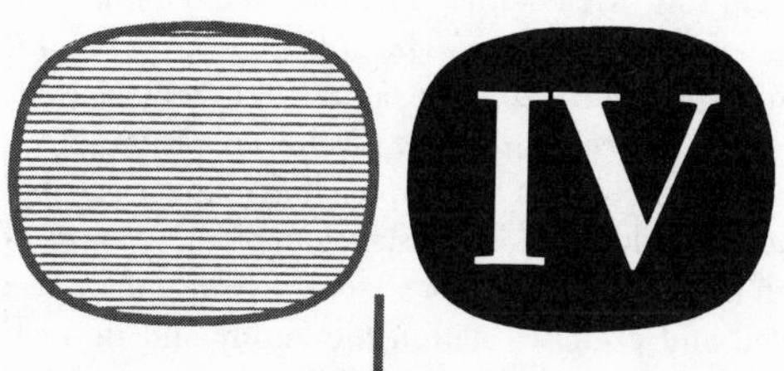

PSYCHOANALYSIS, GENDER, AND RACE

Studies of cinema have been vastly enriched by the contributions of recent psychoanalytic theory, particularly as propounded by the French theoretician Jacques Lacan and advanced by such film critics as Christian Metz. Informed by structuralism, psychoanalytic film theory has shifted away from the study of the individual artist, from pathology, and from interpretation of the content of behavior to an examination of how meaning is structured and how this structuring is a paradigm for the spectator's experience of cinema. In psychoanalytic film theory, the screen itself is likened to a mirror and the spectator to the pre-Oedipal child who finds in the image of the film a sense of wholeness associated with this early phase of development prior to the entry of the father and, with him, the child's entry into language and culture, what Jacques Lacan refers to as the Symbolic order.

According to psychoanalytic theory, the language of the unconscious denies history and difference. Moreover, individual subjectivity is constructed in such a way as to guarantee the sense that the world exists to enhance the individual. But this sense of unity is never complete or final, and its provisional nature can be located in language that reveals the fragmentary nature of identification. Psychoanalysis seeks to identify elements that are loci of the repressed and call attention not only to the text's constituted nature but to its roots in repression and misrecognition. Melodrama, because of its stylization, its references to affective experience, its focus on subjectivity and on issues of identity, and its focus on familial relations, becomes a congenial arena for psychoanalytic criticism to explore the ways in which texts construct the subject. This construction is based on the Oedipal conflict and on the experience of sexuality and gender identification and has implications for the positioning of individuals within the social order.

Geoffrey Nowell-Smith's "Minnelli and Melodrama" identifies melodrama (like psychoanalysis) historically in the rise of the bourgeoisie. The distinctive aspect of this melodrama is its psychosocial determinations located in the bourgeois family. Nowell-Smith indicates that melodrama does not "reflect" social and psychic conditions but is instrumental in articulating them, and he proposes a tandem reading of the social and psychological determinations of the individual. In his discussion of the nature of bourgeois melodrama, Nowell-Smith finds that its forms of address involve a discourse of presumed equals. Power is located and exercised within the family and through private property. If tragedy raises the issue of the exercise of public power in terms of legitimacy, melodrama raises the issue of the father's power in terms of the family. The active-passive opposition of the western genre which is also an opposition between male and female is transposed in the melodrama where females are protagonists. The male is presented in terms of vulnerable masculinity. The female's sexuality is unknown, and impotence is the cause of suffering for both males and females. This impotence is played out in the "family romance" which involves paternity, the child's identity within the family, and heterosexual relations. Oedipal conflict can be identified in the text's stylistic generation of an excess which defies the so-called happy endings. These moments of excess, of "undischarged emotion," can be read in the formal elements of the film as symptoms. Like the workings of hysteria, these symptoms are displaced from the affect onto the mise-en-scène as hysterical symptom is displaced from language onto the body. A reading of the text would thus be alert to the ways in which such displacements occur.

Psychoanalysis has also been influential in recent feminist film theory. The earlier feminist preoccupation with content in art has shifted to a concern with the generation of meaning in cultural and social texts in the hope that, as E. Ann Kaplan in *Women in the Cinema: Both Sides of the Camera* suggests, this form of investigation can help to unlock the secrets of sexual politics, of how individuals internalize gender. In their quest for an alternative to the restrictions of patriarchy, feminists have, therefore, not only sought to develop alternatives toward the creation of new cultural imperatives but have sought to locate in the existing discourses both the terms of their traditional position under patriarchy and indications of resistance of it.

From a feminist position, Griselda Pollock addresses Geoffrey Nowell-Smith's comments on the concept of the family romance and the applicability of conversion hysteria to the workings of melodrama. She acknowledges that it may be correct to identify the bourgeois melodrama as an Oedipal drama, but she objects to the general and abstract application of theory in the texts without a corresponding historicizing of psychoanalytic processes. Moreover, she sees difficulties in conflating the notion of the family as a social institution with the family as a site of ideological contention. She finds the unexamined correlation between hysteria and femininity equally problematic. Most particularly, her essay adcknowledges that though the family melodrama exposes the negation of female desire, it does not allow for the possibility of the surfacing of a female voice. Films such as Sirk's *All That Heaven Allows* are rife with psychosexual conflict. They expose class and generational conflict, but they reproduce the subjugation of female sexuality in the recuperation of the mother's role. Pollock's criticism is specifically directed at the ways women's sexuality is untheorized by critical applications of psychoanalysis which address neither the issue of female sexuality outside the familial context nor the issue of female spectatorship. The preoccupation with the male Oedipal drama continues to neglect, if not mystify, female desire.

Mary Ann Doane's analysis of the maternal melodrama addresses some of the problems raised in Pollock's critique. She turns to the women's film where female issues are developed and where the traces of female desire are more accessible. Doane finds the maternal melodramas of the 1930s and 1940s paradigmatic of the women's film. In her discussion of *Stella Dallas*, she introduces the issue of spectatorship, finding that the female spectator within the film, like the external female spectator, is implicated in her own negation. Transformed from a real human being into a symbol of motherhood, the woman's tearful gaze becomes the sign of her negation and loss. Hence Doane describes the maternal melodrama as a "ritualized mourning of women's losses in a patriarchal society."

Through the figure of the mother, these films confront more directly than the family melodrama the constraints on women's sexuality. Motherhood is the site of multiple contradictions. The maternal melodramas amply portray the nature and constraints of mothering within a patriarchal society, but they also reveal the underlying disruptiveness and threat of the maternal figure. Extrapolating from the work of Luce Irigaray and Julia Kristeva, Doane finds that in the films' polarization of maternal excess can be located a more fundamental fear associated with the maternal figure in her association with nondifferentiation. Motherhood threatens the boundaries between subject and object, thus deconstructing the notion of identity upon which patriarchal differentiation thrives.

Melodrama and the maternal are congruent. Both strive to express the ineffable, having recourse to a primal language through looking, gesturing, and, above all, music. Both strive to return to a sense of fullness which is associated with plenitude. The discourse of melodrama is based on the desire to recover the sense of presence and unity associated with the maternal, and the recognition of absence and difference is blocked and displaced. These displacements are communicated through mistiming. The characters are frequently too late. They miss the train; the letters get mislaid; the wrong people appear. These mistimings are related to separation and loss. Maternal melodramas thrive on the dramatization of the female's attachment to an inappropriate love object, as in the frequent instance of the son who replaces the dead father as the object of desire. Doane finds a large measure of sadism generated in the text and in the viewing experience where violence is displaced onto sentimentalism. This "violent emotionalism" forces the viewer into an uncomfortable complicity with the text.

Linda Williams's essay also focuses on the maternal melodrama. Drawing on the work of such writers as Simone de Beauvoir, Adrienne Rich, Nancy Chodorow, Luce Irigaray, and Julia Kristeva, Williams discusses the contradiction in Western culture of the elevation of motherhood and the simultaneous devaluing of the maternal position. There is no high cultural tragedy of the mother as there is of the father, but this does not mean that there are no narratives involving maternal conflicts. Willaims locates maternal narratives in melodrama where the terrain of conflict is the domestic sphere in which women and children are dominant. Their power is based on virtuous suffering, the source of female wish-fulfillment. The nature of the female identification with virtuous suffering, whether it represents a source of oppression or constitutes a form of freedom, is, Williams argues, not clear.

The basic issue in her essay, whether women speak to one another within patriarchy, has been a central one for recent feminist theory. Williams's argument relies on the Freudian hypothesis of the Oedipal asymmetry between male and female development in which the boy develops his identity through rejection of the mother, while the girl develops hers through identification with her. In the traditional view of the Oedipal scenario, the female is envisaged as the powerful phallic mother or as castrated and powerless. What is disregarded is the domain of women's pleasure which cannot be assessed in terms comparable to the phallic. The body as the site of pleasure is also the site of female language, the medium through which women might communicate with one another. However, Williams does not situate language solely in the pre-Oedipal. Women also participate in the Symbolic order.

In her analysis of *Stella Dallas*, Williams identifies moments in the film when the mother-and-daughter bond is cemented in the face of social and class pressures, but this bond disintegrates as does the mother's identity. At first, Stella steadfastly refuses to relinquish either her motherhood or her quest for pleasure, flaunting her femininity through her dress and makeup. Williams discusses how Stella becomes for others an "overdone masquerade of what it means to be a woman." Her outrageous appearance and behavior, typical of the fetishized woman, seem out of place in the women's film that is built on female victimization. Stella comes to signify a masquerade of femininity for herself and for the external spectator. Reading the film differently from others, Williams argues that it offers more than another portrait of the female punished for her refusal to conform. Williams finds that the film is built on shifting perspectives which undermine a monolithic view of the protagonist. She is seen from conflicting points of view, dispersed through the other characters' conflicts. The film thus cannot conceal the contradictions inherent in Stella's struggle to be "something else besides a mother." The implications of Williams's position are that women are not totally victimized, that the audience is not merely the victim of yet another scandal of misrepresentation, and that filmic discourse in the maternal melodrama is not totally closed. There are spaces in which contradiction can surface and be recognized as such.

Jane Gaines's essay is one of the few on melodrama to focus on a consideration of race. Using the silent film *The Scar of Shame* as an exemplary text, Gaines tests current theories of melodrama on a Hollywood film addressed to a black audience. An understanding of the film, she asserts, is dependent on knowing that it was produced for a black audience. Though the film does not make explicit reference to white society, it is haunted by bourgeois ideology. The society it offers is no different from the society that is the source of black oppression. Through its racial uplift philosophy, through the elevation of individual responsibility and the deployment of sentiment, the film seeks to conceal this contradiction. Melodrama thrives on masking social conflicts through its emphasis on pathos and victimization, but, as Gaines argues, the resolutions call attention to inconsistencies. Most particularly, the film offers the illusion of power at the same time that it dramatizes the inevitability of failure and resignation.

A major strategy of the uplift philosophy often hinges on the representation of women's virtue. The mulatto protagonist in *The Scar of Shame* serves this function. She represents a number of contradictory significations. She is a figure of guilt for the white society, a symbol of aspiration to black bourgeois society (prior to the 1930s), a concession to white society that the black woman could be accorded the designation of woman, and a reminder that her lighter color, which places her closer to whites, is a mark of higher development. The film's caste and class bias is conveyed through an emphasis on color. Examining how style plays with the various aspects of the color, caste, and class issues, Gaines asks whether it is possible to read *The Scar of Shame* as an example of subversive stylistics in the manner critics have read the 1950s melodramas. Her answer is negative. She states that a knowing spectator is required for a subversive reading. The contemporary viewer of the film would be aware of two narratives, the one involving interracial strife, the other involving life in a racist society. In discussing the subversive potential of melodrama, Gaines suggests that the subversion is not in the text's stylistic properties alone or in the point of view of the director but in the spectator's awareness of another story.

Minnelli and Melodrama

GEOFFREY NOWELL-SMITH

What this paper claims is that the genre or form that has come to be known as melodrama arises from the conjunction of a formal history proper (development of tragedy, realism etc), a set of social determinations, which have to do with the rise of the bourgeoisie, and a set of psychic determinations, which take shape around the family. The psychic and social determinations are connected because the family whose conflicts the melodrama enacts is also the bourgeois family, but a complexity is added to the problem by the fact that the melodrama is also a particular form of artistic representation. As artistic representation it is also (in Marxist terms) ideology and (in Freudian terms) "secondary revision," but it cannot be simply reduced to either. As artistic representation it does not "reflect" or "describe" social and psychic determinations. Rather, it *signifies* them. This act of signifying has two aspects: on the one hand it produces a narrated or represented content, the life of people in society; and on the other hand it narrates and represents to and from a particular standpoint or series of standpoints, "subject positions." Now it might be thought that the former aspect, concerning the content, is a question for social (historical-materialist) analysis, and the latter, concerning the form, a matter for psychology or psychoanalysis. What I shall claim is that this is not the case and that the positions of the narrating are also social

Geoffrey Nowell-Smith's "Minnelli and Melodrama" originally appeared in *Screen*, Vol. 18, no. 2 (Summer 1977), pp. 113–19. Reprinted by permission of the author and *Screen*. The paper was presented at a weekend school held in London, March 25–27, 1977, by the Society for Education in Film and Television (SEFT). The weekend school was devoted to the study of melodrama and its place in ideology. "A note on 'Family Romance' " at the end of the essay is by Stephen Heath and Geoffrey Nowell-Smith.

positions, while what is narrated is also psychical. The "subject positions" implied by the melodrama are those of bourgeois art in a bourgeois epoch, while the "represented object" is that of the oedipal drama.

Melodrama and Tragedy

Melodrama originally meant, literally, drama—melos (music) and this eighteenth-century sense survives in the Italian *melodramma*—grand opera. In its early form melodrama was akin to pastoral, and differentiated from tragedy in that the story usually had a happy end. Not much of the original meaning has survived into later—Victorian and modern—usages of the term, but the differentiation from tragedy has become, if anything, more marked. The principal differences are two, both of them the result of developments in art forms generally that began in the eighteenth century and were consolidated later. The first of these concerns modes of address and the second the representation of the hero(ine). At the time it should be noted that in many other respects the melodrama is the inheritor of many tragic concerns, albeit transposed to a new situation.

Melodrama as Bourgeois Form

One feature of tragic and epic forms up to (roughly) the eighteenth century is that they characteristically deal with kings and princes, while being written by, and for the most part addressed to, members of a less exalted social stratum (The authors, even Homer, are broadly speaking "intellectuals," while the audience is conceived of, however inaccurately, as "the people"). With the advent of the novel (cf. Scarron's "Le Roman Bourgeois") and the "bourgeois tragedy" of the eighteenth century, the situation changes. Author, audience and subject matter are put on a place of equality. As Raymond Williams has noted (*Screen*, v. 18 n. 1, Spring 1977), the appeal is directly to "our equals, your equals." Mystified though it may be, the address is from one bourgeois to another bourgeois, and the subject matter is the life of the bourgeoisie. This movement of equalisation generally goes under the name of (or is conflated with) realism, but it also characterises forms which in other respects are not conspicuous for their realism, such as the melodrama.

In so far as melodrama, like realism, supposes a world of equals, a democracy within the bourgeois strata (alias bourgeois democracy), it also supposes a world without the exercise of social power. The address is to an audience which does not think of itself as possessed of power (but neither as radically dispossessed, disinherited, oppressed) and the world of the subject matter is likewise one in which only middling power relations are present. The characters are neither the rulers nor the ruled, but occupy a middle ground, exercising local power or suffering local powerlessness, within the family or the small town. The locus of power is the family and individual private property, the two being connected through inheritance. In this world of circumscribed horizons (which corresponds very closely to Marx's definition of "petit bourgeois ideology") patriarchal right is of central importance. The son has to become like his father in order to take over his property and his place within the community (or, in variant structures, a woman is widowed and therefore inherits, but the question posed is which man she can pass the property onto by remarriage; or, again, the father is evil and the son must grow up different from him in order to be able to redistribute the property at the moment of inheritance etc, etc). Notably, the question of law or legitimacy, so central to tragedy, is turned inward from "Has this man a right to rule (over us)?" to "Has this man a right to rule a family (like ours)?" This inward-turning motivates a more directly psychological reading of situations, particularly in the Hollywood melodrama of the 50s.

Action and Passion

Aristotle defined History as "what Alcibiades did and suffered." Doing and suffering, action and passion, are co-present in classical tragedy, and indeed in most art forms up to the romantic period. There is then a split, producing a demarcation of forms between those in which there is an active hero, inured or immune to suffering, and those in which there is a hero, or more often a heroine, whose role is to suffer. Broadly speaking, in the American movie the active hero becomes protagonist of the Western, the passive or impotent hero or heroine becomes protagonist of what has come to be known as melodrama. The contrast active/passive is, inevitably, traversed by another contrast, that between masculine and feminine. Essentially the world of the Western is one of activity/masculinity, in which women cannot figure except as receptacles (or occasionally as surrogate males). The melodrama is more complex. It often features women as protagonists, and where the central figure is a man there is regularly an impairment of his "masculinity"—at least in contrast to the mythic potency of the hero of the Western. It cannot operate in the simple terms of a fantasy affirmation of the masculine and disavowal of the feminine, but the way it recasts the equation to allow more space for its women characters and for the representations of passion undergone throws up problems of its own. In so far as activity remains equated with masculinity and passivity with femininity, the destiny of the characters, whether male or female, is unrealisable; he or she can only live out the impairment ("castration") imposed by the law. In their struggle for the achievement of social and sexual demands, men may sometimes win through, women never. But this fact about the plot structure is not just an element of realism, it reflects an imbalance already present in the conceptual and symbolic structure. "Masculinity," although rarely attainable, is at least known as an ideal. "Femininity," within the terms of the argument, is not only unknown but unknowable. Since sexuality and social efficacy are recognisable only in a "masculine" form, the contradictions facing the women characters are posed in more acutely problematic form from the outset. For both women and men, however, suffering and impotence, besides being the data of middle-class life, are seen as forms of a failure to be male—a failure from which patriarchy allows no respite.

The Generation Game

To describe as patriarchy the law which decrees suffering and impairment (if only as motors for dramatic action) and decrees them unequally for men and for women is also to raise the problem of generations. The castration which is at issue in the melodrama (and according to some writers in all narrative forms) is not an a-historical, a-temporal structure. On the contrary it is permanently renewed within each generation. The perpetuation of symbolic sexual division only takes place in so far as it is the Father who perpetuates it. It is not just the place of the man relative to the woman, but that of the parent (male) relative to the children, which is crucial here. Melodrama enacts, often with uncanny literalness, the "family romance" described by Freud—that is to say the imaginary scenario played out by children in relation to their paternity, the asking and answering of the question: whose child am I (or would I like to be)? In addition to the problems of adults, particularly women, in relation to their sexuality, the Hollywood melodrama is also fundamentally concerned with the child's problems of growing into a sexual identity within the family, under the aegis of a symbolic law which the Father incarnates. What is at stake (also for social-ideological reasons) is the survival of the family unit and the possibility for individuals of acquiring an identity which is also a place within the system, a place in which they can be both "themselves" and "at home," in which they can simultaneously enter, without contradiction, the symbolic order and bourgeois society. It is a condition of the drama that the attainment of such a place is not easy and does not happen without sacrifice, but it is very rare for it to be seen as radically impossible. The problems posed are always to some extent resolved. Only in Ophuls' *Letter from an Unknown Woman,* where Lisa dies after the death of her (fatherless) child, are all the problems laid out in all their poignancy, and none of them resolved.

Hysteria and Excess

The tendency of melodramas to culminate in a happy end is not unopposed. The happy end is often impossible, and, what is more, the audience knows it is impossible. Furthermore a "happy end" which takes the form of an acceptance of castration is achieved only at the cost of repression. The laying out of the problems "realistically" always allows for the generating of an excess which cannot be accommodated. The more the plots press towards a resolution the harder it is to accommodate the excess. What is characteristic of the melodrama, both in its original sense and in the modern one, is the way the excess is siphoned off. The undischarged emotion which cannot be accommodated within the action, subordinated as it is to the demands of family/lineage/inheritance, is traditionally expressed in the music and, in the case of film, in certain elements of the mise-en-scène. That is to say, music and mise-en-scène do not just heighten the emotionality of an element of the action: to some extent they substitute for it. The mechanism here is strikingly similar to that of the psychopathology of hysteria. In hysteria (and specifically in what Freud has designated as "conversion hysteria") the energy attached to an idea that has been repressed returns converted into a bodily symptom. The "return of the repressed" takes place, not in conscious discourse, but displaced onto the body of the patient. In the melodrama, where there is always material which cannot be expressed in discourse or in the actions of the characters furthering the designs of the plot, a conversion can take place into the body of the text. This is particularly the case with Minnelli. It is not just that the characters are often prone to hysteria, but that the film itself somatises its own unaccommodated excess, which thus appears displaced or in the wrong place. This is the case both in the musicals (*Pirate, Meet Me in St Louis*, etc.), which tend to be much more melodramatic than others from the same studio and where the music and dancing are the principal vehicles for the siphoning of the excess but where there may still be explosions of a material that is repressed rather than expressed; and in the dramas proper, where the extreme situations represented turn up material which itself cannot be represented within the convention of the plot and mise-en-scène.

It should be stressed that the basic conventions of the melodrama are those of realism: ie what is represented consists of supposedly real events, seen either "objectively" or as the summation of various discrete individual points of view. Often the "hysterical" moment of the text can be identified as the point at which the realist representative convention breaks down. Thus in the scene in *The Cobweb* where the lake is being dragged for Stevie's body there is no certainty either as to what is being represented (is the woman Stuart is talking to Meg or is it Karen?) or as to whose point of view, if anybody's, is being represented. The breakdown of the stable convention of representation allows such questions to be temporarily suspended in favour of what is, at one level, simple narrative cnfusion, but on another level can be seen as an enactment of a fantasy that involves all the characters whom the plot has drawn together. At the level of this collective fantasy, Stevie is Stuart's and Meg's "child" and therefore the child Stuart could have had by Meg, did he not already have children by Karen (from whom he is estranged). The possibility of Stevie being dead brings this submerged fantasy to the surface, but not directly into the articulation of the plot. Realist representation cannot accommodate the fantasy, just as bourgeois society cannot accommodate its realisation.

Provisional Conclusion

Melodrama can thus be seen as a contradictory nexus, in which certain determinations (social, psychical, artistic) are brought together but in which the problem of the articulation of these determinations is not successfully resolved. The importance of melodrama (at least in the versions of it that are due to Ophuls, Minnelli, Sirk) lies precisely in its ideological failure. Because it cannot accommodate its problems, either in a real present or in an ideal future, but lays them open in their shameless contradictoriness, it opens a space which most Hollywood forms have studiously closed off.

A Note on "Family Romance"

The term "family romance," whose interpretation is at issue in the foregoing material, was introduced by Freud in his correspondence with Fliess in 1897–98. Its first mentions (*Standard Edition*, vol. 1, 244, 265) link it specifically to paranoia, but subsequently its application becomes more extended. Commenting on a story by C. F. Meyer, *Die Richterin*, which he sees as activating a defence against the memory of an incestuous affair, Freud writes: "The only remarkable thing is that this happens exactly as it does in neurosis. All neurotics create a so-called family romance (which becomes conscious in paranoia); on the one hand it serves the need of self-aggrandisement and on the other as a defence against incest. If your sister is not your mother's child you are relieved of guilt" (*The Origins of Psychoanalysis*, p. 256). The major statement of the concept is in the paper "Der Familienroman der Neurotiker" (1909: translated as "Family Romances," *SE* IX, pp. 235–41). Here the child's family romance is seen as part of a movement of estrangement from the parents and as having two stages, one (prepubertal and asexual) in which the existing parents are replaced by superior ones, and a second one (developing from increased sexual knowledge) in which only paternity is challenged and the mother is pictured as engaging in secret infidelities. The motives in this second stage can include sexual curiosity about the mother, a revenge against the parents for punishing sexual naughtiness in childhood and even a revenge against brothers and sisters who are bastardised in the romance while (in a curious variant) the author sees himself/herself as legitimate. Freud notes: ". . . if there are any other particular interests at work they can direct the course to be taken by the family romance; for its many-sidedness and its great range of applicability enable it to meet every sort of requirement" ("Family Romances," *SE* IX, 240).

Two points may be made here. The first concerns the "many-sidedness" of this activity of fantasy, the importance of the topic of family relations in the pubertal period and the role of the family romance as an effort to regulate anxieties in the late moments of the working out of the Oedipus complex. Hence in a note added to the 1920 edition of the *Three Essays on Sexuality* (*SE* VII, 226n) Freud refers to family romance in connection with pubertal fantasies "distinguished by their very general occurrence and by being to a great extent independent of individual experience." Secondly there is in the connection made between family romance and art via "imaginative activity." This is evident not only in the treatment of the Meyer story and in the 1909 paper but in "Creative Writers and Daydreaming" (1908: *SE* IX, 141–53) where creative writing is seen as a correction of reality, "reconciling" pleasure and reality principles, allowing "full play to erotic and ambitious wishes," etc. The connection is present in the term *Familienroman* itself, variously translatable as "romance" and as "novel."

The relevance of the concept to art, and melodrama in particular, lies not so much in the presumed universality of the family romance (which would still leave each romance the private fantasy property of the romancer) as in the intersection of the one constitutive moment (the fantasy *per se*) with others in terms of the radical heterogeneity of subject formation. Thus, while the history of the subject described by psychoanalysis is specific, that specificity has to be seen as heterogeneous, inscribed into and inscribing itself on historical, linguistic, social, sexual, etc determinations. It is on such a heterogeneity that institutions like the cinema turn in their ideological functioning, and to understand melodrama in the cinema is necessarily to attempt to focus the investment in a constant repetition of family romance fantasising both in its themes and in its processes of relations and positions of the subject-spectator.

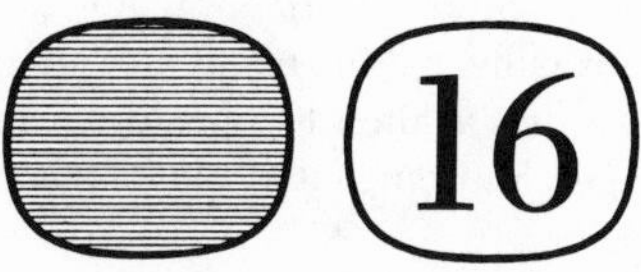

Report on the Weekend School

GRISELDA POLLOCK

Female chastity alone, protects social relations from complete disorder

—E. van Hartmann, *The Philosophy of the Unconscious*, 1868.

Hollywood melodrama can be read as an instance of exposed contradications within bourgeois ideology. This is the conclusion reached, for example, at the end of Geoffrey Nowell-Smith's paper where he refers to melodrama "opening up a space that most Hollywood forms have studiously closed off."

It is this "opening" which constitutes the attraction of a justification for a theoretical analysis of Hollywood melodrama. But one cannot ignore the considerable "pleasure" still generated by viewing the movies of Sirk and Minnelli and it is therefore as much a necessity to locate the current interest in a study of them as to determine the social, psychical and artistic forces in the production and consumption of melodramas in America of the fifties. The terms and approaches used in the weekend school reflected present cultural and political preoccupations. Thomas Elsaesser's paper, "Tales of Sound and Fury," reprinted from *Monogram* 4 (1973), was an early intervention into film history and theory at a time when the commercial cinema of Hollywood had not yet been recognised as worthy of serious attention. This initial work has since been followed up notably with work on Douglas Sirk at Edinburgh in 1972 (see L. Mulvey

---

Griselda Pollock's "Report on the Weekend School" originally appeared in *Screen*, Vol. 18, no. 2 (Summer 1977), pp. 105–13. The weekend school was held March 25–27, 1977, in London by the the Society for Education in Film and Television (SEFT) and was devoted to the study of melodrama and its place within ideology.

and J. Halliday, eds.: *Sirk*, Edinburgh Film Festival 1972). Geoffrey Nowell-Smith's paper for the weekend elaborated Freudian concepts of conversion hysteria with respect to the films of Vincente Minnelli, continuing work adumbrated at the Psychoanalysis and Cinema event at the 1976 Edinburgh Film Festival. Feminist analysis was brought to bear on melodrama's concentration on women's sexuality and the family in Laura Mulvey's paper which discussed the problem of these films' address to a putative/real female audience and the way in which the contradictions for women under patriarchal culture are exposed within them.

Most of these terms of reference were accepted (within the narrow limits of a self-selected audience, of course) but they were used with unwarranted abandon, often rendering banal and innocent concepts and notions that are still highly problematic. For it is precisely the obscured dialectic between class politics and sexual politics, bourgeois ideology and the patriarchal order that is one of the most pressing political issues at the moment. I would also argue that this dialectic significantly determines the process of production and consumption of Hollywood melodrama both as an historical object and as an area of study that continues to be attractive and available to both film buffs and film theorists at the present time. Furthermore, it is that specific nexus of contradictions which renders Hollywood melodrama so fruitful a field for investigation of an intersection of patriarchal and bourgeois ideologies.

The weekend as a whole was good. The school had been well prepared by its organisers who actually circulated the papers beforehand and provided an introductory statement of the main concerns to be addressed at the weekend. In addition to Steve Neale's succinct and interesting outline and Elsaesser's early piece there were papers on each of the directors whose films were screened. The choice of films was apt and closely linked to the papers: Minnelli's *Home from the Hill* and *The Cobweb* and Sirk's *All that Heaven Allows*. The organisation of time between screening, seminars and plenary sessions produced valuable discussions and allowed detailed study of individual films in the light of the specific points raised by the papers.

Despite the extremely useful and valuable work done at the weekend, there were for me three major areas of dissatisfaction and theoretical concern.

In his introductory paper, Steve Neale quickly dismissed both auteur and generic approaches to Hollywood melodrama and proposed instead a perspective based on current theoretical work on the cinema and ideology. He quoted from Stephen Heath's article *Jaws*, Ideology and Film Theory" (*Framework* No. 4) which demanded an analysis of cinema not simply as a combination of parts—text, industry and consumption—but rather set within a complex set of relationships which constitute the "cinematic machine." The reports from the seminar groups in the final session revealed how many different lines of inquiry had been pursued within each. Analysis of the contradictions and ideological character of the films ranged wide: family relations within class society, the problem of the reception of the movies and the supposed female spectator, the significance of the political and social climate of Eisenhower's post-war America are just a few topics that were mentioned beside substantive discussion of the papers. Such fragmentation is, however, in contradiction to the stated intention of the weekend of articulating relations between these factors within a notion of the cinematic machine. While it is perhaps inevitable (and indeed useful as a means of preliminary identification of relevant issues) that small groups follow up some points in detail to the exclusion of others, the failure to integrate cannot be explained merely in organisational terms. The demand for a non-object centred film theory must be met with a radically new practice and inscribed into the language of the discussion.

In the second place, all the papers focussed on issues of sexuality and the family. I quote from Steve Neale's introduction:

> Within this perspective melodrama (and in particular the Hollywood melodrama of the 1950s) can be seen as the locus of contradiction and of a potential subversion and disruption of the dominant ideologies and their operations, most conspicuously in relation to the family and sexuality. One of the main areas of narrative action in the melodrama is the family. What is offered as the basis for plot is a constellation of family relations, with individual characters marked as sites for the articulation and interaction of these relations. . . . In either case the set of relations into which the characters are bound is seen as restrictive, its pressure potentially, if not actually, destructive. In interpreting this restrictiveness a psychoanalytical approach may be taken. . . . The specific correlation of melodrama and the concerns of psychoanalysis is pinpointed by the fact that Freud's category of "Family Romance" is in many ways an apt alternative title for melodrama. (p. 2)

While I cannot pretend to comprehend fully what is meant in Freudian terms by "Family Romance" (*Familienroman* is imprecisely translated by that term anyway), I am sure this is a misuse in this context. Freud seems to have coined this phrase to describe specific childhood fantasies of noble parentage. However there is the further complication that Heath has used this term to describe a filmic notion of narrativisation and memory which concerns process rather than content or setting (see "Screen Images, Film Memory," *Edinburgh '76 Magazine*, pp. 33–42). It is therefore dangerously misleading to use this term in the light of the lack of clear and agreed definition of its meaning. There is yet another point to be made about the correlation between psychoanalytic approaches and melodrama. In the section of his paper entitled "Where Freud Left his Marx in the American Home" Elsaesser rightly discussed the explicit imprint of America's adoption of Freudianism on the character of Hollywood melodrama. This demands a theoretical refinement and a more double-edged approach which can take into account both the significance of the conscious reference to Freudian issues within the film texts and the quite specific relevance of a psychoanalytic perspective on precisely these films. This is extremely important for the identification of the particular contradictions exposed within the Hollywood melodrama. In general terms Geoffrey Nowell-Smith may be correct to identify the represented object of bourgeois melodrama as the "oedipal drama," but that must be modified by articulating within the significant determinations on the melodrama of the fifties the preoccupation with psychoanalysis both within the text and also in the culture of the audience. The family may well be the focus of socio-sexual initiation and the construction of subjectivity, but one needs to question exactly how a concern with those processes operates within ideology at a certain date, and further, with the necessary reflex, ask therefore what both determines and conditions the use of psychoanalytic approaches to film in the present conjuncture. Furthermore it is necessary to distinguish between the family as a social institution and a place of socialisation which does invite (and indeed generated) psychoanalytic analysis, and the representation of the family in an ideological revision, film. At that remove what does the family signify? Is it to be read as an interrogation of bourgeois family relations or is it a displacement of contradictions in social relations as a whole, or indeed, may it be a condensation of the two?

A film like *Home from the Hill* raises this problem of articulating the relations between the contradictions within the bourgeois family and the contradictions of bourgeois social relations within the social formation. The space of action is not merely the family but rather the small town in which the family of Wade Hunnicutt (Robert Mitchum) is dominant, owning much of the town, its industries and most of the surrounding countryside. While familial issues of paternal authority and the legality and suitability of inheritance do play an obvious and important role, the overall dynamic of the narrative and its placement of positions for the characters is located on an inside/outside opposition in which places—homes for instance—are contrasted with other spaces outside, in the woods and finally and most significantly beyond the frame (both literally and figuratively) of the reference of the film. In this more complex interrelation of spaces and positions the importance of mise-en-scène as opposed to plot or story line becomes crucial. Admittedly most of the papers did discuss mise-en-scène, giving it at times a central place (which I will discuss in a moment). But one final observation needs to be made here in relation to the confusions surrounding the use of psychoanalysis. There seemed to be an excessive emphasis of the literary and dramatic sources of the Hollywood melodrama in the novel, tragedy or theatre. These forms are without doubt important—most particularly the first, since Hollywood melodramas are so often adaptations of novels. But the ignorance of the concurrent development of narrative painting in the nineteenth century, with its particular elaboration of "mise-en-scène" in order to spatialise and render visually legible novelistic forms, is a serious and puzzling omission in the study of film.

The notion of mise en scène offering an ironic commentary or functioning as a countercurrent leads on to one of the other important issues raised by the weekend which I think needs further work. The eruption of excesses in a film text which cannot be contained and which render any closure forced and expose irreconcilables at the point of the attempted "happy ending" can be identified in the contradictions between plot and mise-en-scène. Geoffrey Nowell-Smith suggested an analogy between this process and the mechanisms of conversion hysteria in which "energy attached to an idea that has been repressed returns converted into a bodily symptom." At this stage one moves closer to Heath's notion of the cinematic machine by addressing not the components of the film's object but the process, in this case with the notion of the hysterical text in which the repressed returns to the body of the film in its discontinuities, dislocation of placement and confusion of identity. While this is a valuable observation, it still remains to identify the "repressed" of which stylistic deformation is but the symptom and to remark, at this stage only in passing, on the classical correlation between hysteria and femininity.

Finally one comes to the issues raised by feminist analyses of Hollywood melodrama. These were specifically explored by Laura Mulvey's paper on Sirkian films in which she emphasised the ways in which films like *All That Heaven Allows* expose the impossibility of female desire under a patriarchal order. Once again there is the problem of definition for it is dangerous if not indeed politically suspect to naturalise by repeated and imprecise usage a term which is still in the process of theoretical elaboration. Laura Mulvey rightly stated the difference between "the project of giving voice to the problems and frustrations of women from the female point of view and that of examining tensions, where, although women play a central part, their point of view does not dominate" ("Douglas Sirk and Melodrama," p. 2). For there is a difference, at least theoretically useful, between the lived contradictions and repression of women in a phallocentric order and the appropriation of sexuality in ideological representation.[1]

One can read a film like *All That Heaven Allows* in terms of the repression of female desire as Laura Mulvey originally states it. Cary (Jane Wyman), a widowed mother of two college aged children, falls in love with a younger man, Ron (Rock Hudson), but Ron is not only younger than she is, a fact which invites the horrified reactions of her friends and family in the town, but also an outsider and a social inferior, her gardener in fact, who lives outside the town, cultivating trees and living according to the ideals of Thoreau which as Mulvey points out represents a lost American ideal. On the level of narrative Cary's sexual indiscretion in being attracted to a younger man and the difficulties they encounter in the pursuit of the relationship receive an almost excessive prominence; but the spectator is also witness to less explicit conflicts of class and to the opposition between the small-town community and the free self-directing individual at one with nature recuperating and living out the lost ideal. One could accommodate these strands within the framework of overdetermination but one also needs to separate out the various levels of contradiction from the process of condensation and displacement which foregrounds the family and sexuality but leaves traces of further meanings.

There is indeed a grave danger of reifying sexuality outside the social formation. The subjugation of female sexuality to the demands of reproduction is one of the fundamental forms of the oppression of women while at the same time it can be identified as necessary to the existing social order (precisely how and why remains to be precisely elaborated).[2] The contradictions that *All That Heaven Allows* exposes are between social positions and are not simply concerned with irreconcilable desires or the sexuality of women. The closures of these Hollywood melodramas are revealing of this in so far as they end with the relocation of women in their socially determined place as mothers. Fathers may be dismissed in the end, dispatched by each other or by a son as in *Home from the Hill*, returned to professional silence as in *The Cobweb* or reduced to infant dependency as *All That Heaven Allows*, but the mothers remain in possession of the screen. Hanna (Eleanor Parker) accepts her maternal role by agreeing to go and live with her husband's illegitimate son and caring for her own grandson, the "trouble" in *The Cobweb* ends with Karen's (Gloria Grahame) solicitous care of Stevie (John Kerr) and in *All That Heaven Allows* Cary nurses a supine and childlike Ron.

On the other hand one needs to understand the extraordinary and disruptive role played by the women's uncontained, withheld or frustrated sexuality in the dynamic of the narrative which is often disguised or inverted at the point of its explicit expression. For instance, it is clear that Hanna in *Home from the Hill* plays an important role in motivating the action of the plot. The breakdown in the family results from her refusal to sleep with Wade after her discovery of his premarital transgression, which produces the impossible positions for her real and his illegitimate son; it is her narration of these events which precipitates Theron's (George Hamilton) rift with his father; and she initiates the reconciliation and in the end puts both sons' names on the tombstone acknowledging a paternity the father did not. But for all this she remains most shadowy and undeveloped on the level of both characterisation and identification. On the other hand in *All That Heaven Allows*, a film that ostensibly places a woman, Cary, prominently in view, she in fact plays a profoundly passive role and is offered as the spectacle of the impotent spectator (one is given privileged access to her look within the text) which is ironically signalised by the stunned and speechless reflection of her in the TV screen at the moment of her paralysing realisation of the impossibility of the choice condoned by her children and the town, whereafter she develops hysterical symptoms of headaches. In *The Cobweb* two of the most significant moments of discontinuity and excess erupt around women. One is the scene on the riverbank with the loss of clear position as to the identity of the two women Meg and Karen, finally stated by Meg's "Who do you think I am?" and the other more perplexing is the extraordinary scene between Stuart (Richard Widmark) and his daughter who thereafter disappears definitively from the visual field of the film.

These two observations leave two problems, the precise significance attached to female sexuality outside familial roles, and the identification of the positions for the spectator male and female, both of which I suggest can be illuminated by positing the notion of the repressed feminine. Such a notion must be grasped in its two-sidedness, its recto and verso, namely on the one side the feminine position as a loss for the masculine at the oedipal moment, and on the other the contradictions between the placement of the female subject as signifier of non-male in a patriarchal order and the appropriation of woman, and of the family relations signified by the mother as crucial terms in bourgeois society. What follows is an attempt to map out some theoretical basis for future work and is, I am fully aware, tentative and perhaps dangerously superficial.

Three points will amplify what I am suggesting.

It is important to restate that, in Freudian terms, the rejection of the feminine position is one of the marks of the oedipal moment through which the masculine emerges in its dominance and privilege while the feminine passes into unspoken negativity (not therefore unknown and unknowable but silenced and repressed). Hence it is possible to identify the return of the repressed manifested in the hysterical text as the return of the repressed and displaced feminine. In using psychoanalytic theory however there are dangers. It is possible to confuse substantive statements made by Freud and other theorists from within "patriarchal" culture with the more important principles of unconscious processes. The one-sided recognition of a masculine oedipal drama in every film text can serve to restate the status quo and obscure in a merely revisionist manner the more important undertaking, which is to identify from the principles of unconscious processes the points of radical rupture and potential transformation. Furthermore in so far as Freudian theory correctly describes the laws by which we are placed as subjects within a particular social formation, is also posits an inevitable resistance outside clinical or quite specific situations to the very knowledge that psychoanalysis offers. Thus, even within a film theory that uses the concerns of psychoanalysis, these resistances operate to counter the radical possibilities offered by the use of the theory. There is therefore every likelihood that the repression of the feminine is doubly ensured even at the point of potential exposure in theoretical analysis of film.

The second point concerns the position of women in bourgeois society. In early forms of bourgeois society one can identify the particular role allotted to women at the cost of their autonomous sexuality within an opposition inside/outside, private/public, the untroubled home and the world of production and class contradiction. Woman was located in the family home and became the guardian of "human values" in a dehumanised world of capitalist social relations and within the bourgeois family itself woman functioned as the keeper of social stratification through elaborate rituals surrounding marriage and society. The form of the family and its ideological representation have of course undergone considerable transformation in subsequent history; but it is not without significance, I suggest, that in the years after the second world war the dislocation of the economy and attempts to restore peacetime conditions coincided with a major attempt to relocate women in the home and in their familial roles.

From this dynamic of historical process and available modes of representation (which contain quite contradictory impulses) one comes to the problem of the position offered to the spectator, any consideration of which must take into account both the largely female audience in the fifties and the continuing popularity of Hollywood melodrama in contemporary film culture. The articulation of the positions of the female and male spectator lies at the intersection of patriarchal and bourgeois ideologies seized in their simultaneity and their historical specificity, and in attempting to do this one returns to the nexus of contradictions which the authors of the papers see exposed within the Hollywood melodrama. A variety of these contradictions is indeed revealed but, as Laura Mulvey mentioned in her paper, art forms can function as necessary safety valves within a culture. I wonder whether many of the contradictions whose rehearsal leads to a progressive reading of the Hollywood melodramas of Sirk and Minnelli are really secondary and therefore recuperable by bourgeois culture. That which remains outside both patriarchal and bourgeois orders, and therefore irrecuperable, is the "feminine," which includes both the feminine position and the foregone phallic sexuality of women. The repression of this feminine produces the particular uncontained excesses which can only be restored by forced closure, what Sirk aptly and ironically calls the invocation of the *deus ex machina* happy ending. In the films discussed at the weekend this closure provides for the simultaneous repression of the feminine and reconstitutes the family through the acceptance of the only available position for women in both patriarchy and bourgeois society, the mother.

I suggest that it is along these lines that the notion of the cinematic machine can be elaborated in relation to Hollywood melodrama and the fragmentation of the discussion at the weekend overcome so as to identify the precise determinations and the primary contradictions and engage in the most necessary theoretical work at the present time, the dialectic between sex and class.

Notes

1. This is of course to some extent an artificial and dangerous separation for, as Heath ("Screen Images," p. 40) clearly states, it is a matter of simultaneity. However, not only are social

formations undergoing transformations and changes resulting in different subject positions, but the process of placement and construction of the subject is not a "once and for all" affair. The narration of these processes has therefore a historical specificity. In order to approach this in the context of Hollywood melodrama it is necessary to distinguish between femininity as a *position*, woman as a *signifier* in filmic discourse, and women as a *sex* whose position in culture and society is historically one of impotence, silence, negativity and appropriability.

2. While Marxist-feminists have given much prominence to the attempt to elaborate a theory of reproduction little has been done on the construction of the female subject as reproducer. Freud made some attempts at a theory of femininity without much success. But one should note in passing two points which bear on the following discussion. (1) The oedipal drama for the female subject is not a mere mirror image of the male and it has always been recognised to be considerably more problematic, and potentially so inconclusive as to persist into adult life and to be reactivated by motherhood. (2) The basic Freudian formulation concerns a transference of sexual interest from clitoral/phallic sexuality to a rather more nebulous responsiveness of the vagina, the birth canal itself, despite such physiological evidence as exists which discredits a biological basis for such a distinction. Freud's notion may well merit a further investigation as an almost metaphorical attempt to articulate not what actually happens to women's sexuality but what is necessary in order to forego phallic sexuality so as to function as mother.

The Moving Image: Pathos and the Maternal

MARY ANN DOANE

There is a scene in *Mildred Pierce* (1945) in which Mildred attempts to convince her daughter Veda to give up her job as a singer in a rather seedy nightclub and return home. When Mildred visits Veda in her dressing room backstage, one of Veda's coworkers comments upon learning Mildred's identity, "I didn't know you had a mother." Veda replies, "Everyone has a mother." In a similar scene in *The Reckless Moment* (1949), the blackmailer, Donnelly, referring to Mrs. Harper's daughter Bea, remarks, "She's lucky to have a mother like you." Mrs. Harper's immediate response is, "Everyone has a mother like me. You probably had one, too."

Everyone has a mother, and furthermore, all mothers are essentially the same, each possessing the undeniable quality of motherliness. In Western culture, there is something *obvious* about the maternal which has no counterpart in the paternal. The idea that someone might not have a mother is constituted as a joke; it is articulated in the mode of the ridiculous or absurd.[1] For the suggestion questions the unquestionable, and the status of the unquestionable is, of course, the natural. Paternity and its interrogation, on the other hand, are articulated within the context of issues of identity, legality, inheritance—in short, *social* legitimacy. To generate questions about the existence of one's father is, therefore, to produce an insult of the highest order.

The semantic valence, the readability, of the two functions is closely associated with an epistemological construction. Knowledge of maternity is constituted in terms of immediacy (one only has to look and see). Knowledge of paternity, on the other

---

Mary Ann Doane, "The Moving Image: Pathos and the Maternal," from *The Desire to Desire: The Woman's Film of the 1940s* (Bloomington: Indiana University Press, 1987). Reprinted by permission of the author and the Indiana University Press.

hand, is mediated—it allows of gaps and invisibilities, of doubts in short. It therefore demands external regulation in the form of laws governing social relations and the terms of inheritance. Maternity is self-regulating, it has its own internal guarantees. The logic of the sexual division of labor in relation to the upbringing of children derives its force, more than any other aspect of sexual difference, from a purported fidelity to the dictates of the biological. Although the connotations of the maternal as social position far surpass its biological aspects, the biological nevertheless infuses it with meaning and is activated as an anchor to prevent any slippage of the concept. The biological fact of motherhood is utilized to reduce all argumentation to the level of the "obvious," to statements (e.g., "Men cannot have babies") which, in their sheer irrefutability, block or preclude all analysis. These "obviousnesses" then lend credibility to another level, a different order of interpretation of sexual difference which assigns fixed positions to mother, father, and child—positions authorized by the weight of a primal configuration.

A discourse of the obvious thus grounds an understanding of the maternal in terms of the sheer ease of its readability. It is therefore not surprising that the privileged form in the cinema for the investigation of issues associated with maternity is melodrama. The dilemmas of the mother are rarely tragic; they are much more frequently contextualized in the mode of melodrama. Melodrama and the maternal: two discourses of the obvious which have a semiotic resonance. Both are inscribed as sign systems which are immediately readable, almost *too* explicit. Peter Brooks traces the historical origins of melodrama as a popular form and claims that it is "radically democratic, striving to make its representations clear and legible to everyone."[2] Arguing that melodrama, in its desire to "say everything," breaks down the mechanism of repression, Brooks locates its meaning on the surface, in terms of primal psychic integers.

> To stand on the stage and utter phrases such as "Heaven is witness to my innocence" or "I am that miserable wretch who has ruined your family" or "I will pursue you to the grave" is to achieve the full expression of psychological condition and moral feeling in the most transparent, unmodified, infantile form. Desire triumphs over the world of substitute-formations and detours, it achieves plenitude of meaning. . . . In the tableau more than in any other single device of dramaturgy, we grasp melodrama's primordial concerns to make its signs clear, unambiguous, and impressive.[3]

In its striving for a directness in the relation to the spectator, melodrama's semiotic straining is evidenced as a form of excess, a will-to-transparency which is self-negating through its very obviousness. In this sense, the form is inherently contradictory. For the term "melodramatic" in colloquial language connotes excess, the artifice of theatricality.

It is certainly arguable that the term "melodrama," given its vagueness and the range of its potential and actual applications (particularly in relation to the cinema), is virtually useless for analysis. While the label "melodrama" has most recently been activated primarily in the criticism of '50s family melodrama, it has also been applied in discussions of Griffith and silent cinema, crime films and film noir, and even the Western (to which it is also frequently opposed). Moreover, some critics have gone so far as to claim that the cinema itself is essentially melodramatic,[4] basing the argument on the cinema's unique organization and direction of affect, together with its orchestration of a heterogeneous group of signifying materials. Nevertheless, critical essays such as Thomas Elsaesser's "Tales of Sound and Fury: Observations on the Family Melodrama" and the *Screen* "Dossier on Melodrama"[5] demonstrate that, whether or not the term melodrama is capable of defining and delineating a specific group of films, it does pinpoint a crucial and isolable signifying tendency within the cinema which may be activated differently in specific historical periods.

Some of the characteristics of the melodramatic mode, according to Elsaesser, are: the nonpsychological conception of the characters (". . . significance lies in the structure and articulation of the action, not in any psychologically motivated correspondence with individualized experience");[6] the consequent externalization of internal emotions and their embodiment within the mise-en-scène or decor; the claustrophobia of the settings, which are most frequently domestic and/or limited to the small towns of middle America; a concentration on the rhythm of experience rather than its content, a strategy linked to the "foreshortening of lived time in favor of intensity" which is characteristic of melodrama; and the activation of the psychical mechanisms of condensation and displacement which underlie the frustrations emerging when desire is attached to an unattainable object. The contradiction between the notion that melodrama deals with a nonpsychological conception of character and the resort to psychical categories (such as condensation and displacement) for their explanatory power is only apparent. For it is not the psychical dimension which is negated by the films but interiority which is eschewed. The narrative conflict is located *between* characters rather than *within* a single mind. As Robert B. Heilman points out, the latter situation (internal conflict) is typical of tragedy; in melodrama, on the other hand, "dividedness is replaced by a quasi-wholeness, and we find the security of an ordering monopathy."[7] The drama is thus played out within a complex nexus of relationships and the characters' major activity is that of reading, constantly deciphering the intentions, desires, and weaknesses of other characters. In the closed world of melodrama, as Elsaesser claims, the "characters are, so to speak, each others' sole referent."[8]

Hence, melodrama does have its own specificity in relation to characterization, temporality, setting, and the organization of affect. But even more importantly, for the purposes of this study, the melodramatic mode is often analyzed in terms which situate is as a "feminine" form, linking it intimately with the woman's film in its address to a female audience. Thus, Geoffrey Nowell-Smith, in the *Screen* dossier, contrasts the melodrama with the Western:

> Broadly speaking, in the American movie the active hero becomes protagonist of the Western, the passive or impotent hero or heroine becomes protagonist of what has come to be known as melodrama. The contrast active/passive is, inevitably, traversed by another contrast, that between masculine and feminine. . . . [The melodrama] often features women as protagonists, and where the central figure is a man there is regularly an impairment of his "masculinity"—at least in contrast to the mythic potency of the hero of the Western.[9]

The difference is inscribed as a spatial one as well: while the wide open spaces of the Western suggest a range of options and freedom of action, in the melodrama alternatives appear to be closed off and limited by a constricting domestic sphere. The impairment of masculinity or castration which Nowell-Smith points to is generalizable—whether the character is a man or a woman, "suffering and impotence, besides being the data of middle-class life, are seen as forms of a failure to be male."[10] While Elsaesser does not explicitly delineate the (negative) feminization of the protagonist as Nowell-Smith does, he describes the major character in terms which denote passivity and impotence: the protagonist fails to act in "a way that could shape events," the characters are "acted upon." and melodrama "confers on them a negative identity through suffering."[11] More specifically, as Jacques Goimard maintains, pathos—the central emotion of melodrama—is reinforced by the disproportion between the weakness of the victim and the seriousness of the danger so that, as Goimard points out and Northrop Frye emphasizes, "the pathetic is produced more easily through the misfortunes of women, children, animals, or fools. . . ."[12] Melodrama closely allies itself with the delineation of a lack of social power and effectivity so characteristic of the cultural positioning of women.

From this point of view, it is not surprising that the social function most rigorously associated with femininity—that of motherhood—should form the focus of a group of films which exploit the pathetic effect and which bear the label *maternal melodrama*.[13] Maternal melodramas are scenarios of separation, of separation and return, or of threatened separation—dramas which play out all the permutations of the mother/child relation. Because it foregrounds sacrifice and suffering, incarnating the "weepie" aspect of the genre, the maternal melodrama is usually seen as the paradigmatic type of the woman's film. Already a popular genre in the 1920s (*Way Down East* [1921], *Stella Dallas* [1925], *Madame X* [1920, 1929]), it reaches its American apotheosis in the 1930s with films like the 1937 version of *Madame X*, *Blonde Venus* (1932) and, perhaps most importantly, King Vidor's 1937 remake of *Stella Dallas*. In a study of the maternal melodrama from 1930 to 1939, Christian Viviani isolates the thematic matrix of the form:

> A woman is separated from her child, falls from her social class and founders in disgrace. The child grows up in respectability and enters established society where he stands for progress. . . . The mother watches the social rise of her child from afar; she cannot risk jeopardizing his fortunes by contamination with her own bad repute. Chance draws them together again, and the partial or total rehabilitation of the mother is accomplished, often through a cathartic trial scene.[14]

Although this thematic matrix is modified or inflected in various ways by particular films, all of the texts bring into play the contradictory position of the mother within a patriarchal society—a position formulated by the injunction that she focus desire on the child and the subsequent demand to give up the child to the social order. Motherhood is conceived as the always uneasy conjunction of an absolute closeness and a forced distance. The scenario of "watching the child from afar" thus constitutes itself as a privileged tableau of the genre, and it is clear why *Stella Dallas* has become its exemplary film.

While King Vidor's version of *Stella Dallas* (1937) does not, strictly speaking, fall within the time period analyzed in this study, its significance as a model of the form makes it evident that it warrants some detailed attention.[15] Viviani's investigation of '30s maternal melodrama demonstrates that the films tend to establish an intimate relationship between the problems of the mother and issues of social class and/or economic status. Motherhood is marginalized, situated on the cusp of culture (it is more compatible with nature)—looking in from the outside as it were—because it is always a source of potential resistance to the child's entry into the social arena. Thus, as Viviani points out, the child often stands for some sort of social "progress," in contradistinction to the mother. The mother's negotiation of a relation to her child is placed in opposition to his/her social or even economic recognition—according to the logic of the films the two must be incompatible. The price to be paid for the child's social success is the mother's descent into anonymity, the negation of her identity (quite frequently this descent is justified by the narrative on the surface by making her an unwed, and hence explicitly guilty, mother). She must be relegated to the status of silent, unseen and suffering support. As Viviani points out, this is a particularly cruel fate in the '30s: ". . . the mother now pays for her fault no longer through a veritable degradation but by being condemned to anonymity, the true curse in the Hollywood thematics of the Thirties, totally geared to the success story and the rise to fame."[16] Stella Dallas (Barbara Stanwyck) pathetically incarnates this fate at the end of the film when she is deprived of even the frills and jewelry, the excesses in clothing which mark her identity throughout the film. Her presence is not recognized by any of the participants of the drama she watches through the window.

Stella is the victim of desires which exceed her social status. The film prefigures its own ending by situating Stella very early as a movie spectator, but this time a dissatisfied one who measures the distance between herself and the figures on the screen and would like to collapse that difference. As Stephen and Stella leave the movie theater, Stella tells him about her dreams of social mobility, "I want to be like all the people you're around—educated and, you know, speaking nice." When Stephen urges her to be "like herself," Stella objects—"No, I don't want to be like myself, like the people around here. I want to be like the people in the movie—you know, do everything well-bred and refined." What Stella desires is movement, process, a change in the social status represented by her own working class family and, in particular, her mother, who is represented as devoid of energy or even desire. The trajectory of the film, however, succeeds in situating her in her "proper" place, as contented and passive spectator, weeping but nevertheless recognizing and accepting her position on the margins of the social scene, in a space outside.

Stella Dallas demonstrates that "being what you are" involves *not* mimicking those of another social class, allowing them to remain "on the screen." What Stella is, naturally, is a mother. But her downfall is directly linked to her desire to be what is forever outside her grasp since it is inconsistent with her social origins—a refined and respectable lady. Her inability to assume that position is represented as a process of misreading. Stella, misunderstanding what is involved in refinement and respectability, overcompensates, views her access to a higher social position as a matter of excess, addition, *more* of everything—more jewelry, more frills, more perfume. Calling attention to itself, her dress is aggressive, lacking the proportion necessary to refinement. And this tendency gains momentum as the film progresses, until Stella, weighted down by the burden of an inordinate amount of jewelry and accessories, is caricatured by her daughter Laurel's friends and labelled a "Christmas tree." As Viviani points out, the Americanization of the maternal melodrama is in part accomplished by transforming the mother's "moral sin" of the European version into the more typically American "social error."[17] Stella does not commit a social error, she *is* that social error. Consequently, it is embarrassment rather than guilt and punishment which is at stake.

Although soon after Stella becomes obsessed by her maternal duties she largely forgets her earlier social aspirations, displacing them onto Laurel, her excesses in dressing remain as the trace of forbidden desires of social mobility.

And the separation between mother and child is ultimately predicated upon this lack of proportion on the part of Stella, the fact that she is an embarrassment to Laurel, who has outstripped her mother in the social arena (inheriting her refinement, no doubt, from her father). Stella's displacement of her desires onto her daughter is revealed as a constant need to dress Laurel (a major function of mothering in *The Reckless Moment* is also insuring that the child is well-clothed). While Laurel's father sends her books as a birthday present, Stella works at the sewing machine to produce a birthday dress and complains that books are free at the library but a fur coat is not. Although Laurel accepts the dress with pleasure (in contrast to Veda in *Mildred Pierce* whose refusal of a dress is the first sign of a difficulty in the mother/daughter relation), her greatest degree of refinement is evidenced by her rejection of the frills which are specific to her mother's pleasure. Mrs. Morrison, whose dress is more careful, basic, and proper, represents a more appropriate mother for Laurel.

The incredibly pathetic effect of *Stella Dallas* is in part the result of the fact that Stella is the embodiment of the very mechanism of pathos—disproportion (between means and ends, desires and their fulfillment). Her separation from Laurel is the consequence of her misunderstanding or denial of what is "proper" insofar as that word connotes the sign which is fully adequate to, "right" for, its referent. This is particularly regrettable since what is "proper"—propriety—is supposed to be an attribute of women, especially mothers, who must see to it that their children are properly dressed, have the proper manners, etc. Stella's signifiers are askew—they do not match the signifieds for which they are intended. She is a misplaced spectacle. But Laurel does not really perceive this until she sees her mother via the mediation of the instrument of the proper so closely associated with female narcissism—the mirror.

A mirror is always a proper representation of its referent, and the specular relation is one to which women are expected to adhere. Laurel's gradual disengagement from her mother is figured into two separate scenes in which a mirror dominates the mise-en-scène and acts as a relay of glances. In the first, Stella applies cold cream to her face and peroxide to her hair as Laurel speaks admiringly of Mrs. Morrison. Concentrating on her image in the mirror, Stella inadvertently smudges with cold cream the photograph of Mrs. Morrison which Laurel shows her. Laurel reacts with a kind of horror which is the effect of the radical divergence between the photograph, reflecting an easy and composed attractiveness, and the mirror image of Stella, revealing through curlers and cold cream the straining, the excessiveness of her cumbersome narcissistic machinery. In a subsequent shot both mother and daughter are reflected, side by side, in the mirror. Looking at her mother via the mediation of two images—photographic and specular—Laurel sees her differently. The mirror, site of identity and narcissism, initiates the disjunction between mother and daughter. The second scene that stages a specular mediation of the daughter's gaze at the mother takes place at a soda fountain. Laurel and her date are sitting slightly apart from a crowd of young people, facing a large mirror, when Stella walks in in her "Christmas tree" attire. Laurel's friends begin to whisper and make mocking comments about Stella. Presently, Laurel looks up, sees her mother reflected in the mirror, and runs out of the shop, acutely embarrassed. Her gaze mediated via the gazes of others and the mirror, Laurel finally recognizes an accurate, or "proper," reflection of her mother's disproportion. It is as though the closeness of the mother/daughter relation necessitated the deflection of the gaze, its indirection, as a precondition for the establishment of difference.

Stella Dallas is exemplary as a maternal melodrama because Stella figures so blatantly the psychical import or trajectory of mothering. The mother, as a mother, represents a fullness, a presence, a wholeness and harmony which must ultimately be broken. Although the film appears to isolate the issue of Stella's excessiveness in dress and manners from the issue of her mothering, to assume that there is no pertinent relation between the two, her disproportion does stand in direct opposition to the harmonious wholeness associated with motherhood. The "good mother" sacrifices herself for her child because she cannot possibly sustain that impossible image of wholeness. Stella's sacrifice/separation is made more extreme by the fact that she literally *embodies* this inability as excess, a disproportion of parts. Although her behavior toward Laurel is that of the "good mother," her image is not. Yet, Stella is simply a hyperbolization of all mothers, who are inevitably deficient in relation to this image of unity and perfection. As Linda Williams points out, "The device of devaluing and debasing the actual figure of the mother while sanctifying the institution of motherhood is typical of 'the woman's film' in general and the subgenre of the maternal melodrama in particular."[18] All mothers share the same predicament. This is why Mrs. Morrison emphathizes so strongly with Stella. In the scene in which the two women meet, the distance between them is gradually reduced as Mrs. Morrison moves closer and closer to Stella, her spatial proximity signifying an increasing amount of empathy. The communication between them is almost instantaneous and eschews linguistic foundation: when Stephen reads the letter from Stella which claims that she no longer wants Laurel, Mrs. Morrison demands, "Couldn't you read between those pitiful lines?" Mrs. Morrison is the perfect reader of this text (or of its empty spaces), and, being a perfect reader, she recognizes another—it is Mrs. Morrison who insures that the curtains are left open so that Stella can see her daughter's wedding.

Stella is a lesson for the female spectator in more ways than one—what she learns and figures at the window is distance. But the position of the distanced spectator can be assumed by her only at the cost of an identity, of recognition. Nevertheless, Stella, at the window, is not, cannot be, a voyeur despite the policeman's exhortation to move on (and hence the suggestion of the illegality of her vision). Her visual pleasure is not (at least explicitly) a sexual one—it must be mixed with tears and suffering. Although much of my analysis of the woman's film stresses the refusal to attribute the gaze to the woman in a nonproblematic way, there is also a sense in which the woman is socially positioned as a spectator—asked to assume a place *outside* the "real" arena of social relations and power, with all the connotations of passivity, waiting, and watching normally attached to the function of spectatorship. But, in *Stella Dallas*, the production of a distanced spectatorial position for the woman is synonymous with her own negation as mother, at least in any material sense. Her sacrifice, her very absence from the scene, nevertheless insures her transformation into an Ideal of Motherhood.

When the policeman tells Stella to "move on" at the end of the film, she pleads with him, "Oh please let me see her face when he kisses her." What Stella desires, as spectator, is a close-up. When she walks away smiling, toward the camera and into close-up, she becomes that close-up for the spectator, who empathizes with her fate. The distance achieved by Stella is collapsed at an entirely different level. Through the insistent invitation to overidentify with the female protagonist, the maternal melodrama becomes a ritualized mourning of the woman's losses in a patriarchal society.

But this is the classic '30s articulation of maternal melodrama. In the '40s, the form is witness to a number of aberrations. In fact, the maternal melodrama loses much of its coherence as a subgenre, as a structural and iconographic logic which supports a grouping of films. Instead, a sustained effort to conceptualize the maternal surfaces in a number of different types of films—from those which closely resemble overt propaganda (*Tender Comrade* [1943], *Since You Went Away* [1944]), to films informed by the iconography of film noir (*Mildred Pierce* [1945], *The Reckless Moment* [1949]), to the biography of the "great woman" (*Blossoms in the Dust* [1942], *Lydia* [1941]), in which mothering is institutionalized as the founding and directing of an orphanage. Coincident with a wartime reorganization of sexual roles and the corresponding introduction of ambivalence about mothering, the maternal becomes a fractured concept in the '40s, necessitating its dispersal in different genres. Only a few films (e.g., *To Each His Own* [1946], *The Great Lie* [1941]) explicitly and intensively activate the classic figures of the '30s form. The separation which is most frequently narrativized is that dictated by the war: the separation between a husband and his wife and family. As the literalism of the title of *Since You Went Away* indicates, the narrative's time is telescoped into the "meanwhile" of the husband's absence, the points between his departure and return. Mother and child, far from being separated, remain together as a demonstration that the home front is a united front.

The war, quite predictably, mobilizes the ultraconservative aspects of the cultural construction of motherhood. Ann Hilton's (Claudette Colbert's) major duty as a mother in *Since You Went Away* is to maintain things "as they are." Hugging the empty bathrobe which signifies her husband's absence, she sobs, "I'll try to keep all the good things as they were. I'll keep the past alive. Like a warm room for you to come back to." The maternal is appropriated as a signifier for all that American soldiers are fighting for. Nazimova, playing a newly arrived working-class immigrant, presents Mrs. Hilton with a speech about the significance of the Statue of Liberty and then tells her, "You are what I thought America was." The identification of America with the ideal wife and mother allows a political discourse to expropriate an entire constellation of connotations associated with the maternal—comfort, nurturance, home, containment/stasis, community, closeness, affect—in the service of a nationalistic cause.[19] This process enables the naturalization of the political cause through a kind of contamination effect. For maternal characteristics are given as the most natural thing in nature. This strategy of imbricating the concept of the maternal with that of a nationalistic patriotism also succeeds in giving the woman a significant position in wartime which does not constitute a threat to the traditional patriarchal order—a symbolic role which counteracts the effects of the woman's new and necessary role in production. Thus in *Since You Went Away*, Ann Hilton's employment as a welder is an afterthought of the narrative structure, and in *Tender Comrade*, the only shots of the women actually working in a large airplane hangar are denaturalized through the use of a rear projection process which uncannily introduces a division between the women and the space of production.[20] The sheer weight of the symbolic role of motherhood offers a strong resistance to the potentially profound implications of the socioeconomic roles now accessible to women in production. Material reality yields to melodrama, which becomes a historical document.

The mirror, which in *Stella Dallas* mediated a traumatic deflection of the gaze between mother and daughter, in *Since You Went Away* intensifies the relation between the mother and an absent husband whose representation enables her own. After Ann Hilton ascends the stairs, clasping two photographs of her husband, she stops at the door of their bedroom. Her voice-over, addressed to the absent husband, fixes her nonidentity—"You know I have no courage"—and there follows a cut to an empty mirror on the dressing table, reflecting nothing, accompanied by the continuation of the voice-over, "and I have no vision." The camera moves slightly forward toward the mirror as Ann moves into its frame and places the two pictures of her husband on either side of it, framing her own reflection. Deprived of vision and a narcissistic identification, maternal subjectivity is annihilated in the movement which brackets the woman's mirror image between the memories of the absent male. In an earlier section of this opening scene the camera hysterically documents the traces of the paternal presence and the signifiers of an impending wartime absence—the imprint of a body in a favorite soft chair, a sleeping bulldog at its foot, a carton labeled "Military Raincoats," a Western Union telegram containing instructions to proceed to camp, mementos of the couple's wedding trip and their children. The scene activates the construction of a loss which haunts the entire narrative. References to and representations of absent males (husbands and sons) abound in *Tender Comrade* as well—each of the women keeps a photograph of an absent husband next to her bed so that the all-female house is laced with reminders of male presence. And in *Since You Went Away*, a huge mural depicting men fighting overshadows and dwarfs a group of young women (including the Hilton daughter) who are taking a nurse's aide oath. Yet, these images of men have a different valence or inflection than those of women in the classical Hollywood text—absence and hence photographability do not connote the erotic. Rather, the photographs (and other images) act as memory traces of authority-in-absence—an authority which is just as, if not more, powerful in its absence.

In the '40s, the issues of social class so important to the maternal melodrama of the '30s are repressed or marginalized (with the exception, perhaps, of *Mildred Pierce*, where Mildred's problems are a direct result of her desire to move up the social scale). The families of *The Reckless Moment* and *Since You Went Away* are decidedly middle class. Yet, while social class is made to appear insignificant given the democratic tendencies of the films, social inequalities emerge on the sidelines, in the use of black servants. In this respect, it is significant that there is a '30s version of *Imitation of Life* and a '50s version, but no '40s remake. Racial issues are too central to the film—in the '40s maternal melodramas these issues are present but marginalized. Black servants haunt the diegeses of films like *The Great Lie*, *Since You Went Away*, and *The Reckless Moment*. Furthermore, black servants are frequently used to buttress central ideologies and to invalidate any claims of racial inequality through their representation as essential and legitimate (unquestionable) appendages of the nuclear family. Female black servants in particular act to double and hence reinforce the maternal function. In *The Reckless Moment*, the black maid, Sybil, consistently occupies the background of shots which chronicle the family's dilemma. As the locus of otherness and an instinctive and unspecifiable form of maternal knowledge, she can distinguish between those who will

ultimately protect the family structure (the blackmailer Donnelly played by James Mason) and those who threaten it (Donnelly's less sentimental partner, Nagel). Sybil assumes a maternal function in relation to Mrs. Harper (constantly questioning her as to whether she's had enough to eat, etc.) and hence becomes a kind of meta-mother. This representation—and others in the films—are fully consistent with psychological theories of the 1940s which held that the black woman symbolized "the primitive essence of mother-love."[21] Perceived as closer to the earth and to nature and more fully excluded from the social contract that the white woman, the black woman personifies more explicitly the situation of the mother, and her presence, on the margins of the text, is a significant component of many maternal melodramas.

Because the films tend to posit an ideal of democracy and hence to deny any functional differences based on either class or race (at the level of their manifest discourse), they also tend to situate any sociopolitical differentiation in the realm of pure ideology divorced from material constraints. The most "propagandistic" of the films—*Tender Comrade* and *Since You Went Away*—present, primarily through dialogue, a war of ideologies which are linked in curious ways to forms of sexuality. For instance, in *Tender Comrade* the character (Barbara) who articulates and advocates an isolationist policy is also represented as sexually promiscuous. A discussion about whether or not Barbara should be dating other men while her husband serves in the Navy (Ginger Rogers: "I should think that with Pete out there on a ship you might play it straight") is linked syntagmatically to an argument about the political implications of hoarding. Barbara, who is excessive in the realm of sexuality, also desires what the film, upholding a wartime economy of scarcity, posits as an excessive desire for material goods, a tendency toward overconsumption. She situates herself as a proponent of isolationism by complaining about "shipping butter to foreigners" and "fighting for a lot of foreigners." In *Since You Went Away*, the character who unpatriotically hoards goods is excessive in the register of speech—she is the town gossip. Veda's negative characterization in *Mildred Pierce* as a type of consumer vampire ("There are so many things that we should have and haven't got," she complains to Mildred) echoes this excessive relation to commodities. Economics and sexuality are inextricably linked in this algebra whereby a wartime economy of lack or scarcity is seriously threatened by excessive female sexuality.

But from our point of view the most interesting aspect of this political economy is its relation to the register of the maternal. In this respect, promiscuous sexuality is comparable to excessive mothering—both are dangerous aspects of femininity, and both are represented as maintaining a close affinity with a detrimental politics of isolationism. The mother who is too close to her son strives to keep him out of the arena of world affairs. In *Tomorrow Is Forever* (1946) and *Watch on the Rhine* (1943), the mother's desire to prevent her son from enlisting or fighting for democracy is clearly stigmatized as an isolationist tendency. It is worth stressing that these films frequently articulate an anti-isolationist politics with a maternal ideology. In other words, the historical articulation of the maternal obligation to surrender the son is merged with an anti-isolationist politics. A careful balancing of closeness and distance within the nuclear family is crucial to the maintenance of democratic nationalistic ideologies.

What the maternal melodramas of the '30s and '40s demonstrate, almost inadvertently, is that motherhood, far from being the simple locus of comfort and nostalgic pleasure—a position to which a patriarchal culture ceaselessly and somewhat desperately attempts to confine it—is a site of multiple contradictions. In the '40s these contradictions are reduced to a single governing opposition which polarizes maternal possibilities. Figured spatially, the oppositional terms are an overcloseness between mother and child which signals, on the political plane, the dangers of isolationism (in *Tomorrow Is Forever* and *Watch on the Rhine*) and, conversely, the maintenance of a dangerous distance from and hence neglect of the child (in other words, the situation of the working mother in films like *Mildred Pierce* or *To Each His Own*). The maternal is represented as its two excesses which are controlled and contained through their narrativization.[22]

Yet, the films of the '40s simply effect a historical specification of a more generalizable psychical configuration associated with patriarchy. As Monique Plaza points out, "Responsible for too much or not enough, the Mother is submitted to contradictory injunctions which are a function of the representation that the theoreticians make of the child, and of the well-adjusted adult."[23] The mother is allowed no access to a comfortable position of moderation. Rather, the polarization of the two maternal excesses creates a textual problematic quite conducive to the manipulation of simple moral absolutes or primal psychic integers which Brooks claims is characteristic of melodrama. In this sense, the films conform to what he labels the "logic of the excluded middle."[24] Nevertheless, this polarization acts as a kind of decoy to distract attention from an entirely different kind of fear associated with the maternal. It is an ideological strategy for defusing, minimizing the effects of another diametrically opposed understanding of the maternal as the site of the collapse of all oppositions and the confusion of identities. This conceptualization of the material is elaborated in detail in much contemporary feminist theory, including the work of such writers as Irigaray and Kristeva.

Luce Irigaray is perhaps the most insistent spokesperson for the necessity of delineating a female specificity—an autonomous symbolic representation for the woman. The difficulty of such a project is, however, evidenced by the constant production of figures which are by no means autonomous but gain much of their force in direct (and thus dependent) opposition to patriarchal representations of masculinity. Thus, in the text where she confronts most directly the question of the maternal—"And the One Doesn't Stir Without the Other"[25]—the specification of a maternal space clearly opposes itself to and hence departs from a notion of paternal law as the site of separation, division, differentiation. The essay is constructed as the pre-Oedipal daughter's lament to the mother, and in this context the mother is represented as all-powerful, engulfing, paralyzing. The suffocating closeness of the relation is exacerbated by its anticipation of a future in which the daughter is doomed to assume the mother's place, to repeat the configuration in relation to her own daughter. In this sense, the essay is a dramatization or theatricalization of the Freudian scenario of the mother/child relation. The plenitude and nondifferentiation associated with the maternal space is evidenced by the constant slippage and confusion of the shifters designating mother and daughter (the "you" and the "I") in the essay.

From its opening statement, "With your milk, Mother, I swallowed ice," Irigaray's essay situates the process of mothering by tracing the figures of orality. The maternal space is the realm of pure need, and mothering is obsessively linked to nurturing, feeding, the provision of an object for the oral drives. But nurturing here does not receive a positive valence as it does in much American feminist theory. The child is not simply satiated but glutted by the mother's milk/love, which is always in excess. In overinvesting her desire in the child, the mother becomes herself the perverse subject of the oral drive—the agent of an engulfing or devouring process which threatens to annihilate the subjectivity of the child. In this respect, Irigaray's analysis approaches that of Julia Kristeva in *Powers of Horror.* Kristeva associates the maternal with the abject—i.e., that which is the focus of a combined horror and fascination, hence subject to a range of taboos designed to control the culturally marginal.[26] In this analysis, the function of nostalgia for the mother-origin is that of a veil, a veil which conceals the terror attached to nondifferentiation. The threat of the maternal space is that of the collapse of any distinction whatsoever between subject and object. Within the Freudian schema, incorporation is the model for processes of identification (between "subject" and "object," mother and child) which have the potential to destroy the very notion of identity.

Kristeva elsewhere emphasizes a particularly interesting corollary of this aspect of motherhood: the maternal space is "a place both double and foreign."[27] In its internalization of heterogeneity, an otherness within the self, motherhood deconstructs certain conceptual boundaries. Kristeva delineates the maternal through the assertion, "In a body there is grafted, unmasterable, an other."[28] The confusion of identities threatens to collapse a signifying system based on the paternal law of differentiation.

It would seem that the concept of motherhood automatically throws into question ideas concerning the self, boundaries between self and other, identity. Perhaps this is why a patriarchal society invests so heavily in the construction and maintenance of motherhood as an identity with very precise functions—comforting, nurturing, protecting. The horror of nondifferentiation is suppressed through a process of attaching a surplus of positive attributes to the maternal. It might also explain why there exists a specific genre—maternal melodrama. The films of this genre play out the instabilities of maternal identity in order to locate it more solidly.[29] In films like *The Great Lie, To Each His Own,* and *Stella Dallas,* biological maternity and social maternity may not coincide, but the true function and responsibilities of the mother are made quite clear. The mother must be present (as both *The Great Lie* and *To Each His Own* demonstrate) and she must be an adequate mirror for the child (the failure of Stella Dallas). The constant return in the films to the themes of mistaken identity, distance and separation, knowledge and recognition indicates the obsessiveness of a compulsion to repeat which strives to allay, through a kind of slow erosion, any danger associated with the potentially radical aspects of the maternal.

Above and beyond all other specifications, the true mother is defined in terms of pure presence: she is the one who is *there.* In *To Each His Own,* after a traumatic confrontation with the child who does not recognize her as his mother, Jody tells her friend and secretary, "I'm not his mother, not really. Just bringing a child into the world doesn't make you that. It's being there always, nursing him . . . all the things I've missed." Although presence does not exhaust the attributes essential to motherhood—in itself it is not sufficient—it is absolutely necessary for adequate mothering. Paternal power, on the other hand, often manifests itself more strongly through absence (this is the case in films like *The Reckless Moment* and *Since You Went Away*). In *The Great Lie*, Bette Davis makes use of assumptions based on the association of presence and mothering to sustain her husband's belief that the child is actually hers. In this way she manages to manufacture a lie (the "great lie") from an iconic system. Yet, it does not have the affective valence of a lie—after all, Bette Davis is *there*, while Mary Astor is not. And the (rather abrupt) closure of the film affirms the spectator's sense that Bette Davis is the "true" mother.

Circumscribed in this way, the concept of the maternal is compatible with the language of melodrama—the two discourses support one another through a mutual reinforcement of certain semes: presence, immediacy, readability. According to Peter Brooks, the melodramatic mode strives to resuscitate an originary language theorized in the eighteenth century by writers such as Diderot and Rousseau in terms of a notion of gesture as an unmediated sign and its corresponding attributes of purity and presence. In Diderot's aesthetic theory, gesture and cry signify more fully because they are the language of nature and hence accessible to all.[30] The nostalgia implicit in such a formulation is apparent in Rousseau—as Brooks points out, "Gesture appears in the *Essai* to be a kind of pre-language, giving a direct presentation of things prior to the alienation from presence set off by the passage into articulated language."[31] And according to the *Encyclopédie*, gesture is "the primitive language of mankind in its cradle."[32] This "originary language" is, of course, theorized as a maternal tongue. Although Brooks does not explicitly indicate this, references to "nature," a "pre-language," "mankind in its cradle," forcefully connect the primal language he delineates to a maternal space. The "feminine" connotations attached to melodrama are no doubt at least partially derived from this tendency.

The desire of melodrama to recover an originary language which is not structured through difference is manifested in the genre's strategy of deflecting signifying material onto other, nonlinguistic registers of the sign—gesture, looks, music, mise-en-scène. In this group of films, little is left to language. The texts, in fact, exhibit a distrust of language, locating the fullness of meaning elsewhere. At the end of *The Reckless Moment*, the bars of the staircase which appear to imprison the mother (Joan Bennett) undermine the forced optimism of her telephone conversation with the absent husband. The memory-flashback which structures the bulk of the narrative in *To Each His Own* is constituted as the repudiation of a casual remark made by a young woman to Jody as she waits in the train station for the arrival of her son: "You can't imagine what it's like to be in love with a flier." Jody proceeds to imagine/remember this and more in the production of the film's narrative. The pathetic quality of the scene in which Jody fails to disclose her secret to her son is encapsulated less in the dialogue whereby she denigrates her own right to claim the status of motherhood than in the prominence accorded an absurd balloon in the shape of a horse (Carol, the Queen of the Corral) within the mise-en-scène. The constant presence of the horse which haunts and doubles her own image underlines the futility of her desire. Insofar as gesture is concerned, in *Johnny Belinda* the full force of the mute Belinda's maternal desire is conveyed by her constant repetition of the sign language signifiers for the phrase, "I want my baby" (signifiers which include the gesture of rocking an imaginary baby back and forth in one's arms).

But the register of the sign which bears the greatest burden in this yearning for a full language is that which authorizes the label "melodrama"—music. Music marks a deficiency in the axis of vision. Because emotion is the realm in which the visible is insufficient as a guarantee, the supplementary meaning proffered by music is absolutely necessary. The cinematic relation between music and the image is explicitly spelled out in *Lydia* when a blind pianist teaches children colors through music and produces an entire concerto as a "description" of Lydia's face. As the pianist maintains, "No one can really see what he loves," and music marks the excess. The incessent recourse to music in maternal melodrama and its heightening effect suggest that the rationality of the image is a disadvantage.[33]

In this sense, the melodramatic discourse aims to do what Brooks claims psychoanalysis accomplishes in relation to the unconscious—to recover for meaning what is outside meaning. Gesture, music, and mise-en-scène are deployed to represent that which is unrepresentable—the "ineffable." The project of the maternal melodrama is from the beginning an impossible one insofar as it strives to retrieve that which is fundamentally contradictory—a language of presence. Doubly impossible insofar as it strives to represent the maternal as a form of pure presence. And because the imaginary signifier of the cinema, as Metz has shown, is based on absence to a greater degree than other languages which activate multiple sensory registers, the melodramatic film has a greater stake in masking this absence. It does so by intensifying and displacing the presence, immediacy, and closeness which purportedly characterize the connection between sign and referent onto the relation between film and spectator. The film invests in the possibility of immediate understanding, and the immediacy of its communication is evidenced by the unthought, uncontrollable tears which it produces. The form of affect associated with maternal melodrama, pathos, connotes a violent sentimentalism.

This pathetic effect is facilitated, as mentioned earlier in the analysis of *Stella Dallas*, by a sense of disproportion—between desires and their fulfillment or between the transgression (e.g., the "sin" of the unwed mother) and the punishment associated with it. As the nurse in *To Each His Own* tells Jody, "You've sinned. You'll pay for it the rest of your life." And she does. *To Each His Own* exemplifies the classic maternal melodrama insofar as its rapid plot reversals and convolutions, its blockages of communication, all seem to serve the same function—to construct and maintain an unbridgeable distance between the female protagonist and the object of her desire, a distance which is rationalized by her originary transgression. From this perspective, it is worth exploring *To Each His Own* in some depth.

In the beginning of the film, which is predominantly structured as a flashback, Jody Norris (Olivia de Havilland) is a middle-aged American woman in London who happens to save the life of an Englishman, Lord Desham, when he falls off a roof during air raid maneuvers. When Lord Desham in gratitude takes Jody to dinner, she has a chance encounter with a soldier from her hometown who informs her that someone else from the same town is arriving on the train that night. Because that "someone else," as the spectator later learns, turns out to be Jody's son, she rushes to the train station only to find that the train has been delayed. The bulk of the film's narrative takes the form of a flashback memory which fills the time of her waiting at the train station.

As mentioned earlier, the flashback is a response to (and a repudiation of) a young woman's casual remark to Jody, "You can't imagine what it's like to be in love with a flier." In the first scene of her memory-flashback, Jody discourages one potential beau

(Max, a slick salesman) in the name of her desire for "true romance" and turns down the marriage proposal of another (Alec, who marries another woman, Corrine, on the rebound). But then Jody meets a romantic young flier who descends from the sky seemingly for the sole purpose of making love to her and fulfilling her dreams and then ascends once more only to be shot down in a battle. From their one night of romance, she becomes pregnant. The speed with which the love story of the first section of the film is displaced by the maternal melo of the second is rather remarkable. As Wolfenstein and Leites point out in their description of the film, "A recurrent theme in these films of the heroine and her son is the absence of the father, who may descend from heaven in an airplane to beget the child and then fly off never to be seen again (*To Each His Own*)."[34] Wolfenstein and Leites interpret the film as an instance of Otto Rank's myth of the birth of the hero which "reduces the relation of the mother and father to a transient contact" and "gratifies the son's longing to exclude the father and have the mother to himself."[35] This analysis is, however, based on the premise that the film should be interpreted from the point of view of the son—a premise which has little credibility given the organization of affect in the film and the terms of its address.

But Jody's pregnancy and her motherhood are riddled with problems. When the doctor tells her she is pregnant he also informs her that she is sick and either must have an operation in which she will lose the baby or die. Jody is preparing to go to New York and have the operation when she hears the news of her flier's death. This turn of events prompts her to have the baby regardless of the threat to herself in order to preserve the father's memory. Despite the doctor's warning, the baby and Jody are both healthy after the delivery in New York City. Jody devises a scheme whereby she has the baby left on a doorstep in her hometown (the doorstep of a woman who already has eight children) and plans to intervene herself with the offer to adopt the baby. But the plan miscarries when Alec and Corrine, whose first child has just died, find out about the foundling and adopt it before Jody can make her claim. Jody sees how happy Corrine is with the baby in her arms and leaves him with her, although she visits him constantly. Tension develops between Corrine and Jody over both the baby and Alec, who ultimately admits that he still loves Jody. When Jody's father dies, she asks Corrine if she can act as the baby's ("Griggsy's") nursemaid. When Corrine jealously refuses, Jody decides to tell her that the baby is hers and produces a birth certificate (a recurrent sign in scenes of recognition in melodrama). But Corrine and Alec have had the baby legally adopted to protect themselves against such a possibility, and Jody has no legal right to the child.

Upon hearing this news, Jody leaves her hometown and goes to New York to work. She becomes rich and influential as the president of Lady Vyvyan cosmetics. Several years pass and Alec occasionally brings Griggsy to New York so that Jody can get a glimpse of her son. Jody learns that Corrine and Alec are on the verge of bankruptcy and literally blackmails Corrine into giving her Griggsy. However, the little boy (who is now approximately five or six years old) soon misses his "mother" (Corrine), and in a poignant scene Jody recognizes this and is forced to let him return to his adoptive family. Hoping to displace all her energies from motherhood to work, she tells an associate, "Let me go to London. Find me fourteen hours of work a day."

Thus ends the flashback portion of the film as Jody still waits at the train station for her now fully grown son who has become, like his father, an air force pilot. Jody, of course, recognizes him immediately (perhaps because the same actor—John Lund—

takes the roles of both father and son). The son now has a girl, however—a WAC who is also on leave—and he is more concerned with her and with the obstacles to their desire to get married than with "Aunt" Jody. But Lord Desham, arriving for a date with Jody, learns about the situation and by means of his high-level contacts arranges a wedding and longer leaves for the young couple. In the last scene the son, primarily through the intervention of his girlfriend (who says of Jody: "I saw her watching you. Anyone would think you were her only son"), finally recognizes that Jody is his real mother. The son approaches Jody and says, "I think this is our dance, mother."

I have delineated the plot of *To Each His Own* in such extended detail in order to specify the various ways in which the narrative structure meticulously constructs blockade after blockade against maternal desire. Even at the end of the film, when recognition finally takes place, it does so only through the mediation of a father figure (Lord Desham) and in the context of a ritual whereby the son is passed on to another woman. Despite the absence of a literal father in much of the film, father figures do play a crucial role in the narrative trajectory. Not only does Lord Desham almost miraculously provide closure, but Jody's father, earlier in the film, determines to a large extent the course of events. When Corrine and Alec decide to adopt the child found on the doorstep early in the film, Jody prepares to tell them that the child is really hers. But her father intervenes claiming, "He's my grandchild, he's not going to be brought up a marked child. Can't you hear people whispering, 'He hasn't a father—never had one.' " The lack of a father and its social consequences are determinant in the initiation of Jody's trajectory of pain and suffering. When her own father dies, Jody tries to retrieve the child but it is too late (her timing is off), and the birth certificate she produces as proof of the child's identity is now useless. From this point of view, it is quite significant that recognition takes place at the end of the film via a stand-in (Lord Desham) for the absent father. The separation between mother and son, that is, the movement of the son into the social order, must be insured before any possibility of reunification of the two can be acknowledged.

This is why the presence of Liz—the girlfriend—is so crucial at the end of the film. She effectively blocks a process which had been gaining momentum throughout the film—the eroticization of the mother/son relation—and which culminates in the use of the same actor to play the roles of both lover and son. This eroticization is registered primarily as a scopophiliac relation. Jody keeps a scrapbook filled with photographs of her son and frequently looks with longing at these photos. Caught in the act of doing so by her former beau, Max the salesman (who does not see the subject of the photographs), she has a lengthy conversation with him based on his misunderstanding that the object of her gaze is a beau (Max asks her about "obstacles" to their marrying). When "Griggsy" comes to live with Jody briefly in New York, she can't keep her eyes off of him until Griggsy finally asks, "Is my face dirty? You keep looking at it so hard." Absence and distance only intensify that love which is doomed to failure. *To Each His Own* seems to dramatize most explicitly the Freudian notion that a woman's love is always mistimed, always subject to a displacement from father to son (a psychoanalytic thematics which will be discussed more thoroughly later in this chapter). Jody must witness and accept her replacement as object of desire by Liz at the end of the film.

To Each His Own also dramatizes what Elsaesser refers to as the impotency of displacement as a method of attaining emotional ends in melodrama.[36] The money stockpiled by Jody for her son only increases the pathos of her failure to relate to him. When she learns that Corrine and Alec have adopted her son she substitutes hard work and economic success for the joys of mothering. Many of the maternal melodramas of the '40s elaborate this type of binary logic whereby mothering and economic success are opposed to one another and, in most cases, constituted as absolutely incompatible. In this way the films manage to effectively demarcate and separate the realms of production and reproduction. This is the case in *To Each His Own*, *Mildred Pierce*, and *The Reckless Moment*. In *The Reckless Moment*, Mrs. Harper is so absorbed by the processes of mothering that she finds herself entirely excluded from the language of economics. When she attempts to get a loan in order to pay off her daughter's blackmailer, she stumbles over the words ("I'd like to *make* a loan . . . *get* a loan").

The pathetic effect of the scene in which Jody, having literally bought Griggsy from Corrine and Alec, finds that she cannot satisfy his desire for his mother, is a result of this absolute disjunction between the maternal and economic activities. Jody's large, well-decorated house only underlines Griggsy's loneliness and the extent to which he misses the woman he believes to be his mother. In an earlier scene, Alec had taken Griggsy to a rodeo in order to provide a situation in which Jody could see and talk to her son. At the rodeo it becomes clear that Griggsy would like to have a ridiculous-looking balloon that the peddler refers to as "Carol, the Queen of the Corral." Jody attempts to buy the balloon but the peddler informs her that this particular balloon is not for sale since it is used as a "come-on." Later, when Griggsy has come to live with her, Jody tells him that she has a surprise for him. The little boy becomes very excited when the surprise is referred to as a "lady," but is dismayed to find that it is "Carol, the Queen of the Corral." When Jody asks him why he is so sad he replies, "I thought maybe it was my mother" and runs into a bedroom. In the following shot of Jody, "Carol, the Queen of the the Corral"—the balloon that was not for sale—occupies the background as a grotesque reminder and caricature of Jody's deficiency as a mother.

At this point, Jody's friends urge her to tell Griggsy that she is his real mother, and there follows a scene which is one of the most moving of the film, based as it is on an almost total blockage of communication and Griggsy's nonrecognition of his mother. When Jody attempts to reveal her identity, he misunderstands and, thinking that she is referring disparagingly to the fact that he is adopted (a situation Corrine has clearly warned him about), he runs crying into the bathroom. As Elsaesser points out, "Pathos results from noncommunication or silence made eloquent. . . ."[37] Jody can only walk over to the mirror, whose reflection seems to confirm her nonidentity as a mother. For the function of a mother, as Jody defines it, is "being there always." The slippage between the mirror image and what she desires also mirrors the female spectator's relation to the text of pathos.

Of the various subgenres of the woman's film, the maternal melodrama is the one which appears to fully earn the label "weepie." The plight of the mother with respect to her child, the necessary separations, losses, and humiliations she must suffer are always moving and often "move" the spectator to tears. The films obsessively structure themselves around just-missed moments, recognitions which occur "too late," and blockages of communication which might have been avoided. In this sense, the pathetic text appears to insist that the gap between desire and its object is not structural but accidental and therefore to reconfirm the possibility of a fullness in signification—a complete and transparent communication. Tears testify to the loss of such a fullness but also to its existence as a (forever receding) ideal.

But what activates crying as the spectatorial response to (or defense against) a text? For Franco Moretti it is a matter of timing, and in some cases it is even possible to locate a precise textual moment which triggers the tears. Although Moretti's investigation of "moving literature" focuses on boy's literature ("texts with 'boys' both as their protagonists and as their ideal readers"),[38] the pathos associated with this genre has a great deal in common with that of the woman's film. For both boys and women are "presubjects"; they are denied access to the full subjectivity bestowed on the adult male within a patriarchal culture. Occupying the margins of the social field, they are both allowed to cry. There is a difference of course. The projected future of the boy always assumes an access to subjectivity—he must simply wait. The woman, on the other hand, is always a "presubject"—she will always wait for that moment (scenarios in which the woman *waits* abound in the woman's film). "Boy's literature" represents for its addressee a form of preparation for the assumption of full subjectivity within society. As Moretti points out, the texts thus enact a mourning for the narcissistic losses which must inevitably accompany such an access to subjectivity. They can therefore be analyzed with reference to the *Bildungsroman*. Not so the maternal melodrama in which no *Bildung* takes place.

The moving effect is generated by what Moretti describes as a "rhetoric of the too late." All literary narrative is characterized by shifting points of view which are ultimately submitted to a process of hierarchization in the text's resolution. This is the moment of agnition or recognition. What is specific to "moving" literature is not the hierarchization of points of view or the device of agnition itself but the *timing* of that agnition—"Agnition is a 'moving' device when it comes *too late*. And to express the sense of being 'too late' the easiest course is obviously to prime the agnition for the moment when the character is on the point of dying."[39] Pathos is thus related to a certain construction of temporality in which communication or recognitions take place but are mistimed. Moving narratives manifest an unrelenting linearity which allows the slippage between what is and what should have been to become visible. What the narratives demonstrate above all is the irreversibility of time.

> And this irreversibility is perceived that much more clearly if there are no doubts about the *different direction* one would like to impose on the course of events.
>
> This is what makes one cry. Tears are always the product of *powerlessness*. They presuppose two mutually opposed facts: that it is clear how the present state of things should be changed—and that this change is *impossible*. They presuppose a definitive estrangement of facts from values, and thus the end of any relationship between the idea of *teleology* and that of *causality*.[40]

The "moving effect," then, is tied to a form of mistiming, a bad timing, or a disphasure. This is perhaps most visible in a woman's film which is not, strictly speaking, a maternal melodrama, but is a "weepie" nevertheless—*Back Street*. In the 1941 version of this film, the female protagonist literally misses the boat, and her bad timing insures that her fiancé will leave and ultimately marry another woman. That one missed moment will determine her future, relegating her to the back street of his life until she dies. The film goes so far as to provide the spectator with a means to measure the distance between what was and what should have been by supplying the missing image of their encounter at the boat landing—after both of the characters have died.

Maternal melodramas, on the other hand, favor a specific form of mistiming which allows the films quite often to corroborate Freud's theories about maternal love and the relation between the sexes. For Freud, the most perfect human relationship is that between mother and son. In his lecture on "Femininity," he notes the importance of the pre-Oedipal period in the formation of the future mother. The psychical characteristics acquired by the woman in this period later attract the man who sees in her his own mother. Freud's interpretation is somewhat despairing: "How often it happens, however, that it is only his son who obtains what he himself aspired to! One gets an impression that a man's love and a woman's are a phase apart psychologically."[41] This disphasure is echoed in Laean's formulation, "There is no sexual relation." In the maternal melodramas, the son (or sometimes a daughter) often quite blatantly assumes the place of the father in the mother's sexual life. In films like *Tomorrow Is Forever* and *Watch on the Rhine*, the son's desire to enlist or to become active in world affairs renews the threat of a lost love. The timing of the two world wars—a generation apart—allows for the narratives' exploitation of repetition in the relation between a woman and her husband and that between a woman and her son (*To Each His Own, Tomorrow Is Forever, Watch on the Rhine* are examples of this tendency). In *Letter from an Unknown Woman* or even *Now, Voyager* the child takes over the space of the absent lover. The most striking example is *To Each His Own*, discussed earlier, in which a series of mistimings results in the separation between mother and son and the subsequent eroticization of the mother's (scopophiliac) relation to the son (whose role, it is worth repeating, is taken by the same actor as the now dead father). In this sense, weepies trace the outline of an inevitable mistiming or disphasure which is constitutive of feminine sexuality in a patriarchal culture.

This alleged "fault" or "flaw" in female sexuality (the woman's misdirected desire—her insistence on striving after the "wrong" object) is given extensive representation within the maternal melodramas. Maternal desire is frequently revealed as actively resistant to the development of a love story. In *Mildred Pierce*, a potential love relationship between Mildred and Monty is aborted almost before it begins by Mildred's growing involvement with a business venture designed to satisfy her daughter Veda's desires. In *The Reckless Moment*, the most aberrant and even, at times, subversive of maternal melodramas, Mrs. Harper (Joan Bennett), concentrating on the protection of her daughter, does not even recognize that she is involved in a love story with the blackmailed Donnelly until it is too late. As the editors of *Framework* point out in their insightful analysis of the film, motherhood is delineated as the repression of desire (Mrs. Harper's strict regulation of her daughter's sex life) and the body (she is constantly telling her son to put on more clothes—"Pull up your socks," "Put on a shirt," etc.).[42] An inordinate amount of film time is spent on a scene in which Mrs. Harper laboriously and in silence (there is no music on the track, only the sound of lapping waves) drags Darby's body down the beach to the boat in order to take it away and conceal it—in what is basically a literalization of the "maternal function" of hiding (or repressing) the body. A mother's instinct to protect the fully legalized institution of the family is, interestingly enough, itself outside of the law.

Particularly pertinent, then, is *The Reckless Moment*'s presentation to its female spectator of a fantasy of flirting with otherness, represented in the film by the underworld. Although the *Framework* article treats the film primarily as a family melodrama which, riddled with tensions and contradictions, tends to subvert the stability of the family as a structure, the film is based on a short story from *Ladies' Home Journal*,[43] and its mode of address is partially codified by the demands of this form. Much of its appeal lies in its status as a story of a forbidden or illicit love and the attraction of a character played by James Mason—an attraction which is strengthened by his association with illegality and the underworld. The spectator's knowledge or awareness of the love affair exceeds that of the female protagonist, who is totally oblivious to the "female fantasy" aspect of the film—being loved by a blackmailer—until the end when she must recognize it as a lost object. In this sense, the film laboriously constructs that loss for her.

When the blackmailer Donnelly first appears in the film he functions, structurally, as an erotic replacement for the absent father. The sustained tracking shot which follows Mrs. Harper down the stairs (the pivot of the mise-en-scène in the film) to meet Donnelly for the first time echoes that in which she descends the stairway in order to talk to her husband on the phone. During Mrs. Harper's conversation with Donnelly, her son enters and the camera placements emphasize a triangular spatial relationship between the three figures—mother, son, and, structurally, "father." Furthermore, it is almost as though all communications addressed to the husband-father were intercepted by Donnelly. Early in the film, Mrs. Harper writes a letter to her husband, censoring a version in which she details her anxieties about her daughter and substituting for it the standard clichés of a love letter. Several scenes later, as though the letter had reached the wrong destination, Donnelly reads to her the clichéd love letters which were, in fact, written by her daughter. The "real" father in the film is never imaged; he is represented only as a voice at the other end of the line, and that voice is merely implied, never actually heard. But Donnelly literally takes his place at the other end of the line. When he speaks with Mrs. Harper on the phone, he is given both an image and a voice.

Yet, it becomes clear fairly quickly that Donnelly's status as lover-husband figure is only an apparent one. For, what he is actually seduced by is the maternal. As Mrs. Harper fully assumes the maternal function, becoming more and more concerned about her family, Donnelly is progressively more attracted to her. The film is, in a sense, a fantasy about the power of mothers—even criminality is confounded and subdued by the maternal. In the drugstore scene, Donnelly provides Mrs. Harper with change for the phone, carries her packages, and even buys her a present (which she does not recognize as such). Later, he goes so far as to offer her his half of the blackmail money. The blackmailer is fully domesticated. At the end of the film this transformation of the potentially erotic into filial devotion is evidenced most fully by a speech in which Donnelly admits that Mrs. Harper invokves in him the memory of his own mother ("My mother wanted to make a priest out of me. I never wanted to do a decent thing until I met you. . . . Don't make the same mistake my mother did"). It is the image of the mother, not the woman, which prompts desire and reformation.

Mrs. Harper is not even aware of the possibility of another type of relationship with Donnelly—or of the possibility that she might perform a role different from that of the maternal—until she loses him when he sacrifices himself for the family she sought to protect throughout the film. But here the mother's desire for something outside of or other than the family (a desire which the spectator possesses long before Mrs. Harper) is thwarted by the process of its inclusion within that familial structure. The blackmailer, tinged with the excitement of the illicit, the underworld, is reduced to a son, paying homage to a maternal ideal. This inclusion of the external object of desire within the closed web of the family is marked by lighting. Throughout the film, a uniformly lit and clear image is associated with the inside of the Harper house and the activities of the family, while film noir lighting characterizes the scenes external to the house—on its fringes or in the boathouse, scenes associated with the intrusion of the underworld. But in the final section of the film, film noir lighting invades the household, contaminating the bedroom—site of Mrs. Harper's lost desire—as she lies on the bed, crying violently. This collapse of the opposition between inside and outside in relation to the family exemplifies the status of the maternal as a closed circuit of desire. Donnelly is a pivotal figure here insofar as he explicitly demonstrates the slippage whereby a lover figure becomes a son. Mrs. Harper's tears testify to the pathos associated with this inevitability. In the final scene of the film, the image of Mrs. Harper sobbing, as she carries on a banal phone conversation with her husband about the color of the family Christmas tree, is not only framed by the bars of the staircase which verify her imprisonment within the family, it is also haunted by the presence of her son, finally and fully dressed, occupying the background of the image.

In films like *The Reckless Moment*, pathos is generated by a situation in which maternal love becomes a sign of the impossibility of female desire, which must remain unfulfilled precisely because it is "out of synch" with the proper order of generations. In more "standard" maternal melodramas, such as *To Each His Own* or *The Great Lie*, *Stella Dallas* or *That Certain Woman*, pathos is associated with the actual or potential separation between mother and child. Nevertheless, given the variety of instanciations of pathos and the generality of a definition linking it to a fundamental split between causality and teleology, it is difficult to support any claim which would make pathos a specifically feminine signifying strategy. And yet it is also clear that the "moving" and the maternal maintain an intimate relationship. Furthermore, it is important to keep in mind that words etymologically related to "pathos"—e.g., sympathy, empathy—are evocative of the culturally constructed understanding of the woman's relation to the other.

The maternal melodrama is maintained as a feminine genre by means of its opposition to certain genres specified as masculine (e.g., the Western, the detective film, the boxing film)—an opposition which in its turn rests on another, that between emotionalism and violence. But theories of scopophilia, the imaginary relation of spectator to film, and the mirror phase all suggest that aggressivity is an inevitable component of the imaginary relation in the cinema. In the Western and detective film aggressivity or violence is internalized as narrative content. In maternal melodrama, the violence is displaced onto affect—producing tear*jerkers*. Its sentimentality is, in some respects, quite sadistic.

This sadism generates metaphors within the critical discourse surrounding melodrama which are fully informed and inflected by ideologically complicit understandings of sexual difference. Claude Beylie, for instance, in an article entitled "Propositions on the Melo," attempts to describe the peculiarly melodramatic effect and it is not accidental that he arrives at the metaphor of rape: "The Greeks had a word for designating this, the art of captivating immediately and violently a public apparently reticent, in reality complicit (like a masochistic girl, who adores, at bottom, being violated): the word *pathos*."[44] Pathos, then, is a kind of textual rape and it is understandable from this point of view that it should frequently be perceived as lacking a certain aesthetic legitimacy. The opposition emotion/violence can be maintained at the level of generic content only by collapsing it in the film's terms of address and producing a violent emotionalism. Insofar as the spectator is feminized through pathos (transformed into a "masochistic girl"), the film is perceived as cheating or manipulating its viewer. The cultural denigration of the "weepies" is complicit with an ideological notion of sexually differentiated forms of spectatorship. From this perspective, it is not at all surprising that the maternal melodrama tends to produce the uncomfortable feeling that someone has been had.

Notes

1. The lack of a mother also connotes the precise opposite—an absolute sadness—as in the blues song, "Sometimes I feel like a motherless child . . . ," which signifies a state of complete loss of identity, homelessness, etc. The lack of a father, or illegitimacy, on the other hand, signals the impairment of identity, not its obliteration.
2. Peter Brooks, *The Melodramatic Imagination: Balzac, Henry James, Melodrama, and the Mode of Excess* (New Haven: Yale University Press, 1976), p. 15.
3. Ibid., pp. 41, 48.
4. See, for instance, Claude Beylie, "Propositions sur le mélo," *Les Cahiers de la Cinematheque: Pour Une Histoire du Mélodrame au Cinéma*, no 28, pp. 7–11. Peter Brooks in *The Melodramatic Imagination* also refers to the cinema as a whole as a continuation of the melodramatic stage tradition, particularly in its use of music.
5. Thomas Elsaesser, "Tales of Sound and Fury: Observations on the Family Melodrama," *Monogram*, no. 4 (1972), pp. 2–15; and Griselda Pollock, Geoffrey Nowell-Smith, and Stephen Heath, "Dossier on Melodrama," *Screen*, vol. 18, no. 2 (summer 1977), pp. 105–19.
6. Elsaesser, "Tales of Sound and Fury," p. 2.
7. Robert Bechtold Heilman, *Tragedy and Melodrama: Versions of Experience* (Seattle: University of Washington Press, 1968), p. 86.
8. Elsaesser, "Tales of Sound and Fury," p. 10.
9. Nowell-Smith, "Dossier on Melodrama," p. 115.
10. Ibid., p. 116.
11. Elsaesser, "Tales of Sound and Fury," p. 9.
12. Jacques Goimard, "Le mélodrame: le mot et la chose," *Les Cahiers de la Cinematheque: Pour Une Historie du Mélodrame: au Cinéma*, no. 28, p. 51. My translation.
13. Films discussed in this chapter include: *Stella Dallas* (King Vidor, 1937); *That Certain Woman* (Edmund Goulding, 1937); *The Great Lie* (Edmund Goulding, 1941); *Blossoms in the Dust* (Mervyn LeRoy, 1941); *Lydia* (Julien Duvivier, 1941); *Now, Voyager* (Irving Rapper,

1942); *Tender Comrade* (Edward Dmytryk, 1943); *Watch on the Rhine* (Herman Shumlin, 1943); *Since You Went Away* (John Cromwell, 1944); *Mildred Pierce* (Michael Curtiz, 1945); *To Each His Own* (Mitchell Leisen, 1946); *Tomorrow Is Forever* (Irving Pichel, 1946); *Letter from an Unknown Woman* (Max Ophuls, 1948); *Johnny Belinda* (Jean Negulesco, 1948); *My Foolish Heart* (Mark Robson, 1949); *The Reckless Moment* (Max Ophuls, 1949).

14. Christian Viviani, "Who Is Without Sin? The Maternal Melodrama in American Film, 1930–39," *Wide Angle*, vol. 4, no. 2 (1980), p. 7.
15. Two other feminist analyses of *Stella Dallas* with somewhat different overall emphases are E. Ann Kaplan, "The Case of the Missing Mother: Maternal Issues in Vidor's *Stella Dallas*," *Heresies*, no. 16, pp. 81–85; and Linda Williams, " 'Something Else Besides a Mother': *Stella Dallas* and the Maternal Melodrama," *Cinema Journal*, vol. 24, no. 1 (fall 1984), pp. 2–27.
16. Viviani, "Who Is Without Sin?" p. 15.
17. Ibid., p. 15.
18. Williams, "Something Else Besides a Mother," p. 2.
19. For a fuller discussion of this process, which she refers to as trait-stripping, see Anne Norton, "Maternal Metaphors in Politics: Three Studies," unpublished manuscript.
20. Wartime "Rosie the Riveter" imagery is also denaturalized, but in a different way—through an emphasis on its exceptionality, its incompatibility with or reversal of existing norms of femininity.
21. See Barbara Ehrenreich and Deirdre English, *For Her Own Good: 150 Years of the Experts' Advice to Women* (Garden City: Anchor Books, 1979), p. 220.

22. The mother who escapes these excesses—e.g., Ann Hilton (Claudette Colbert) in *Since You Went Away*—is abstracted and idealized until she becomes a symbol for something beyond the maternal—America in its unity and identity. The film constantly flirts with the possibility of Ann having an extramarital affair with Tony (Joseph Cotten), but is ultimately quite explicit about the impossibility of such a liaison—it would tarnish the ideal image of Mrs. Hilton.
23. Monique Plaza, "The Mother/The Same: Hatred of the Mother in Psychoanalysis," *Feminist Issues*, vol. 2, no. 1 (spring 1982), p. 88.
24. Brooks, *Melodramatic Imagination*, p. 36.
25. Luce Irigaray, "And the One Doesn't Stir Without the Other," trans. Hélène Vivienne Wenzel, *Signs*, vol. 7, no. 1 (autumn 1981), pp. 60–67.
26. Julia Kristeva, *Powers of Horror* (New York: Columbia University Press, 1983).
27. Julia Kristeva, "Maternité selon Giovanni Bellini," *Polylogue* (Paris: Éditions du Seuil, 1977), p. 409. My translation.
28. Ibid.
29. Films like *Psycho* (and other more contemporary horror films) indicate the underside of this, the terror attached to the maternal, the repression of the mother's other aspect as outlined in *Powers of Horror.*
30. Brooks, *Melodramatic Imagination*, pp. 67–68.
31. Ibid., p. 66.
32. *Encyclopédie;* s.v. "Geste" (Paris, 1757), quoted in Brooks, *Melodramatic Imagination*, p. 66.
33. See Claudia Gorbman, "The Drama's Melos: Max Steiner and *Mildred Pierce*," *The Velvet Light Trap: Review of Cinema*, no. 19 (1982), pp. 35–39, for an illuminating analysis of the music Max Steiner composed for a number of women's pictures including, in particular, *Mildred Pierce*.
34. Martha Wolfenstein and Nathan Leites, *Movies: A Psychological Study* (New York: Atheneum, 1970), p. 133.
35. Ibid.

36. Elsaesser, "Tales of Sound and Fury," p. 10.
37. Ibid., p. 14.
38. Franco Moretti, *Signs Taken for Wonders: Essays in the Sociology of Literary Forms*, trans. Susan Fischer, David Forgacs, David Miller (London: New Left Books, 1983), p. 159.
39. Ibid., p. 160.
40. Ibid., p. 162.
41. Sigmund Freud, "Femininity," *The Standard Edition of the Complete Psychological Works of Sigmund Freud*, ed. James Strachey (London: The Hogarth Press and the Institute of Psychoanalysis, 1964), p. 134.
42. Members of the *Framework* editorial board, "The Reckless Moment" and "The Family in 'The Reckless Moment,' " *Framework*, no. 4 (autumn 1976), pp. 17–24.
43. Elisabeth Saxony Holding, "The Blank Wall," *Ladies' Home Journal* (October 1947), pp. 37–223.
44. Beylie, "Propositions sur le mélo," p. 7. My translation.

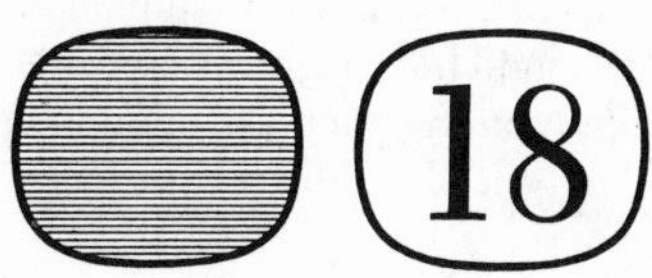

"Something Else Besides a Mother": *Stella Dallas* and the Maternal Melodrama

LINDA WILLIAMS

> Oh, God! I'll never forget that last scene, when her daughter is being married inside the big house with the high iron fence around it and she's standing out there—I can't even remember who it was, I saw it when I was still a girl, and I may not even be remembering it right. But I am remembering it—it made a tremendous impression on me—anyway, maybe it was Barbara Stanwyck. She's standing there and it's cold and raining and she's wearing a thin little coat and shivering, and the rain is coming down on her poor head and streaming down her face with the tears, and she stands there watching the lights and hearing the music and then she just drifts away. How they got us to consent to our own eradication! I didn't just feel pity for her; I felt that shock of recognition—you know, when you see what you sense is your own destiny up there on the screen or on the stage. You might say I've spent my whole life trying to arrange a different destiny![1]

These words of warning, horror, and fascination are spoken by Val, a character who is a mother herself, in Marilyn French's 1977 novel *The Women's*

Linda Williams's " 'Something Else Besides a Mother': *Stella Dallas* and the Maternal Melodrama" originally appeared in *Cinema Journal*, Vol. 24, no. 1 (Fall 1984), pp. 2–27. Reprinted by permission of the author and *Cinema Journal*.

Room. They are especially interesting for their insight into the response of a woman viewer to the image of her "eradication." The scene in question is from the end of *Stella Dallas*, King Vidor's 1937 remake of the 1925 film by Henry King. The scene depicts the resolution of the film: that moment when the good hearted, ambitious, working class floozy, Stella, sacrifices her only connection to her daughter in order to propel her into an upper-class world of surrogate family unity. Such are the mixed messages—of joy in pain, of pleasure in sacrifice—that typically resolve the melodramatic conflicts of "the woman's film."

It is not surprising, then, that Marilyn French's mother character, in attempting to resist such a sacrificial model of motherhood, should have so selective a memory of the conflict of emotions that conclude the film. Val only remembers the tears, the cold, the mother's pathetic alienation from her daughter's triumph inside the "big house with the high iron fence," the abject loneliness of the woman who cannot belong to that place and so "just drifts away." Val's own history, her own choices, have caused her to forget the perverse triumph of the scene: Stella's lingering for a last look even when a policeman urges her to move on; her joy as the bride and groom kiss; the swelling music as Stella does not simply "drift away" but marches triumphantly toward the camera and into a close-up that reveals a fiercely proud and happy mother clenching a handkerchief between her teeth.

It is as if the task of the narrative has been to find a "happy" ending that will exalt an abstract ideal of motherhood even while stripping the actual mother of the human connection on which that ideal is based. Herein lies the "shock of recognition" of which French's mother-spectator speaks.

The device of devaluing and debasing the actual figure of the mother while sanctifying the institution of motherhood is typical of "the woman's film" in general and the sub-genre of the maternal melodrama in particular.[2] In these films it is quite remarkable how frequently the self-sacrificing mother must make her sacrifice that of the connection to her children—either for her or their own good.

With respect to the mother-daughter aspect of this relation, Simone de Beauvoir noted long ago that because of the patriarchal devaluation of women in general, a mother frequently attempts to use her daughter to compensate for her own supposed inferiority by making "a superior creature out of one whom she regards as her double."[3] Clearly, the unparalleled closeness and similarity of mother to daughter sets up a situation of significant mirroring that is most apparent in these films. One effect of this mirroring is that although the mother gains a kind of vicarious superiority by association with a superior daughter, she inevitably begins to feel inadequate to so superior a being and thus, in the end, to feel inferior. Embroiled in a relationship that is so close, mother and daughter nevertheless seem destined to lose one another through this very closeness.

Much recent writing on women's literature and psychology has focused on the problematic of the mother-daughter relationship as a paradigm of a woman's ambivalent relationship to herself.[4] In *Of Woman Born* Adrienne Rich writes, "The loss of the daughter to the mother, mother to the daughter, is the essential female tragedy. We acknowledge Lear (father-daughter split), Hamlet (son and mother), and Oedipus (son and mother) as great embodiments of the human tragedy, but there is no presently enduring recognition of mother-daughter passion and rapture." No tragic, high culture equivalent perhaps. But Rich is not entirely correct when she goes on to say that "this cathexes between mother and daughter—essential, distorted, misused—is the great unwritten story."[5]

If this *tragic* story remains unwritten, it is because tragedy has always been assumed to be universal; speaking for and to a supposedly universal "mankind," it has not been able to speak for and to womankind. But melodrama is a form that does not pretend to speak universally. It is clearly addressed to a particular bourgeois class and often—in works as diverse as *Pamela, Uncle Tom's Cabin,* or the "woman's film"—to the particular gender of woman.

In *The Melodramatic Imagination* Peter Brooks argues that late eighteenth and nineteenth century melodrama arose to fill the vacuum of a post-revolutionary world where traditional imperatives of truth and ethics had been violently questioned and yet in which there was still a need for truth and ethics. The aesthetic and cultural form of melodrama thus attempts to assert the ethical imperatives of a class that has lost the transcendent myth of a divinely ordained hierarchical community of common goals and values.[6]

Because the universe had lost its basic religious and moral order and its tragically divided but powerful ruler protagonists, the aesthetic form of melodrama took on the burden of rewarding the virtue and punishing the vice of undivided and comparatively powerless characters. The melodramatic mode thus took on an intense quality of wish-fulfillment, acting out the narrative resolution of conflicts derived from the economic, social, and political spheres in the private, emotionally primal sphere of home and family. Martha Vicinus notes, for example, that in much nineteenth century stage melodrama the home is the scene of this "reconciliation of the irreconcilable."[7] The domestic sphere where women and children predominate as protagonists whose only power derives from virtuous suffering thus emerges as an important source of specifically female wish-fulfillment. But if women audiences and readers have long identified with the virtuous sufferers of melodrama, the liberatory or oppressive meaning of such identification has not always been clear.

Much recent feminist film criticism has divided filmic narrative into male and female forms: "male" linear, action-packed narratives that encourage identification with predominantly male characters who "master" their environment; and "female" less linear narratives encouraging identification with passive, suffering heroines.[8] No doubt part of the enormous popularity of *Mildred Pierce* among feminist film critics lies with the fact that it illustrates the failure of the female subject (the film's misguided, long-suffering mother-hero who is overly infatuated with her daughter) to articulate her own point of view, even when her own voice-over introduces subjective flashbacks.[9] *Mildred Pierce* has been an important film for feminists precisely because its "male" film noir style offers such a blatant subversion of the mother's attempt to tell the story of her relationship to her daughter.

The failure of *Mildred Pierce* to offer either its female subject or its female viewer her own understanding of the film's narrative has made it a fascinating example of the way films can construct patriarchal subject-positions that subvert their ostensible subject matter. More to the point of the mother-daughter relation, however, is a film like *Stella Dallas,* which has recently begun to receive attention as a central work in the growing criticism of melodrama in general and maternal melodrama in particular.[10]

Certainly the popularity of the original novel, of the 1925 (Henry King) and 1937 (King Vidor) film versions, and finally of the later long-running radio soap opera, suggests the special endurance of this mother-daughter love story across three decades of female audiences. But it is in its film versions in particular, especially the King Vidor version starring Barbara Stanwyck, that we encounter an interesting test case for many recent theories of the cinematic presentation of female subjectivity and the female spectator.

Since so much of what has come to be called the classical narrative cinema concerns male subjects whose vision defines and circumscribes female objects, the mere existence in *Stella Dallas* of a female "look" as a central feature of the narrative is worthy of special scrutiny. Just what is different about the visual economy of such a film? What happens when a mother and daughter, who are so closely identified that the usual distinctions between subject and object do not apply, take one another as their primary objects of desire? What happens, in other words, when the look of desire articulates a rather different visual economy of mother-daughter possession and dispossession? What happens, finally, when the significant viewer of such a drama is also a woman? To fully answer these questions we must make a detour through some recent psychoanalytic thought on female subject formation and its relation to feminist film theory. We will then be in a better position to unravel the mother-daughter knot of this particular film. So for the time being we will abandon *Stella Dallas* to her forlorn place in the rain, gazing at her daughter through the big picture window—the enigma of the female look at, and in, the movies.

Feminist Film Theory and Theories of Motherhood

Much recent feminist film theory and criticism has been devoted to the description and analysis of Oedipal scenarios in which, as Laura Mulvey has written, woman is a passive image and man the active bearer of the look.[11] The major impetus of these forms of feminist criticism has been less concerned with the existence of female stereotypes than with their ideological, psychological, and textual means of production. To Claire Johnston, the very fact of the iconic representation of the cinematic image guarantees that women will be reduced to objects of an erotic male gaze. Johnston concludes that "woman as woman" cannot be represented at all within the dominant representational economy.[12] A primary reason for this conclusion is the hypothesis that the visual encounter with the female body produces in the male spectator a constant need to be reassured of his own bodily unity.

It is as if the male image producer and consumer can never get past the disturbing fact of sexual difference and so constantly produces and consumes images of women designed to reassure himself of his threatened unity. In this and other ways, feminist film theory has appropriated some key concepts from Lacanian psychoanalysis in order to explain why subjectivity always seems to be the province of the male.

According to Lacan, through the recognition of the sexual difference of a female "other" who lacks the phallus that is the symbol of patriarchal privilege, the child gains entry into the symbolic order of human culture. This culture then produces narratives which repress the figure of lack that the mother—former figure of plenitude—has become. Given this situation, the question for woman becomes, as Christine Gledhill puts it: "*Can women speak, and can images of women speak for women?*"[13] Laura Mulvey's answer, and the answer of much feminist criticism, would seem to be negative:

> Woman's desire is subjected to her image as bearer of the bleeding wound, she can exist only in relation to castration and cannot transcend it. She turns her child into the signifier of her own desire to possess a penis (the condition, she imagines, of entry into the symbolic). Either she must gracefully give way to the word, the Name of the Father and the Law, or else struggle to keep her child down with her in the half-light of the imaginary. Woman then stands in patriarchal culture as signifier for the male other, bound by a symbolic order in which man can live out his phantasies and obsessions through linguistic command by imposing them on the silent image of woman still tied to her place as bearer of meaning, not maker of meaning.[14]

This description of the "visual pleasure of narrative cinema" delineates two avenues of escape which function to relieve the male viewer of the threat of the woman's image. Mulvey's now-familiar sketch of these two primary forms of mastery by which the male unconscious overcomes the threat of an encounter with the female body is aligned with two perverse pleasures associated with the male—the sadistic mastery of voyeurism and the more benign disavowal of fetishism. Both are ways of not-seeing, of either keeping a safe distance from, or misrecognizing what there is to see of, the woman's difference.

The purpose of Mulvey's analysis is to get "nearer to the roots" of women's oppression in order to break with those codes that cannot produce female subjectivity. Her ultimate goal is thus an avant-garde filmmaking practice that will break with the voyeurism and fetishism of the narrative cinema so as to "free the look of the camera into its materiality in space and time," and the "look of the audience into dialectics, passionate detachment."[15] To Mulvey, only the radical destruction of the major forms of narrative pleasure so bound up in looking at women as objects can offer hope for a cinema that will be able to represent not woman as difference but the differences of women.

It has often been remarked that what is missing from Mulvey's influential analysis of visual pleasure in cinematic narrative is any discussion of the position of the female viewing subject. Although many feminist works of film criticism have pointed to this absence, very few have ventured to fill it.[16] It is an understandably easier task to reject "dominant" or "institutional" modes of representation altogether than to discover within these existing modes glimpses of a more "authentic" (the term itself is indeed problematic) female subjectivity. And yet I believe that this latter is a more fruitful avenue of approach, not only as a means of identifying what pleasure there is for women spectators within the classical narrative cinema, but also as a means of developing new representational strategies that will more fully speak to women audiences. For such speech must begin in a language that, however circumscribed within patriarchal ideology, will be recognized and understood by women. In this way, new feminist films can learn to build upon the pleasures of recognition that exist within filmic modes already familiar to women.

Instead of destroying the cinematic codes that have placed women as objects of spectacle at their center, what is needed, and has already begun to occur, is a theoretical and practical recognition of the ways in which women actually do speak to one another within patriarchy. Christine Gledhill, for example, makes a convincing case against the tendency of much semiotic and psyochoanalytic feminist film criticism to blame realist representation for an ideological complicity with the suppression of semiotic difference. Such reasoning tends to believe that the simple rejection of the forms of realist representation will perform the revolutionary act of making the viewer aware of how images are produced. Gledhill argues that this awareness is not enough: the social construction of reality and of women cannot be defined in terms of signifying practice alone. "If a radical ideology such as feminism is to be defined as a means of providing a framework for political action, one must finally put one's finger on the scales, enter some kind of realist epistemology."[17]

But what kind? Any attempt to construct heroines as strong and powerful leaves us vulnerable, as Gledhill notes, to the charge of male identification:

> However we try to cast our potential feminine identifications, all available positions are already constructed from the place of the patriarchal other so as to repress our 'real' difference. Thus the unspoken remains unknown, and the speakable reproduces what we know, patriarchal reality.[18]

One way out of the dilemma is "the location of those spaces in which women, out of their socially constructed differences as women, can and do resist."[19] These include discourses produced primarily for and (often, but not always) by women and which address the contradictions that women encounter under patriarchy: women's advice columns, magazine fiction, soap operas, and melodramatic "women's films." All are places where women speak to one another in languages that grow out of their specific social roles—as mothers, housekeepers, caretakers of all sorts.[20]

Gledhill's assertion that discourses about the social, economic, and emotional concerns of women are consumed by predominantly female audiences could be complemented by the further assertion that *some* of these discourses are also differently inscribed to necessitate a very different, female reading. This is what I hope to show with respect to *Stella Dallas*. My argument, then, is not only that some maternal melodramas have historically addressed female audiences about issues of primary concern to women, but that these melodramas also have reading positions structured into their texts that demand a female reading competence. This competence derives from the different way women take on their identities under patriarchy and is a direct result of the social fact of female mothering. It is thus with a view to applying the significance of the social construction of female identity to the female positions constructed by the maternal melodrama that I offer the following cursory summary of recent feminist theories of female identity and motherhood.

While Freud was forced, at least in his later writing, to abandon a theory of parallel male and female development and to acknowledge the greater importance of the girl's pre-Oedipal connection to her mother, he could only view such a situation as a deviation from the path of "normal" (e.g., male heterosexual) separation and individuation.[21] The result was a theory that left women in an apparent state of regressive connection to their mothers.

What Freud viewed as a regrettable lack in a girl's self development, feminist theorists now view with less disparagement. However else they may differ over the consequences of female mothering, most agree that it allows women not only to remain in conection with their first love objects but to extend the model of this connectedness to all other relations with the world.[22]

In *The Reproduction of Mothering* the American sociologist Nancy Chodorow attempts to account for the fact that "women, as mothers, produce daughters with mothering capacities and the desire to mother."[23] She shows that neither biology nor intentional role training can explain the social organization of gender roles that consign women to the private sphere of home and family, and men to the public sphere that has permitted them dominance. The desire and ability to mother is produced, along with masculinity and femininity, within a division of labor that has already placed women in the position of primary caretakers. Superimposed on this division of labor are the two "oedipal asymmetries"[24] that Freud acknowledged: that girls enter the triangular Oedipal relation later than boys; that girls have a greater continuity of pre-Oedipal symbiotic connection to the mother.

In other words, girls never entirely break with their original relationship to their mothers, because their sexual identities as women do not depend upon such a break. Boys, however, must break with their primary identification with their mothers in order to become male identified. This means that boys define themselves as males negatively, by differentiation from their primary caretaker who (in a culture that has traditionally valued women as mothers first, workers second) is female.

The boy separates from his mother to identify with his father and take on a masculine identity of greater autonomy. The girl, on the other hand, takes on her identity as a woman in a positive process of becoming like, not different than, her mother. Although she must ultimately transfer her primary object choice to her father first and then to men in general if she is to become a heterosexual woman, she still never breaks with the original bond to her mother in the same way the boy does. She merely *adds* her love for her father, and finally her love for a man (if she becomes heterosexual) to her original relation to her mother. This means that a boy develops his masculine gender identification in the *absence* of a continuous and ongoing relationship with his father, while a girl develops her feminine gender identity in the *presence* of an ongoing relationship with the specific person of her mother.

In other words, the masculine subject position is based on a rejection of a connection to the mother and the adoption of a gender role identified with a cultural stereotype, while the female subject position identifies with a specific mother. Women's relatedness and men's denial of relatedness are in turn appropriate to the social division of their roles in our culture: to the man's role as producer outside the home and the woman's role as reproducer inside it.[25]

Chodorow's analysis of the connectedness of the mother-daughter bond has pointed the way to a new value placed on the multiple and continuous female identity capable of fluidly shifting between the identity of mother and daughter.[26] Unlike Freud, she does not assume that the separation and autonomy of the male identification process is a norm from which women deviate. She assumes, rather, that the current social arrangement of exclusive female mothering has prepared men to participate in a world of often alienated work, with a limited ability to achieve intimacy.[27]

Thus Chodorow and others[28] have questioned the very standards of unity and autonomy by which human identity has typically been measured. And they have done so without recourse to a biologically determined essence of femaleness.[29]

Like Nancy Chodorow, the French feminist psychoanalyst Luce Irigaray turns to the problems of Freud's original attempt to sketch identical stages of development for both male and female. In *Speculum de l'autre femme* Irigaray echoes Chodorow's concern with "Oedipal asymmetries." But what Irigaray emphasizes is the *visual* nature of Freud's scenario—the fact that sexual difference is originally perceived as an absence of the male genitalia rather than the presence of female genitalia. In a chapter entitled "Blind Spot for an Old Dream of Symmetry," the "blind spot" consists of a male vision trapped in an "Oedipal destiny" that cannot *see* woman's sex and can thus only represent it in terms of the masculine subject's own original complementary other: the mother.[30]

"Woman" is represented within this system as either the all-powerful (phallic) mother of the child's pre-Oedipal imaginary or as the unempowered (castrated) mother of its post-Oedipal symbolic. What is left out of such a system of representation is the whole of woman's pleasure—a pleasure that cannot be measured in phallic terms.

But what Freud devalued and repressed in the female body, Irigaray and other French feminists engaged in "writing the female body" in an *ecriture feminine,*[31] are determined to emphasize. In *Ce sexe qui n'en est pas un* (This sex which is not one) Irigaray celebrates the multiple and diffuse pleasures of a female body and a female sex that is not just one thing, but several. But when forced to enter into the "dominant scopic economy" of visual pleasure she is immediately relegated, as Mulvey has also pointed out with respect to film, to the passive position of "the beautiful object."[32]

Irigaray's admittedly utopian[33] solution to the problem of how women can come to represent themselves to themselves is nevertheless important. For if women cannot establish the connection between their bodies and language, they risk either having to forgo all speaking of the body—in a familiar puritanical repression of an excessive female sexuality—or they risk an essentialist celebration of a purely biological determination. Irigaray thus proposes a community of women relating to and speaking to one another outside the constraints of a masculine language that reduces everything to its own need for unity and identity—a "female homosexuality" opposed to the reigning "male homosexuality" that currently governs the relations between both men and men, and men and women.[34]

A "female homosexual economy" would thus challenge the dominant order and make it possible for woman to represent herself to herself. This suggests an argument similar to that of Adrienne Rich in her article "Compulsory Heterosexuality and Lesbian Existence." Rich argues that lesbianism is an important alternative to the male economy of dominance. Whether or not a woman's sexual preferences are actually homosexual, the mere fact of "lesbian existence" proves that it is possible to resist the dominating values of the male colonizer with a more nurturing and empathic relationship similar to mothering.[35] The female body is as necessary to Rich as it is to Irigaray as the place to begin.

Adrienne Rich's critique of psychoanalysis is based on the notion that its fundamental patriarchal premises foreclose the envisioning of relationships between women outside of patriarchy. Irigaray's recourse to the female body ironically echoes Rich's own but it is constructed from *within* psychoanalytic theory. The importance of both is not simply that they see lesbianism as a refuge from an oppressive phallic economy—although it certainly is that for many women—but that it is a theoretical way out of the bind of the unrepresented, and unrepresentable, female body.

The excitement generated when women get together, when they go to the market together "to profit from their own value, to talk to each other, to desire each other," is not to be underestimated.[36] For only by learning to recognize and then to represent a difference that is not different to other women, can women begin to see themselves. The trick, however, is not to stop there; woman's recognition of herself in the bodies of other women is only a necessary first step to an understanding of the interaction of body and psyche, and the distance that separates them.[37]

Perhaps the most valuable attempt to understand this interaction is Julia Kristeva's work on the maternal body and pre-Oedipal sexuality. Like Irigaray, Kristeva attempts to speak the pre-Oedipal relations of woman to woman. But unlike Irigaray, she does so with the knowledge that such speech is never entirely authentic, never entirely free of the phallic influence of symbolic language. In other words, she stresses the necessity of positing a place from which women can speak themselves, all the while recognizing that such places do not exist. That is, it cannot be conceived or represented outside of the symbolic language which defines women negatively.[38]

Thus, what Kristeva proposes is a self-conscious dialectic between two imperfect forms of language. The first is what she calls the "emiotic": a pre-verbal, maternal language of rhythm, tone and color linked to the body contact with the mother before the child is differentiated by entrance into the symbolic. The second is the "symbolic" proper, characterized by logic, syntax, and a phallocratic abstraction.[39] According to Kristeva, all human subjects articulate themselves through the interaction of these two modes. The value of this conception is that we no longer find ourselves locked into an investigation of different sexual *identities*, but are freed rather into an investigation of *sexual differentiations*—subject positions that are associated with maternal or paternal functions.

Speaking from the mother's position, Kristeva shows that maternity is characterized by division. The mother is possessed of an internal heterogeneity beyond her control:

> Cells fuse, split and proliferate; volumes grow, tissues stretch, and body fluids change rhythm, speeding up or slowing down. Within the body, growing as a graft, indomitable, there is an other. And no one is present, within that simultaneously dual and alien space, to signify what is going on. "It happens, but I'm not here."[40]

But even as she speaks from this space of the mother, Kristeva notes that it is vacant, that there is no unified subject present there. Yet she speaks anyway, consciously recognizing the patriarchal illusion of the all-powerful and whole phallic mother. For Kristeva it is the dialectic of two inadequate and incomplete sexually *differentiated* subject positions that is important. The dialectic between a maternal body that is too diffuse, contradictory, and polymorphous to be represented and a paternal body that is channeled and repressed into a single representable significance makes it possible for woman to be represented at all.

So, as Jane Gallop notes, women are not so essentially and exclusively body that they must remain eternally unrepresentable.[41] But the dialectic between that which is pure body and therefore escapes representation and that which is a finished and fixed representation makes possible a different kind of representation that escapes the rigidity of fixed identity. With this notion of a dialectic between the maternal unrepresentable and the paternal already-represented we can begin to look for a way out of the theoretical bind of the representation of women in film and at the way female spectators are likely to read *Stella Dallas* and its ambivalent final scene.

"Something Else Besides a Mother"

Stella's story begins with her attempts to attract the attention of the upper-class Stephen Dallas (John Boles), who has buried himself in the small town of Milhampton after a scandal in his family ruined his plans for marriage. Like any ambitious working-class girl with looks as her only resource, she attempts to improve herself by pursuing an upper-class man. To distinguish herself in his eyes, she calculatingly brings her brother lunch at the mill where Stephen is the boss, insincerely playing the role of motherly caretaker. The refinement that she brings to this role distinguishes her from her own drab, overworked, slavish mother (played by Marjorie Main, without her usual comic touch).

During their brief courtship, Stella and Stephen go to the movies. On the screen they see couples dancing in an elegant milieu followed by a happy-ending embrace. Stella is absorbed in the story and weeps at the end. Outside the theater she tells Stephen of her desire to "be like all the people in the movies doing everything well-bred and refined." She imagines his whole world to be like this glamorous scene. Her story will become, in a sense, the unsuccessful attempt to place herself in the scene of the movie without losing that original spectatorial pleasure of looking on from afar.

Once married to Stephen, Stella seems about to realize this dream. In the small town that once ignored her she can now go the "River Club" and associate with the smart set. But motherhood intervenes, forcing her to cloister herself unhappily during the long months of pregnancy. Finally out of the hospital, she insists on a night at the country club with the smart set that has so far eluded her. (Actually many of them are a vulgar *nouveau-riche* lot of whom Stephen, upper-class snob that he is, heartily disapproves.) In her strenuous efforts to join in the fun of the wealthy, Stella makes a spectacle of herself in Stephen's eyes. He sees her for the first time as the working-class woman that she is and judges her harshly, reminding her that she once wanted to be something more than what she is. She, in turn, criticizes his stiffness and asks *him* to do some of the adapting for a change.

When Stephen asks Stella to come with him to New York City for a fresh start as the properly upper-class Mrs. Dallas, she refuses to leave the only world she knows. Part of her reason must be that to leave this world would also be to leave the only identity she has ever achieved, to become nobody all over again. In the little mill town where Stephen had come to forget himself, Stella can find herself by measuring the distance traveled between her working-class girlhood and upper-class wifehood. It is as if she needs to be able to measure this distance in order to possess her new self from the vantage point of the young girl she once was with Stephen at the movies. Without the memory of this former self that the town provides, she loses the already precarious possession of her own identity.

As Stephen drifts away from her, Stella plunges into another aspect of her identity: motherhood. After her initial resistance, it is a role she finds surprisingly compelling. But she never resigns herself to being *only* a mother. In Stephen's absence she continues to seek an innocent but lively pleasure—in particular with the raucous Ed Munn. As her daughter Laurel grows up, we observe a series of scenes that compromise Stella in the eyes of Stephen (during those rare moments he comes home) and the more straight-laced members of the community. In each case Stella is merely guilty of seeking a little fun—whether by playing music and drinking with Ed or playing a practical joke with itching powder on a train. Each time we are assured of Stella's primary commitment to motherhood and of her many good qualities as a mother. (She even says to Ed Munn, in response to his crude proposal: "I don't think there's a man livin' who could get me going anymore.") But each time the repercussions of the incident are the isolation of mother and daughter from the upper-class world to which they aspire to belong but into which only Laurel fits. A particularly poignant moment is Laurel's birthday party where mother and daughter receive, one by one, the regrets of the guests. Thus the innocent daughter suffers for the "sins" of taste and class of the mother. The end result, however, is a greater bond between the two as each sadly but nobly puts on a good face for the other and marches into the dining room to celebrate the birthday alone.

In each of the incidents of Stella's transgression of proper behavior, there is a moment when we first see Stella's innocent point of view and then the point of view of the community or estranged husband that judges her a bad mother.[42] Their judgment rests on the fact that Stella insists on making her motherhood a pleasurable experience by sharing center stage with her daughter. The one thing she will not do, at least until the end, is retire to the background.

One basic conflict of the film thus comes to revolve around the *excessive presence* of Stella's body and dress. She increasingly flaunts an exaggeratedly feminine presence that the offended community prefers not to see. (Barbara Stanwyck's own excessive performance contributes to this effect. I can think of no other film star of the period so willing to exceed both the bounds of good taste and sex appeal in a single performance.) But the more ruffles, feathers, furs, and clanking jewelry that Stella dons, the more she emphasizes her pathetic inadequacy.

Her strategy can only backfire in the eyes of an upper-class restraint that values a streamlined and sleek ideal of femininity. To these eyes Stella is a travesty, an overdone masquerade of what it means to be a woman. At the fancy hotel to which Stella and Laurel repair for their one fling at upper-class life together, a young college man exclaims at the sign of Stella, "That's not a woman, that's a Christmas tree!" Stella, however, could never understand such a backward economy, just as she cannot understand her upper-class husband's attempts to lessen the abrasive impact of her presence by correcting her English and toning down her dress. She counters his efforts with the defiant claim, "I've always been known to have stacks of style!"

"Style" is the war paint she applies more thickly with each new assault on her legitimacy as a woman and a mother. One particularly affecting scene shows her sitting before the mirror of her dressing table as Laurel tells her of the "natural" elegance and beauty of Helen Morrison, the woman who has replaced Stella in Stephen's affections. Stella's only response is to apply more cold cream. When she accidentally gets cold cream on Laurel's photo of the ideal Mrs. Morrison, Laurel becomes upset and runs off to clean it. What is most moving in the scene is the emotional complicity of Laurel, who soon realizes the extent to which her description has hurt her mother, and silently turns to the task of applying more peroxide to Stella's hair. The scene ends with mother and daughter before the mirror tacitly relating to one another through the medium of the feminine mask—each putting on a good face for the other, just as they did at the birthday party.

"Stacks of style," layers of make-up, clothes, and jewelry—these are, of course, the typical accouterments of the fetishized woman. Yet such fetishization seems out of place in a "woman's film" addressed to a predominantly female audience. More typically, the woman's film's preoccupation with a victimized and suffering womanhood has tended, as Mary Ann Doane has shown, to repress and hystericize women's bodies in a medical discourse of the afflicted or in the paranoia of the uncanny.[43]

We might ask, then, what effect a fetishized female image has in the context of a film "addressed" and "possessed by" women? Certainly this is one situation in which the woman's body does not seem likely to pose the threat of castration—since the significant viewers of (and within) the film are all female. In psychoanalytic terms, the fetish is that which disavows or compensates for the woman's lack of a penis. As we have seen above, for the male viewer the successful fetish deflects attention away from what is "really" lacking by calling attention to (over-valuing) other aspects of woman's difference. But at the same time it also inscribes the woman in a "masquerade of femininity"[44] that forever revolves around her "lack." Thus, at the extreme, the entire female body becomes a fetish substitute for the phallus she doesn't possess. The beautiful (successfully fetishized) woman thus represents an eternal essence of biologically determined femininity constructed from the point of view, so to speak, of the phallus.

In *Stella Dallas*, however, the fetishization of Stanwyck's Stella is unsuccessful; the masquerade of femininity is all too obvious; and the significant point of view on all this is female. For example, at the fancy hotel where Stella makes a "Christmas tree" spectacle of herself she is as oblivious as ever to the shocking effect of her appearance. But Laurel experiences the shame of her friends' scorn. The scene in which Laurel experiences this shame is a grotesque parody of Stella's fondest dream of being like all the glamorous people in the movies. Stella has put all of her energy and resources into becoming this glamorous image. But incapacitated by a cold, as she once was by pregnancy, she must remain off-scene as Laurel makes a favorable impression. When she finally makes her grand entrance on the scene, Stella is spied by Laurel and her friends in a large mirror over a soda fountain. The mirror functions as the framed screen that reflects the parody of the image of glamour to which Stella once aspired.

Unwilling to acknowledge their relation, Laurel runs out. Later, she insists that they leave. On the train home, Stella overhears Laurel's friends joking about the vulgar Mrs. Dallas. It is then that she decides to send Laurel to live with Stephen and Mrs. Morrison and to give Laurel up for her own good. What is significant, however, is that Stella overhears the conversation at the same time Laurel does—they are in upper and lower berths of the train, each hoping that the other is asleep, each pretending to be asleep to the other. So Stella does not just experience her own humiliation; she sees for the first time the travesty she has become by sharing in her daughter's humiliation.

By seeing herself through her daughter's eyes, Stella also sees something more. For the first time Stella sees the reality of her social situation from the vantage point of her daughter's understanding, but increasingly upper-class, system of values: that she is a struggling, uneducated woman doing the best she can with the resources at her disposal. And it is *this* vision, through her daughter's sympathetic, mothering eyes—eyes that perceive, understand, and forgive the social graces Stella lacks—that determines her to perform the masquerade that will alienate Laurel forever by proving to her what the patriarchy has claimed to know all along: that it is not possible to combine womanly desire with motherly duty.

It is at this point that Stella claims, falsely, to want to be "something else besides a mother." The irony is not only that by now there is really nothing else she wants to be, but also that in pretending this to Laurel she must act out a painful parody of her fetishized self. She thus resurrects the persona of the "good-times" woman she used to want to be (but never entirely was) only to convince Laurel that she is an unworthy mother. In other words, she proves her very worthiness to be a mother (her desire for her daughter's material and social welfare) by acting out a patently false scenario of narcissistic self-absorption—she pretends to ignore Laurel while lounging about in a negligee, smoking a cigarette, listening to jazz, and reading a magazine called "Love."

In this scene the conventional image of the fetishized woman is given a peculiar, even parodic, twist. For where the conventional masquerade of femininity can be read as an attempt to cover up supposedly biological "lacks" with a compensatory excess of connotatively feminine gestures, clothes, and accouterments, here fetishization functions as a blatantly pathetic disavowal of much more pressing social lacks—of money, education, and power. The spectacle Stella stages for Laurel's eyes thus displaces the real social and economic causes of her presumed inadequacy as a mother onto a pretended desire for fulfillment as a woman—to be "something else besides a mother."

At the beginning of the film Stella pretended a maternal concern she did not really possess (in bringing lunch to her brother in order to flirt with Stephen) in order to find a better home. Now she pretends a lack of the same concern in order to send Laurel to a better home. Both roles are patently false. And though neither allows us to view the "authentic" woman beneath the mask, the succession of roles ending in the final transcendent self-effacement of the window scene—in which Stella forsakes all her masks in order to become the anonymous spectator of her daughter's role as bride—permits a glimpse at the social and economic realities that have produced such roles. Stella's real offense, in the eyes of the community that so ruthlessly ostracizes her, is to have attempted to play both roles at once.

Are we to conclude, then, that the film simply punishes her for these untimely resistances to her proper role? E. Ann Kaplan has argued that such is the case, and that throughout the film Stella's point of view is undercut by those of the upper-class community—Stephen, or the snooty townspeople—who disapprove of her behavior. Kaplan notes, for example, that a scene may begin from Stella's point of view but shift, as in the case of an impromptu party with Ed Munn, to the more judgmental point of view of Stephen halfway through.[45]

I would counter, however, that these multiple, often conflicting, points of view—including Laurel's failure to see through her mother's act—prevent such a monolithic view of the female subject. Kaplan argues, for example, that the film punishes Stella for her resistances to a properly patriarchal view of motherhood by turning her first into a spectacle for a disapproving upper-class gaze and then finally into a mere spectator, locked outside the action in the final window scene that ends the film.[46]

Certainly this final scene functions to efface Stella even as it glorifies her sacrificial act of motherly love. Self-exiled from the world into which her daughter is marrying, Stella loses both her daughter and her (formerly fetishized) self to become an abstract (and absent) ideal of motherly sacrifice. Significantly, Stella appears in this scene for the first time stripped of the exaggerated marks of femininity—the excessive make-up, furs, feathers, clanking jewelry, and ruffled dresses—that have been the weapons of her defiant assertions that a woman *can* be "something else besides a mother."

It would be possible to stop here and take this ending as Hollywood's last word on the mother, as evidence of her ultimate unrepresentability in any but patriarchal terms. Certainly if we only remember Stella as she appears here at the end of the film, as Val in French's *The Women's Room* remembers her, then we see her only at the moment when she becomes representable in terms of a "phallic economy" that idealizes the woman as mother and in so doing, as Irigaray argues, represses everything else about her. But although the final moment of the film "resolves" the contradiction of Stella's attempt to be a woman *and* a mother by eradicating both, the 108 minutes leading up to this moment present the heroic attempt to live out the contradiction.[47] It seems likely, then, that a female spectator would be inclined to view even this ending as she has the rest of the film: from a variety of different subject positions. In other words, the female spectator tends to identify with contradiction itself—with contradictions located at the heart of the socially constructed roles of daughter, wife, *and* mother—rather than with the single person of the mother.

In this connection the role of Helen Morrison, the upper-class widowed mother whom Stephen will be free to marry with Stella out of the way, takes on special importance. Helen is everything Stella is not: genteel, discreet, self-effacing, and sympathetic with everyone's problems—including Stella's. She is, for example, the only person in the film to see through Stella's ruse of alienating Laurel. And it is she who, knowing Stella's finer instincts, leaves open the drapes that permit Stella's vision of Laurel's marriage inside her elegant home.

In writing about the narrative form of daytime soap operas, Tania Modleski has noted that the predominantly female viewers of soaps do not identify with a main controlling figure the way viewers of more classic forms of narrative identify. The very form of soap opera encourages identification with multiple points of view. At one moment, female viewers identify with a woman united with her lover, at the next with the sufferings of her rival. While the effect of identifying with a single controlling protagonist is to make the spectator feel empowered, the effect of multiple identification in the diffused soap opera is to divest the spectator of power, but to increase empathy. "The subject/spectator of soaps, it could be said, is constituted as a sort of ideal mother: a person who possesses greater wisdom than all her children, whose sympathy is large enough to encompass the conflicting claims of her family (she identifies with them all), and who has no demands or claims of her own (she identifies with no character exclusively)."[48]

In *Stella Dallas* Helen is clearly the representative of this idealized empathic but powerless mother. Ann Kaplan has argued that female spectators learn from Helen Morrison's example that such is the proper role of the mother; that Stella has up until now illicitly hogged the screen. By the time Stella has made her sacrifice and become the mere spectator of her daughter's apotheosis, her joy in her daughter's success assures us, in Kaplan's words, "of her satisfaction in being reduced to spectator. . . . While the cinema spectator feels a certain sadness in Stella's position, we also identify with Laurel and with her attainment of what we have all been socialized to desire; that is, romantic marriage into the upper class. We thus accede to the necessity for Stella's sacrifice."[49]

But do we? As Kaplan herself notes, the female spectator is identified with a variety of conflicting points of view as in the TV soap opera: Stella, Laurel, Helen, and Stephen cannot resolve their conflicts without someone getting hurt. Laurel loses her mother and visibly suffers from this loss; Stella loses her daughter and her identity; Helen wins Stephen but powerlessly suffers for everyone including herself (when Stella had refused to divorce Stephen). Only Stephen is entirely free from suffering at the end, but this is precisely because he is characteristically oblivious to the suffering of others. For the film's ending to be perceived as entirely without problem, we would have to identify with this least sensitive and, therefore, least sympathetic point of view.

Instead, we identify, like the ideal mother viewer of soaps, with *all* the conflicting points of view. Because Helen is herself such a mother, she becomes an important, but not an exclusive, focus of spectatorial identification. She becomes, for example, the significant witness of Stella's sacrifice. Her one action in the entire film is to leave open the curtains—an act that helps put Stella in the same passive and powerless position of spectating that Helen is in herself. But if this relegation to the position of spectator outside the action resolves the narrative, it is a resolution not satisfactory to any of its female protagonists.

Thus, where Kaplan sees the ending of *Stella Dallas* as satisfying patriarchal demands for the repression of the active and involved aspects of the mother's role, and as teaching female spectators to take their dubious pleasures from this empathic position outside the action, I would argue that the ending is too multiply identified, too dialectical in Julia Kristeva's sense of the struggle between maternal and paternal forms of language, to encourage such a response. Certainly the film has constructed concluding images of motherhood—first the high-toned Helen and finally a toned-down Stella—for the greater power and convenience of the father. But because the father's own spectatorial empathy is so lacking—Stephen is here much as he was with Stella at the movies, present but not identified himself—*we* cannot see it that way. We see instead the contradictions between what the patriarchal resolution of the film asks us to see—the mother "in her place" as spectator, abdicating her former position *in* the scene—and what we as empathic, identifying female spectators can't help but feel—the loss of mother to daughter and daughter to mother.

This double vision seems typical of the experience of most female spectators at the movies. One explanation for it, we might recall, is Nancy Chodorow's theory that female identity is formed through a process of double identification. The girl identifies with her primary love object—her mother—and then, without ever dropping the first identification, with her father. According to Chodorow, the woman's sense of self is based upon a continuity of relationship that ultimately prepares her for the empathic, identifying role of the mother. Unlike the male who must constantly differentiate himself from his original object of identification in order to take on a male identity, the woman's ability to identify with a variety of different subject positions makes her a very different kind of spectator.

Feminist film theorists have tended to view this multiple identificatory power of the female spectator with some misgiving. In an article on the female spectator, Mary Ann Doane has suggested that when the female spectator looks at the cinematic image of a woman, she is faced with two main possibilities: she can either over-identify (as in the masochistic dramas typical of the woman's film) with the woman on the screen and thus lose herself in the image by taking this woman as her own narcissistic object of desire; or she can temporarily identify with the position of the masculine voyeur and subject this same woman to a controlling gaze that insists on the distance and difference between them.[50] In this case she becomes, as Laura Mulvey notes, a temporary transvestite.[51] Either way, according to Doane, she loses herself.

Doane argues that the only way a female spectator can keep from losing herself in this over-identification is by negotiating a distance from the image of her like—by reading this image as a sign as opposed to an iconic image that requires no reading. When the woman spectator regards a female body enveloped in an exaggerated masquerade of femininity, she encounters a sign that requires such a reading. We have seen that throughout a good part of *Stella Dallas* this is what Stella does with respect to her own body. For Doane, then, one way out of the dilemma of female over-identification with the image on the screen is for this image to act out a masquerade of femininity that manufactures a distance between spectator and image, to "generate a problematic within which the image is manipulable, producible, and readable by women."[52]

In other words, Doane thinks that female spectators need to borrow some of the distance and separation from the image that male spectators experience. She suggests that numerous avant-garde practices of distanciation can produce this necessary distance. This puts us back to Mulvey's argument that narrative pleasure must be destroyed by avant-garde practices. I would argue instead that this manufacturing of distance, this female voyeurism-with-a-difference, is an aspect of *every* female spectator's gaze at the image of her like. For rather than adopting either the distance and mastery of the masculine voyeur or the over-identification of Doane's woman who loses herself in the image, the female spectator is in a constant state of juggling all positions at once.

Ruby Rich has written that women experience films much more dialectically than men. "Brecht once described the exile as the ultimate dialectician in that the exile lives the tension of two different cultures. That's precisely the sense in which the woman spectator is an equally inevitable dialectician."[53] The female spectator's look is thus a dialectic of two (in themselves) inadequate and incomplete (sexually and socially) differentiated subject positions. Just as Julia Kristeva has shown that it is the dialectic of a maternal body that is channeled and repressed into a single, univocal significance that makes it possible for women to be represented at all, so does a similar dialectic inform female spectatorship when a female point of view is genuinely inscribed in the text.

We have seen in *Stella Dallas* how the mediation of the mother and daughter's look at one another radically alters the representation of them both. We have also seen that the viewer cannot choose a single "main controlling" point of identification but must alternate between a number of conflicting points of view, none of which can be satisfactorily reconciled. But the window scene at the end of the film would certainly seem to be the moment when all the above contradictions collapse into a single patriarchal vision of the mother as pure spectator (divested of her excessive bodily presence) and the daughter as the (now properly fetishized) object of vision. Although it is true that this ending, by separating mother and daughter, places each within a visual economy that defines them from the perspective of patriarchy, the female spectator's own look at each of them does not acquiesce in such a phallic visual economy of voyeurism and fetishism.

For in looking at Stella's own look at her daughter through a window that strongly resembles a movie screen,[54] the female spectator does not see and believe the same way Stella does. In this final scene, Stella is no different than the naive spectator she was when, as a young woman, she went to the movies with Stephen. In order to justify her sacrifice, she must *believe* in the reality of the cinematic illusion she sees: bride and groom kneeling before the priest, proud father looking on. We, however, *know* the artifice and suffering behind it—Laurel's disappointment that her mother has not attended the wedding; Helen's manipulation of the scene that affords Stella her glimpse; Stella's own earlier manipulation of Laurel's view of her "bad" motherhood. So when we look at Stella looking at the glamorous and artificial "movie" of her daughter's life, we cannot, like Stella, naively believe in the reality of the happy ending, any more than we believe in the reality of the silent movements and hackneyed gestures of the glamorous movie Stella once saw.

Because the female spectator has seen the cost to both Laurel and Stella of the daughter's having entered the frame, of having become the properly fetishized image of womanhood, she cannot, like Stella, believe in happiness for either. She knows better because she has seen what each has had to give up to assume these final roles. But isn't it just such a balance of knowledge and belief (of the fetishist's contradictory phrase "I know very well but just the same . . .")[55] that has characterized the sophisticated juggling act of the ideal cinematic spectator?

The psychoanalytic model of cinematic pleasure has been based on the phenomenon of fetishistic disavowal: the contradictory gesture of *believing* in an illusion (the cinematic image, the female penis) and yet *knowing* that it is an illusion, an imaginary signifier. This model sets up a situation in which the woman becomes a kind of failed fetishist: lacking a penis she lacks the biological foundation to engage in the sophisticated game of juggling presence and absence in cinematic representation; hence her presumed over-identification, her lack of the knowledge of illusion[56] and the resulting one, two, and three handkerchief movies. But the female spectator of *Stella Dallas* finds herself balancing a very different kind of knowledge and belief than the mere existence or non-existence of the female phallus. She *knows* that women can find no genuine form of representation under patriarchal structures of voyeuristic or fetishistic viewing, because she has seen Stella lose herself as a woman and as a mother. But at the same time she *believes* that women exist outside this phallic economy, because she has glimpsed moments of resistance in which two women have been able to represent themselves to themselves through the mediation of their own gazes.

This is a very different form of disavowal. It is both a *knowing* recognition of the limitations of woman's representation in patriarchal language and a contrary *belief* in the illusion of a pre-Oedipal space between women free of the mastery and control of the male look. The contradiction is as compelling for the woman as for the male fetishist, even more so because it is not based on the presence or absence of an anatomical organ, but on the dialectic of the woman's socially constructed position under patriarchy.

It is in a very different sense, then, that the psychoanalytic concepts of voyeurism and fetishism can inform a feminist theory of cinematic spectatorship—not as inscribing woman totally on the side of the passive object who is merely seen, as Mulvey and others have so influentially argued, but by examining the contradictions that animate women's very active and fragmented ways of seeing.

I would not go so far as to argue that these contradictions operate for the female viewer in every film about relations between women. But the point of focusing on a film that both addresses female audiences and contains important structures of viewing *between* women is to suggest that it does not take a radical and consciously feminist break with patriarchal ideology to represent the contradictory aspects of the woman's position under patriarchy. It does not even take the ironic distancing devices of, for example, the Sirkian melodrama to generate the kind of active, critical response that sees the work of ideology in the film. Laura Mulvey has written that the ironic endings of Sirkian melodrama are progressive in their defiance of unity and closure:

> It is as though the fact of having a female point of view dominating the narrative produces an excess which precludes satisfaction. If the melodrama offers a fantasy escape for the identifying women in the audience, the illusion is so strongly marked by recognisable, real and familiar traps that the escape is closer to a daydream than a fairy story. The few Hollywood films made with a female audience in mind evoke contradictions rather than reconciliation, with the alternative to mute surrender to society's overt pressures lying in defeat by its unconscious laws.[57]

Although Mulvey here speaks primarily of the ironic Sirkian melodrama, her description of the contradictions encountered by the female spectator apply in a slightly different way to the very un-ironic *Stella Dallas*. I would argue that *Stella Dallas* is a progressive film not because it defies both unity and closure, but because the definitive closure of its ending produces no parallel unity in its spectator. And because the film has constructed its spectator in a female subject position locked into a primary identification with another female subject, it is possible for this spectator, like

Val—the mother spectator from *The Women's Room* whose reaction to the film is quoted at the head of this article—to impose her own radical feminist reading on the film. Without such female subject positions inscribed within the text, the stereotypical self-sacrificing mother character would flatten into the mere maternal essences of so many motherly figures of melodrama.

Stella Dallas is a classic maternal melodrama played with a very straight face. Its ambivalences and contradictions are not cultivated with the intention of revealing the work of patriarchal ideology within it. But like any melodrama that offers a modicum of realism yet conforms to the "reconciliation of the irreconcilable" proper to the genre,[58] it must necessarily produce, when dealing with conflicts among women, what Val calls a "shock of recognition." This shock is not the pleasurable recognition of a verisimilitude that generates naive belief, but the shock of seeing, as Val explains, "how they got us to consent to our own eradication." Val and other female spectators typically do *not* consent to such eradicating resolutions. They, and we, resist the only way we can by struggling with the contradictions inherent in these images of ourselves and our situation. It is a terrible underestimation of the female viewer to presume that she is wholly seduced by a naive belief in these masochistic images, that she has allowed these images to put her in her place the way the films themselves put their women characters in their place.

It seems, then, that Adrienne Rich's eloquent plea for works that can embody the "essential female tragedy" of mother-daughter passion, rapture, and loss is misguided but only with respect to the mode of tragedy. I hope to have begun to show that this loss finds expression under patriarchy in the "distorted" and "misused" cathexes of the maternal melodrama. For unlike tragedy, melodrama does not reconcile its audience to an inevitable suffering. Rather than raging against a fate that the audience has learned to accept, the female hero often accepts a fate that the audience at least partially questions.

The divided female spectator identifies with the woman whose very triumph is often in her own victimization, but she also criticizes the price of a transcendent "eradication" which the victim-hero must pay. Thus, although melodrama's impulse towards the just "happy ending" usually places the woman hero in a final position of subordination, the "lesson" for female audiences is certainly not to become similarly eradicated themselves. For all its masochism, for all its frequent devaluation of the individual person of the mother (as opposed to the abstract ideal of motherhood), the maternal melodrama presents a recognizable picture of woman's ambivalent position under patriarchy that has been an important source of realistic reflections of women's lives. This may be why the most effective feminist films of recent years have been those works—like Sally Potter's *Thriller,* Michelle Citron's *Daughter Rite,* Chantal Akerman's *Jeanne Dielman . . . ,* and even Jacques Rivette's *Celine and Julie Go Boating*—that work *within and against* the expectations of female self-sacrifice experienced in maternal melodrama.

Notes

1. *The Women's Room* (New York: Summit Books, 1977), 227.
2. An interesting and comprehensive introduction to this sub-genre can be found in Christian Viviani's "Who Is Without Sin? The Maternal Melodrama in American Film, 1930–1939," *Wide Angle* 4, no. 2 (1980): 4–17. Viviani traces the history of maternal melodrama in American films back to the original French play *Madame* X about an adulterous woman who expiates her sin in lifelong separation from a son whose social rise would be jeopardized by the revelation of her relation to him. Two successful twenties screen versions of *Madame* X set a pattern of imitators. Within them Viviani traces two different "veins" of this melodramatic sub-genre: those films with European settings in which the originally sinning mother descends to anonymity, and those films with American settings where the more "Rooseveltian" mother displays a greater energy and autonomy before descending to anonymity. Viviani suggests that King Vidor's *Stella Dallas* is the "archetype" of this more energetic, American vein of maternal melodrama. He also adds that although Stella is not actually guilty of anything, her unwillingness to overcome completely her working class origins functions as a kind of original sin that makes her seem guilty in her husband's and finally in her own eyes.

   B. Ruby Rich and I have also briefly discussed the genre of these sacrificial maternal melodramas in our efforts to identify the context of Michelle Citron's avant-garde feminist film, *Daughter Rite*. Citron's film is in many ways the flip side to the maternal melodrama, articulating the daughter's confused anger and love at the mother's sacrificial stance. "The Right of Re-Vision: Michelle Citron's *Daughter Rite*," *Film Quarterly* 35, no. 1 (Fall 1981):17–22.
3. *The Second Sex*, trans. H. M. Parshley (New York: Bantam, 1961), 488–89.
4. An excellent introduction to this rapidly growing area of study is Marianne Hirsch's review essay, "Mothers and Daughters," *Signs: Journal of Women in Culture and Society* 7, no. 1 (1981): 200–22. See also Judith Kegan Gardiner, "On Female Identity and Writing by Women," *Critical Inquiry* 8, no. 2 (Winter 1981): 347–61.
5. *Of Woman Born* (New York: Bantam, 1977), 240, 226.
6. *The Melodramatic Imagination: Balzac, Henry James, Melodrama and the Mode of Excess* (New Haven: Yale University Press, 1976).
7. Martha Vicinus, writing about the nineteenth century melodrama, suggests that melodrama's "appropriate" endings offer "a temporary reconciliation of the irreconcilable." The concern is typically not with what is possible or actual but what is desirable. "Helpless and Unfriended: Nineteenth Century Domestic Melodrama," *New Literary History* 13, no. 1 (Autumn 1981): 132. Peter Brooks emphasizes a similar quality of wish-fulfillment in melodrama, even arguing that psychoanalysis offers a systematic realization of the basic aesthetics of the genre: "If psychoanalysis has become the nearest modern equivalent of religion in that it is a vehicle for the cure of souls, melodrama is a way station twoard this status, a first indication of how conflict, enactment, and cure must be conceived in a secularized world" (202).
8. Most prominent among these are Claire Johnston's "Women's Cinema as Counter Cinema" in *Notes on Women's Cinema*, BFI Pamphlet (September 1972); and Laura Mulvey's "Visual Pleasure and Narrative Cinema," *Screen* 26, no. 3 (Autumn 1975): 6–18.
9. The list of feminist work on this film is impressive. It includes: Pam Cook, "Duplicity in

Mildred Pierce," in *Women in Film Noir,* ed. E. Ann Kaplan (London: BFI, 1978), 68–82; Molly Haskell, *From Reverence to Rape: The Treatment of Women in the Movies* (N.Y.: Holt, Rinehart and Winston, 1973), 175–80; Annette Kuhn, *Women's Pictures: Feminism and Cinema* (London: Routledge and Kegan Paul, 1982), 28–35; Joyce Nelson, "*Mildred Pierce* Reconsidered," *Film Reader* 2 (January 1977): 65–70; and Janet Walker, "Feminist Critical Practice: Female Discourse in *Mildred Pierce,*" *Film Reader* 5 (1982): 164–71.

10. Molly Haskell only gave the film brief mention in her chapter on "The Woman's Film" *From Reverence to Rape: The Treatment of Women in the Movies* (N.Y.: Holt, Rinehart and Winston, 1973), 153–88. Since then the film has been discussed by Christian Viviani (see note 2); Charles Affron in *Cinema and Sentiment* (Chicago: University of Chicago Press, 1983), 74–76; Ben Brewster, "A Scene at the Movies," *Screen* 23, no. 2 (July–August 1982): 4–5; and E. Ann Kaplan, "Theories of Melodrama: A Feminist Perspective," *Women and Performance: A Journal of Feminist Theory* 1, no. 1 (Spring–Summer 1983): 40–48. Kaplan also has a longer article on the film, "The Case of the Missing Mother: Maternal Issues in Vidor's *Stella Dallas,*" *Heresies* 16 (1983): 81–85. Laura Mulvey also mentions the film briefly in her "Afterthoughts on 'Visual Pleasure and Narrative Cinema' Inspired by 'Duel in the Sun' (King Vidor, 1946)," *Framework* 15/16/17 (Summer 1981): 12–15—but only in the context of Vidor's much more male-oriented western. Thus, although *Stella Dallas* keeps coming up in the context of discussions of melodrama, sentiment, motherhood, and female spectatorship, it has not been given the full scrutiny it deserves, except by Kaplan, many of whose arguments I challenge in the present work.
11. Mulvey, 11. See also most of the essays in *Re-Vision: Essays in Feminist Film Criticism,* eds. Mary Ann Doane, Patricia Mellencamp, and Linda Williams (Los Angeles: AFI Monograph Series, 1983).
12. Claire Johnston, for example, writes, "Despite the enormous emphasis placed on women as spectacle in the cinema, woman as woman is largely absent." "Woman's Cinema as Counter-Cinema," *Notes on Woman's Cinema,* Screen Pamphlet 2, ed. Claire Johnston, 26.
13. Christine Gledhill, "Developments in Feminist Film Criticism," *Re-vision: Essays in Feminist Film Criticism,* eds. Mary Ann Doane, Patricia Mellencamp, and Linda Williams (Los Angeles: American Film Institute Monograph Series, 1983), 31. Originally published in *Quarterly Review of Film Studies* 3, no. 4 (1978): 457–93.
14. Mulvey, 7.
15. Mulvey, 7, 18.
16. The few feminists who have begun this difficult but important work are: Mary Ann Doane, "Film and the Masquerade: Theorizing the Female Spectator," *Screen* 23, no. 3–4 (Sept.–Oct. 1982): 74–87; Gertrud Koch, "Why Women Go to the Movies," *Jump Cut* 27 (July 1982), trans. Marc Silberman: 51–53; Judith Mayne, "The Woman at the Keyhole: Women's Cinema and Feminist Criticism," *Re-Vision: Essays in Feminist Film Criticism,* 44–66; and Mulvey herself in "Afterthoughts on 'Visual Pleasure and Narrative Cinema' Inspired by 'Duel in the Sun' (King Vidor, 1946)," *Framework* 15/16/17 (Summer 1981): 12–15; B. Ruby Rich, in Michelle Citron et al., "Women and Film: A Discussion of Feminist Aesthetics," *New German Critique* 13 (1978): 77–107; and Tania Modleski, *Loving with a Vengeance: Mass Produced Fantasies for Women* (Hamden, Conn.: Archon Books, 1982). Since I wrote this article, two important new books on women and film have appeared. Both take considerable account of the processes by which the female spectator identifies with screen images. They are: E. Ann Kaplan's *Women and Film: Both Sides of the Camera* (N.Y.: Methuen, 1983); and Teresa de Lauretis, *Alice Doesn't: Feminism, Semiotics, Cinema* (Bloomington: Indiana University Press, 1984).
17. Gledhill, 41.
18. Gledhill, 37.

19. Gledhill, 42.
20. Gledhill, 44–45.
21. Freud begins this shift in the 1925 essay, "Some Psychological Consequences of the Anatomical Distinction between the Sexes," *Standard Edition of the Complete Psychological Works* (Hogarth Press, 1953–74), vol. XIX. He continues it in the 1931 essay "Female Sexuality," vol. XXI.
22. Marianne Hirsch's review essay, "Mothers and Daughters," *Signs: Journal of Women in Culture and Society* 7, no. 1 (Autumn 1981): 200–22, offers an excellent summary of the diverse strands of the continuing re-appraisal of the mother-daughter relation. Hirsch examines theories of this relation in Anglo-American neo-Freudian object relations psychology (Chodorow, Miller, Dinnerstein), in Jungian myth criticism, and in the French feminist theories developing out of structuralism, post-structuralism, and Lacanian psychoanalysis. A recent study of how female connectedness affects female moral development is Carol Gilligan's *In a Different Voice* (Cambridge: Harvard Univ. Press, 1982).
23. Chodorow, *The Reproduction of Mothering: Psychoanalysis and the Sociology of Gender* (Berkeley: University of California Press, 1978), 7.
24. "Oedipal asymmetries" is Chodorow's term, 7.
25. Chodorow, 178.
26. Marianne Hirsch surveys the importance of this point in her review essay "Mothers and Daughters," 209. So, too, does Judith Kegan Gardiner in "On Female Identity and Writing by Women," *Critical Inquiry: Writing and Sexual Difference* 8, no. 2 (Winter 1981): 347–61.
27. Chodorow, 188.
28. These others include: Dorothy Dinnerstein, *The Mermaid and the Minotaur: Sexual Arrangements and the Human Malaise* (New York: Harper and Row, 1976); Jessie Bernard, *The Future of Motherhood* (New York: Dial Press, 1974): and Jean Baker Miller, *Toward a New Psychology of Women* (Boston: Beacon Press, 1976).
29. This is the real advance of Chodorow's theories over those of an earlier generation of feminist psychoanalysts. Karen Horney, for example, found it necessary, as both Juliet Mitchell and Jane Gallop point out, to resort to generalizing statements of women's essential, biologically determined nature, thus leaving no possibility for change. Horney, "On the Genesis of the Castration Complex in Women," *International Journal of Psycho-Analysis* V, 1924: 50–65.
30. Paris: Editions de Minuit, 1974.
31. Other French feminists involved in this "feminine writing" are Hélène Cixous, Monique Wittig, Julia Kristeva, and Michele Montrelay. A critical introduction to these writers can be found in Ann Rosalind Jones, "Writing the Body: Toward an Understanding of L'Ecriture feminine," and Helene Vivienne Wenzel's "The Text as Body/Politics: An Appreciation of Monique Wittig's Writings in Context," both in *Feminist Studies* 7, no. 2 (Summer 1981): 247–87.
32. "Ce sex qui n'en est pas un," trans. Claudia Reeder, *New French Feminisms*, ed. Elaine Marks and Isabelle de Courtivron (Amherst: University of Mass. Press, 1980), 100–1.
33. Anglo-American feminists have thus been critical of the new French feminists for two different reasons: American feminists have criticized an essentialism that would seem to preclude change (see, for example, the essay by Jones referred to in note 31); British feminists have criticized their apparent failure to account for the way the female body is mediated by language (see, for example, Beverly Brown and Parveen Adams, "The Feminine Body and Feminist Politics," *m/f*, no. 3 (1979): 35–50).
34. Irigaray, 106–7.
35. Rich, *Signs* 5, no. 4 (Summer 1980); 631–60.
36. Irigaray, 110.

37. Mary Ann Doane, "Woman's Stake: Filming the Female Body," *October* 17 (Summer 1981): 30.
38. Kristeva's work has been translated in two volumes: *Desire in Language: A Semiotic Approach to Literature and Art*, trans. Thomas Gora, Alice Jardine, Leon S. Roudiez (New York: Columbia University Press, 1980); and *About Chinese Women*, trans. Anita Barrows (New York: Horizon Books, 1977).
39. Alice Jardine, "Theories of the Feminine: Kristeva" *enclitic* 4, no. 2 (Fall 1980): 13.
40. Kristeva, "Motherhood According to Giovanni Bellini," in *Desire in Language*, 237–70.
41. Jane Gallop, "The Phallic Mother: Freudian Analysis," in *The Daughter's Seduction: Feminism and Psychoanalysis* (Ithaca, N.Y.: Cornell University Press, 1982), 113–31.
42. Ann Kaplan emphasises this "wrenching" of the filmic point of view away from Stella and towards the upper-class values and perspectives of Stephen and the townspeople. "The Case of the Missing Mother," 83.
43. Doane, "The Woman's Film: Possession and Address," in *Re-Vision: Essays in Feminist Film Criticism*, 67–82.
44. The term—originally used by Joan Riviere—is employed in Mary Ann Doane, "Film and the Masquerade: Theorizing the Female Spectator," *Screen* 23, no. 34 (Sept.–Oct. 1982): 74–87.
45. Ann Kaplan, "The Case of the Missing Mother," 83.
46. Ibid.
47. Molly Haskell notes this tendency of women audiences to come away with a memory of heroic revolt, rather than the defeat with which so many films end, in her pioneering study *From Reverence to Rape: The Treatment of Women in the Movies* (New York: Holt, Rinehart and Winston, 1973), 31.
48. Modleski, "The Search for Tomorrow in Today's Soap Opera: Notes on a Feminine Narrative Form," *Film Quarterly* 33, no. 1 (Fall 1979): 14. A longer version of this article can be found in Modleski's book *Living with a Vengeance: Mass Produced Fantasies for Women* (Hamden, Conn.: Archon Books, 1982): 85–109.
49. Kaplan, "Theories of Melodrama," 46.
50. Doane, "Film and the Masquerade," 87.
51. Mulvey, "Afterthoughts on 'Visual Pleasure and Narrative Cinema' Inspired by 'Duel in the Sun' (King Vidor, 1946)," 13.
52. Doane, 87.
53. Ruby Rich, in Michelle Citron et al., "Women and Film: A Discussion of Feminist Aesthetics," *New German Critique* 13 (1978): 87. Although Rich goes on to suggest that this dialectic is an either/or choice—"to identify either with Marilyn Monroe or with the man behind me hitting the back of my seat with his knees"—I think the more proper sense of the word would be to construe it as a continuous conflict and tension that informs female viewing and which in many cases does not allow the choice of one or the other.
54. Ben Brewster has cited the many cinematic references of the original novel as an indication of just how effective as an appeal to reality the cinematic illusion has become. "A Scene at the Movies," *Screen* 23, no. 2 (July–Aug. 1983): 4–5.
55. Freud's theory that the little boy believes in the maternal phallus even after he knows better because he has seen evidence that it does not exist has been characterized by Octave Manoni as a contradictory statement that both asserts and denies the mother's castration. In this "Je sais bien mais quand même" (I know very well but just the same), the "just the same" is the fetish disavowal. Manoni, *Clefs pour l'imaginaire* (Paris: Seuil, 1969), 9–30. Christian Metz later applied this fetishistic structure of disavowal to the institution of the cinema as the creator of believable fictions of perceptually real human beings who are nevertheless absent from the scene. Thus the cinema aims all of its technical prowess at the disavowal of the lack on which its "imaginary signifier" is based. *The Imaginary Signifier: Psychoanalysis and the*

Cinema, trans. Celia Britton, Annwyl Williams, Ben Brewster, and Alfred Guzzetti (Bloomington: Indiana University Press, 1982), 69–76.
56. Doane, "Film and the Masquerade," 80–81.
57. Mulvey, "Notes on Sirk and Melodrama," 1 *Movie* 25 (n.d.): 56.
58. Vicinus, 132.

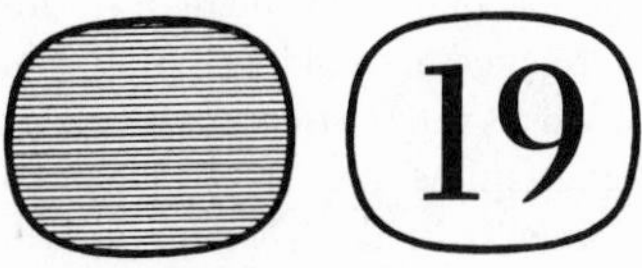

The Scar of Shame: Skin Color and Caste in Black Silent Melodrama

JANE GAINES

When blacks began to finance and direct their own films in the teens and early 1920s, they consistently produced domestic melodramas. Some of these early productions have racial themes which reorganize the world in such a way that black heritage is rewarded over white paternity; they are schematic renunciations of the prevailing order of things in white American society where, historically, the discovery of black blood meant sudden reversal of fortune, social exclusion, or banishment.[1] Feminist studies of literary, cinematic, and theatrical melodrama have suggested that the melodramatic world view favors the weak over the strong as it adheres to a moral order which privileges the lesser and handicaps the greater. Since these new theories have shown that there is something genuinely affirming for women readers in narratives which organize the world around the female character and her domestic haven in the home, I wondered if domestic melodrama had ever produced an analogous position for black viewers or "readers," female or male.[2] What I found surprised me. Although the black viewer is not exactly "affirmed" in the silent film text, this viewer is implicated in it in a way that is still pertinent to the whole project of understanding the subversive potential of domestic melodrama. At the outset I did not expect that it would be necessary to reconstruct the black viewer in history. Nor did I expect to find that cinema aesthetics and the aesthetics of racial distinction could be so closely linked. In fact, as I will argue, they are one and the same.

My reading of *The Scar and Shame* (1927), one of the few silent melodramas with

Jane Gaines's "*The Scar of Shame*: Skin Color and Caste in Black Silent Melodrama" originally appeared in *Cinema Journal*, Vol. 26, no. 4 (Summer 1987), pp. 3–21. Reprinted by permission of the author and *Cinema Journal*.

an all-black cast available for rental in the United States, is also an attempt to see how theories of literary and cinematic melodrama can be applied to Afro-American culture. Since, with a few exceptions, this heritage has not been submitted to any systematic analysis as mass culture, I offer this approach as an example of how we might deal with cultural products which are politically offensive to later generations of black American viewers.[3] The advantage of this approach is that since it does not measure mass culture against high culture, the people who enjoy popular entertainment are not condemned by association with it. In order to consider the black viewer in 1927, whom we will never exactly "know," and about whom we can always ask more, I will take up the problems of melodramatic mode of address, the use of the mulatta type, the subversive aspects of style, and the reception of the "happy ending." An attempt to reconstruct the spectator in history seems especially pressing with this film, even though it will probably baffle the contemporary viewer who might see *The Scar of Shame* screened for the first time in the context of a black film history retrospective. This viewer will undoubtedly note that the narrative represents the tragedy in the film as the consequence of a social class division within the black community. What, then, is meant by the intertitles which lay the blame on a caste system? Why the use of a term that denotes a social ranking scheme that is even more rigid than a class-based system?[4]

Immediately, *The Scar of Shame* raises issues regarding the race and class constitution of the audience which bear on its mode of address. To begin with, the history of black motion picture production and exhibition shows that "race movies," or those films produced specifically for all-black audiences, were created by the black bourgeoisie, often in collaboration with whites, for the entertainment and edification of the group below them. In the 1920s, this class difference would have been further emphasized by the northern urban versus southern rural distinction as the increased migration of southern blacks created a new proletariat that became the audience for the black theatrical product. Two other factors suggest that black entrepreneurs addressed a group of social unequals who would have been finding diversion at the movies. First, "respectable" blacks, who could claim this distinction merely by virtue of having lived longer in the North, held themselves above popular entertainments which were not sanctioned by their churches. Second, literacy levels suggest that motion pictures and popular musical recordings more than printed material provided entertainment for the new arrivals from the South.[5]

Some clarification about the class structure of urban black society in the United States in the 1920s is essential here since the configuration has been historically misunderstood and systematically ignored by blacks as well as whites. Briefly, toward the end of the nineteenth century, black society was characterized by a small group of aristocrats at the top and a small group of social outcasts at the bottom. The group between, made up of 80 to 90 percent of the black population, is difficult to compare with the white middle-class in the same period. Although income level and occupation would place individuals in this group below those in the white structural middle, persons in this group had a claim to respectability within the black community. The rearrangement of this center was under way by the 1920s, as the black structure came to resemble the upper-, middle-, and lower-class breakdown of the dominant society.[6]

The Scar of Shame gropes for a target audience in this social shuffle. Thus, the film creates a phantom social hierarchy in which black society struggles to make its own illusory "middle" while economic conditions having to do with the black migration north are enlarging the lower group. My argument depends on seeing race films as part of bourgeois ideology, but at the same time as playing to a race and class consciousness even upper-class blacks would have by virtue of their antagonistic relationship to capital. I will be less interested in making direct connections between political positions espoused in the film and the race and class positions of the producers, although later I will find out the production history of the film in these terms. The melodramatic text is not, after all, the place where such positions are set out clearly as in a debate; rather, it is the place where they encounter trouble.

British work on film melodrama as bourgeois form helps explain the coexistence within the same film of the "bootstraps" philosophy informing so many of the race movie narratives from this period and the melodramatic world view. As a literary form which has thrived in the bourgeois epoch, melodrama carries bourgeois assumptions about power—it presumes that everyone has a little.[7] This assumption that "something can be done" is carried by the bourgeois voice of responsibility—the intertitles which assign fault to the top and bottom classes (e.g., "Our people have much to learn"). This portrait of a self-contained black society makes no reference to the white outer world, but I would argue that the willing self-critical tone of the intertitles betrays a judgmental presence. *The Scar of Shame* is haunted by white society. If the intertitles carry the self-confident bourgeois assumptions about power, the narrative carries a vision of a world in which the strings are pulled somewhere else. The marks of a melodramatic narrative construction—the use of coincidence and ironic twists of fate—create a sense that control is always out of one's hands, confirming the point of view of the disenfranchised. Martha Vicinus, among other critics, distinguishes melodrama from tragedy on the basis of the power position it confirms: "Tragedy appeals to those who feel, however erroneously, that they have some control over lives ruined by personal decision and error; melodrama to those who feel that their lives are without order and that events they cannot control can destroy or save them."[8] The "racial uplift" pitch is attached to a film that speaks defeat in its downward narrative spiral. Melodrama has no trouble with such contradictions, but actually camouflages social inconsistencies by focusing on their traumatic consequences—victimization, despondency, and pathos, although, as theories of melodrama have shown, these inconsistencies are not so easy to disguise in the last moment when the form calls for resolution.

Melodrama reenacts a moral pattern which coincides with the value system in operation within a community at a particular point in history. In the parallel world constructed by melodrama, it is safe to raise emotionally volatile issues and test traumatic outcomes. Because the moral pattern, the distribution of reward and punishment in melodrama, is always tailor-made to fit local assumptions and prevailing theses, it stirs an audience in its time but may never strike a chord for another generation. An extremely malleable and susceptible genre, melodrama accommodates the social problems of every new decade, translating them into hypothetical scenarios.[9] Melodrama, then, may accommodate both the address which assumes some power and the order of events which counsels resignation. Thus it combines a sense of the way things have come down historically in the black community with the bourgeois uplift strategy, saying in effect: "Because we haven't helped ourselves enough, we are still subject to discrimination, disaster, and degradation." Racial uplift stories lend themselves to melodramatic treatment because the uplift philosophy, like melodrama, is built upon a basic paradox. Explaining the peaceful coexistence of oppositional values and traditional norms within the same genre. Vicinus identifies the paradox of melodrama. As she puts it, ". . . while defending an ideal against a vengeful society, in the name of a higher moral order, in actuality this moral order is a reflection of the current values of the very society presumably being attacked."[10] What was problematic about the black bourgeois uplift philosophy was that the better society it proposed was not significantly different from the one that held all blacks down.

The history of the tragic mulatta type in black-authored literature calls our attention to another aspect of the uplift strategy constituting one of the conventional battlefields of melodrama—woman's virtue. I refer here to the type which was first used in the abolitionist melodramas such as *Clotel* (1853) and *Iola Leroy* (1895) and was carried over into such 1920s Harlem Renaissance novels as *Quicksand* (1928), *Passing* (1929), *Plum Bun* (1928), and *There is Confusion* (1924).[11] This character, which finds its prototype in Clotel, Iola Leroy, and even Eliza Harris, is intelligent, refined, educated, virginal, and exquisitely beautiful according to Caucasian standards. She is like the white romance novel heroine in every way—except that her legal status as slave places her in degrading and compromising situations, designed to play on the guilt of the white reader who would be appalled by the defilement of a genteel lady. The black abolitionist novelist's use of this character as an ideal certainly indicates the hegemony of white physical standards of beauty, but we might also suppose that giving white readers something other than what they thought they were getting—their own idealized heroine who was *not* white—was a canny trick. This character (who of course did not appear at all in the white antebellum literature) was, in the use black authors made of her, an eloquent statement against several generations of southern male sexual license.[12]

From a contemporary point of view, this type is offensive to blacks, but the portrait of the mulatta as talented and beautiful because of her white paternity might have been flattering to light-skinned readers before 1930. The portrayal of the type as tragic and pitiable would later be insulting to blacks as it was used to argue that the mulatta was miserable because she had been denied her rightful place in a society that excluded others of the same race because they were darker.[13] Seen in a historical perspective, the type has more to say about white supremacist ideology than about actual black persons, although the condition of real historical black women can be inferred obliquely from the construction. As Barbara Christian has analyzed the ideological function of the refined mulatta, her "qualities"—traditional femininity and moral purity—were arguments necessary to proving that she was even a woman.[14] If she was a woman, then her honor had to be defended, and she could certainly not be the cause of white male sexual transgression.[15] The type is thus like a several-sided cube which can be made to face in one direction while another side is concealed. In these early versions, the mulatta heroine could be used as a ruse to turn the tables on whites, or as a political strategy, or even as a utopian vision of security and transcendence.

Louise Howard, the mulatta heroine in *The Scar of Shame*, rehearses some of the disputes over the territory of the black woman's body raised by her literary predecessors. In the negative sense, she fulfills the prophecy of the poor (black) rather than the fine (white) ingredient of her paternity. Further, since in the 1920s lightness had come to stand for opportunity rather than rightful heritage, following this uplift interpretation she dies because she does not use the advantage her whiteness affords her; her tragedy of lost possibility is a setback for the entire race. As she combines exquisite white features and lower-class background, Louise is like those young women within the black community who once earned the snide reference, "a waste of color."[16] The meaning of the tragic mulatta character is not settled once and for all within this film, but she surfaces again as a recurring problem—that of racial respectability as it has been historically bound up with the virtue which black women were not supposed to have.[17] *The Scar of Shame* explores and exhausts all of the possible explanations for Louise's victimization as it thrashes around looking for culprits within the black community, even resurrecting the old nightmare of the loose mulatta.[18]

The Scar of Shame

In 1969, a 35mm original print of *The Scar of Shame* (1927) was discovered among other nitrate films in a trash can in the basement of an empty theater in Detroit, Michigan.[19] Now restored and in 16mm distribution, this silent feature with an all-black cast has become one of the most frequently exhibited examples of our black cinema heritage, and has become source material for new black independent film and video-making, as evidenced in the reference to it in Kathy Collins's *Losing Ground* (1982).[20] One of at least three films produced by the Colored Players of Philadelphia, *The Scar of Shame* represents a typical division of labor between black and white artists producing race movies in that period.[21] Produced specifically for black motion picture audiences, *The Scar of Shame* was directed and photographed by white professionals and improvised by black actors from a story written by the white producer, David Starkman.[22] Although the Philadelphia production group was really run by Starkman, the idea for the Colored Players originally came from black vaudeville comedian Sherman H. Dudley, Jr., who started a theatrical group with the same name in Washington, D.C. Dudley and Starkman, owner of a black theater in Philadelphia, organized the new company in 1926, and the black comedian, listed in the credits as producer of *The Scar of Shame*, also served as company president.[23]

The central victim of the story, Louise Howard (Lucia Lynn Moses), is molested by her "ne'er do well" father Spike, and rescued by Alvin Hillyard, an aspiring composer and pianist (Harry Henderson). Hillyard marries Louise to protect her from the father who continues to assault her, thus lifting her out of the lower class. After their marriage, the father's gambler friend Eddie Blake conspires with him to kidnap Louise and put her to work as a "lure" in a speakeasy. Caught in pistol crossfire between Eddie and Alvin, who tries to prevent the abduction, Louise is wounded in the neck, "her beauty marred for life," according to the newspaper report. Alvin goes to jail for the crime, and Louise takes up a life of prostitution and gambling. When Alvin escapes from jail and the two meet again, he has become engaged to the daughter of the powerful black lawyer Hathaway who frequents Eddie's speakeasy and becomes Louise's lover. Louise tries to win Alvin back, and when she fails, she takes poison. Louise's suicide note, which confesses that she had been wounded by Eddie's gun and not Alvin's, symbolically frees Alvin to marry Alice Hathaway, his social equal.

The opening titles, almost a short lecture on social Darwinism, direct the viewer to interpret the film in terms of social class distinctions:

> Environment—Surroundings, childhood training . . . shapes our destinies and guides our ambitions. If no loving hand lights the lamp of knowledge . . . through lack of love will come sorrow and SHAME!

The social class moral is reiterated in the final titles as the lawyer Hathaway speaks, bestowing his blessing on his daughter and Alvin Hillyard: "A child of environment! If she had been taught higher hopes, finer things in life, she would not be lying cold in death! Our people have much to learn."[24] In 1927, social Darwinism would have provided one of the more progressive challenges to theories of genetic determinism, and certainly would have been complementary to the philosophy and goals of Negro improvement and advancement. The titles proclaim that environment, rather than any person, is the villain, but the urban social condition provides its own anthropomorphic villainous agents in the scum it breeds—Eddie and Spike.[25] What is important to note here is that in blaming the environment, *The Scar of Shame* sidesteps the more devastating color critique, the criticism of black social stratification based on skin color graduations which would later become a harsh indictment in E. Franklin Fraser's *Black Bourgeoisie.*[26] There would be advantages to the black bourgeois social program in shifting the emphasis from the skin color distinction, about which an individual could do nothing, to education, employment, and income—relatively attainable indicators of status. Understandably, black history and sociology would support such a shift of emphasis from the "pettiness" of physiological distinctions which characterized earlier periods, to other signs of differentiation.[27]

In retrospect, we can appreciate the strategy, but, in the determination of social rank, we cannot easily extricate one sign of difference from another, and in American society, race seems to encompass a multitude of distinctions. My emphasis on skin color here is an attempt to fill out the larger picture which *The Scar of Shame* refers to in its silence, to look harder at the visible/invisible dialectic of "racial difference," which, like the signified "breeding," has not always required a signifier in highly stratified societies.

In the preferred version of social conflict in *The Scar of Shame*, however, the highest and lowest classes in black society are responsible for the reputation of the lower orders and especially for the degradation and mistreatment of black women. The black dual responsibility interpretation encourages the discovery of a second victim—Alvin (who his landlady, Mrs. Lucretia Green, expects will become "the leading composer of our race"). Alvin is imprisoned as the direct consequence of the downward pull of the more disreputable Negro element—Eddie, Spike, and Louise (as she works in league with them). Louise's confession reveals not only that it was the shot from Eddie's gun which injured her, but that Eddie and Spike prevented her from telling the truth at the time of the trial. Is the most compelling victim in the film then also a villainess? The film seems to hesitate here, at least long enough for one critic to interpret Louise as "wicked."[28] After all, she is no longer the pure mulatta heroine. I would argue, however, that Louise's villainy is effectively cancelled since she is so sympathetically and lovingly coded as tragic heroine. Treated to a good deal of soft focus attention in close-up against a dark background, Louise is featured in the same photographic style used on D. W. Griffith's haloed innocents. This sympathetic visual interpretation of Louise is part of my case for seeing an oppositional discourse in the codes of lighting and framing which I discuss in a later section. Following the preferred reading, however, Louise and Alvin, in competition as victims, contribute to the portrait of black self-victimization on which the "if only" and the "what might have been" appeals are based. Because their fates are linked, Louise's act of sacrifice is pitiable but not glorious, and the union of Alice and Alvin is proper rather than happy. Although one "hope of the race" is rescued and his reputation restored, the resolution is ragged, and like the often discomforting melodramatic closure, which I will discuss in the conclusion, it leaves the viewer with a bitter taste.

The structure of *The Scar of Shame* further supports the case for the culpability of the upper and lower classes. Plotting to separate Alvin and Louise by sending a fake telegram to Alvin which states that his mother is seriously ill, Eddie and Spike pull Louise back to the gutter. The aristocratic class contributes to the desecration of the black woman in another way. The arrival of the fake telegram occasions Alvin's confession to Louise that his mother does not know that they have married. (Title: "Caste is one of the things mother is very determined about. You don't belong to our set.") The Negro aristocracy and the lower orders then act in league with one another. This characterization of the two classes at the extreme ends of the social spectrum corresponds with a kind of scapegoating seen in the black community during this period. While the lower classes were viewed as dragging others down, the higher were seen as holding up impossible hurdles for other blacks while clamoring upward on their backs.[29]

This joint villainy of the lower and the upper classes is elaborately coordinated in the abduction scene as it is cross-cut between Eddie and Spike outside the boarding house, Alvin driving to the suburbs and returning, and Louise alone in her bedroom. Here Louise is the vehicle for elaborating the toll these conflicts take on families—expressed in terms of emotional turmoil, and represented by shots of her discovery of the letter from Alvin's mother (shown earlier). The mother's letter states that she hopes her son will marry Helen Smith, who plays the piano and is "very lovely, a lady, and one of our set." Inserts of the letter are alternated with shots of Alvin driving away, and the directionality of these shots suggests his allegiance to his mother and her social position. The mother, although not present in the film, is powerfully evoked by the letter as well as by the uniformed black butler who receives Alvin at the suburban home. After Louise finds the letter in Alvin's dresser drawer and reads it, she slowly rips the paper into fine pieces. The following shot, from her point of view, is an insert of her wedding certificate. Here, the decorous quaintness of this icon is incongruous with the moment. As Louise starts to tear the stiff parchment decorated with garlands of orchids and embossed with the words "Holy Matrimony," the film cuts to Alvin racing to his mother. From here, the film cuts back to the slow vertical movement of Louise ripping the sacred document. As Alvin leaves his mother's house and drops his door key, the film cuts to close-ups of Louise's hand as she twists off her wedding band. The cross-cutting pattern, then, establishes a cause and effect relationship between the elitism of the aristocracy and the breakup of black families.

Melodrama, as contemporary critics have asserted, translates ideological dilemmas into private predicaments.[30] The family context serves to intensify these struggles—cruelty and brutality "carry an additional emotional force because they occur between family members."[31] The social injustice of the Negro upper class is here represented in terms of Louise's torn heart. But in this emotional whirlpool, Louise's distress is made to seem the cause of the breakup rather than the effect of political conditions beyond her control. Thus, as Alvin is racing back to Louise, his marriage is being destroyed *by her hand*. By the time Eddie arrives to try to abduct Louise, the damage is done; the remnants of respectability lie shredded on the lace doily on top of a chest of drawers.

I have already noted the debt *The Scar of Shame* owes to Afro-American literture and theatrical melodrama. However, aesthetically the film owes all to D. W. Griffith. *The Scar of Shame* seems constructed out of memorable moments from *Intolerance* (1916) and *Broken Blossoms* (1919). Louise's struggles with her father refer to Lucy's beatings in *Broken Blossoms;* the scene in which Spike breaks into his daughter's room is an ugly homage to the elongated rape and murder scene for the earlier film.[32] The shooting scene is likewise almost lifted intact out of the modern story from *Intolerance*. Like the scene in which The Boy is set up for the killing of The Musketeer, this scene is organized around the fire escape. Alvin is forced to enter up the fire escape because he has lost his key, and he surprises Eddie and Louise as he comes through the window. Also as in the scene from *Intolerance*, the innocent person is framed because of the disappearance of the guilty one.[33] In addition to these direct quotations, the intricate cross-cutting of the rescue scene reminds us of all the last-minute interventions in silent cinema premised on saving the virtue of a woman. Critics have linked the convention as Griffith used it with his championing of the American home and family. As Nick Browne describes the fantasy behind this use of parallel editing: "This scenario of rescue is essentially a chivalrous project couched in a kind of medieval and allegorical idiom that has as its end the stabilization of the place and integrity of the bourgeois family against the threat of abandonment, dismemberment, homelessness, or worse. . . ."[34] Ironically, the structure which D. W. Griffith used in *Birth of a Nation* (1915) to signify the black threat to white womanhood and the glorious rush to save it is recruited here to rally around the protection of black womanhood. The double movement in this scene, suggesting Alvin's divided allegiance, shows that this marriage cannot be saved. For Alvin Hillyard, thrust into the heroic position within the cross-cutting structure, the rescue of his wife and the maintenance of his family is an impossibility; he walks into a trap. The conflicted black hero cannot protect and will not triumph.

After Louise destroys her marriage certificate, the film shifts premises, as though it, too, must continue without the benefit of marriage, and at this point offers a justification for the symbolic annulment of the union. Although Alvin has acted to protect his rightful marriage, the film represents the cross-caste marriage as wrong from the start. The wrongness of Alvin's marriage is born out in one clear way—by the kind of evidence pointed to by old wives tales through the ages. The sad story is told here by the intertitle which separates Alvin's impassioned proposal to Louise from the first shot representing their married life. From the intertitle "Three months later," the film cuts to a close-up of a dark-skinned baby doll in white christening gown and bonnet. In the second shot, the only one with the family intact, Louise cradles the doll, which is remarkably darker than either parent. The faked motherhood tells the tale of Louise's fondest hopes and worst expectations—the marriage is infertile. Later, in the desertion scene, when Alvin tells Louise that she cannot go with him to his mother's home because she doesn't know that they have been married, the toy plays another role. The surrogate baby becomes a third victim in the film—and its fate is the most heart-wrenching. As Alvin picks up his suitcase to leave, the doll is accidentally knocked to the floor, and on his way out the door, unknowingly, he steps on its head.[35] Two exterior shots follow, one locating Spike lurking in the street and another showing Alvin getting into his convertible. Then, the film cuts back to the interior showing the doll in close-up without its head. The title carries Louise's exclamation: "Poor little thing! A victim of caste." The disaster of this marriage is told in Louise's tender attentions to the headless doll which she first clasps to her and then throws into the corner, and in this gesture we recognize a familiar argument against marriages which go against social convention—children neglected and abused.

Caste and Class

But is the child a victim of caste as the title says, or of class prejudice? This usage, as I have noted, is one of the more curious aspects of the film encountered by the contemporary viewer, and the issues with which the film is dealing are easily missed by the white viewer with no background in Afro-American history. To black audiences in 1927, class and caste would have had resounding significance. The upper or aristocratic class held to an elaborate rationale for maintaining their distinctness from the lower levels, and this engendered certain hostility. Hortense Powdermaker describes how the rest of black society participated in this deference by default as they begrudgingly adhered to the values which reinforced the hierarchy: "The Negro upper class acts out for its race the denial that Negroes are inferior; it demonstrates that they too can be educated, moral, industrious, thrifty. This class also reaps a fair share of resentment from other members of its race, but here resentment is far less keen and less conscious, and is offset by substantial advantages, among which is to be numbered a very gratifying prestige."[36] Philadelphia, the home of the Colored Players, had a very old aristocratic society of Negroes as well as a rich literary tradition that paralleled the Harlem Renaissance.[37] The justification for separateness offered by those who considered themselves superior was that by example they would inspire the lower orders to improve themselves. The author of *Sketches of Colored Society* (1841) writes: "If the virtuous and exemplary members of society should not keep aloof from the vicious and worthless, they would furnish no example to the latter to strive to make themselves reputable, and of like consideration. By associating with such persons we not only thereby give countenance to their doings, but we degrade ourselves to their level, and are adjudged accordingly."[38] Thus their strategy was that full acceptance depended upon proving that blacks could be equal to whites in their cultured tastes and their achievements, hence the tight circle dedicated so fiercely to pursuing "finer things." Although sensitive about being mistaken for the serving class, some elite families saw nothing inconsistent in employing other blacks as servants. In his turn-of-the-century study of Philadelphia, W.E.B. Du Bois found that in the 277 upper-class families he studied, fifty-two kept servants. It was Du Bois's conviction that the upper classes should help the lower to rise, but he found that this group was too economically unstable and strategically self-protective to do so. As Du Bois explains it, "the class which should lead refuses to head any race movement on the plea that thus they draw the very color line against which they protest."[39] Or, to take a position against racial discrimination would be to distinguish themselves even further from whites, and thus cut themselves off from the small, and possibly imagined, advantage they enjoyed. This group of blacks, then, as John Dollard describes them, "stood beating at the caste barrier, competent and disciplined in the sense desired by our society but categorically debarred from full status." In the sociological literature on race in the period of Reconstruction through the 1940s, caste designates the fixed line between the races one technically could never cross. In the South, the caste division essentially replaced slavery.[40] Theoretically, caste defines a more rigid separation than class, which allows for some fluidity. In the United States, then, there would be social classes within caste, and within the black caste, the class system would operate at particular periods in deference to the whole, according to the rules of caste.[41]

The history of miscegenation and the phenomenon of crossing over or passing in American society has a bearing on *The Scar of Shame* as it fills out our knowledge about the black spectator. Pertinent here is the white society's vacillation regarding the meaning and the value of racial mixing. Originally, during the period of slavery, the established scale of valuation gave a social advantage to Negroes with white blood and an economic advantage to the masters who could claim a higher sale price for slave property with white features. Later, the house slave versus field slave distinctions established by percentage of white blood became the basis of the earliest "blue vein" societies in the northern cities. As black society observed preferential treatment and absorbed white cultural biases, it came to embrace the same physiological ideals. This connection between light skin and economic success was born out again during Reconstruction when the first profits in black economic ventures were handed to those who bore the greatest likeness to whites.[42]

Abruptly, white society withdrew the favors offered to the relatively lighter few, taking the position that no fraction of Negro blood was acceptable. Some lighter blacks adjusted to this by passing, but this was a phenomenon more mythic than real, and, especially in the 1920s, racial pride may have kept a check on the practice.[43] Whereas white ancestry had once been a sign of esteem, by the 1940s it would be a sign of disgrace in many communities.[44] The black aristocratic class was slow to respond to the loss of their edge of privilege and continued to insist on it, holding over the tribute to and convenient defense of white supremacy.[45] Also held over were the stubborn tastes and preferences for light skin, Caucasian facial features, and white hair-form. In 1927, there would be deference to a skin color hierarchy in the black community at the same time that there would be antagonism toward it.

The Political Aesthetics of Skin Color

My sense of *The Scar of Shame* is that it accommodates both the deference and the antagonism. However, it seems to me that the way in which it is open to the antagonism is a way which forces us to reconsider theories of the subversive potential of domestic melodrama, particularly the British Marxist work on cinema produced in the early 1970s. The model proposed and refined by the British critics finds a subversive space in melodrama that is not there in other American genres. This space is found in the difference between narrative and mise-en-scène, which are understood as having a kind of contrapuntal relationship.[46] In this two-tiered textual arrangement, the stylistic level below can comment on, and even criticize, the surface level which carries the plot line, characterized as carrying the bourgeois world view.

This theory of subversive stylistics developed out of an interest in the flamboyant 1950s melodramas of Ophuls, Minnelli, and Sirk. Thus theories of stylistic contradiction in silent melodrama have so far been formulated in relation to an exceptional moment in the 1950s. In Thomas Elsaesser's formulation, for instance, there is a line of development from silent film stylistics (which evolved as a cinema language to compensate for the lost expressivity of speech) and the aesthetics made possible in the 1950s by technical innovations such as Technicolor, power zooms, and dolly shots. The 1950s auteurs, in this account, stand for the fullest realization of melodramatic expressivity in cinema history.[47] Immediately, there are several problems with adapting this theory to the black audience melodrama. First, there are different degrees of "stylistic comment" in both silent and 1950s melodrama. Most expressivity in silent cinema could not be considered as parodic as, for instance, the Sirkian use of the slow motion cut-glass baubles in the opening credits of *Imitation of Life* (1959), which offer the famous "through a glass darkly" vision of bourgeois family life.[48] Second, this theory of stylistic orchestration really calls for the hand of the auteur who can be credited with making the text reveal its contradictions. Third, the space which opens up the possibilities for resistance is an empty one. A space in and of itself cannot split a gaping text. What is required is a critic or a reader who is either politically primed or slightly jaundiced.[49] Finally, I would mention the psychoanalytic aspect of this theory which hypothesizes a cause and effect relationship between the stylistic expressivity or excess and the impossibililty of closure. The mark of style, like an hysterical symptom, manifests itself before the ending, and the film, like the psychoanalytic patient, must repress the tabooed, which returns in another guise as the formal symptom. I will return momentarily to the issue of closure and the politics of the hysterical text, but first I want to take up the question of the reader-viewer's space.

In *The Scar of Shame*, the stylistic discourse carrying the melos is connected to the aesthetics of skin tone and hair texture played out in light, shadow, and shade. This color scheme or code would be known in its finer gradations and variations only to black audiences—to the group that would read a wealth of significance in the difference between processed and unprocessed coiffure, and would be sensitive to all kinds of hair-splitting along caste lines.

At the end of the film this color scheme becomes stylistically highlighted in the cross-cutting between Alice and Louise. Here the empathetic effects clearly favor the latter. Where Alice is filmed in silhouette, backlit against black drapery, Louise is framed full-face in long, languid, glowing close-ups. While the accomplished Alice is playing the piano (unaware that she may be the diegetic source for the melos which evokes sympathy for her rival), Louise is dying. Visual style elaborates the contrast between the two worlds—an elegant candelabra provides the illumination behind Alice, while Louise's life is snuffed out as a single candle burns down. The full-bodied, suffering woman is preferred over the ethereal but still adolescent piano pupil, and in Alice, with her shiny long dark curls and thin delicate nose, there is an intimation that the sheltered Negro class, living out lives of deference and imitation, is finally anemic.

The mise-en-scène here provides commentary, but can the signifiers in and of themselves cause much trouble in the text? (We are also handicapped in our analysis of those silent films which do not have original orchestral, organ, or piano scores. This music might have functioned as ironic comment much as Elsaesser's calliope or organ grinder, particularly if a black pianist were simultaneously responding to the audience and interpreting the screen action in an all-black theater.)[50] What is really required to resist, split, or rupture a text is the skeptical audience member who notes that the text is saying more than one thing at once, as texts will do. But we also have to consider that historically situated viewers accommodate contradictions and multiple meanings in much the same way that texts combine levels of signification. Would the text necessarily "rupture" if the black viewer accommodated its split by means of a double consciousness developed as an ingenious adjustment to living in two societies at once?

I find two stories in *The Scar of Shame*. In an earlier part of this essay I discussed the story about an interracially divided community, the story the intertitles hold to and the narrative structure supports. In contrapuntal opposition, in the mise-en-scène, I find the ghost of a second story about life in a racist society, and I would maintain that this other story has not been orchestrated in the authorial sense. But neither is it exactly the doing of the text. "Criticism," says Terry Eagleton, "is not a passage from text to reader; its task is not to redouble the text's self-understanding, to collude with its object in a conspiracy of eloquence. Its task is to show the text as it cannot know itself, to manifest those conditions of its making (inscribed in its very letter) about which it is necessarily silent."[51] *The Scar of Shame* is not able to speak about its own subtle racism or about the racism in the black film industry in the 1920s. On the screen the actors playing Louise, Alvin, Alice, and the baser element, Eddie, appear exactly the same degree of light brown. The actor playing Spike, Louise's father, seems darker than the other actors (with the exception of the inhabitants of the local bar). Since this darkness might be connoted by the stubble on his face, the father's crude behavior could be motivated by either enviromental factors (the slovenly habits of the underclass) or by genetic factors (race). Since we are presented with a basically monochromatic cast, it would seem that "on the face of it," *The Scar of Shame* is about the rift within black society and not about color caste distinctions based on the white model at all. Let us assume that the film means what the titles insist it means for a moment—if that is possible—and consider something else.

Could a film which was frankly about color caste within black society have been made at all in 1927, considering the discriminating color caste system operating within the black film industry? At that time, the color bar in Hollywood worked in reverse of the ban in the white world. That is, light-skinned blacks could not find work in white motion pictures. Black and white film stock registered too much truth—on the screen racially mixed actors looked white. Conversely, the dark-skinned blacks preferred by white producers were unacceptable in star roles in race films. They were not idealized (i.e., white) enough.[52] In 1927, it would have been impossible to have made a popular vehicle about an exquisitely beautiful black woman who was cut out of elite blue vein society because she was too dark. A black production company could not have cast such a film.[53]

While the monochrome appearance of the actors guarantees that *The Scar of Shame* is about intraracial strife, the casting qualifies this message. Realism, that unacknowledged attempt to make the screen world correspond with popular notions about the real world so that audiences are not confused, betrays the assumptions that inform the ghost film. Louise and Alice may be the same skin shade, but of the two, on a scale of physical characteristics that also matches hair texture and facial features, Alice, the upper-class woman, is more white. Or, *The Scar of Shame argues* that environmental factors determine social standing, but *represents* a society divided in terms of racial characteristics socially read as percentage of white blood; it pleads for community unity, but warns about the consequences of crossing racial as well as class lines.

Conclusion

"The tendency of melodrama to culminate in a happy end is not unopposed. The happy end is often impossible, and, what is more, the audience knows it is impossible," Nowell-Smith says in the context of his discussion of fifties melodrama.[54] Further, he says, melodramatic stylistics, the hysterical "symptoms" referred to earlier, are a by-product of commitment to the "realistic" portrayal of a social problem. Here, the analogy between the text and the unconscious does not help the cause of race and class struggle. What kind of political strategy can be forged if racial antagonism is located in the depths of the unconscious?[55] The stylistics of *The Scar of Shame* speaks that which is unspeakable, but the aesthetic excess lavished in the comparison of Louise and Alice tells most as it declares itself socially rather than pyschoanalytically symptomatic. If an adherence to representing the situation "the way things are" cannot be consistently maintained through to a happy outcome, it is because of political realities outside the text. The opposition to the happy end comes from the preceding events, but also, Nowell-Smith suggests, it comes *from the viewers who know the odds of one outcome over another based on their own expert knowledge of social life.*[56] This comment, one of the few direct references to reception to be found in all of the British melodrama theory from the 1970s, allows that aesthetic excess is not just a matter of auteurist insight or the text's formal properties. A reader is required. Further, as this theory of the imperfect happy ending has been interpreted, the opposition to neat closure has to do with the audience's estimation of the character's chances for happiness in bourgeois society.[57] The epilogue to *The Scar of Shame*, with its union of Alice and Alvin and the uplift benediction delivered by the corrupt lawyer Hathaway, Alice's father and Louise's client, is ill-fitting. The death of Louise is an unsatisfactory condition of uplift and the marriage an unsatisfying solution. In a racist society, these bonds may prove brittle.

What of my original question regarding the position of the viewer in the domestic melodrama produced for black audiences? I do not see that *The Scar of Shame* offers the black "reader" the privileged place that is offered, for instance, in such novels as *Iola Leroy*, which shows black characters as morally superior to whites and mulatto characters choosing black society over white. More needs to be done on this question, and the research is complicated by the fact that so few black-produced films from this period remain. To some degree, we also have to admit that merely seeing images of black life on the screen in a motion picture theater would have been affirming for the 1927 audience. Beyond that, we still need to consider the therapeutic function of melodrama theorized in the feminist analysis of romance fiction, the gothic novel, and soap opera, which shows how readers may be invited to rehearse their own victimization and its reversal within the same plot.[58] The feminist re-evaluation which sees the domestic melodrama as meaningful confrontation rather than escape and avoidance suggests that the end of *The Scar of Shame* could simultaneously fan smoldering resentments and convey hope: "Happy endings do not necessarily ignore issues; rather melodrama places the most profound problems in a moral context and thereby makes them manageable. By insisting on the ultimate triumph of social and personal justice, melodrama is able to provide consolation and hope without denying the social reality that makes goodness and justice so fragile."[59] For black readers, then, domestic melodrama would have made the cruel irrationality of social and political disenfranchisement seem manageable; cast in personal terms, injustice could almost seem to be dealt with finally and absolutely. Ideals of fairness and equality could appear to win out at least temporarily over bigotry, heartlessness, and malevolence. The advantage of this argument is finally the way in which it credits the audiences of *The Scar of Shame* who might have viewed the film in these terms.

With ingenuity the viewer could also glean some political satisfaction in seeing these domestic melodramas produced for black audiences but projected with whites looking over their shoulders. I even imagine the black viewer in 1927 performing a kind of transposition which would go beyond seeing the upper class as effete and impotent. The title of the film identifies a central metaphor and a peculiar inversion. Before the black pride movement, blacks in the United States might have seen color as a stigma either carried by or projected onto themselves, but tied up in some way with interracial conflicts. *The Scar of Shame*, however, carefully shows that Louise is stigmatized as the result of *intraracial* class strife. Like the drop of black blood, Louise's scar, although not visible, still dooms her to a life of dissipation, a strange harkening back to the loose mulatta from earlier antebellum literature. *Intraracial* class distinctions in 1927 might well have been experienced and understood in much the same terms as *interracial* black-white differences. Class difference within black society was then analogous to caste difference between races in the United States, and, therefore, the term *caste* in a metaphoric and slightly exaggerated sense would stand for all such invidious distinctions, and would function characteristically in melodrama to stir emotions and touch raw nerves.

Notes

1. After the advent of sound and the Depression, this product was a mix of genres—comedy, Western, musical, as well as melodrama. In the black turn-about melodramas, black heritage is generously rewarded, as in *By Right of Birth* (1921) in which a California coed is forced to leave school when she finds she is part Negro. She later inherits a fortune in land, and is reunited with a lost parent. *Call of His People* (1922) holds up a light-skinned hero whose success in the business world is certain as long as his race is undetected, but the darker-skinned woman he loves and her brother dramatize the choice he must make between his black birthright and his career. His decision to acknowledge his race is rewarded by a seeming miracle—his employer turns out to be unexpectedly liberal. The best source for these plot descriptions is Harry T. Sampson, *Blacks in Black and White: A Source Book on Black Films* (Metuchen, N.J.: Scarecrow Press, 1977).
2. See, for instance, Janice Radway, *Reading the Romance: Women, Patriarchy, and Popular Literature* (Chapel Hill: University of North Carolina Press, 1985). Jane Tompkins, "Sentimental Power: *Uncle Tom's Cabin* and the Politics of Literary History," in *The New Feminist Criticism: Essays on Women, Literature, and Theory,* ed. Elaine Showalter (New York: Pantheon, 1985), 81–104, analyzes the power position of the weak in abolitionist literature.
3. Exceptions to this pattern of condemnation are Henry Gates, Jr.'s "Introduction" to Harriet E. Wilson, *Our Nig; or, Sketches from the Life of a Free Black* (1859; rpt. New York: Random House, 1983), which he discusses as part sentimental fiction and part slave narrative. Barbara Christian in "The Uses of History: Frances Harper's *Iola Leroy, or Shadows Uplifted,*" *Black Feminist Criticism: Perspectives on Black Women Writers,* ed. Barbara Christian (New York: Pergamon Press, 1985), 165–70, discusses the first novel published by a black woman in the United States as a popular form, but in her earlier *Black Woman Novelists: The Development of a Tradition, 1892–1976* (Westport, Conn.: Greenwood Press, 1980), 43, she criticizes Jessie Fauset because "her plots seldom rise beyond the level of melodrama."
4. Thomas Cripps, in " 'Race Movies' as Voices of the Black Bourgeoisie: *The Scar of Shame,*" in *American History/American Film,* ed. John E. O'Connor and Martin A. Jackson (New York: Ungar, 1979), 49–50, says that the "title cards refer frequently to 'caste' when they must mean 'class'." Cripps called my attention to this article after I had already written my composition. He has a similar explanation for the use of the term *caste,* although this is not central to his argument.
5. Cripps, "Race Movies," 42, 46.
6. David Gordon Nielson, *Black Ethos: Northern Urban Negro Life and Thought* (Westport, Conn.: Greenwood Press, 1977), 76, 51, 53, 61. I am also indebted to Thomas Cripps for this important reference which contains one of the few attempts to construct a sociology of black society in the 1920s.
7. Geoffrey Nowell-Smith, "Minnelli and Melodrama," *Screen 18* (Summer 1977): 115.

8. Martha Vicinus, " 'Helpless and Unfriended': Nineteenth-Century Domestic Melodrama," *New Literary History* 13 (Autumn 1981): 152.
9. Here I am drawing on John Cawelti, *Adventure, Mystery, and Romance: Formula Stories as Art and Popular Culture* (Chicago: University of Chicago Press, 1976), and Peter Brooks, *The Melodramatic Imagination: Balzac, Henry James, Melodrama and the Mode of Excess* (New Haven: Yale University Press, 1976).
10. Vicinus, "Helpless and Unfriended," 141.
11. Technically, William Wells Brown's *Clotel, or The President's Daughter* is the first novel written by a black American (published in England in 1853, it went through several different versions: *Miralda; or, the Beautiful Quadroon* and *Clotelle*; or, *The Colored Heroine: A Tale of the Southern States*). A number of novels with a melodramatic structure written by black women have been republished in Henry Louis Gates, Jr., ed. *The Schomburg Library of Nineteenth-Century Black Women Writers*, Vols. 1–30 (New York: Oxford University Press, 1988). See, for instance, Frances E. W. Harper, *Iola Leroy, or Shadows Uplifted* (1892; rpt. New York: Oxford University Press, 1988); and Pauline E. Hopkins, *Contending Forces* (1900; rpt. New York: Oxford University Press, 1988). Also see Harriet E. Wilson, *Our Nig* (1859; rpt. New York: Random House, 1983); Nella Larsen, *Quicksand* and *Passing*, ed. Deborah E. McDowell (New Brunswick, N.J.: Rutgers University Press, 1986); Jessie Fauset, *Plum Bun* (New York: Fredrick Stokes, 1928); Jessie Fauset, *There Is Confusion* (New York: Boni and Liveright, 1924). Thanks to Kenny Williams for originally leading me to this fiction.
12. Kristin Herzog, *Women, Ethnics, and Exotics: Images of Power in Mid-Nineteenth Century American Fiction* (Knoxville: University of Tennessee Press, 1983), 125; Barbara Christian, "Shadows Uplifted," in *Feminist Criticism and Social Change*, ed. Judith Newton and Deborah Rosenfelt (New York: Methuen, 1985), 190.
13. Jim Pines, *Blacks in Film* (London: Cassell & Collier Macmillan, 1975), 37. See T. E. Perkins, "Rethinking Stereotypes," in *Ideology and Cultural Production*, ed. Michelle Barrett et al. (London: Croom Helm, 1979), 134–59, for an especially rich theory of stereotyping which understands these popular images as like ideology, both true and false.
14. Christian, "Shadows Uplifted," 209.
15. Ibid., 190.
16. In conversation with Ed Hill, Director of the Mary Lou Williams Black Cultural Center, Duke University, Durham, N.C.
17. See my "White Privilege and Looking Relations: Race and Gender in Feminist Film Theory," *Cultural Critique* 4 (Fall 1986), for some discussion of the shifting definitions of black women's sexuality and the implications this has for feminist theory.
18. Christian, "Shadows Uplifted," 192.
19. Research Report, Andrew C. McKay (22 June 1973) in *The Scar of Shame* file, Museum of Modern Art Film Library.
20. Distributed by Black Filmmaker Foundation, 1 Centre St., New York, NY 10007. Also distributed by BFF is Denise Oliver and Warrington Hudlin's *Colour* (1982), 30 min., a contemporary black-produced film dealing with color caste.
21. Thomas Cripps, *Slow Fade to Black: The Negro in American Film, 1900–1942* (New York: Oxford University Press, 1977), 198; Pines, *Blacks in Film*, 38.
22. Other films the Colored Players are known to have produced are *A Prince of His Race* (1926), *Ten Nights in a Bar Room* (1926), and *Children of Fate* (1928).
23. Cripps, "Race Movies," 48–49; Cripps, *Slow Fade to Black*, 195; Thomas Cripps, "Black Films and Film Makers: Movies in the Ghetto, B. P. (Before Poitier)," *Negro Digest* (Feb. 1969): 25; Thomas Cripps, *Black Film as Genre* (Bloomington: Indiana University Press, 1978), 67; Stephen Zito, "The Black Film Experience," *American Film Heritage: Impressions from the American Film Institute Archives*, ed. Tom Shales and Kevin Brownlow et al. (Washington, D.C.: Acropolis Books, 1972), 65.

24. Daniel J. Leab, *From Sambo to Superspade: The Black Experience in Motion Pictures* (Boston: Houghton Mifflin, 1975), 74, quotes this title as: "If only she had turned her mind to the higher things in life." This mistake in the transposition may account for his uncritical acceptance of Norman Kagan's interpretation of Louise as destroyed because of her "base instincts" ("Black American Cinema," *Cinema* 6, no. 2, as quoted in Leab, 3).
25. This diffused villainy is consistent with the historical development of melodrama in which the earlier villainy of the natural disaster or the slimy character was replaced by social institutions. Michael Walker, in "Melodrama and the American Cinema," *Movie* 29/30 (Summer 1982): 35, suggests that as patriarchal laws and class structures took over for the villain, prohibition replaced wickedness:

> The prohibitions and repressions which these generate are in place of the villain's wicked deeds. And such a shift inevitably introduces problems. On the one hand, the ideology endeavours to affirm the laws of patriarchy, the class and gender determined position, as "good," and punishes transgressions; on the other, audience sympathy is usually with the transgressing characters. When the punishments, often directed against female characters, lead to the same sort of sufferings as in traditional melodrama, the ideology is unconsciously functioning as the villain.

26. E. Franklin Fraser, *Black Bourgeoisie* (1955; rpt. New York and London: Collier Macmillian, 1975).
27. Cripps, in "Race Movies," 42, suggests these other indicators of status.
28. Pines, *Blacks in Film*, 38.
28. Nielson, 76, quotes Rayford Logan, "The Hiatus—A Great Negro Middle Class," *Southern Workman* 58 (Dec. 1929): 53, on this scapegoating:

> The lower classes resent being used as a stepping stone to help the lawyer or doctor or teacher to remove himself from their intellectual society, and economic orbit; the upper classes condemn the lower for "making it hard for us." The professional class approach the masses with the typical twentieth century "uplife" psychosis; the masses have the perfectly natural reaction of suspecting ulterior motives on the part of their self-professed friends.

30. Thomas Elsaesser, "Tales of Sound and Fury: Observations on the Family Melodrama," *Monogram* 4 (1973): 3; rpt in *Movies and Methods II*, ed. Bill Nichols (Berkeley: University of California Press, 1985): 167–94.
31. Vicinus, "Helpless and Unfriended," 129.
32. See Julia Lesage, "Artful Rape, Artful Violence," *Jump Cut* 26 (Dec. 1981): 51–55, for an analysis of rape and incest in *Broken Blossoms*.
33. Walker, "Melodrama and the American Cinema," 8.
34. "Griffith's Family Discourse: Griffith and Freud," *Quarterly Review of Film Studies* 6 (Winter 1981): 79.
35. Cripps, in "Race Movies," 51, attributes this action to Louise. Where my analysis differs significantly from his is in the interpretation of Louise.
36. *After Freedom: A Cultural Study in the Deep South* (New York: Viking Press, 1939), 334–35.
37. See Vincent Jubilee, "In the Shadow of Harlem," *The Pennsylvania Gazette* 79 (May 1981): 37–40, for one of the few descriptions of the Black Opals, Philadelphia's literary answer to the Harlem Renaissance.
38. Joseph Wilson, *Sketches of Higher Class of Colored Society in Philadelphia* (Philadelphia: Merrihew and Thompson, 1841), 66–67.
39. W. E. Burghardt Du Bois, *The Philadelphia Negro: A Social Study* (1899; rpt. New York: Schocken, 1967), 317, 177.
40. John Dollard, *Caste and Class in a Southern Town*, revised ed. (Garden City, N.Y.: Doubleday, 1949), 449, 62.

41. Dollard, 63, 74; see also W. Lloyd Warner, "American Caste and Class," *American Journal of Sociology* 22, no. 2 (1936): 234–37, for the first scholarly treatment of caste in the United States which established the usage in American sociology.
42. Joseph R. Washington, *Marriage in Black and White* (Boston: Beacon Press, 1970), 99, 101, 102.
43. Sterling Brown, in *The Negro in American Fiction* (Washington, D.C.: The Association in Negro Folk Education, 1937), 149, comments on this in what remains one of the most insightful discussions of the representation of color and class in black literature.
44. Charles S. Johnson *Growing Up in the Black Belt: Negro Youth in the Rural South* (Washington, D.C.: American Council on Education, 1941), 274.
45. Washington, *Marriage*, 105.
46. Nowell-Smith, "Minnelli and Melodrama," 118, describes this subversive opportunity which melodrama provides: "The importance of melodrama (at least in the versions of it that are due to Ophuls, Minnelli, Sirk) lies precisely in its ideological failure. Because it cannot accommodate its problems, either in a real present or in an ideal future, but lays them open in their shameless contradictoriness, it opens a space which most Hollywood forms have studiously closed off."
47. Elsaesser, "Tales of Sound and Fury," 6.
48. The phrase is Sirk's, as quoted in Paul Willeman, "Distanciation and Douglas Sirk," *Douglas Sirk*, ed. Laura Mulvey and Jon Halliday (Edinburgh Film Festival, 1972), 26. For one of the most important attempts to theorize melodrama, cinema aesthetics, and black suffering in a discussion of the 1959 version of *Imitation of Life*, see Richard Dyer, "LANA: Four Films of Lana Turner," *Movie* 25 (Winter 1977–78): 40–52.
49. Jane Feuer, in "Melodrama, Serial Form and Television Today," *Screen* 25 (Jan.–Feb. 1984): 6, makes this point about authorship in her discussion of British melodrama theory, along with the point that another problem with the "space" theory is that the other discourse can only be read by "an elite audience already committed to subversive ideas."
50. Elsaesser, "Tales of Sound and Fury," 2–3.
51. Terry Eagleton, *Criticism and Ideology* (London: Verso, 1978), 43.
52. Ralph Matthews, "Too Light for the Movies," *The Afro-American Week*, 25 March 1933; Ray Buford, "Color in Hollywood," Los Angeles, 21 December 1934 (clippings file, Schomberg Center for Research in Black Culture, New York Public Library).
53. The Hollywood film which is most notorious for using skin color variation to create types is *Carmen Jones*, and the indictment of it is James Baldwin, "*Carmen Jones*: The Dark Is Light Enough," in *Notes of a Native Son* (New York: Dial Press, 1964), 50–51.
54. Nowell-Smith, "Minnelli and Melodrama," 117.
55. Christine Gledhill, in "Recent Developments in Feminist Criticism: *Quarterly Review of Film Studies* 3 (Fall 1978), 483, makes a similar point. Reprinted in Mary Ann Doane, Patricia Mellencamp, and Linda Williams, eds., *Re-Vision: Essays in Feminist Film Criticism* (Frederick, Md.: University Publications of America, 1984), 18–45.
56. Nowell-Smith, "Minnelli and Melodrama," 117.
57. Christopher Orr, in "Closure and Containment: Marylee Hadley in *Written on the Wind*," *Wide Angle* 4, no. 2 (1980): 28–35, considers Marylee's future; and Feuer, "Melodrama, Serial Form," 12, in reference to the same scene, suggets that the audience may have some concern about Mitch and Lucy's future.
58. See Tania Modleski, *Loving with a Vengeance: Mass-Produced Fantasies for Women* (New York: Methuen, 1984).
59. Vicinus, "Helpless and Unfriended," 132.

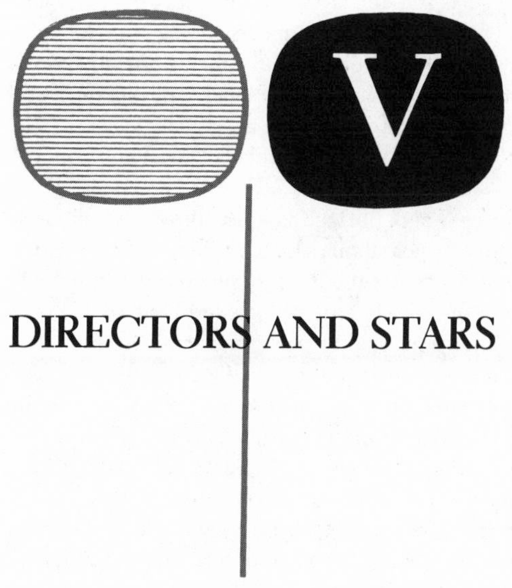

V DIRECTORS AND STARS

If we now regard cinema as a serious object of study, it is due in part to the work of those critics who developed what came to be known as the "politique des auteurs." Rescuing the popular cinema from neglect or impressionism, the French New Wave critics and the American critic Andrew Sarris examined the work of certain European and American filmmakers with an eye to locating thematic, personal, and stylistic preoccupations that run through the corpus of a director's works. The elevation, however, of the auteur was accomplished often at the expense of other contributions to the production of the film such as the role of the studio, the writers, the stars, the camerapersons, genre, and social history. As in literary criticism, the tendency was to create a sense of the legitimacy of certain filmmakers and hence the cinema by creating a canon closely resembling the high cultural canon. The essays in this section address, and in some instances challenge, the determining role of directors and stars in melodrama.

A. Nicholas Vardac explores the techniques D. W. Griffith employed to enhance his melodramas, making them more sentimental and romantic. Griffith's dominant technique was to fuse the romance elements in the narrative with more realistic photography in the presentation of character. Through his uses of lighting, his employment of the close-up, cross-cutting, a more restrained form of acting, the dependence on historical narratives, and the dependence on spectacle involving large casts, Griffith enhanced the romance elements of the melodrama, freeing them from the rigid conventions of his precursors.

Characteristic of auteur analysis, Alan Casty's essay discusses the distinct style of

D. W. Griffith's film which Casty describes as the convergence of the personal and the cultural. Unlike the European silent spectacles, Griffith infused his films with action and feeling. Casty attributes Griffith's success to the favorable conditions of production under which the films were made as well as to Griffith's understanding of melodrama which owed much, as Sergei Eisenstein had indicated, to nineteenth- and early-twentieth-century melodrama and to the novel. But Griffith's real contribution lay in his transformation of the traditional techniques of melodrama through his experimentation with cinematic techniques that were fused with his particular social and political vision.

John Belton's discussion of the films of Frank Borzage addresses the contributions of Borzage to the development of cinematic melodrama. Like Griffith, Borzage developed a style that added depth to character, eschewing the two-dimensional treatments of traditional melodrama. The characters in Borzage's works are charged with an intensity of feeling that endows the films with vitality and immediacy. But Borzage's melodramas differ from Griffith's in their emphasis on spirituality, in his strategies for transcending the physical details of the narrative. In his disregard for physical space, in his treatment of objects as metaphors, in his relegation of economic and political issues to the background, and in his foregrounding of spiritual and moral relationships, Borzage's films avoid the harsh extremes of Manicheanism so characteristic of much melodrama. Belton finds that in his transmutation of the physical world to the spiritual, Borzage produces a broader and more accepting sense of relationships and conflict than conventional melodrama.

Probably Douglas Sirk is the most discussed of all the melodrama directors. The attention that his work has received can be traced to the convergence of several factors in film study: auteur study, critical work on genre, feminist theory, and reevaluations of popular culture. With the assistance of auteur theory, it was possible to identify in Sirk's melodramas a clearly-marked personal style and thematics that speaks to the disaffections and contradictions of American society. The films, addressed to 1950s' audiences at a time when the political commitments of the 1930s and the World War II era had receded, when the retreat from the public sphere into the domestic was most pronounced, and when the Cold War exploited anxieties over nuclear holocaust and resurrected fears of totalitarianism, are a rich source for understanding how the domestic arena is not a neutral zone but a political battleground. Auteur study produced a reexamination of melodrama, redeeeming the genre from charges of banality, sentimentality, and escapism through identifying the broad cultural basis of its representations. Through stylistic analysis, it was possible to locate where melodramatic texts addressed psychic and social issues. It became clear that melodramas were not mere legitimations of the status quo. As with other genres, it became possible to read the narratives against the grain, to locate where they subvert dominant values. In particular, through an analysis of Sirks' uses of lighting, *mise-en-scene*, music, color, and other distanciation strategies, the Sirkian irony became apparent. And, as feminists were quick to recognize, Sirk's films brought to the surface contradictions particularly relating to women's position in the family, contradictions which are at the center of bourgeois family life.

Christopher Orr's essay on Sirk's film, *Written on the Wind*, addresses the ways in which the narrative functions to rupture conventional melodramatic expectations. Orr suggests that the usual description of the Sirkian style as residing in the opposition between the manifest content of the film and the style that undercuts it is not appropriate to this film where style and content fuse in the portrait of the oppressive nature of the Hadley wealth and its corrosiveness. Orr finds that the figure of Marylee Hadley is the locus of the excesses that the film cannot contain and that comment on the sexual and class conflict. Her sexuality signifies the decadence of affluence but also the legitimacy of sexual desire. She exposes the impotence of the men—Mitch, Kyle, and her father—but the text does not discipline her. The pleasure of the happy ending with the coming together of Mitch and Lucy is called into question, if not negated, by the film's stylistics as well as by the treatment of Marylee. The image of the closing of the gates behind the couple as if to lock them out, the drabness of the couple's costumes, and the image of Marylee alone under the picture of her dead father as she cradles the model of the oil derrick undercuts any pleasure that the spectator might anticipate at the usual romantic coupling.

Melodrama is alive, if not well, in the historical melodramas of two recent filmmakers, Francis Ford Coppola and Michael Cimino. Naomi Greene likens their films to Verdi's operas which allegorize history. Films like *The Deerhunter, Godfather I* and *II*, and *Heaven's Gate* are similarly preoccupied with history and spectacle. The films are also produced at a time of national crisis. The American films differ from the Verdi operas and films of Lucchino Visconti in their less analytic, more affective, and spectacular mode of presentation. Unlike earlier Hollywood melodramas, spectacle in the contemporary melodramas overwhelms narrative. Greene regards the overweighting of spectacle and the fracturing of narrative structures as having ideological significance, representing a loss of faith in meaningful action. The emphasis on the grotesque creates a climate in which violence and pessimism triumph. The juxtaposition of past and present only reinforces a sense of lament for a world that is gone. In this context, melodrama does not embody resistance to or subversion of dominant values. Greene argues that these films herald the death of melodrama.

Christine Saxton's essay calls into question the primacy accorded the director as constituted through auteur analysis. Rather than regarding the auteur solely in personal terms, she suggests that the position of auteur is a collective one which encompasses a number of practices and individuals including the spectator. Instead of asking "who is an author," she askes "what is an author" and attempts to orchestrate the various functions of authorship. Using Sirk's *Written on the Wind* as a case study, she explores the multiple determinants on the text in an effort to counteract the readings of Sirk that derive from conventional auteur analysis.

While the role of the director has been amply discussed and debated in the study of cinema, the role of the star has not. Numerous books are written regularly on the Hollywood stars, mainly from the point of view of gratifying voyeurism or, in a more scholarly vein, from a sociological perspective in terms of the star's role in society. The works of some feminist critics such as Molly Haskell have sought to link the images of particular stars with the positioning of women in society. Not until recently has there been any attempt to account systematically for the star's contributions, presence, and impact on the films themselves. The concerns with directors, themes, genres, social history, and cinema history have not addressed the contributions of the star phenomenon to cinematic representation.

In his article on Lana Turner, Richard Dyer describes how the self-conscious element of her being manufactured as a glamorous star image is increasingly integral to the roles she played. Rather than concealing this aspect of construction, the films exploit it. Moreover, the roles she played bear some relation to the conflicts in her life which were highly publicized. The publicity, rather than having an adverse effect on her career, only added a deeper dimension to the image of a woman who was "born to be bad" not through malevolence but through impulsiveness. In her role of Cora in *The Postman Always Rings Twice*, the public and the private aspects of her image merged as she played a woman who is the victim of impulse and whose impulses lead her and others to destruction. By the time she did *The Bad and the Beautiful*, the ordinariness with which she had been associated was replaced by the image of glamorousness. When she made Sirk's *Imitation of Life*, her troubled private life was available for the world to experience. The role she plays in the film fuses her public and cinematic images. She is always onstage, and her acting in the film is appropriate to the title, an imitation of life in its posturing, its detachment from the other characters to the point of noninteraction with her acting partners. The only moment of authenticity in her presentation comes at the end but in an image of total collapse.

Jean-Loup Bourget analyzes Joan Crawford's contributions to the women's picture. The styles of actresses such as Joan Crawford, Bette Davis, Gene Tierney, Barbara Stanwyck, and Lana Turner share responsibility for having initiated the women's film and are an integral part of the genre's signifying system. Bourget comments on how Bette Davis's nervous acting becomes a major factor in producing pathos. In the case of Joan Crowford, it is her extreme stylization. While Davis's persona is based on strength which ironically becomes the means of her destruction, Crawford's is based on weakness. Bourget describes the tension in the Crawford characters between simplicity and sophistication. Unlike Jane Wyman, who is often used to represent a harmony between nature and culture, Crawford's fleeting contact with nature is problematic in most of her films. The male characters against whom she is pitted are the *Wildermann* who is identified with nature and the flouting of social conventions and the upper-class villain who is sophisticated. The *Wildermann* brings out her sophistication, the upper-class villain her simplicity. Bourget also identifies two styles in Crawford's films. The films she made with Frank Borzage stress lyricism and sentiment, while those she made with Michael Curtiz and David Miller are identified with a sophisticated milieu. Borget's and Dyer's studies chart directions for future work on stars' contributions to the development of the language and social implications of melodramatic representation.

Realism and Romance: D. W. Griffith

A. NICHOLAS VARDAC

D. W. Griffith entered motion pictures in 1907. He began as author and actor, writing a number of scripts this first year and appearing in Porter's *Rescued from an Eagle's Nest* (Edison, 1907). Born in the South in 1880, he was openly exposed from childhood to its romanticism and sentimentality. "The sentimental bias implanted in Griffith by his father (a former Confederate colonel) was reinforced by the boy's love of poetry in the Victorian manner."[1] He became an actor in the provincial theatre of the South, playing in residence or touring with the sentimental and sensational melodramas of the period. He took this theatre seriously enough to plan his career as playwright in its manner, and had gained some recognition for his play, *A Fool and a Girl*, presented in Washington and Baltimore in 1907. Having spent his conditioning years in close and constant contact with this romantic theatre, Griffith suddenly found himself in the position of writer, actor, and director—a creative artist in the most realistic art medium ever known. He was reluctant at first to jeopardize his standing in the legitimate theatre, but he gradually recognized that the screen might enable him to achieve in a much more realistic manner the same romanticized concepts with which he had been involved on the stage. He accepted his first directoral assignment with the Biograph Company in 1908.

Productional conditions were still poor at this time. Progress since Porter's *Train Robbery* was negligible. *The Snow-man*, produced at about the time of Griffith's entry into motion pictures, is indicative of the methods in use. Indoor photography had not become practical until 1906. The delay in productional progress was partly due to the

---

A. Nicholas Vardac, "Realism and Romance: D. W. Griffith," from *Stage to Screen* (Cambridge: Harvard University Press, 1949). Reprinted by permission of the author.

furious strife over patent rights in which the industry was embroiled from 1897 to 1908. This condition was eliminated on January 1, 1909, shortly after Griffith's debut as a director. On this date the Motion Pictures Patents Company was formed by the seven American manufacturers, Edison, Biograph, Vitagraph, Lubin, Kalem, Essanay, and Selig; the two French firms of Pathé and Méliès; and finally the distributor, Kleine. This organization, which became known as the "trust," pooled all patent claims and agreed to issue no further licenses, thus removing the padlocks from the cameras and paving the way for progress on a peaceable basis. The industry assumed the cloak of dignity and respectability.

This legal reorganization called for productional and aesthetic reforms. Frank Woods, an early film critic, "now set about to criticize the pictures with the same seriousness with which he would have criticized the theater. He bought books about Indians and let the producers know there was a difference between the Hopi and the Apache and the Navajo."[2] Griffith was forced into high standards of productional realism, for early screen criticism followed stage patterns.

His first release, *The Adventures of Dolly* (Biograph, July 14, 1908), borrowed a melodramatic subject previously treated by Porter in *Stolen by Gypsies* and used a similar editorial structure. It was an outdoor film, hence pictorially realistic. To this realism Griffith added his own romantic touch. In the Porter film, Dolly had been accidentally found and recognized by her former nurse years after her kidnaping, and then simply rescued from the gypsies by the police. But in the Griffith picture, the gypsies hid her

> in a water cask, put it on their wagon and sped away. As they pass over a stream, the cask falls off the wagon and into the water where it is carried by a strong current downstream, over a waterfall, through seething rapids, finally to enter the quiet cove of the first scene. Fishing boys hearing strange sounds from the cask break it open and discover Dolly. Soon she is safe in the arms of her overjoyed papa and mama.[3]

To the hard-edged melodrama of Porter, Griffith began by adding a fuller pictorial development, both sentimental and romantic.

With such romantic material he began to refine Porter's editorial approach with techniques directed toward a more thorough realism. In his filming of *For Love of Gold*, from Jack London's romantic melodrama, *Just Meat*, he made progress in the realistic presentation of character. Previous to this, the usual method for revealing the mental reaction of a character had been with a double-exposure "dream balloon" flashed above his head. Griffith eliminated this conventional technique by cutting down the editorial unit from a full scene "take" to a single "shot." The climactic scene in this picture, showing two thieves dividing their latest plunder, developed out of the fear of each that the other suspected a double-cross. Suspense and drama arose over which would first succeed in getting rid of the other, and how. This was, in its small way, the beginning of a long line of psychological thrillers, since the thieves managed to poison each other's coffee. Dramatic climax was developed through the use of a single "shot" within the scene "take." Instead of playing the entire scene before a stationary camera, with action proceeding as if on a stage, both actors visible at once, and with "dream balloons" coming to the aid of their pantomime, Griffith shifted his camera to shoot one or the other as the dramatic focus demanded. Where whole scenes had been the previous editorial unit, single shots were used here. The result was greater realism in the presentation of character and a more fluid cinematic continuity.

This use of the single shot as editorial unit had a still further effect. By eliminating all distractive elements at the moment when the reaction of the individual character became the significant dramatic value, it reduced the necessity for exaggerated acting and overplaying. Restraint in acting, hence greater realism of character, became possible.

With this start toward a more realistic treatment of character and toward a smoother and more articulate editorial pattern, Griffith sought next to improve the realism of the photography itself through an aesthetic approach to lighting. In *Edgar Allan Poe* (Biograph, 1909), he achieved a three-dimensional quality, therefore greater realism in photography, with the use of light and shade. It is of interest, too, that this new photographic realism was again coupled with a subject straight from the heart of nineteenth-century romance, dealing, as it did, with Poe's *The Raven* and incidents in the poet's baroque and abnormal life. The need for this realism in photography led Griffith into further successful experiments with lighting. In *A Drunkard's Reformation* (Biograph, 1909), he photographed fire burning in a fireplace in a darkened room. The weird, grotesque effect, with its ephemeral shadows and fugitive figures, created a startling and realistic illusion on the screen. In *Pippa Passes* (Biograph, 1909), he discarded the usual editorial form of melodrama and in a simple, direct story leaned heavily upon the pictorial appeal of his realistic lighting. Morning, Noon, Evening, and Night, the four parts of the film, were realistically filmed. And while Browning was the most rarified dramatic stuff up to date, it was reported that "the adventurous producers who inaugurated these expensive departures from cheap melodrama are being overwhelmed by offers from renting agents."[4] The appeal of simple pictures realistically presented by means of the new developments in film lighting equaled the box-office draw of melodrama.

This advance in realistic photography was followed by further progress in the articulation of motion-picture syntax and in realistic character portrayal. A one-reel version of *Enoch Arden*, rechristened *After Many Years* (Biograph, 1908), sacrificed both melodramatic structure and the usual chase sequence. Much of its success came out of the editorial technique. It was the first film to use the "close-up" to reveal more realistically than could the full shot what was going on in the minds of the characters. The visualization of a state of mind arose out of the manner in which the close-up was worked into the fabric of the film. For instance, from a close-up of Annie brooding in her seaside cottage over the fate of her long-departed Enoch the camera dissolves to a shot of Enoch shipwrecked on the desert island. The juxtaposition of these two strips of film suggested to the spectator a psychic relationship between the two which, with its reduction of spatial limitations, was not only a marvel of pictorial realism but marked the beginnings of subjective revelation of character in the cinema.

The Lonely Villa (Biograph, 1909) indicated further advance in the realism of the pictorial medium with a cross-cutting technique which left little to the imagination of the audience. A husband leaves wife and children alone in their remote villa to drive twenty miles away to fetch his mother. Robbers break into the villa. The husband's car breaks down. He calls his wife on the telephone just in time to hear her terrified cries before the wires are cut. Between these parallel lines of action a cross-cutting techinque, new in its rapidity and dynamic development, was employed. Both lines of action were trasferred to the screen exactly as they were progressing. The visual impact of the rapid-fire succession of "takes" developed a dynamic crescrendo of suspense which was relieved only at the breaking point by the husband's last-minute arrival to effect a rescue. This cross-cutting technique was repeated in *The Lonedale Operator* (Biograph, 1911), heightening the melodramatic values through facile and realistic pictorial presentation and thus perfecting the technique employed many years before in the melodrama of the stage.

Griffith worked continually to increase graphic realism. It seems that every refinement in editorial technique was associated with this desire. In *Ramona* (Biograph, 1910), he combined the long shot with the full shot and the close-up. This of itself marked progress toward a fluid cinematic structure. But at the same time the underlying significance of this development is that each type of shot was devoted to that special purpose which seemed "right" or real in view of the dramatic value of the particular scene being filmed. The vantage point of the camera was changed in the same way that an ideal spectator, wishing to gain a real view of the action without being distracted, would change his position. The technique of photography joins here with that of editing to cast off elements of conventionality and to attain a truer realism. Action was now shown as an ideal spectator would wish to see it had he actually been present.

With the use of the full shot, more restrained acting had become possible than in the early filming of a full scene before a static camera. Similarly, the close-up allowed for more realistic acting than did the full shot. In *The New York Hat* (Biograph, 1912), this refinement in the articulation of the camera made possible a break away from the broad, stereotyped, robust, and artificial pantomime of the earlier films.

Griffith ever sought new methods and fresh areas. The Biograph Company, on the other hand, was more conservative. Experiments, innovations, and improvements were welcomed as long as they were successful and as long as they remained in the areas of editorial technique and camera articulation, for here no productional investment was necessary. Longer films, with costly production, were as yet unproved and here Biograph opposed the genius of Griffith. He succeeded, despite opposition from the company officials, in refilming *Enoch Arden* in two reels in 1911. He defied the policy of Biograph in this case on the basis of a film which relied as much on the spectacle appeal of California backgrounds as upon the popularity of a well-known stage subject.

It was becoming increasingly difficult to add new and more realistic refinements to the editorial structure established by Porter. Griffith began to look in new directions. Editorial and photographic advancements had been achieved; productional expansion appeared to be the next logical step. His first attempt at a longer film had been stymied by the conservative Biograph policy, which forced a single-reel release of the two-reel version of *Enoch Arden*. Consequently, his next attempt at a spectacle film, *The Battle* (Biograph, 1911), retained the single-reel form but involved a larger pictorial conception, employing hundreds of soldiers fighting in trenches, on the run, on the march, suggesting what was later to be fully developed in *The Birth of a Nation*. Large-scale spectacle became a part of the fabric of the melodramatic photoplay.

The psychology of a bevy of village lovers is conveyed in a lively sweethearting dance. Then the boy and his comrades go forth to war. The lines pass between hand-waving crowds of friends from the entire neighborhood. These friends give the sense of patriotism in mass. Then as the consequence of this feeling, as the special agents to express it, the soldiers are in battle. By the fortunes of war the onset is unexpectedly near to the house where once was the dance.

The boy is at first a coward. He enters the old familiar door. He appeals to the girl to hide him, and for the time breaks her heart. He goes forth a fugitive not only from battle, but from her terrible girlish anger. But later he rallies. He brings a train of powder wagons through fires built in his path by the enemy's scouts. He loses every one of his men, and all but the last wagon, which he drives himself. His return with that ammunition saves the hard-fought day.

And through all this, glimpses of the battle are given with a splendor that only Griffith has attained.[5]

This combination of spectacle and melodrama was so successful, and the treatment in this short picture so popular, that even after the feature-length film has been established, *The Battle* was reissued June 11, 1915, four years after its original production.

In 1912 the second significant American spectacle film and the first to recognize the challenge of current European spectacles was produced. This was Griffith's *The Massacre* (Biograph, 1912). Again the enlargement of the scope of film melodrama was attained through the addition of spectacle. Again, a romanticized historical subject was reproduced with realism. Custer's last stand came to life. On the West Coast, far from the dingy offices of Eastern film magnates, cries for budget reduction fell unheard. Hundreds of cavalrymen and scores upon scores of Indians were unleased. Costumes and sets reached a new high for lavishness in American films. But the release came too late, for new European spectacles of a more magnificent scale had already reached American exhibitors and Griffith's *Massacre* passed unnoticed in the crowd.

Within the single-reel form Griffith had aimed, first of all, at heightening the realism of the camera, of acting, and of the production; secondly, toward a refinement and articulation of the melodramatic cinematic syntax originally demonstrated by Porter; and thirdly, at an enlargement of the pictorial and productional conception of the film through the addition of spectacle. Throughout the last years of this single-reel development, the influence of the foreign film was being felt and it must have reached Griffith, for, either under its stimulus or in his own creative spontaneity, he had begun to offer a certain competition to European importations. A steadily increasing stream of historical spectacles shows an early recognition of the cinematic possibilities of this form. *The Slave* (Biograph, 1909) was a melodrama set in Roman times, supported by "a series of most beautiful pictures of the Romanesque type."[6] In the following week came *The Mended Lute*, with a great deal of authentic spectacle

based on the life and customs of the American aboriginals. . . . Much thought and time were given the many details, and we may claim that as to costumes, manners and modes of living, it is more than reasonably accurate, these details having been supervised by an expert. . . . The subject as a whole is a combina-

> tion of poetical romance and dramatic intensity, the canoe chase being the most picturesque and thrilling ever shown.[7]

The addition of historical spectacle to melodrama was consciously taking place in a large body of the Biograph output. *The Death Disc* (1909) exploited historical costumes of the Cromwellian period; *The Call to Arms* (1910) was a story of the Middle Ages with picturesque period paraphernalia and background; *Wilful Peggy*, of the early days in Ireland; *The Oath and the Man*, of the French Revolution; *Rose o' Salem Town*, of Puritan witchcraft; *Heartbeats of Long Ago*, of fourteenth-century Italy; *The Spanish Gypsies*, of sunny Andalusia, and so on. A full series of Spanish and Mexican films was produced. Browning's *A Blot on the 'Scutcheon* was produced with complete costumes in 1912. *Lena and the Geese* (1912) went to old Holland for its locale. Two reels were devoted to *A Pueblo Legend* (1912), authentically spectacular and filmed on location in Old Pueblo of Isleta, New Mexico. Costume plates and shields, weapons and accessories were loaned by the Museum of Indian Antiques at Albuquerque.[8] The success of these authentic historical spectacles on the screen demonstrates the continuation by the film of the approach and the manner of the nineteenth-century stage.

Griffith's romanticism was as evident in his choice of players as in his subject matter. Lewis Jacobs has observed that "all his heroines—Mary Pickford, Mae Marsh, Lillian Gish, Blanche Sweet—were, at least in Griffith's eye, the pale, helpless, delicate, slim-bodied heroines of the nineteenth century English poets."[9] It was this same romantic bias which, when added to the stimulus supplied by the success of lavish European spectacles, suggested the subject for an early attempt at supremacy in the field of the spectacle film.

Working in comparative secrecy in the town of Chatsworth, far from the Los Angeles film colony, Griffith began production in 1912 of a Biblical spectacle. In the following year he completed *Judith of Bethulia*, the first American four-reel film designed for feature-length exhibition. The picture was not released until 1914, and in the interim Griffith's association with Biograph had terminated. His reckless extravagance in this production led the company to request his resignation as director. The balm of appointment as producer-adviser in the productions of newer directors was insufficient to prevent his complete separation from Biograph and his immediate entrance into the Majestic-Reliance Company.

Judith of Bethulia borrowed its material from the scriptural spectacle of the same name by Thomas Bailey Aldrich, currently successful upon the stage. Needless to say, the stage production, impeded by physical limitations, was dwarfed by Griffith's screen version. An entire army of Assyrians, authentically garbed and marshaled in the manner of the period, was thrown against the city walls. The production involved feats of engineering.

> Between two mountains was the location chosen for the great wall against which Holofernes hurls his cohorts in vain attacks. Eighteen hundred feet long, and broad enough to permit of the defenders being massed upon it, the wall rose slowly until it was a giant's causeway connecting the crags on either side. Within, a city sprang up, in whose streets take place some of the most thrilling scenes in the picture. Beyond it, in the valley, was pitched the great armed camp

> of the Assyrians. In the chieftains' tent alone were hangings and rugs costing thousands of dollars.[10]

This was the most expensive production Biograph had yet attempted. Great numbers, more than one thousand people and about three hundred horsemen, were marshaled. The monstrous scale of the conception did not interfere with the development of details and authentic properties.

> The following were built expressly for the production: a replica of the ancient city of Bethulia; a faithful reproduction of the ancient army camps embodying all their barbaric dances; chariots, battering rams, scaling ladders, archer towers, and other special war paraphernalia of the period.
>
> The following spectacular effects: the storming of the walls of the city of Bethulia; the hand-to-hand conflicts; the death-defying chariot charges at breakneck speed; the rearing and plunging horses infuriated by the din of battle; the wonderful camp of the terrible Holofernes, equipped with rugs from the Far East; the dancing girls in their exhibition of the exquisite and peculiar dances of the period, the routing of the command of the terrible Holofernes, and the destruction of the camp by fire.[11]

Vachel Lindsay, in his excellent description of this film, has pointed out that the structure of this spectacle employed an editorial form utilizing four sorts of scenes. There were scenes showing (1) the particular history of Judith and Holofernes; (2) the wooing of Naomi by Nathan; (3) the streets of Bethulia massed with the people in their sluggish mass movement; and finally, (4) scenes of the assault, with camp and battle scenes interpolated, to unify the continuity.[12] Spectacle had, at the cost of $32,000,[13] assumed the salient position and melodrama existed only as a means for exploiting spectacle. And it was through editorial patterns demonstrated in the melodrama that the preceding four types of scenes were integrated. The story of Judith and Holofernes and the courtship of Nathan and Naomi were subsidiary to the spectacle and derived their dramatic stature and significance from the spectacle. Nathan and Naomi, for instance, "are seen among the reapers outside the city or at the well near the wall, or on the streets of the ancient town. They are generally doing the things the crowd behind them is doing, meanwhile evolving their own little heart affair."[14] This heart affair of two black and white figures flickering across the screen gained its dramatic power through editorial association with the huge, spectacular environment and with the masses whose mob mind could be visually dramatized upon the screen. Naomi and Nathan transcended the personality of mortals. Their own little personal drama, woven into the vast tapestry of the spectacle, gained thereby an emotional significance which far exceeded the possibilities of simple chase melodrama. The limitations of conventionalized character portrayal were removed by an editorial pattern involving elements of spectacle. When Naomi is rescued by her sweetheart, Nathan, this "act is taken by the audience as a type of the setting free of all the captives."[15] Judith similarly derives her stature from Bethulia, and Holofernes achieves his dramatic identity as the personification of the Assyrian army, Thus, through a clever editorial form, the dramatic as well as the pictorial scale of the cinema was extended. Spectacle values had become absolutely necessary to the development of the silent motion picture. And it was a recognition of these values that had prompted Griffith's entrance into the feature film with *Judith of Bethulia*.

With the arrival of the feature film came improvement in the use of musical accompaniment. Stage melodrama and early screen melodrama had, of course, both used musical accompaniment to the action. It had been stereotyped, direct, and bold in its intention, oftentimes the impromptu creation of the pianist or organist bred to the work. For *Judith*, however, a complete musical accompaniment with specific predetermined cues was provided.

> Open with *Maritana* (Wallace) until Judith in Prayer:
> Then *The Rosary* (Nevin) until she leaves woman with child:
> Then *Maritana* until "The Army":
> Then *William Tell* (Rossini) the last movement. Play this to end of reel:
> Then *Pique Dame*, overture (Suppe) all through:
> Then *Poet and Peasant*, overture (Suppe) until "Water and Food Famine":
> Then *Simple Aven* (Thome) until "The King":
> Then *Peer Gynt*—Suite II, opus 55 (Grieg) until Judith has vision:
> Then *Woodland Sketches I & II* (MacDowell) until she dons fine clothes:
> Then *Lament of Roses* (Sonnakolb) until "The King":
> Then *Peter Gynt*—Suite II, opus 55 (Grieg) until end of reel.[16]

Music, an integral part of nineteenth-century melodrama and spectacle, was utilized here by the screen in the same fashion. The quality of the music, obviously enough, was calculated in its naïve way to heighten the intensity of the scene.

Through the work of D. W. Griffith in the period from 1908 to 1913, motion pictures progressed from single-reel storyettes and topical episodes to successful experiment with the feature-length spectacle film. Griffith had come to the films with a rich background of Victorian romanticism both in the theatre and in his general approach to life. Without sacrificing any of his strong romantic bias, he developed the realistic capacities of this medium to serve in the exploitation of his romantic conceptions. Whatever progress Griffith made in the development of a cinematic syntax had always been motivated by his quest for a greater and more fluid screen realism, whether for character portrayal, scenic production, or narrative development. In this way, he pioneered in the evolution of a technique for this new art form, which was originally derived from the forms of the nineteenth-century stage but which succeeded in eliminating the restrictions and conventions with which this stage had been fettered.

In the search for greater realism Griffith carried this editorial development to a point beyond which improvement was difficult. And at about this time the influence of foreign spectacle films was being felt in this country. Responding to these two coincidental conditions, Griffith made his first attempt at a feature-length film on the basis of a spectacular production with *Judith of Bethulia*. He took his material directly from the stage and surpassed the stage in its production. In this way, presenting a romanticized historical spectacle in an authentic and lavish fashion within the melodramatic cinematic structure, Griffith produced the first American four-reel photoplay. He appears, then, as the strongest and most successful of the early screen continuators of nineteenth-century melodrama and spectacle, of realism and romance.

Notes

1. Louis Jacobs, *Rise of the American Film A Critical History* (New York: Harcourt Brace and Company, 1939), p. 96.
2. Linda A. Griffith, *When the Movies Were Young*, (New York: E.P. Dutton and Co., 1925), p. 65.
3. *Biograph Catalogue*, Bulletin 151 (July 14, 1908), film 3454.
4. *New York Times*, October 10, 1909.
5. N. Vachel Lindsay, *Art of the Moving Picture*, (New York: Macmillan, 1943), pp. 43–44.
6. *Biograph Catalogue*, Bulletin 261 (July 29, 1909), film 3598.
7. *Ibid.*, Bulletin 263 (August 5, 1909), film 3601.
8. *Ibid.*, *Bulletin* (August 29, 1912), film 3994.
9. Jacobs, *Rose of the American film*, p. 97.
10. *The Biograph Weekly*, vol. I, no. 2 (New York, September 12, 1914), p. 11.
11. From a contemporary review (unidentified) quoted in Lindsay, *Art of the Moving Picture*, p. 59.
12. Lindsay, *Art of the Moving Picture*, p. 60.
13. Griffith, *When Movies Were Young*, p. 225.
14. Lindsay, *Art of the Moving Picture*, p. 62.
15. *Ibid.*, p. 64.
16. Clarence E. Sinn, "Music for Pictures," *Motion Picture World*, vol. XX, no. 1 (April 4, 1914), p. 50.

21

The Films of D. W. Griffith: A Style for the Times

ALAN CASTY

The title itself had an almost uncanny aptness. For David Wark Griffith's first full-length feature, *The Birth of a Nation*, was in many important ways the true birth of an art. It not only brought together for the first time all that was being discovered about the essential characteristics of the motion picture; it fused these in a distinct style, a style that reflected both a man and his times, so deeply, perhaps even excessively, was Griffith attuned to the cultural and social assumptions of the period and the moral and aesthetic expectations of its audiences. Since it is the first fully wrought style in the medium, it is especially useful in tracing the process that determines style: the selection, extension, and combination of possible elements and structures, the choice of subjects, the crucial interplay between typical manner and typical material. In Griffith's work we can see that for the film, as for the other arts, style is a structuring of feeling—an embodiment in form of attitudes toward the world and toward the art itself. In the words of Gertrude Stein, "The composition in which we live makes the art which we see and hear."

In practical terms, the time was ripe for an American film of feature length, intense dramatic emotion and identification, and epic sweep of action and spectacle. His most recent films had led up to it in action and scope, and increasing length. Foreign historical spectacles continued to be successful. In France, Sarah Bernhardt appeared in *Queen Elizabeth*, and the screen was already full of the panoramic tales of other famous ladies in *Camille*, *Cleopatra*, *Gypsy Blood*, *Theodora*. In 1912 and 1913, the

---

Alan Casty's "The Films of D. W. Griffith: A Style for the Times" originally appeared in *Journal of Popular Film*, Vol. 1, no. 2 (Spring 1972), pp. 67–79. Reprinted by permission of the author and *Journal of Popular Film*.

young Italian industry had brought forth the largest and most successful of the spectacles—*Quo Vadis*, *Cabiria*, and *The Last Days of Pompeii*. But for all their epic intentions, these films were in the main static and stuffed, mere pageants, stage drama on a vast scale, their exaggerated histrionics and their spectacles unredeemed by visual movement and rhythm.

By 1915, the year of the production of *The Birth of a Nation*, Griffith had seen that on film a dramatic situation, a scene, a panorama, was a sequence of shots. That the expressiveness of the sequence of shots was a result of selection—of materials in the shot, of distance from the materials, angles, lighting and camera movements. And a result of ordering, arranging—the reconstitution of the materials through editing. He and others had discovered the grammar; the enthusiasm over making this a language contributed to the sweeping scope of his first major attempt. The excited fascination with the possibilities contributed to the overt, insistent display of these resources, to the zealous extremes of manipulation in their application.

The new production and distribution system in American allowed him to bring these new approaches to a vast audience. Competition had been accelerated with the rendering ineffectual of the ruling trust, The Motion Picture Patent Company. Independent producers were increasing, studios were being built, stars were being nurtured and paid, new and larger theaters were in need of products that would suit the new economics of the motion picture industry. There were still those who scoffed at the length (twelve reels) and cost ($100,000) of Griffith's new venture, but its impact and financial success were immediate and monumental—despite instances of protest and rioting.

It is hard to assess the role prejudice against the negro played in this success. The subsequent and continuing praise of the film, even among liberal critics, adds credence to the judgment that its primary appeal was the impact of its emotional expressiveness, not its specific thesis. Griffith was concerned with what would make the audience feel, what would move the mass sitting in the darkened theater. This devotion to hyperbolic emotionalism as the essence of drama influenced his hyperbole of subject, his largeness of scope, his exclamatory use of emphasis in depicting it. His world on film would be a world of intense high points, of irreconcilable poles of emotion.

On one level, his work fused form and content. The expressive extremes of his technique were well suited to the extreme melodrama of the contents. But on a deeper, more historical level, the fusion is, finally, a false one. For the two kinds of extremes feed each other, glut each other on excess until the superior element, the technique, is itself marred. Or, when it is unmarred, it must be extricated from the weaknesses of content, viewed arbitrarily and artificially, without the interacting wholeness of the highest levels of art. In a like manner, while his films are concerned with a realistic depiction of detail—even imitating historical photographs down to the smallest physical data—the detail must serve other ends, the heightened expression of emotion or idea. And again a lapse, a gap, develops between a single element and the impression of the whole.

The thesis that shaped the total impression of the details of *Birth* was the most direct and specific expression in his work of his own family background. Its attack on Reconstruction and negroes in general, its heroic justification of the rise of the Klu Klux Klan are surely inheritances of his youth in the South. But more than racial or political prejudices were nurtured there. Griffith's father was a doctor, was wounded three times in defense of his romantic ideals of the Old South, whose vision he never ceased expounding. He declaimed Shakespeare in public with a booming voice (thus his nickname Roaring Jack Griffith). Griffith's sister read aloud to him from the romantic poets. The results were a blend, not untypical, of the hardness of antagonistic prejudice and the softness of idealistic moralism. The insistent, exaggerated caricatures of all the blacks in *The Birth of a Nation* were really no different than Griffith's treatment of all of his villains, whatever the specific subject. The unblemished purity of the women of the South, the noble heroism of the white men were found in the heroines and heroes of all of his films. His was a world without mixtures—of black and white in more ways than one—a world of certitudes absolutely expressed. And with a booming voice. It was the world of 19th Century melodrama.

Eisenstein was the first to examine the significant relationship between Griffith and Dickens, although citations of Griffith's references to Dickens to support his own use of parallel editing had appeared earlier. In "Dickens, Griffith, and the Film Today" (still one of the most intricately wrought and persuasively argued pieces ever written on the film art), Eisenstein particularly focuses on this similarity of technique—the use of physical detail and closeups and especially the use of abrupt shifts of scene to build tempo and emotion. He does remark in passing on similarities of content, attitude and world view, but he does not penetrate far enough. For what we have in Griffith is the surface of Dickens—that which made him so popular because it touched on the surface nerves of the public—but not the wit or penetration, the insight into complexity and emotional depths that underlay the surface simplicities, the types, the sentimentalities of situation and emotion. What is left is the energetic rendering of the shell: Griffith's cinematic embodiment of exaggerated, sentimental emotionalism, naive, simplistic conflict and tension, and one-dimensional character stereotypes.

In it there is still much of late nineteenth and early twentieth century stage melodrama and popular fiction. The melodrama in particular had imparted to the young film industry the impetus of its own technical development. The theater of Max Reinhardt and others had moved toward more and more surface realism—conceived as the presence on the stage of real objects and settings. It had moved toward the rendering of impossible spectacle—locomotives, fires, sawmills, ice flows—had developed accelerated shifts of scene as it had produced a flourishing of physical action in fights, chases, and last minute rescues. but it had done more. It had provided the film-makers and the audiences who would smoothly make the transition from stage melodrama to film with a pervasive habitual conception of dramatic over-simplification of character, emotion, conflict, and theme. Griffith, along with others, was to move beyond this melodrama in terms of the inventiveness, the verve and vitality of tempo with which he could render the melodrama. He would apply it more seriously and sincerely to serious problems of the world. But even here his themes were more simplistic *theses*, naively applied, without the depth of conception or powers of self-analysis to see the contradiction in following the sensationalized bigotry and prejudice of *The Birth of a Nation* with an equally sensationalized attack on bigotry and prejudice in *Intolerance*. In 1944, in a late and rare statement of his aims, he replied to a question about what makes a good film:

> One that makes the public forget its troubles. Also, a good picture tends to make folks think a little, without letting them suspect that they are being inspired to think. In one respect, nearly all pictures are good in that they show the triumph of good over evil.

This approach to human problems—in terms of clear-cut absolute distinctions between the forces of lightness and darkness—was the legacy of melodrama. But it also was a typical popularization of the ideals and attitudes of the Progressive Era in the first decade and a half of the century in America. More than a political movement, Progressivism seemed to capture a national tone: an innocent optimistic faith in progress and human potential, in the efficacy of change; a moralistic seriousness, a no-nonsense soberness; a mixture of sentimental idealism and gruff, athletic confidence. Theodore Roosevelt was the type writ large; the movies, it was felt, were to be, in Vachel Lindsay's phrase, the prophet-wizard of the new millennium. Lindsay was one among many who stressed the role of the movies in uplifting society. An especially instructive voice of the times was that of Louis Reeves Harrison, an influential spokesman within the industry, the critic for the *Moving Picture World*. With insistent regularity Harrison repeated his belief that we—especially in America—"seem to be at the dawn of enlightenment" and that it was the film that would hasten that dawn, with "its cultivation of the social muscle," its ability "to affect the manners and habits of the people, to cultivate their taste for the beautiful, to soften harsh temperament by awakening tender sympathy, to correct primitive egotism and avarice, to glimpse history and travel, to nourish and support the best there is in us."

The expressive style of Griffith, and of the period, reflected these attitudes—the innocent enthusiasm of discovery and progressive amelioration, the extreme polarization and emphasis of melodrama and moral absolutism. Like the histrionics and mannerisms of the acting that has become one of its most bothersome aspects, it was a bold and bald iconography of broad gestures. This stylization did not produce a break with realism (except in the case of the German Expressionists). The sense of tangible reality that the film image could produce was certainly valued, yet taken for granted (as much of the critical writing of the period illustrates) in the zeal for displaying and capitalizing on the medium's technical resources. The realistic image was not to be contradicted or denied; it was to be used, without intentionally breaking the illusion, for an obtrusive manipulation of time and space, an intensification, an expressive heightening that gave new significance to what Pudovkin called the "dead objects" of literal reproduction.

Griffith's parallel editing most fully exemplifies his personal version of this collective style and its relationship to the conglomeration of attitudes—emotionalist, melodramatic, progressive, reactionary, absolutist—he brought to his films. Emotionally, it produced the extremes of tension and emotion that he sought, the roaring climaxes of his favorite narrative structures. Technically, it freed the film from the limitations of time and space. But even more importantly, it intensified the facile, absolute oppositions of his plot conflicts. It became the visual structure for his feelings about a world of totally distinct, but directly opposed forces, of irreconcilable poles of good and evil. It is a split world, but clearly, neatly split. For all the rapidity and variety of his parallel editing, it is a clearly oriented, sharply demarking, ordering editing. Unlike the rapid editing of today—and its context of relativity and ambiguity—it does not seek to blur, or overlap, or dislocate.

In *The Birth of a Nation*, some of the instances of parallel editing produce contrasts between relatively static and undeveloped material, contrasts that give visual expression to the ideological simplifications: A shot of old people at home praying intercut with shots of trenches piled high with bodies. A shot of the Southern girl Margaret being proposed to by a Northern soldier followed by a shot of her brothers being killed, then a shot of her refusal.

But the major instances of parallel editing involve the development of dynamic, dramatic action in sequences of shots that manipulate space, time, and movement. In the recreation of the assassination of Lincoln, a sequence of some 55 shots, alternates, with varying tempo and selection, between the stage, the audience, Lincoln in his box, the hallway behind, the balcony, Lincoln's guard, John Wilkes Booth, in the gallery, on the balcony, in the hall, in the box, on stage.

It is more characteristic for Griffith's peak parallels to fuse three separated but simultaneous actions. This recurrent triadic pattern is revealing: the two antagonistic forces of the world in combat over natural innocence, over the very soul of the world. Within the three-way pattern, there are often further embellishments. In the evil Gus' chase of Flora through the woods and the attempt of Ben to save her (this time with an untypical lack of success), there is not only cutting between the three, but an effective alternation of long shots and close shots of Flora's frantic, wild course. In other cases, the three-way tension is achieved by cutting between an innocent one and a force of evil who are in one place and then between them and the force of good at another place.

In *Birth*'s climactic double rescue, Griffith first alternates slots within two similar but separate situations; then he fuses them for the climactic three-way rescue. First, at the mansion of the villainous mulatto leader, Lynch, the threat of his forced marriage to the good, sweet, and white Elsie is intercut with shots of the Klan gathering. After some 65 shots, we switch to the good Camerons besieged in a cabin by wild, evil Negro militia, again intercut with the gathering of the Klan, their number swelling. In the third part of the sequence, we alternate between all three places, the mansion, cabin, and Klan—as the Klan achieves the rescue and rides through the streets of the town. In the latter stages, time is markedly impeded and suspense stretched by delays at the points of rescue and the breakup of the action into close shots of many component details; while tempo is accelerated by the increasing brevity of shots and increasing rapidity of alternation between the three points of focus.

This emotional and didactic intensity and expressive heightening of reality is effected by other means as well. The film has a visual richness, a purely visual excitement, as much from the number and variety of devices as from their individual effectiveness. It is a film more of devices and of movement—within shots, by camera, or between shots—than of perfection of composition of shots. Even in the climax just discussed, the composition of the shots of the Klan bursting upon the militia in the streets is not the equal of the momentum achieved by the editing. Among the many other devices of shooting, printing or editing, one other type of editing should be mentioned. This is selective editing—the breakup of a scene into separate shots of varying content, angle and distance from content. As a result, the film has some 1375 shots, as compared to less than 100 in most of the comparable continental spectacles. Yet this breakup of the scene into shots does not produce fragmentation or refraction. It is ordered to build the clearcut emotional and ideological conflicts and support the insistent points of emphasis within them.

This emphasis is most often achieved through Griffith's important development of the intensity and expressiveness of the close-up. Again, these close-ups confirm; they do not dislocate or fragment. They varied widely in the sophistication of what they sought to express and how they expressed it, typically less sophisticated when they were most strongly icons of good and evil. A tight close-up of the gun in the hand of John Wilkes Booth is illustrative of the baldness of some of the emphases, while a wonderful sudden bust shot of a confederate soldier, in the midst of longer shots of a battle, emphasizes in much more sophisticated form the passion and fury of the battle. Shot from behind his own cannon, the nose of the cannon projecting into the frame, he is captured, with a yell on his face, at the peak of a movement of thrusting a primer into the cannon's mouth. For expression, physical objects are treated symbolically, again with varying sophistication: a close shot of parched corn in the South; the hands of the good "Little Colonel" caressing a bird; an ecstatic Elsie embracing a bedpost.

For Griffith, a thematic connection and continuity existed between this tale of the unjust travail imposed on the South by the North (as well as the unjust attacks made on him by some after the release of the film) and his next film *Intolerance*, released in August of 1916. For in the latter he would portray the more universal basis of his position—a protest against intolerance and injustice, a cry for love and justice—and he would portray this by interweaving four separate plots in which the good people are beset by and, in three out of four of the cases, destroyed by the evil, intolerant ones. The flaws in his conception of this connection or in his working out of the universalized thesis in *Intolerance* are revealing but in one important sense irrelevant. For to clear away reams of forced high seriousness offered by critics and historians, there are probably few who have ever responded deeply to this film in terms of the kind of metaphoric arc of meaning between immediate detail and theme through which significance rises from a work of art.

It is a film of paradoxes—beyond those ironies intended by Griffith. Its grandiose conception weighs it down. Its thesis is too broad and vague. Its four plots don't clearly develop its thesis in a consistent manner: In the modern plot, the most extended of the four, intolerance might apply to the actions of the lady Do-gooders, but not to the bosses who mistreat workers, the police who shoot them down, the criminal who misuses the girl and boy, the boy who, through bad luck and sheer stupidity, twice gets caught holding a gun, the court which stupidly sentences him to death for murder, or the ludicrous coincidences of the murder itself. Its sheer flood of detail gets in the way of even maintaining a response to the plots as plot, especially when so many of the plot details are bathetic, banal, oversimplified. Yet this very grandiosity gives the technique its challenge, gives Griffith the opportunity to carry it out with a plastic vitality, a flow of movement, an audacious inventiveness that, especially in the last third of the movie, is, for all of its artificiality, awesome.

The key is again parallel editing—on a monumental scale. The basic structure embodies Griffith's intuition of the space and time fluidity of film technique. Throughout, he juggles all four plots simultaneously, intercutting from one to the other.

Through roughly two-thirds of the film, the segments of each plot are several minutes long, with some exceptions, and with some parallel intercutting within the segment. At the climax points of the four plots, he accelerates the momentum of the intercutting between the plots. From one, however—Christ moving to his crucifixion—relatively few shots appear. In the other three, he intensifies the editing within the plot to the peak of his characteristic three-way chase and rescue pattern. Thus, in the last third of the movie, the three-way structures within each of the three plots are in turn part of what is basically a three-way structure among the three plots.

In the contemporary episode there is actually a double chase as well, or a chase in two movements. In the first movement, the boy is being readied for execution by hanging, while the girl speeds in a racing car to catch the Governor's speeding train. Griffith cuts back and forth among these three elements, and then he cuts to a parallel three-cornered situation in the French Huguenot plot. Here the girl and her family are inside their house, the besieging Army in the streets, her lover racing across the city to save her. Again, Griffith cuts back and forth among the three elements, and then cuts to a parallel three-cornered situation in the Babylonian plot. Here, the Babylonians are celebrating a previous victory, while the evil hordes move on the city and a young servant girl races in a chariot to warn the Babylonians. Again, the three-way cutting, and then back to the three elements of the contemporary plot.

At the successful climax of the first movement of the contemporary rescue—the stopping of the train—Griffith achieves his most striking juxtaposition of shots. Without the intervening title that he often uses in his transitions between the plots, he cuts from a shot of the girl's happy success to a shot of the Huguenot girl being stabbed by her tormentor. From this point on the continuing suspense of the race back to save the boy (and intercutting between the two points) is interleaved with the tragic final stages of the other two plots. With reversed contrast, the last shots of the defeated Babylonians are followed by the successful last minute rescue of the boy. By this point the acceleration produces a flurry of images, with shots of shorter and shorter duration within each sequence and equally accelerated alternation between sequences. By fragmenting space and action into their selected component details, this acceleration again produces a corollary sense of impeding time as well.

The virtuosity and excitement of this sustained crescendo of editing burst the bindings of ideological and aesthetic conception; still, the basic stylistic structure underlies them. For all the visual fireworks, the images still build the conventional rhythm of emotion and linear progression of the dualistic narrative. In *Intolerance*, however, Griffith does use contrast editing with a sharper, ironic sense of counterpoint. The ironic reversals reinforce the clearcut oppositions, rather than undercutting with any skeptical ambiguity: Between plots, the trial of the boy and the trial of Christ; within a plot, the "Vestal Virgins of Reform" visit the workers' homes to save their souls and in the next scenes the workers are denied work and shot down by the militia. Immediate visual juxtapositions reinforce the situational irony: the lavish home of the boss and the plain room of "The Dear One"; "Bablyon's greatest noble" served wine with great pomp at the feast and "The Mountain Girl" milking a goat in a poor section of Babylon to get a drink for herself.

The selection of close-ups is one last indication of the mixed nature of the film's multitude of effects. A sudden cut to the eyes of one actress, another to the lower part of an actress's face, a shot in the shadows of the face of Mae Marsh ("The Little Dear One") as she returns to her child and darkened room after the trial, the brief shot of her stoic face at the verdict—these are in sharp contrast to the many facial close-ups of banal, exaggerated expressions. The shot of Mae Marsh in the courtroom is immediately followed by the famous close-up of her hands, twisting together, gripping tightly in anguish—the two shots together expressing her character, her state of mind and heart. But it should not be forgotten that the selective nuance of these two close-ups had been preceded by dozens of other shots of her face and hands, intercut with shots of the boy, as she encourages him during the trial, twisting her handkerchief, biting the end of it, blinking her eyes, essaying a flickering smile again and again and again. In Griffith's Armaggedon, even the quiet nuance is shaped into the hyperbole of the booming voice.

Somehow, in the film's excessiveness lay its wonder, and its weakness. The same might be said of its creator.

And so it might be understood, to some degree, how and why he had already reached its high point. The exuberance of technical discovery and a deep sincerity had more than kept a balance with the limitations of his conceptions. But now advances in technique were haltered by the limitations of the uses to which technique would be put. Even the style seemed to collaborate with the reductive conceptions, restricting the kinds and degrees of felt life that could become the content of the work. A film like *Isn't Life Wonderful* (1924) showed some traces of wrestling free, and even within the hardening pattern there were major exceptions; but in the main, exciting extremes gave way to repetitious exaggerations. Among the numerous subsequent films Griffith directed, several might be mentioned to indicate some of the higher and some of the significant points in the pattern of decline.

The basic content pattern was the same: the dear pure hearts of the world beset by the forces of evil, whatever their particular name or uniform. In some, the personal tales were again enmeshed in historical spectacle of some sort, but never again with the lavishness of *Intolerance.* In *Hearts of the World* (1918) the expected villains are the Huns, the contrast editing juxtaposes German atrocities and pure sweetness, German debauchery with the death of a French Mother; the climactic rescue is made by French, English and American soldiers. In *Orphans of the Storm* (1921) it is the French Revolution (with allusions to the evils of the Russian Revolution) with many repetitions of technique, some of them quite striking. *America* (1924) transfers the entire pattern to the American Revolution.

The same need to repeat what had worked produced similar reapplications of the same techniques even to those movies of smaller dramatic scope, including two of the best of these, *Broken Blossoms* and *Way Down East* (1920). In *Way Down East* the obligatory rescue of the harassed dear one is from a floe of ice over a waterfall; for all its repetitiousness, it has a fine sense of movements within shots and between them. In *Broken Blossoms* (1919) the parallel-edited rescue attempt is too late; moreover, not only does the innocent girl die, but there is a further turn to the pattern. The Chinese lover kills her brute of a father and then himself.

More than the ending was powerful and distinct. There was something in the situation of the harassed waif sheltered and loved by a kind Chinese storekeeper (only to have her father shatter the blossom of the dream) that ignited a creative sincerity in

Griffith, that overbalanced the bathos and sentimentality. The stylized acting is probably the best consort of performances in a Griffith film, often captured tellingly by the lighting, tinting, soft and changing focus, selection of shot detail and angle. Richard Barthelmess made escellent use of his slender body, arching, poised, head tilted, tense but tender, a sweetness of face captured in numerous close-ups. The franticness of Lillian Gish is climaxed by an amazing scene in which (photographed partly from above) she spins wildly around and around in a tiny closet while her father pounds on the door. Donald Crisp's brute is tremendously physical, constantly on the move; even a shot of his angry face is given a sense of physical energy as Griffith cuts from a close-up to a tighter close-up to an extremely tight close-up. It is Griffith's most consummate evocation of naive, maudlin sentimentality, touched with a special grace this time by a feeling for the fragility of purity and love that was deeper and truer than anything in the artificial repetitions of his later work.

The material touched something deep within Griffith, became a concrete, activating metaphor for his shaping sense of the unequivocal, irreconcilable opposition of good and evil. The extreme, melodramatic poles of emotionality are still present, still unequivocal; but the material seemed to generate a tangible, experienced tenderness that kept in check the usual imposition of final progressive affirmation. The elements of his expressive style are still dominant, selected and combined as always: the polar simplicities of the dramatic plot, the emotional and narrative intensifications of parallel editing, the ordering of conflict by composition in shots, the iconographic emphasis of close-ups. But there use in *Broken Blossoms* provides a specially muted version of the hyperbolic structure of feeling that Griffith drew from and provided for his times.

Souls Made Great by Love and Adversity: Frank Borzage

JOHN BELTON

One of the reasons that melodrama—and great film-makers like D. W. Griffith and Frank Borzage who work its conventions—remains in critical disrepute is that it tends to externalise, to transform, a character's inner conflicts into external events.[1] Nineteenth century melodramatic literature traditionally presents two-dimensional characters, often at the mercy of a hostile environment or an extension of that environment (villain). Though the genre's lack of complexity has a primitive "purity" to it, it becomes, if handled poorly, its chief drawback and greatest limitation. The best—that of Dickens, Ibsen, Chekhov—makes use of the melodramatic form but avoids its flaws. By adding depth to characterisation through descriptive detail, it steers clear of simplistic externalisations of conflict. Griffith and Borzage, like their literary predecessors, use and believe in the melodrama as a way of seeing the world but also, by shifting their focus from the melodramatic situation itself to the *characters* in that situation, they gave the form a new dimension; Griffith's and Borzage's wholehearted commitment to a melodramatic world view, apparent in the intensity of feeling behind each shot in their films, invests their work with a transcendent emotional level because it confers upon the characters presented an integrity which is a sign of both innocence and vitality.

What distinguishes Borzage's melodramas from Griffith's is their spirituality. Where Griffith concerns himself primarily, like Dickens, with the restitution of the family unit or the creation of a new family-like unit, Borzage's interests lie chiefly in the salvation of his characters—not with external but internal order.

John Belton's "Souls Made Great by Love and Adversity" originally appeared in *Monogram*, Vol. 3 (1972), pp. 20–23. Reprinted by permission of the author and *Monogram*.

Where Griffith's characters possess an irrepressible physical vitality—a vitality which makes his films immediate and direct—Borzage's characters radiate from within a unique, spiritual energy that makes them seem luminously unreal. Yet Borzage's characters also project a captivating but wholly innocent sensuality; they possess a fascinating mixture of spiritual purity and physical attractiveness. Where Griffith tends to evoke either madonna-like innocence (Gish) or wholesome physicality (Dempster), Borzage inextricably combines both these qualities in his characters (Farrell, Gaynor). This sensuality of Borzage's characters is rooted in their Edenic ignorance of the state of sin; it denies an awareness of physical corporeality. In short, Borzage's films concern themselves more with the exploration of the essences behind physical reality: unlike Griffith, he attempts to deal purely with the souls of his characters.

Borzage himself explains that "in every face I see I find a story. It doesn't seem hard. The story is right there lying on top, easily visible. You can take it and make something real, vital out of it. . . . By face I don't mean face literally . . . I mean the characters in my story."[2] Borzage's inarticulateness is only verbal. The first few shots of *Street Angel* (1928), perhaps the director's greatest silent film, describe this spirituality—the stories behind faces—far better than words ever could. The first title of the film sets the mood: "Everywhere . . . in every town . . . in every street . . . we pass, unknowing, human souls made great by love and adversity." After this remarkably explicit title, Borzage's camera wanders through the crowded streets of Naples, observing policemen making their rounds in the market place, lovers walking arm in arm, a beggar girl sitting desolately at the foot of some stairs, circus gypsies arguing with a sausage vendor. Finally, Borzage cuts to an apartment in which a doctor is telling a girl (Angela) that she must buy some medicine in order to save her sick mother.

Each character we encounter in the opening shots of the film (similar to a later scene in which Gino looks for Angela in the crowded streets) has some story behind him and each wears that story on his face. By shooting the sequence and directing the actors as he does, Borzage captures the essence of their stories—he penetrates beneath the physical surface of every action, every gesture, and every face. Though all the stories occur independently of one another, Borzage ties them together into a single, spiritual event by use of connective camera movement and editing. This makes no sense logically, as it would in Griffith, but it does work intuitively, to define the limits of the spiritual system that exists in the film. Yet in this and most other Borzage films it is much less rigid and limited than the term "spiritual system" implies. In fact, the beauty of the opening sequence in *Street Angel* rests on the complexity of characterisation which prevents any inflexible schematization of spiritual values.

Borzage's love relationships in *Street Angel* and other films reveals a highly visual romanticism with roots in the spiritual transparency of his characters, deliberately set off against the sordidness of the social condition. Angela, escaping from the police when arrested for theft while soliciting, runs away with the circus gypsies and eventually meets Gino, an itinerant artist. When they fall in love, Gino paints her portrait. His painting, a fantastic metaphor for the film itself, captures her not as she is, but as he sees her (her soul). In order to eat, they sell the painting to an art dealer. Yet even though it has been sold, the painting and its absence exert a powerful influence on the lovers. When Borzage cuts to shots of the bare wall where the painting was hung, the empty space conveys even more directly the painting's metaphysical significance. Meanwhile, the art dealer, hoping to make a great deal of money on Gino's painting, hires another artist to retouch it and to forge out of it an Old Master. Several times during the film Borzage cuts back to the painting of Angela: as she herself becomes more and more transformed by her love for Gino, the painting, now depicting a madonna, has also undergone a transformation.

The parallel is both ironic and symbolically true, and when Angela, without Gino's knowledge, is taken back to jail after spending her last hour with him, Borzage cuts to a shot of the forger painting a halo over her head.

Borzage's editing of love sequences, in its total disregard for physical space, goes beyond the surfaces of specific places or actions directly to the spiritual origins of his lovers' relationships. In his first sound film, *Sound O' My Heart* (1930), the lovers, Sean and Mary, are separated, first by a forced marraige of her to another man and, then, by sheer physical distance. When Sean sings "The Rose of Tralee" just before he leaves Ireland for a concert tour in the US, Mary, hearing their old love song, is drawn across the village to him and stands in his doorway, listening to him sing. Later, as Sean sings the same song in a New York concert, Borzage cuts back to (the dying) Mary in Ireland looking out of her window at falling leaves and, seemingly, listening to a song that is sung thousands of miles away. Similarly, in *I've Always Loved You* (1946) former lovers Myra Hassman and Leopold Goronoff, her piano teacher, play the same piece of music on the piano at the same moment, though miles apart. By cutting back and forth between the lovers, Borzage creates a strong, spiritual bond between them.

This spiritual quality of Borzage's love relationships is partly achieved by the narrative backgrounds with which they are contrasted: the hostile environments of war or depression or both appear at the same time as the obstacle to their happiness and the very condition of their love. *Seventh Heaven* (1927), *Farewell to Arms* (1932), *A Man's Castle* (1933), *Little Man, What Now?* (1934), *Three Comrades* (1938), *The Mortal Storm* (1940) and *Till We Meet Again* (1944) all contain hostile backgrounds which Borzage's central characters ultimately transcend. Yet the often-chaotic worlds which surround these characters are no more "real" in a physical sense than the characters themselves are. In other words, the backgrounds do not impose real or physical danger on the central characters; the chaos of the backgrounds is not a physical but a spiritual one. In *Farewell to Arms* when Lieut. Frederick Henry, deserting the Italian army (including his cynical friend, Major Rinaldi, and what Rinaldi represents), goes back to search for Catherine Barkley, his lover, Borzage surrounds him with scenes of death, destruction, explosions, and horrible human misery in the ranks of the wounded and retreating soldiers. Lieut. Henry's search for Catherine, set in the midst of all this spiritual bleakness, becomes a metaphorical journey and, because of the strength and explicitness of its images, the sequence emerges as one of the most powerful direct thematic statements in the film.

The background of *Little Man, What Now?* set in the post-war depression of '20s Germany, is filled with voices crying out in the streets—voices like that of the speaker in the park who preaches equality in the film's rain-drenched opening sequence, or cynics like the communist who blames "them" for the death of his wife, or emotionally twisted characters like the grotesque Kleinholz family or the crazy relationship between Mia

Pinnenberg and her dog. It is the spiritual message of these voices that threatens Hans Pinnenberg, not the physical fact of economic depression. Only the innocence and purity of his relationship with Lammchen—symbolised in part by the birth of their child at the end of the film—enables Hans to escape the human wasteland that surrounds him. A *Man's Castle* is played against the background of the American Depression—yet Borzage sees that Depression in terms of its spiritual, not economic chaos. As a result, Bill's aimlessness, represented by his attraction to the sound of the train whistle, and the cynical assurance in his seeming self-sufficiency and independence—an aspect of his character reflected in the self-centred grotesqueness of his promotional costumes (he becomes a walking neon sign, a clown on stilts)—endanger the purity of his relationship with Trina. Even the grim background of war in *The Moral Storm* or *Till We Meet Again* is less materially hostile than spiritually suffocating to Borzage's characters. In *The Mortal Storm*, set in pre-Nazi Germany, fascism becomes an insane social-political backdrop to Borzage's family melodrama: a family fights against an externalised system of evil which threatens to destroy its cohesiveness.[3] On one level, the film works as allegory—Borzage treats the disintegration of the Roth family as a microcosm for the greater collapse of the state and the world. Yet Borzage's handling of the narrative material is less political than moral and spiritual.[4] When Professor Roth's stepsons, Otto and Erich, and his best student, Fritz (also his daughter's fiancé and, as such, would-be member of the family), reveal their conversion to fascism at the professor's birthday party, their betrayal emerges as a betrayal of a system of general, spiritual values more than of a specific political or religious belief.[5] Borzage's editing here, first isolating, then grouping various characters together according to their beliefs, transforms the family from one based originally on ties of blood to one based on a more abstract, yet stronger bond of mutuality and affinity of spirit.

As the family seems to crumble around the professor, what emerges is a new alliance of souls: Freya, becoming more and more disillusioned with Fritz's gradual Nazification, grows closer to Martin, another of her father's students. Borzage's alignment of characters according to spiritual affinity creates two distinct outlooks in the film. Though one seems to overwhelm the other—the professor dies in a concentration camp, Mrs. Roth and her youngest son go to Switzwerland, Freya tries to escape from Germany with Martin but is shot by Fritz and dies in Martin's arms on the Swiss border—the grotesque brutality and barbaric consequences of that outlook take their toll on those who try to adhere to it. In the last few shots of the film, Borzage reaffirms the transcendence of the professor's vision. Otto and Erich visit their now-deserted home. Fritz enters and tells them of Freya's death. After Fritz has gone, they argue about what has happened to their family and Erich, the more dogmatic Nazi, also leaves. Otto, transformed by what he has learned, walks about the empty house; Borzage's tracking camera shows us what he sees and suggests what he remembers. Then, when Otto also departs, the camera, after a moment or two, follows him outside and tracks down the Roths' walk to their gate, focusing on Otto's footprints in the snow as they slowly fill in with new-fallen snow before our eyes.

The power and beauty of this ending, like that of *Farewell to Arms* in which Lieut. Henry holds his dead "wife" in his arms as peace is announced (Borzage cuts to a shot of pigeons flying), lies in the complexity of feelings it evokes. The disillusionment of

Otto with the rigid Nazi dogma that has destroyed his family suggests his conversion to a new awareness. Yet the cost at which his conversion comes, the loss of all that once had meaning to him, qualifies his transformation.

In *Till We Meet Again*, Sister Clothilde's fear of the outside world, brilliantly visualised in her attempts to shut out—through prayer—the gunshots she hears in the film's first sequence, defines that world in terms of its spiritual threat to her. Though Clothilde tries melodramatically to externalise the forces of evil and to locate them solely in the outside world, Borzage, going beyond the limited vision of any one of his characters, undercuts the novice's self-confidence and untested surety in her faith by using that world to make trial of her spiritually. For Borzage, Clothilde's cloistered saintiness gives her spiritual aspirations no meaning because she has only *escaped* not *transcended* the outside world. Her contact with that world, with the aviator and his system of values in particular, deepens her faith and leads her to a more profound understanding of what religion really is. Her crucifixion at the end of the film, representing conversion to a more complex spirituality, marks her transcendence of both the outside world and the cloister. In *Till We Meet Again*, as in other films, Borzage is rarely specific. If the film contains a conversion to a spiritual system, that system is defined more by its flexibility than its orthodoxy. Borzage's characters' transcendence, as a result, is the more moving because they attain a state that is not restricted, defined or limited by dogmatic ideas or set beliefs.

In *Mannequin* (1937), the tangible reality of a light bulb on Jessie's tenement stairway is less important than the intangible flickering it emits. Though the source of the light is shown and the heroine can temporarily correct its malfunctioning, the light becomes, like the sound of the train whistle in *A Man's Castle*, an intangible force that cannot be dealt with physically: later that night the light flickers again and finally goes out, trapping Jessie in the darkness. Light is part of a physical environment (Hester St.) that she is trying to escape: Borzage treats it as a visual metaphor of her spiritual state and of the spiritual atmosphere which surrounds her.

In a way, Borzage's visual style reflects his belief in the immateriality of objects and characters. His images have little to do with real things; rather, like Plato's ideal forms, they refer to an absolute and eternal reality that exists on a purely abstract level. In other words, his images often function as metaphors, revealing his concern for larger, transcendent issues. In *Strange Cargo* (1940), Cambreau, who exerts a strange spiritual influence in the film, draws a map of an escape route from the island's prison in a Bible and leaves it behind for Vern to use when he escapes and follows him and the other prisoners. Though Borzage only cuts to the Bible map once, the image becomes one of the most powerful ones in the film, representing, as it does, the symbolic implications of the prisoners' escape/journey. The explicitness of this brief image, consistent with the explicitness of the film as a whole, illustrates the depth of Borzage's commitment to the metaphorical aspects of his story.

In *The River* (1928) Borzage presents Rosalee, waiting for the return of her convict-lover Marsdon, sitting disconsolately on the river's edge with the crow that Marsdon left her. Borzage intercuts shots of flotsam and debris, caught in the river's current, which disappears into a whirlpool. Reflecting her mood and state of mind, the river and its contents become a metaphor for Rosalee's despair. The appearance of Allen John among the drifting wreckage, since it initially suggests an identification of him with her gloom, ties the two together into a single state of consciousness which, through Allen John's purity and his subsequent efforts to evoke emotion in Rosalee, gradually evolves into a positive, therapeutic relationship that redeems Rosalee from her despondency.

In visual terms, Borzage's backgrounds, like his tonal environments, have a spiritual rather than material quality. In most of his films, he uses studio sets and, as a result, his backgrounds have an unreal, fairy-tale quality. Part of this has to do with the way Borzage lights them—the tones of his backgrounds, often as light as or lighter than his characters' faces, gives his frames a weightless quality. Borzage's lighting, like Griffith's, is even throughout the frame, i.e. each part of the frame seems equally and evenly lit. Yet Borzage's lighting is softer than Griffith's and his frames lack Griffith's precision and tremendous resolution in depth. What is important about Borzage's lighting is that it creates an *evenness* of tone within the frame: though the background and foreground are weightless, they are equally weightless. As a result of this evenness specific objects or backgrounds never exert specific physical force on his characters. The stove in *A Man's Castle* and the mirror-dresser in *Little Man, What Now?* for example, have a force over Borzage's characters which goes beyond their material existence or function. The relationship of characters to objects or to their backgrounds, because of this evenness of tone do not work out in spatial terms (e.g. conflict between foreground and background or between characters and their environment). The flatness of Borzage's backgrounds and their tendency to fall out of focus in medium shot and close-up do not, as they do in, say, Cukor's films, separate characters by dividing the frame into two planes of depth. Instead, Borzage's lighting unifies his frames into a single level of depth, and characters do not derive their spirituality from specific objects or from specific parts of the frame (as in Griffith) but from the tonal quality of the whole frame and the succession of frames around it (i.e. from the editing).

Unlike Hawks, Borzage is not a visual materialist. At the beginning of *Three Comrades*, after the toast to the "comrades living and dead of all men," Borzage introduces his central characters. When one of them, Otto Koster, learns that, because of the armistice, his plane is to be dismantled, he leaves the group and goes outside. Outside, Borzage tracks in on Koster as he approaches his plane. He cuts to an insert shot of a medallion with "Baby" written on it, cuts back to the original set-up as Koster takes the pin out of a grenade, drops it into the plane's cockpit and walks away. Then Borzage cuts back to a shot which tracks away from the plane and from Koster. The camera tracks back until the grenade explodes; then it tracks in again on the burning plane.

What makes the scene so emphatic is that its force hinges on the tracking camera which pulls away from the plane. For me, the tracking shot seems to deny the plane's physical reality, because although Koster destroys his airplane, it's clear that whatever "Baby" is will live on after the demise of its physical reality. In fact, we later see an insert shot of the same medallion on Koster's car which he also sacrifices to achieve a spiritual goal—to pay for the operation of his friend's wife. The scene epitomizes the whole film:

characters give objects and one another, through friendship and love, a life of their own which transcends material existence. Both objects and characters attain an "eternal" reality—something impervious to time and space, to death or physical separation.

There's a sequence in *A Man's Castle* in which Bill, afraid of becoming trapped by Trina's love, leaves her. The scene begins with a two-shot close-up of them together. Bill slowly draws out of the frame, leaving Trina alone on the bed. A train whistle is heard on the soundtrack. After a few moments, Borzage cuts to Bill hopping a freight. Then he begins to cross-cut—back to Trina, then to Bill. The shots of Trina are tremendously powerful—partly because of her angled position in the frame, as if her image were drawing him back through space. Bill first looks back and then jumps off the train to return to her. The cross-cuts here, somewhat like Griffith's in *Intolerance* or *Way Down East*, go beyond the mere mechanic of suspense: implying an ultimate rescue, they have the force of salvation and exert a mysterious power.

In Borzage's films, as suggested above, the space between characters—even in a single frame—has no deterministic force. Where Welles, in the famous breakfast-table time montage in *Citizen Kane*, or the stairway sequences in *The Magnificent Ambersons*, shows the separation of his characters in geographically physical terms—in fact, the space between characters becomes a character itself—Borzage has an altogether nonphysical conception of time and space. The split-screen phone conversations in *Three Comrades* reflect this: a character in one spatial matrix can communicate with another in another spatial matrix. The use of the split-screen foreshadows a sort of relationship, like that in *A Man's Castle* or *I've Always Loved You*, that can transcend space. For this reason, the physical separation of the lovers throughout *Three Comrades* is immensely important to the development of the spirituality of their relationship. Like Koster's plane, it can be seen as another physical reality that Borzage's visual style destroys and transcends. As a result, the dissolve from Pat and the Christmas tree in the mountain sanatorium to Erich and the Christmas tree in Alphons' cafe, like that from Mrs. Dexter's radio to Dean Harcourt's church in *Green Light*, transcends space by suggesting a far greater, spiritual reality that overshadows and encompasses every action in Borzage's universe.

The shooting of *Three Comrades*, like that of Borzage's other '30s work, has a strange, almost mysterious quality to it, as if he were trying to capture in his images the intangible forces that surround his characters. One sequence in particular—the time montage that announces the changing of the seasons—illustrates how far he is prepared to go in his "romanticised" view of the universe. Midway through the film, Borzage cuts to shots of the wind blowing through the trees and through the city streets when winter comes. He transforms time into an almost mystical force that floats his corklike characters along, much as the unseen wind does the newspaper in the streets. At times, his shooting seems to epitomise the emotional state of his characters at specific moments in time. On Erich and Pat's honeymoon, Borzage's long, high-angle shot of Erich carrying Pat along the shore back to their hotel after her sudden collapse seems to transform them, to bring out their inward state and feelings and project them upon the landscape.

At the end of *Three Comrades*, almost every shot serves to capture this essence. The breathtakingly beautiful crane-shot as Pat gets up out of bed after her operation and goes to her balcony to see Erich and Koster for the last time suggests, as does the overhead shooting at the end of *Seventh Heaven* and *Till We Meet Again*, a supernatural presence which oversees her ultimate transcendence of the final physical barrier which separates her from Erich: her body.

Borzage's ending of *Three Comrades*, which differs from *Fitzgerald's* (his screenwriter), takes place in a cemetery outside of the city and shows the three comrades and Pat reunited—a realisation of the film's first lines that toasted "the comrades living and dead of all men." In the last shot, Erich and Koster (surrounded by the ethereal images of Pat and Gottfried) leave the cemetery and talk of going to South America.[6] Like the characters at the end of *A Man's Castle* escaping on the train together or of *Little Man What Now?* with the prospect of a better life in Holland, the characters in *Three Comrades* do not run away from their chaotic, troubled backgrounds as much as they grow out of them spiritually. Borzage so totally transforms them that it becomes impossible for them to go back, as Fitzgerald wanted. Erich and Koster, like Pat and Gottfried, are ultimately liberated from the weight of their own bodies and chaotic backgrounds that threaten to entrap them.

In conclusion, what makes Borzage's melodramas unique is the director's avoidance of extreme conflicts: neither his characters nor their environment struggle mortally with one another. Rather than externalising his plots into moral contests between good and evil in which characters defeat or are defeated by the evil that engulfs them, Borzage, diffusing the conventional melodramatic moral polarity, permits the coexistence of several moral and spiritual systems in his films. He merely makes trial of one by juxtaposing it to another, providing the catalyst for his characters' growth out of one system and emergence into another, more transcendent one. The tolerated presence of inferior spiritual systems in his films only heightens the beauty and integrity of the superior one. For Borzage, it is only through love and adversity that souls are made great.

Notes

1. Corrigan, Robert W., ed., *Laurel British Drama: The Nineteenth Century*, New York, Dell Publishing Co., 1967, pp. 7–8.
2. Milne, Peter, *Motion Picture Directing*, "Some Words From Frank Berzage," New York, Falk Publishing Co., 1922.
3. The insanity of the Nazis is suggested most vividly in their secret meetings and in the terrifying book-burning sequence outside the professor's university window.
4. The film's success upon its release in 1940 rests largely on its political importance as one of the first anti-Nazi Hollywood films. Most contemporary reviews discuss it only on those terms. The author of the book on which the film was based even wrote a political analysis of the film for *The New York Times* (6/16/40).

5. Indeed, Borzage makes very little of Roth's Jewishness. His specific religion is less important than his overall spiritual outlook.
6. In *Crazy Sundays*, Aaron Latham anecdotally discusses F. Scott Fitzgerald's contribution to the film's present ending as escapism. The idea which Fitzgerald wanted to close with was that of "the march of four people living and dead, heroic and inconquerable, side by side back into the fight." *Crazy Sundays*, The Viking Press, New York, 1970, pp. 114–145.

Closure and Containment: Marylee Hadley in *Written on the Wind*

CHRISTOPHER ORR

Toward the end of Douglas Sirk's classic melodrama, *Written on the Wind* (1956), Kyle Hadley (Robert Stack) stumbles out onto the porch of his mansion and falls dead in the driveway. Since the film opened with an abbreviated version of the segment in which Stack dies, this scene closes the circle and we wait for the expected "happy ending" in which the bourgeois hero and heroine escape together from the Hadley mansion. Instead, the camera fades in on a newspaper headline followed by a shot of Mitch Wade (Rock Hudson) and Marylee Hadley (Dorothy Malone). Marylee, Kyle's sister, threatens to implicate the innocent Mitch at the inquest into Kyle's death unless he promises to stay with her. Mitch, who was not only Kyle's best friend but is also in love with his widow, Lucy (Lauren Bacall), refuses. At the inquest, just when it looks as if Mitch will be indicted for Kyle's murder, Marylee breaks down and tells the truth—that Kyle's death was accidental. After a series of shots that position Malone inside the house by herself, the film concludes with the "happy ending" we have been waiting for—the departure of Mitch and Lucy.

Something is wrong. In addition to disrupting the symmetry of the narrative, the diegetic motivation for this extended epilogue is forced and disingenuous. How then can we account for this excess in the film's structure (i.e., this disrupting of the flow of the narrative by the addition of unexpected episodes that make the spectator uneasy)? And, more significantly, to what problems in the film's ideological project does this disruption point? First of all, we cannot explain the epilogue by reference to John

Christopher Orr's "Closure and Containment: Marylee Hadley in *Written on the Wind*" originally appeared in *Wide Angle*, Vol. 4, no. 2 (1980), pp. 29–37. Reprinted by permission of the author and Johns Hopkins University Press.

Cawelti's argument that a major spectacle such as a trial is "at the heart of most social melodramas"[1] since the inquest sequence is not only peripheral, but almost seems to be the beginning of another film. And, while Thomas Elsaesser reads the epilogue as a suggestion of hope ("the possibility of a tangent [the Mitch-Lucy relationship] detaching itself" from the entrapment of the film's circular construction),[2] the Mitch-Lucy relationship can only be seen as hopeful on the most superficial level. More to the point, the epilogue as a whole does not foreground Mitch and Lucy but rather Marylee. Given this foregrounding of Marylee, it follows that the narrational excess—the epilogue—reveals a lack, a sense that Marylee has not been contained within the film's circular structure and hence its ideological project. To comprehend the problematic of Marylee, we need to begin by examining the expectations that the audience brings to bourgeois melodrama and the way in which Sirk's film appears to fulfill those expectations.

A major distinction between melodrama and the noncomic forms that preceded it—tragedy and epic—is, as Geoffrey Nowell-Smith points out, that "author, audience and subject matter are put on a place of equality. . . . Mystified though it may be, the address is from one bourgeois to another bourgeois, and the subject matter is the life of the bourgeoisie."[3] Since the eighteenth century when works such as Richardson's *Clarissa* recorded "the struggle of a morally and emotionally emancipated bourgeois consciousness against the remnants of feudalism," the melodrama has served as an ideological instrument of the bourgeoisie.[4] The function of this ideology, as defined by Robin Wood, has been "to naturalize as eternal truths assumptions that are in fact cultural/historical; [and] to render it impossible to imagine radical alternatives."[5] Thus the manifest content of melodrama in Western culture works to naturalize the assumptions of the inviolability of capitalism and the family within capitalism.

The Sirkian melodrama is often described in terms of the opposition between its complicit manifest content and a style that undercuts that content. The case of *Written on the Wind*, however, is somewhat different. In the scene in which Kyle introduces Lucy to her Miami hotel suite, for example, content and style work together to suggest the theme of the oppressiveness of excessive wealth. Sirk in fact calls *Written on the Wind* his "most gutty picture, . . . a piece of social criticism, of the rich and the spoiled and of the American family."[6] In this sense, the Hadleys (Kyle, Marylee and Jasper, their father) are intended as paradigms of both capitalism ("the rich and the spoiled") and the American bourgeois family (as *nouveau riche* they lack the cultural veneer which the affluent use to isolate themselves from the middle class). The problem with this strategy, however, is that the audience's awareness of the Hadley fortune allows it to refuse to recognize its mirror image in the Hadley family.

Moreover, Mitch and Lucy, by virtue of their economic roles (Mitch Wade is a geologist and Lucy was an executive secretary before her marriage to Kyle) and as embodiments of bourgeois morality, serve as comforting objects of audience identification. On the level of manifest content, their escape from the Hadley mansion at the end of the film can be read by the audience as an affirmation of its values. Thus, in spite of its disavowal of the Hadleys, the film's melodramatic script works to naturalize both capitalism (Mitch never questions his role with the capitalist economic structure) and the family (Lucy, one assumes, will fulfill her expected role as wife and mother now that she has found the "right man").

The place of Marylee within the film is highly problematic. As one of the heirs to the Hadley oil empire and as a woman, her very existence as a sexual being poses a threat to the patriarchal order, i.e., the offspring of a misalliance between a propertied female and a non-propertied male cannot be disavowed as easily as when the sexes are reversed. The containment of female sexuality, the imposition of chastity, is necessary for the legitimate transfer of property in capitalist societies. As a threat to the Law of the Father, Marylee's promiscuity must be suppressed. Hence it is significant that she first appears in the film at a local Hadley bar where Kyle and Mitch, acting in the name of the Father, break up her anticipated liaison with a disreputable (working-class) character. Her brazenness and defiance of the Law—she stands on the seat of the booth drinking while her brother and Mitch battle with Carter in defense of her "honor"—signify to the implied audience that she is the "wrong sort of woman." Yet Marylee is also an object of desire.

Marylee is thus introduced as the site of two desires which the melodramatic film normally satisfies: the bourgeois spectator's desire to feel morally superior to members of an alien and threatening class and the desire to possess vicariously the erotic object of his/her gaze. The locating of both desires in a single character creates a potential for conflict and frustration.

Yet there are several strategies within the melodramatic form through which the eroticized anti-heroine, i.e., the woman who engages in sex outside the proper confines of bourgeois society, can be made to serve ideology. She can be reformed through submission to the male protagonist and thus transformed into a heroine (e.g., the female lead in Sirk's *Shockproof*). We can observe another strategy at work in Murnau's *Sunrise*, where the erring husband, after falling prey to the Vamp's charms, returns to wife and family by the end of the film. The strategy of containment used in *Sunrise* is particularly effective since, on the one hand, it provides a safe outlet for illicit desire through the spectator's vicarious possession of the eroticized anti-heroine and, on the other hand, it relieves the spectator's guilt through the punishment inflicted on the Vamp. Hence the eroticized anti-heroine functions as a scapegoat for the discontent generated by sexual repression which, as Freud reminds us, is the price we pay for civilization. Seen from this perspective, the working out of the Marylee-Mitch relationship calls attention to serious contradictions in the film.

After the fight in the bar, Marylee, while driving Mitch to his job in the oil fields, tells him that the only reason she pursues other men is that he is not interested in her. Mitch's response, that she is too much like a sister to him, recalls an earlier scene in the offices of the Hadley Oil Company where Mitch used the same excuse in replying to Jasper Hadley's efforts to pressure him into marrying his daughter. The composition of the shot in which Mitch answers Marylee's father underlines the falsity of his reply. The prominence of Mitch's head on the left half of the screen creates a diagonal line which begins at the upper left corner of the frame and calls attention to Mitch's hand fidgeting with a pencil in the right foreground. In addition, the juxtaposition of the two faces (although each is on a different plane) and their downward glances creates a triangle, the three points of which are the eyes of the two characters and the pencil grasped in Mitch's hand. The displacement of the emotions generated by this scene onto an inanimate object (the pencil), thereby marking it as a site of overdetermination, suggests that there is more to this than Mitch's "brotherly" feelings. Furthermore, the explanation that Mitch's anxiety is the result of his being in love with Kyle Hadley's wife is implausible since Marylee was available to him long before he met Lucy. Part of this anxiety can be explained by the fact that Jasper Hadley's request places Mitch in a contradictory position. If he accedes to the will of the father by allowing himself to be used as an instrument to contain Marylee (the years he spent looking after Kyle before Kyle's marriage to Lucy testify to his willingness to submit to the father), he violates the injunction against the male succeeding (rising above his class) through his sexuality. However, the ultimate cause of Mitch's anxiety is a fear of female sexuality, i.e., castration.

The sequence in which we find Marylee alone by the river establishes her as a signifier for the sexual Other and hence a source of castration anxiety. This return to a scene of childhood happiness, which occurs after the drive with Mitch to the oil fields and before the party sequence where Marylee tries unsuccessfully to seduce him, is imbued with the trappings of the past, e.g., the initials M.H. and M.W. inscribed on a tree and the off-screen voices of Marylee, Mitch and Kyle as young adolescents.[7] As she stands with her back to the tree and hears the voices from her past, Marylee's face is animated by what appears to be sexual ecstasy. It is a highly personal and intimate moment which the embarrassed spectator/voyeur witnesses directly, i.e., his/her gaze is not authorized by the look of a second character. The representation of Marylee by the river contrasts significantly with the sequence in which she is introduced in the film. In the bar sequence, various signifiers of decadence (the tacky locale; Carter; her tightly fitting, rose-colored [vampish] dress) serve to devalue her, thereby disavowing the threat of castration. In this sequence, on the other hand, Marylee wears jeans and a red and blue checked shirt. The representation of her as eroticized object takes place against a background of childhood voices, river and trees (innocence and nature). What is suggested here is a typical Sirkian theme—the critique of a culture where "an uncompromising, fundamentally innocent energy is gradually turned away from simple, direct fulfillment by the emergence of a conscience, a sense of guilt and responsibility, or the awareness of moral complexity."[8] The juxtaposition of the bar and river sequences and the representation of the Malone character in each reveal an ideological problem. In the bar sequence, Marylee's sexuality is made to stand for the decadence of the affluent classes, whereas in the scene by the river we identify with the legitimacy of her sexual needs. (Marylee's position is analogous to that of Jane Wyman's in *All That Heaven Allows;* the widower tries to convince her to marry him by promising her companionship which he assumes is all she needs.) The film's next sequence—the family party at the Hadley mansion—presents us with a convergence of these conflicting representations of Marylee.

The Hadley party is a celebration of Kyle and Lucy's wedded bliss. Mitch, who is in love with Lucy and not in the mood for a party, sits in an empty room playing a ukulele. Marylee enters the room in a black, strapless dress carrying two drinks. She moves seductively close to Mitch who, after a brief conversation, extricates himself from the situation by taking Marylee back to the party. The final shot of the scene is of the ukulele and the two liquor glasses—Marylee's full and Mitch's nearly empty—on an end table. On a manifest level, Mitch's refusal of Marylee appeals to the moral prejudices and egotism of the film's implied audience. The hero has resisted the temptation of the wealthy and decadent "vamp" in order to remain faithful to the bourgeois heroine who is unfortunately married to someone else. This is discomforting since it conflicts with traditional notions of sex typing. Mitch's refusal also frustrates the spectator's desire for vicarious possession of the erotic object, particularly since the Bacall character, with the exception of the fetishizing shot of her legs early in the film, is not presented erotically. Furthermore, our sympathetic response to Marylee's sexual needs in the previous sequence combined with the visual imagery in this scene suggest a rather different view of Mitch's virtue. As Marylee approaches, there is a medium shot of Mitch in which the position of the ukulele in the frame suggests an erect phallus. When she moves closer, Mitch places the instrument on the table. While this gesture seems insignificant at the time, the privileging of the prone ukulele/phallus in the scene's final shot ultimately serves to underline the hero's impotence.

What makes Sirk's film potentially subversive, in the sense that its embedded structure calls attention to the perversities implicit in the bourgeois ethos, is that Mitch's impotence—his castration by the substitute father, Jasper Hadley—initiates an Oedipal chain of events whereby Marylee acts as an agent of his desire to dispose of the father (and brother) so that he is free to pursue and possess the one representation of the mother in the text—Lucy Hadley. Thus we recognize the perverse logic behind the absence of a mother in Mitch Wade's biological and substitute families. Jasper Hadley's death, like Kyle's, is ostensibly an accident; he collapses on the stairway and dies of a heart attack. Yet there is nothing accidental in the Sirkian melodrama, as the events leading up to Jasper's death and the death scene itself make clear. Shortly after Mitch and Lucy bring a drunken Kyle home from the country club, Marylee appears with two police officers who have rousted her from a motel room she was sharing with a gas station attendant. After an incident in which Jasper Hadley threatens the attendant with a gun (a crime which the police conveniently overlook), Marylee, alone in her room, begins to dance. Accompanied by a jazz recording of "Temptation" that permeates the mansion, she moves about her room wearing a billowy red gown and grasping Mitch's picture in a mad erotic frenzy. It is a sexuality grown uncontrollable out of frustration. Within the body of the text, Marylee functions as a symbol for the return of the repressed and the revenge that repressed desire turned perverse exacts on the agents of repression. (The red *Anthurium* blossoms in her room, with their glossy, plastic-like appearance, are Sirk's *Fleurs du Mal.*) Thus the implicit purpose and effect of Sirk's cutting between Marylee's dance and Hadley as he mounts the stairs and collapses—the father's final attempt to contain his daughter's sexuality—is to implicate Marylee in the crime of parricide. The juxtaposition of the shot of Hadley lying dead at the bottom of the stairs with that of his daughter literally kicking up her heels with joy is truly horrifying. Yet in terms of the conflict between Law and desire (father and daughter), there are no winners except possibly the bourgeois hero and heroine. Marylee, as the representation of desire, cannot act in her own interests—but only as a destructive force. Her manipulation of her brother's jealousy of Mitch and Lucy, which only succeeds in bringing them together and leading to Kyle's death, is, on a psychoanalytic level, eminently logical, i.e., it is motivated by Marylee's need to destroy Lucy because of Lucy's complicty with the Law; Lucy married Kyle rather than Mitch because she was attracted to Kyle as an object to be reformed/castrated. The important point, however, is that while Marylee is in a sense guilty of parricide and fratricide, her actions have served the interests and desires of the hero and heroine as well as the film's bourgeois audience. The audience, because of its desire for the union of Mitch and Lucy (the representation of itself on the screen), implicitly desires and approves the elimination of the obstacles to that union. From this perspective, we can begin to recognize why the film does not end with Kyle's death or, rather, why an epilogue that foregrounds Marylee is ideologically necessary.

As stated previously, the representation of Marylee within the epilogue implies that she has not been contained within the film's circular structure. What is at stake is not simply the disavowal of Marylee because of her function as the site of illicit desire or even as a signifier of the sexual Other. In order to absolve the bourgeois characters and audience from their complicity in parricide and fratricide, the text, as a product of ideology, must work to impose all of the guilt for these crimes onto Marylee.

The efforts of the filmic work to effect these goals can be seen most clearly in the final shots of the inquest sequence and in the shot of Marylee alone at her father's desk as Mitch and Lucy leave together. The ideological message, however, is most effective where it can be made to seem natural or unobtrusive and least effective in the context of such devices as an epilogue (i.e., something added on, a site for information that has not been integrated by the narrative) where it risks becoming didactic, calling attention to itself. Thus the problem with these two examples is that meaning is not fixed, restricted to the intended message. Instead, meaning is open, revealing contradictions which allow for alternative messages.

In the inquest sequence, just when it looks as if Marylee will send Mitch to prison for Kyle's death, there is an exchange of glances between Marylee in the witness box and the accused. In a quivering and seemingly repentant voice, Marylee tells the truth. As she finishes her testimony, she bows her head while the camera dollies in on her black, wide-brimmed hat to fade out the sequence. Thus the inquest sequence is basically an ideological ploy which, by unnecessarily raising the question of legal guilt and exonerating the hero of that guilt, in effect also exonerates him of any symbolic blame. It transfers all blame onto Marylee through the movement of the camera. In the traditional melodramatic fashion, bourgeois morality triumphs over the decadence of the affluent. Yet the high-angle closeup of Mitch opens up other, less comforting possibilities. The pleading expression on Mitch's face as he looks up at Marylee suggests his total vulnerability—Marylee has the power to destroy him. Why then does she choose not to exercise that power? The diegetic explanation, that she saves Mitch because she finally realizes that she cannot have him, is implausible and inconsistent. Why, after being driven to destroy her father and brother out of sexual frustration, should she spare the principal cause of that frustration? The salvation of the hero is clearly arbitrary—a resolution imposed from above. Had Marylee been allowed to act consistently, the film would in fact have revealed to the implied audience the "real conditions" of its existence.

The second example—the shot of Marylee at her father's desk—is also overly insistent. In this shot we have the image of Marylee seated behind the desk in a blue suit and holding a model oil derrick which is duplicated by the portrait of her father on the wall behind her. This shot, according to Sirk, represents his indictment of American capitalism: "Malone has lost everything. I have put up a sign indicating this—

Malone, alone, sitting there, hugging that goddamned oil well, having nothing. The oil well which is, I think, a rather frightening symbol of American society."[9] Yet if Marylee has "nothing," and if her smile is one of madness, then Sirk has provided the spectator with the opportunity to read this shot (and the film) as simply a disavowal of extreme wealth—the reassuring, familiar and ideologically charged message that the rich and powerful are not really happy (cf., Capra's *You Can't Take It With You*). This complicit reading seems at first glance confirmed by the representation of the departure of the hero and heroine. Shortly before Sirk presents us with the image of Marylee in her father's study, we have a shot of Mitch and Lucy as they are about to get into their car. The maid, in the extreme left corner of the frame, glances at Lucy (screen right) who is looking tenderly up at Mitch. Mitch is returning Lucy's gaze and holding her right arm protectively. The background is in soft focus with trees framing the heads of the happy couple. In the final shot of the film, we see the butler closing the gates after Mitch and Lucy have driven away. The formal resemblance between this shot and an earlier one in which the butler removed Jasper Hadley's funeral wreath from the gates establishes an implicit connection between wealth and death. Marylee is not only trapped by the wealth she possesses but is also condemned by it to a state of death-in-life. Thus the bourgeois spectator, in addition to deriving pleasure from the happiness of his/her screen surrogates, can rejoice in the punishment inflicted on a member of an alien class.

There is, however, something ambiguous about the way Marylee smiles at the model oil derrick/substitute phallus—an ambiguity that allows for an alternative reading of the film's conclusion. Is Marylee really mad? We cannot know this with any certainty. Has she really lost everything? The loss of Mitch is more of an imaginary loss than a real one, and the power represented by the object in her hands is certainly very real (the inquest sequence was ironically a testimony to the reality of that power). Moreover, if we look closely at Sirk's treatment of Mitch and Lucy's departure, we perceive that Sirk has subverted his "happy ending," thereby undercutting, even spoiling, the pleasure the implied spectator expects to feel at the representation of the union of Mitch and Lucy. What is particulary striking and disconcerting about the shot of the happy couple as they get into their car is the dominance of cold colors. Mitch, for example, is wearing a gray suit and the shadow from his gray-blue hat covers his eyes as he gazes down at Lucy. Lucy, on the other hand, wears a black cardigan sweater and a pink blouse. The pink blouse, in addition to the color lacking warmth, reinforces our sense of her as de-eroticized object—a pale imitation of female sexuality. The background with its dark greens and somber grays and blues intensifies the coldness of the scene. Also, the background is artificial, signifying the unnaturalness that lies at the base of this relationship. Finally, the notion that Marylee's wealth is an insufferable punishment is contradicted by the lighting of the concluding shot (specifically, the time of day when the shot was taken). The foreground, which includes the driveway, the sides of the gate and, significantly, the area outside of the gate, is in deep shadow. The mansion, on the other hand, is bathed in sunlight. Thus our alternative reading of the conclusion of *Written on the Wind* is that Marylee is not necessarily locked in, but rather that the bourgeois hero and heroine as well as the film's audience are locked out.

Notes

1. John G. Cawelti, *Adventure, Mystery, and Romance* (Chicago: Univ. of Chicago Press, 1976), p. 265.
2. Thomas Elsaesser, "Tales of Sound and Fury: Observations on the Family Melodrama," *Monogram*, No. 4 (1973), p. 10.
3. Geoffrey Nowell-Smith, "Minnelli and Melodrama" *Screen*, 18 (Summer 1977), p. 114.
4. Elsaesser, p. 3.
5. Robin Wood, "The American Family Comedy: From *Meet Me in St. Louis* to *The Texas Chainsaw Massacre*," *Wide Angle*, 3, No. 2 (1979), p. 6.
6. Joh Halliday, *Sirk on Sirk*: Interviews with Jon Halliday (London: Secker and Warburg, 1971), pp. 115–16.
7. Jon Halliday's comments on the theme of the impossibility of regression in *Written on the Wind* ("Introduction" to *Sirk on Sirk*, p. 12) suggest that the intention of this sequence might have been to announce this theme. The effect of the sequence on the spectator, however, is quite different.
8. Elaesser, p. 10. While Elsaesser mentions *Magnificent Obsession*, *Sign of the Pagan*, *All That Heaven Allows* and *Interlude*, he omits any reference to *Written on the Wind*.
9. Halliday, p. 119.

Coppola, Cimino: The Operatics of History

NAOMI GREENE

In retrospect, it seems as if a new kind of cinematic melodrama, exemplified by Francis Ford Coppola's Godfather films and *Apocalypse Now* and by Michael Cimino's *The Deerhunter* and *Heaven's Gate*, developed in the 1970s. Variously described as "historical," "operatic," "choral" or "epic," this melodrama marked a new sensibility in American film, at once deeply theatrical and pessimistic, a sensibility which reflected on the one hand the formal influence of European and especially Italian models and on the other the traumatized social/political climate of post-Vietnam, post-Watergate America. Above all, this sensibility was dominated by a sense of history and a taste for spectacle which were interwoven with each other and with the narrative in unprecedented ways.

Many of the striking features of these films call to mind the defining characteristics of stage melodrama at its inception around the time of the French Revolution: heightened theatricality, characters greater than life, powerful emotions and extreme actions, startling scenic effects and elaborate *mise-en-scène*, as well as a penchant for great contrasts on both the moral level (a Manichean sense of good and evil) as well as the scenic one (contrasts in lights, costumes, and so on). Lastly, they attribute a pivotal role to music (the Godfather theme, the violin accompaniment in *Heaven's Gate*) which was originally *the* defining element of melodrama. The vast social and political fresco against which these films are played out (Vietnam in the case of *Apocalypse Now* and

 Naomi Greene's "Coppola, Cimino: The Operatics of History" originally appeared in *Film Quarterly*, Vol. 38, no. 2 (Winter 1984–85), pp. 28–37. Reprinted by permission of the author and the University of California Press.

The Deerhunter, the immigrant experience in the Godfather films, the "Rustler's War" or the Johnson County Wars in *Heaven's Gate*) suggest, in particular, historical melodrama, which was one of the forms taken by melodrama at an early date. Born at a troubled historical moment—when the old world order, embodied in the French monarchy, was approaching its convulsive death throes, to be followed by decades of turmoil in the Terror and the rise and fall of Napoleon—early melodrama often turned to real events and characters. In the words of one critic, the French Revolution provided excellent models for monstrous villains for "Nothing was improbable to people who had lived through Thermidor."[1]

If these films recall such melodrama, even more so do they evoke one of the paths taken by melodrama in the course of the ninteenth century: opera and, in particular, Verdi. Once again, the vastness of the frescoes they present is such that they suggest less the fairly domestic Verdi of *La Traviata* than the Verdi of the great historical/political operas such as *Rigoletto, I Lombardi,* or *Don Carlos.* In such works, history sets the scene for the portrayal of Romantic passions and conventions: heroes are torn by conflicting loyalties, crushed by Destiny, tangled in tragic conflicts which can end only in murder or self-destruction. In many instances, these tremendously popular operas were enmeshed in the deeply rooted passions surrounding Italian unification: for these reasons, Antonio Gramsci, the great Italian Marxist theoretician, saw them as the Italian equivalent of the "national-popular" literature created in nineteenth-century France by greatly popular authors such as Sue, Dumas, Balzac. In a penetrating article on melodrama, the contemporary critic Thomas Elsaesser describes this phenomenon thus: "In France it is the works of Sue, Hugo and Balzac that reflect most closely the relation of melodrama to social upheaval while the national liberals in Italy during the Risorgimento . . . apparently saw their political aspirations reflected in Verdi's operas."[2]

In general, cinema, with its links to popular culture and its mass audience, its ability to create spectacles, has been seen as the twentieth-century counterpart of both melodrama and opera. It is hardly coincidental that "classical" melodrama died at the same time that cinema was born. As for its link with opera, in an article entitled "Pageants of Violence," Mark Le Fanu observes that: "The emotional charge of opera . . . translated into the 'expressive' *mise-en-scène* of early silent cinema as lighting, gesture, musical accompaniment, could stand as the very definition of melodrama . . . the portrayal of historical events in the cinema inherits opera's emotional intensity in the emphasis it has always placed on violence, gesture and spectacle."[3] Certainly, such a view is confirmed by films considered historical epics: the spectacular elements in films as diverse as Cecil B. De Mille's Biblical frescos, *Reds,* or even *Star Wars,* convey, in Le Fanu's words, the "emotional charge of opera." But what distinguishes these films from, say, both the operas of Verdi and the recent films by Coppola and Cimino is the fact that they do not touch upon issues of national destiny, issues with the potential of stirring deep collective sentiments. *Reds,* for example, may intrigue us intellectually, stir us visually, but it does not touch the raw nerve in the national psyche that was so moved by *The Deerhunter* or the Godfather films. Given this important distinction, it is highly suggestive that, like Verdi's great historical operas, these recent films were made at a deeply troubled historical era, an era which had witnessed not only Watergate and Vietnam, but the end of a certain concept of

America. And, I suggest, largely because of their connection to a traumatic and political era, some of them were able to strike a profoundly responsive chord in audiences. (The failure of *Heaven's Gate* may be partially attributed to the fact that by the time it appeared, the national mood was already changing.) And, as in opera, this chord went so deep, and involved the viewer at such a visceral level, largely through the manipulation of spectacle.

Both the weight given spectacle and the fact that they evoke crucial moments in the national destiny bring these films closer to Italian directors such as Visconti, or the Bertolucci of *1900*, than to American films of recent years. Not surprisingly, these Italian directors have always been seen as quintessentially operatic. To quote Le Fanu once again: "The operatic view of history has a long tradition . . . most vividly exemplified perhaps by movies like Visconti's *Senso* or Rossellini's two dramatisations of 19th century history *Viva L'Italia* and *Vanina Vanini*. In all these films history is mediated through violent and melodramatic passion. . . ."[4] Despite these similarities, Visconti's view of history is essentially different from that found in these American films. History may be "mediated through passion" but, at the same time, his best films such as *Il Gattopardo* or *Senso*, both of which deal with crucial moments in the creation of modern Italy, are deeply analytic in their approach to history, inspired by a Marxian view of social classes and economic structures. Even the extreme estheticism which is evident in his use of *mise-en-scène* and costumes is linked to underlying themes: significant details reveal the spirit of an epoch or of a certain class. And his tone is consistently theatrical, so much so in fact that the stage of history and the stage of spectacle (be it opera or film) emerge as interwoven domains. Like many of Visconti's characters, the Prince of Salina in *Il Gattopardo* is aware of himself as an actor upon a stage which is both that of history and film. His is a distance born of world-weariness as much as philosophy; his theatrical acting corresponds to a world which views reality itself as a phenomenon subject to multiple illusions.

This combination of historical accuracy and analysis, together with a Baroque/illusionist world view which presents history as theater, is not found in these recent American films. As is usually the case in American cinema, their power lies less in analysis than in recreating the feel and climate of certain experiences (such as the horror of war which comes through in *The Deerhunter*), in presenting believable and even ordinary people (Cimino's, in particular, act with great naturalism) who find themselves in extraordinary situations. (*Apocalypse Now* is the exception here since it operates almost exclusively on a mythic level.) In these films, history is often transmuted into myth as it becomes a springboard for general comments involving human destiny, good and evil, the tragedy of power. The Godfather films go beyond the story of a Mafia family as they create a drama of greed, vengeance and power; *Heaven's Gate* is not only a conflict between cattlemen and farmers, or even a class confrontation on a vast scale, but, like *The Deerhunter*, a struggle between good and evil.

This view of history—as a battleground for moral issues which is shaped by individuals and psychology, rather than by economic and social forces—is perfectly in tune with the melodramatic/operatic sensibility underlying these films. While they do not share Visconti's view of the world as spectacle or theater, they are imbued with a heightened theatricality, such as that which characterized early melodrama, which operates on several levels. Within the diegesis itself, this theatricality is underscored by the presence of towering villains (Michael Corleone in the Godfather films, the chief of the cattlemen in *Heaven's Gate*, the Vietcong tortures in *The Deerhunter*), the presence of powerful emotions (fear, passion, revenge), violent actions (betrayal, fratricide, suicide, murder) and tremendous contrasts (the cross-cutting between the church ceremonies and the bloody mob murders in *Godfather II*). And the films often contain performances or theatrical sequences which, to varying degrees, reflect upon the film itself. Both the jungle in *Apocalypse Now* and the old West in *Heaven's Gate* constitute the background for such sequences (go-go dancers perform for the troops in Vietnam, the immigrants stage a cockfight), while in the Godfather films sequences of theater are closely interwoven with the narrative. Vito Corleone goes to see an Italian melodrama where he has his first glimpse of the neighborhood boss (dressed melodramatically in white as he would be in Sicily) whom he will have to kill to begin his own career; on his way to perform the deed he passes a puppet show of Sicilian marionettes jousting to the death; Michael Corleone learns his brother has betrayed him during a theatrical/erotic extravanganza in Havana. In addition to theatrical sequences, important moments are often staged as if they were theater. Vito prowls the New York streets like a latter-day Fantômas and, when he murders the old Don, overhead shots of the streets make it seem as if we are in an opera house: the murder itself is punctuated by ceremonial music and fireworks from a street festival. The first murder in *Heaven's Gate* is seen through a carefully composed hole in the tent which both frames it and suggests many of the other frames (archways, doorways) used in the film. Even the final "tableaux" of stage melodrama find their counterparts here in the family scenes of the Godfather films, the last scene of *The Deerhunter*, or the choral scenes of the immigrants at work in *Heaven's Gate*, all of which are carefully "staged," painterly, designed to imprint themselves upon our memory.

This emphasis upon theatricality is constantly heightened by dramatic lighting, composition, patterns of color and texture. To a certain extent, of course, these have always represented crucial elements in melodrama; in the words of Thomas Elsaesser: "Considered as an expressive code, melodrama might therefore be described as a particular form of dramatic *mise-en-scène*, characterized by a dynamic use of spatial and musical categories, as opposed to intellectual or literary ones." And, in this code, dramatic values are "sublimated into decor, colour, gesture and composition of frame.[5] This is more true than ever in these films where the visual motifs are given such weight they often create a subtext of their own which seems to affect us in a subconscious way: the various locations in *The Deerhunter* create a kind of symphony of reds and blues (the red fires of the steel mill, of the bombs in Vietnam, and the bandanas and blood of the Russian roulette players, the blue of the small town) which merge in the final scene with the American flag, just as the browns and sepia tones, or the repeated shots of water (New York Harbor, the ocean surrounding Cuba, Lake Tahoe) give a special patina to *Godfather II*.

While these motifs may play a more extensive and sophisticated role than they did in earlier films, they are not new. But what is new in these films is the way spectacle, or sequences of spectacle, are intercut with the narrative. In this sense, the films are closer to opera, where the choruses or arias stop and fix the onward narrative flow, than to, say, the films of a Visconti where the narrative is conveyed through spectacle, and where every sequence is part of the spectacle which envelops reality as it does film. In this respect, it is noteworthy that a number of these films are actually structured like opera. *Apocalypse Now* begins with a kind of overture as it shows scenes of the misty jungle, proceeds to Act I—Martin Sheen receiving his orders; Act II—the trip up the river; and Act III—Heart of Darkness, the encounter with Brando-Kurtz.[6] The overture and finale of *The Deerhunter* are set in the small town and the steel mill while the major acts unfold in Vietnam; in *Heaven's Gate* both the overture and the finale are separated from the rest of the action by distance and by decades.

Of course, the weight and even the function accorded spectacle, or the balance between spectacle and narrative if you will, is not the same in all these films. In this respect, the two films about Vietnam are quite different from each other. In *Apocalypse Now,* the narrative is virtually a pretext for one spectacle scene after another: the helicopter raid (to Wagnerian music), the surfers on the river, the surrealistic camp of the demented Brando-Kurtz. In this nightmarish world, the horror of Vietnam has become a pretext for spectacle: the jungle and burning cities appear as a Dantesque inferno often endowed with a strange beauty of its own. The opening scenes of the misty jungle entrance us visually while the final scene of flaming reds and yellows resembles an abstract painting. Psychology and verisimilitude have been displaced by symbolism and myth: the journey up the river, which makes little sense in terms of modern strategic warfare, is a mythic journey to the deepest realm of the self, to the ultimate horror. While spectacle and symbolism are also present in *The Deerhunter* (one has only to think of its jungle scenes, or those of Russian roulette, or those which surround the killing of the deer), unlike *Apocalypse Now,* it is also firmly tied to an American genre (small town friends who go off to war), and to a fairly strong narrative which involves the realistic depiction of place and people. The powerful scenes of war constitute an alien world which contrasts with the scenes at home. And, it may well be that *The Deerhunter* was able to touch a much deeper chord in audiences than *Apocalypse Now* precisely because it was rooted in a reality with which audiences could identify.

Both the Godfather films and *Heaven's Gate* are also rooted, significantly, in archetypal American genres (the gangster film and the Western) and they too intercut scenes of spectacle with the narrative as does *The Deerhunter.* Thus, for example, while the wedding scene in *Godfather I* plays a role which has some functions that are narrative (it introduces us to the major characters) or social (it sets up the ethnicity of the Corleone family), what strikes us most about this sequence is its formal qualities (the sunlight wedding contrasting with the dark interiors) which create a kind of subtext reinforcing the film's theme of claustrophobia and power.

Of all the films, it is in *Heaven's Gate* where sequences of spectacle are given their greatest weight—far more weight and length, in all probability, than ever before in American film. There, while the swirling, vertiginous dances at Harvard Yard which occur towards the beginning may create a mood, they serve little narrative purpose; instead, as we'll see, they are there to be echoed formally later in the film. Here, too, the gains of spectacle seem to be made at the expense of narrative conventions which are treated very casually. (This unusual balance may be one of the reasons, in fact, that the film's initial reception was disastrous; in any case, it was largely these sequences of spectacle which were omitted or drastically cut in the shortened version of the film.)

Audiences used to conventional narrative cannot help but wonder how a man, last seen at a Harvard graduation, turns up as a sheriff on the frontier twenty years later.[7] Or why his Harvard sweetheart would wait thirty years to marry him—thirty years in which she does not age at all. In addition to characters who are not really introduced, to an absence of explicit psychology (one can only guess at motives), scenes which would be emphasized in a conventional narrative (for example, the first murder of the immigrants) go by so quickly that the audience hardly grasps them on first viewing, and the purpose of other, even lengthy scenes (such as the hero's intervention during a cockfight staged by the immigrants) is never really clear. Still other scenes, including the long valedictory address, only become clear in retrospect. Instead of one climactic battle scene, virtually the last hour of the film is devoted to a series of almost unendurable defeats. Narrative conventions are so totally broken, in fact, and expectations so thwarted, that without prior knowledge of the story it takes a very long while before the subject of the film is clear. And the break with narrative conventions is often matched by spatial dislocations. Not only do the battle scenes generate a sense of confusion (it's not clear where anyone is coming from, or going to) but smoke from guns and explosions often obscures any sense of depth so that the figures appear flattened. Renaissance space and narrative conventions have given way to a mythic world of visual icons.

In the past it has been suggested that American film's traditional emphasis on narrative progression—on acts and consequences—revealed a given ideology or world view; in the words of Thomas Elsaesser, the transformation of "spatial and temporal sequences . . . into consequences," the "continuum of cause and effect" in classical American film meant that one was "secure in the knowledge that the scenes fitted into each other like cog-wheels in a clock-work, and that all visual information was purposive, inflected towards a plenitude of significance, saturated with clues that explained motivation and character. Out of conflict, contradiction and contingency the narrative generated order, linearity and articulated energy,"[8] Along similar lines, other critics have linked the narrative thrust in earlier American films to an ideology of progress. But if this is true, or even partially true, then the diminished role accorded narrative in these recent films, as well as the fact that the diegesis is constantly cut by spectacle, can be seen as indicators of an ideological shift whereby the "plenitude of significance," the "order, linearity and articulated energy," if they survive at all, have been greatly weakened, and have given way to a loss of belief in action, a sense that the individual can no longer control his own life.

This theoretical link between formal considerations and ideology is certainly buttressed by the mood of these films which is one of moral nihilism, inevitability and decline. As is often the case in melodrama, the individual seems impotent, caught in a web of destiny which encourages a kind of voluptuous pessimism. A late-Romantic infatuation with the irrational and with death consumes Michael Corleone in the Godfather films as well as Nick in *The Deerhunter.* Like a certain strand of fin-de-siècle literature and art, these films often revel in the grotesque or the pathological. This is especially true of the two films set in Vietnam where war is no longer a testing ground for heroism but a maelstrom of madness and violence. Abnormality reigns in Brando-Kurtz's mad kingdom, reeking of dismembered heads and a savage exoticism, where the final murder is a kind of homoerotic dance, a late romantic marriage of thanatos and eros. The hero of *The Deerhunter* risks his life not to save his friend from the enemy (as in earlier war films) but from a drug-induced obsession with death which compels him to the Russian roulette table in what is probably the strongest scene of the film. Even in those films less prone to emphasize the grotesque, the climate is still one of decline and despair where the individual is prey to murderous forces.

Ultimately, this climate reflects that which haunted a post-Vietnam America which no longer believed in its future or even, for that matter, in what could be seen as the accepted view of its past. It is not coincidental that the rereading of America's past which emerges from some of these films is bleak indeed. The rise of the Mafia family in the Godfather films, for example, has been seen as a parable about the ruthless course of capitalist America.[9] This may well be so but, in addition, Michael's somewhat inexplicable evolution from gallant World War II veteran (when we first meet him he is in uniform) to cold-blooded killer (by the end of the film he tells us that "if History has taught us anything, it's that you can kill anyone") can also be seen as a metaphor for the America that went from its heroic role in the Second World War to the horror of Vietnam. What is seen as self-preservation at the beginning ends in murderous paranoia as Michael slaughters even those who can no longer do him harm. The specter of Vietnam informs the film's sense that enemies can be anywhere and that no one can be trusted, while the lone figure of Michael shrouded in darkness at the end suggests the very lonely, powerful yet impotent America which emerged from the war.

In *Heaven's Gate*, the references to the war in Southeast Asia are more explicit and inescapable, the revisionist view of America's past bleaker, the indictment of United States policy perhaps the strongest ever seen in mainstream film. Its very theme raises the question of class exploitation since it concerns the massacre of homesteading immigrants, who embody a peaceful force in most Westerns, at the hands of rich cattle barons and their mercenary killers who are aided not only by the US Army (the American flag which once signalled that aid was on the way now suggests that murder is about to begin), but by the President himself. Their villainous leader, dressed melodramatically in Russian fur hat and long black coat, tells us that his family includes a governor, a former Secretary of State and a Secretary of War. This official war-machine will crush any individual who gets in its way. Devoid of the solidarity and hope for the future offered by the Marxist perspective in *1900*, lacking perforce that film's catharsis, the film's pessimism becomes almost unbearable. Its beaten and lonely hero (the ties of friendship—so crucial to *The Deerhunter*—have been undermined here by political differences and sexual rivalry) is thrice destroyed as in a kind of epic poem: the homesteading immigrants he is helping are massacred, the woman he loves is murdered, and even the personal integrity granted the Western hero is denied him for, at the end, he is a drained shell of a man, drifting aimlessly on his yacht off Newport Beach. The film's rhythm is one of inevitable decline, a decline broken only by sequences which, in one way or another, have to break the diegesis.

But if the sequences of spectacle break the diegetic flow, they also—and this is true of all the films—reinforce major themes. What makes the "message" of *Heaven's Gate* more powerful than, say, that of other "anti-Westerns" (*A Man Called Horse*, *Tell Them Willie Boy Is Here*, *Soldier Blue*, *Little Big Man*), which give an imperialist cast to their reading of America's past in the light of Vietnam, is due not only to its epic proportions (length, beauty, sweep) and allusions to class warfare, but to the way it manipulates spectacle. Its musical and visual motifs create and reinforce a sense of tremendous loss, a mood of total despair and hopelessness. Mention has been made of the circle motif, accompanied by the same musical strains, which occurs at important points throughout the film. In the words of a French critic, Michael Henry:

> The circle motif structures the *mise-en-scène* of groups. A privileged form of ritual, it [the circle motif] dominates each of these episodes: at Harvard where the Blue Danube Waltz first involves three rings of dancers waltzing in opposite directions (rings enlivened by the dips and swings made by each couple) and then two new, exclusively masculine rings which form around the May Tree; at Sweetwater [on the frontier] where the motif recurs in the rare moments of euphoria (Ella's crazy horse and carriage adventure, the cock fight in the smoky backroom, the rollerskaters' ball . . .); lastly, in the final battle where the murderers are encircled by the immigrants' wagons which are, in turn, encircled by the Cavalry."[10]

Like the repetition of music, each successive visual echo imprints itself more strongly upon our sensibility than the preceding ones since it resonates with what we have already seen. Each time the circle motifs recurs, it evokes the terrible contrast between the idealism and spontaneity of the opening and the subsequent disillusion and despair. The repetition of key family gatherings and celebrations in the Godfather films punctuates and accents the sense of decline in a similar manner. The first scene showing a family united and at peace remains in our mind and is the standard by which we judge, and lament, each successive reunion which reveals the growing decay in family bonds.

The implicit comparison between past and present evoked by resonant motifs or recurring sequences (or, in the case of *Godfather II*, by explicit cross-cutting between scenes which depict the rise of the first, immigrant, Godfather and that of his son, Michael) gives rise in these films (with the exception of *Apocalypse Now*) to a mood of overwhelming nostalgia for an America that has been lost, for the American dream gone astray or betrayed. The explicit lament for the "Good Gone Days" in *Heaven's Gate* haunts all these films. The depiction of immigrant groups in the Godfather films and in the two films by Cimino may reflect the directors' background, but it also plays on the mythology of an America seen as the savior of the needy and the poor. Not only has that America disappeared, but in the wake of the seventies we are led to ask whether it ever existed. The beautiful Western landscape of *Heaven's Gate* has lost none of the mythical power it had in former Westerns, but it has become the breeding ground not of justice but of massacre and class warfare. The contrast between the present and the "golden age" from which we are forever exiled—a world of hope epitomized in the lyrical opening of *Heaven's Gate* celebrating America's rebirth after the trauma of the Civil War—is conveyed by powerful color and visual motifs. As Michael Henry has observed, in *Heaven's Gate* a "network of correspondences, antitheses, and internal rimes" links the opening, idealistic scene at Harvard with the scenes on the frontier: i.e., the scene of the ranked graduates is echoed by the procession of miserable immigrants, the student choruses by the foreign chants of the workers, the candlelit faces of the beautiful young girls by those of the prostitutes.[11] In the Godfather films, the golden-hued New York scenes depicting the life of the old Don (with its moments of hope, generosity, warmth) shine luminously in comparison with the America of his son Michael whose total loss of values and human feeling is mirrored in his bleak Nevada estate; the teeming New York streets have given way to an isolated, policed compound.

One of the central visual motifs of both *Godfather II* and *Heaven's Gate* enhances the sense of loss created by these contrasts between past and present, or between landscape and events. Both films play on the theme of photography which is imbued, per se, with a deep nostalgia, with an aching sense of the past: in the words of Susan Sontag, "Photographs promote nostalgia. Photography is an elegiac art, a twilight art. . . . All photographs are momenti mori."[12] The New York scenes in *Godfather II* recall photographs by reason of their golden hues and soft focus as well as by their accompanying subtitles such as "Ellis Island, 1901." The sepia tones of early photographs also characterize certain scenes in *Heaven's Gate* where, in addition, photography is actually brought into the narrative. Somewhat inexplicably, the hero keeps by his bedside a photograph of himself and his youthful love (a photograph which constantly suggests the idealism and romance of the beginning) while the hard-working immigrants find time to pose for a photographer. In this film, the golden/sepia tones bathe not only the rare moments of release and happiness epitomized by the square dance but also the dreadful scenes of massacre, almost as if these should have been, and now are, photographed for posterity. Is this deliberate or unconscious? Is the film commenting upon its own role as a maker or, in this case, as a debunker of photographs/myths?

But in the very strength with which spectacle creates nostalgia there lies a certain danger. For unlike Verdi's operas which raised people to political passion, the mood of these films gently persuades us that all idealism is empty, all action futile, history and historical awareness unimportant. And the resulting emptiness is all too easily filled by a voluptuous nostalgia, and by the problematical myths and ideological confusion that may have contributed to the perceived decline. This is very clear, for example, in the two war films which, almost certainly inadvertently, are tainted with the ugly racism that characterized the war itself. Brando-Kurtz performs as a white god to teeming Asian masses, while the sadistic Vietcong tortures in *The Deerhunter* would not have felt out of place in a Hollywood film about World War II. *Heaven's Gate* creates a great ambivalence in the audience when it gradually reveals that the slaughered immigrants, innocent victims who should elicit all our sympathy, are for the most part, weak, cowardly and crude, totally in contrast with the altruistic hero who is (incidentally?) a wealthy man. Cimino has remarked that this portrayal of the immigrants was designed to show them as a "new class which is ready to collaborate, to imitate the stockgrowers. The circle closes once again."[13] But I'm not sure that this message, pessimistic as it is, comes through. I think, rather, that we begin—however uneasily—to share the class-inspired scorn the cattle barons feel for those newly arrived masses, and to ask ourselves if democracy and justice for such people is worth defending. The collapse of the American ideal is twofold: historical, since an almost official slaughter occurs, and philosophical, since all idealism is made to seem empty.

Of course, it's also possible that the political ambivalences in these films, in addition to their mood of nostalgia, held a deep appeal for a nation that had been deeply traumatized and defeated for the first time. With *The Deerhunter* we could both condemn war (perhaps even Vietnam) and be touched by an old-fashioned patriotism which had become suspect, while the Godfather films allowed us to criticize contemporary America and yet wax elegiac about a lost world of family values. And *Heaven's Gate* encouraged a postwar cynicism since its overwhelming pessimism suggests that any struggle against the system is futile. This ambivalence also meant that while the overt message of the Godfather films or *Heaven's Gate* might be leftist, the myths upon which they draw (Power and Patriarchy in the one case, Romantic Heroism in the other) could have a reactionary tone. Built into the powerful formal fabric of the film, it is this tone which emerges victorious. The result is that spectacle encourages us to lament the past, to forget history, and to luxuriate in spectacle for its own sake.

Notes

1. Frank Rahill, *World of Melodrama* (University Park: Pennsylvania State University Press, 1967), p. 15.
2. Thomas Elsaesser, "Tales of Sound and Fury: Observations on the Family Melodrama" *Monogram*, No. 4 (1972), p. 4.
3. Mark Le Fanu, "Pageants of Violence: Problems on the Staging of History," *Monogram*, No. 6 (October, 1975), pp. 6–7.
4. Le Fanu, p. 11.
5. Elsaesser, "Tales of Sound and Fury," p. 6.
6. See Ruth McCormick's review of the film in *Cineaste*, Fall, 1979.
7. In an interview with Kris Kristofferson, the critic Charles Champlin was moved to ask if the actor had any ideas about what his character did in the intervening years!
8. Thomas Elsaesser, "The Pathos of Failure: American Films in the 1970's," *Monogram*, No. 6 (1975), p. 13.
9. John Hess, "*Godfather II*: A Deal Coppola Couldn't Refuse," in *Movies and Methods*, ed. by Bill Nichols (Berkeley: University of California Press, 1976), pp. 81–90.
10. Michael Henry, "Le rêve perverti: de *The Deerhunter* à *Heaven's Gate*," *Positif*, No. 246 (September, 1981), p. 13.
11. Ibid.
12. Susan Sontag, *On Photography* (New York: Delta, 1977), p. 15.
13. From an interview with Michael Ciment and Michael Henry published in *Positif*, No. 246 (September, 1981), p. 19.

The Collective Voice as Cultural Voice

CHRISTINE SAXTON

It is well known that the cinematic equivalent of the classical narrative text and its prevailing single "voice" has dominated the commerical cinema since the second decade of this century.[1] This voice, thanks to the tradition of auteur criticism, has commonly been identified with the director, although not all film critics were willing to concede that the thematic and stylistic consistencies of a film text could be credited to the director so simply. They argued that regardless of a film's similarity to a director's other works the fact remained that it had been produced under the aegis of a studio with the participation of writers, camera and lighting crews, set designers, and actors. The auteurists countered such resistance, arguing that not every film had an auteur; indeed a director could only be called an auteur where her or his voice could be heard above the general "noise"[2] of other influences.

The auteurists effectively won this battle, and for the last two and a half decades they have shared dominion only with genre studies over the field of film criticism and most film curricula. Early structuralist work never questioned the role of the director; it either sought to integrate auteurism with the essentially contradictory aspects of genre studies (Kitses, *Horizons West*), or tried to accommodate it (Wollen, *Signs and Meaning in the Cinema*). Recently, however, the idea of the director as author of the film text has come under the scrutiny of theorists schooled in poststructuralist approaches to the text. According to this current school of thought, the voice emerging from the

Christine Saxton's "The Collective Voice as Cultural Voice" originally appeared in *Cinema Journal*, Vol. 26, no. 1 (Fall 1986), pp. 19–30. Reprinted by permission of the author and *Cinema Journal*.

narrative, far from being the expression of an autonomous individual, is a very complex discursive phenomenon. Indeed, Roland Barthes contends in "Death of the Author" that "[w]e know now that a text is not a line of words releasing a single 'theological' meaning (the 'message' of the Author-God) but a multi-dimensional space in which a variety of writings, none of them original, blend and clash. The text is a tissue of quotations drawn from the innumerable centres of culture."[3]

Barthes argues that the reader, or the spectator for film, rather than the author is the source of signification. The author's status is further diminished by the conception of the text as a blend and clash of unoriginal, culturally coded writings. Defining an author, Barthes suggests, "is to impose a limit on that text, to furnish it with a final signified, to close the writing."[4] Clearly, within the context of commercial cinema, the identification of an author continues to be crucial to us. As a popular audience we demand that the polysemy of the text be suppressed and that the film pretend to monological signification. Furthermore, the institutionalized cinema industry insistently continues to produce films according to this formula. Barthes's work demonstrates that the notion of authorship is not only consistent with a tradition of individualism, it also appeases our desire for an enclosed meaningful experience. The author, it would seem, is unavoidable. Yet recent theoretical work has made it possible to consider authorship in something rather than traditional auteurist terms. The author is something built into a text, something that seems to speak to us when we read.

Yet to define an author as a cultural function and her or his voice as the product of "readerly" narrative codes is not to deny the contribution of those engaged in the production of texts. Surely nobody actually goes that far. Nevertheless, perhaps in a reaction to the stranglehold of auteurism, much current theory with its emphasis on the position of the spectator-subject and textual codes is in danger of undervaluing text production. In "Fiction of the Author/Author of the Fiction," the introduction to the final section of his book on authorship, John Caughie cautions against conceiving of "the coherence of the text as a pure 'inside' (producing itself, for an empty spectator, out of its own internal operations), or as a pure 'outside' (given by an originating source). . . ." Instead he suggests that the object is "to formulate the text, and its subjects, as a movement between the two, or as the involvement of the one in the other, destroying the purity of each."[5] The essays Caughie chose to include in this final section reveal a wide range of approaches to the place of the author within the institution of cinema. And cumulatively the section does make it clear that for any study of the cinematic apparatus the codes governing those who participate in the production of films are as important as the codes governing reading.

Accepting Caughie's conclusions as a founding premise, I find it reasonable to make the next step and argue that in the cultural analysis of the film text we must in fact deal with two sets of codes—distinct sub-systems of a more comprehensive system of cinematic representation. In short, as a cultural institution the cinema is a collective process in the largest sense (despite the fact that it is a very private industry when it comes to profit). It involves not only crew, cast, and studio, but also all of us who consume the film. In addition it includes a complex economic industrial network of which we are all a part and a particular system of narrative representation which we have all learned. Film, in other words, is a *cultural collaboration* in which we are all collaborators. Producers and consumers alike all contribute to the polyphony, that "tissue of quotations drawn from the innumerable centre of culture," that we know as cinema discourse.

We have, it seems, been able to dispense with the question, Who *is* the author? And much theoretical inquiry has preferred, along with Barthes, to answer the question, Is there an author? in the negative. However, I would like to reconsider the concomitant question, *What* is an author? in the hope of arriving at a clearer understanding of film as a cultural collaboration.

The four characteristics of the author proposed by Foucault in his essay "What Is an Author?"[6] would seem a good place to start.

1. Discourse has become a kind of "property" whose appropriation is designated by the name of the author. Such an orientation cannot help but produce a tension in an institution like the cinema since the name of the author generally does not coincide with that of the owner. Two ramifications result from this proprietary displacement: It gives sole right of speech to the director, rendering all other contributors to the film's discourse voiceless. Simultaneously it obscures the commercial nature of production (hence the powers that direct the author's speech) in the name of art. The director becomes a kind of *front*. He stands in for all those listed in the credits, implicitly claiming responsibility for everything from script to make-up. Further, in the tradition of artistic genius, the director is allowed to assume creative credit in a medium possessed by its concern with public response and therefore highly conservative in its adherence to conventions of style, story, and theme.

2. The author-function is not attributed to all texts. Indeed, in recent times scientific discourse has commonly been treated as authorless, its credibility depending upon its association with an established system of truths and verifications. While literature and dramatic discourse are emphatically authored, film has followed a more circuitous route. Artistic genius, in other words, was not always considered a possibility in the cinema. Because of the medium's rather dubious standing in the arts many early film directors and actors were not anxious to acknowledge their contributions.

Not until films became a more valuable form of property—even acquiring art status in some cases—did directorial credit become a matter of importance. Even by the end of the first decade of this century the industry's profitability made recognition an issue. In fact, the Motion Picture Patents Company's efforts to suppress the identities of their creative personnel in the interest of proprietary control and profit are regarded as one of the factors that led to its capitulation.[7] Despite notable exceptions, the initial importance of the film product remained more a property and, by extension, profit issue than an aesthetic issue for some time. Furthermore, in the eyes of the public at large film remained mere entertainment.

Only with the advent of the auteur theory in the early 1960s did the American film director begin to acquire much status as an artist.[8] Strikingly, the auteur argument championed by Andrew Sarris was in America, as it had been earlier in France, a demand for the recognition of film as an art form in its own right, worthy of serious attention and, hence, the right of authorship. But advancement of the cinema to the status of an art brought with it the notion of author as artistic genius. The cinema, whose collaborative nature had once been suppressed altogether by the production companies, was now conceived as a pantheon of cult directors. Films became authored texts if the auteur critics liked them, and authorless studio pieces if they did not.

The collective process was regarded as one of the inescapable facts of American feature production that the director had to transcend to achieve auteur status.[9]

3. Authorship, as an alternative system of truth and verification to that provided by science, then ascribes some kind of special sight to the author who therefore becomes the measure of validity of a work. Conceivably the shift from authorlessness to authorship in the history of the cinema has paralleled a transformation in our conception of the medium. Our movement away from an emphasis on the cinema as a technological process that mechanically records the "real world" to that of an art that interprets human experience corresponds to an increasing concern with the *poetic truth* of the film text as opposed to its scientific truth as a reproduced document. (As popular responses to documentary and news broadcasts make evident, this is a transformation that has not yet been finalized.) But what exactly is *poetic truth*, or even mere credibility in a film? We know from recent work on verisimilitude that the classical novel sought to naturalize narrative in two ways: through recourse to detailed description of material objects often peripheral to the story, Barthes's *reality effect*; and by a system of maxims and commonplaces—a system of popular beliefs, in other words—which may be elaborated in the work or left implicit.[10]

As is well known, the cinema's capacity for exact reproduction was one of the characteristics that prevented its being accepted as art. Yet this very realism has enabled narrative cinema to pick up where classical realist fiction left off and to convey the powerful "human truths" which modern western society has commonly regarded as universal. Of course, cinematic representation of human truths, though perhaps more compellingly realistic, derives its credibility from the same cultural repositories as its literary counterpart. The cinema, composed as it is of analogical signs, may be initially easier to read than literature; but to go beyond the level of literal identification requires cultural knowledge and a certain foundational belief consensus on what is true and natural. This is not to say that ideology is necessarily uniform and coherent throughout a culture. However, there does appear to be a level of common ground, a massive construct of commonplaces at once fractured and fluid, which we share as members of that culture. It surfaces most audibly in public discourse and most pervasively in the popular arts. Poetic truth, the aesthetic presentation of universal human truths, and the determinants of credibility derive from this cultural repository.

Since a film far more than a novel is a collective commercial undertaking, deeply dependent on its audience, it stands to reason that even under the control of the most tyrannical and egotistical director the end product will have absorbed as many interpretations as there are contributors, and the production will have been fashioned with audience comprehension and taste in mind. The audience, for its part, will receive the film according to the readerly codes of film consumption and the film's relation to the contemporary social context.

Indeed, the mode of representation as a conventional system has evolved as a kind of contract between producers and audience. Furthermore, the mode of representation along with the narrative tradition are themselves part of the cultural repository internalized by the enculturated individual. Although film producers must learn a distinct subsystem of the codes of production, they nevertheless share not only the classical cinematic paradigm but also more general cultural paradigms of narrative and representation with their audience. Each of the contributors, therefore, including the director, can be conceived as a nexus for all the texts and codifications (cultural, narrative, representational, and specifically cinematic) that might be brought into operation in any given film. We have a situation in which a collectivity of culturally-bound individuals produces a representation whose every facet is drawn from a common reserve of cultural discourse. If a director can be called an author, and thus a speaker of poetic truths, it is only insofar as she or he operates as the overseer of the production of this *cultural collaboration*.

4. The preceding discussion brings us to a point from which we can examine Foucault's final feature. As recent work has demonstrated, the author as we know *her* or *him* is not an actual individual. *It* is a discursive function that arises directly from the text—even as that text extends to other texts—a social function and a narrative function. We have already seen that it is a social function because the text is a tissue of quotations drawn from the cultural repository and organized according to a long narrative tradition and a socio-political-historical context. Further, it is a social function because each of the individuals participating in the production and consumption of a specific film text contributes her or his idiolectic configuration of the cultural material.

The question remains, then, what does the director oversee? Given the ideological-aesthetic bias of consumers and critics, the finished film, however polysemous it may be in fact, must demonstrate a privileged monological signification which, as Barthes says, is what defines an author of a text. To put it another way, the author is a narrative function whose identity as agent issues directly from the processes of textual unification. The director, it might be said, is responsible for seeing to it that this textual author is operative and that the work is unified. Conversely, the reader/spectator is responsible for assuming the subject position thus constructed into the text and, by recourse to a process of reading-hypothesis[11] based on the same system of cinematic representation, reconstituting a unity of signification.

In literary theory it is common practice to distinguish between a narrator and an implied author. This is a simple procedure in the case of an unreliable narrator or a central consciousness, but it becomes much more difficult in a work with an omniscient narrator where the author's position as both enunciator of the text and narrating agent remains essentially indistinguishable. In his recent book, *Point of View in the Cinema*, Edward Branigan attempts to redefine the terms of narration and break away from the traditional conception of the author as real individual reflected implicitly or explicitly in the text. "Narration," he argues, "is . . . a series of levels each, in turn, embedded or framed by a higher level."[12] Point of view, as it is associated with characters at each level in the narration, can therefore be conceived as a means of controlling signification within a hierarchical construction which is bounded finally by "an effaced narrator, a frame which cannot disclose its own act of framing."[13] This final level of narration without an origin, variously referred to as the implied author or an omniscient narrator, Branigan calls "a grand summation of all the points of view—a point of over-view."[14]

Like its literary counterpart, the cinematic agent of narration is also a construction of the text, its origins indeterminate and outside the world of the fiction. According to Foucault's terms of authorship, once we have classified a text as art we designate the producer of the work as origin and agent of the narration. The textual agent, having thus assumed the mantle of authorship, acquires the corresponding role of the Voice of Truth.

Because of the way narrative is represented in film, the author position and the spectator position converge as a subject position determined during production by the placement of the camera. The author-as-narrator is simultaneously effaced and allowed the prerogative of speaking with the Voice of Truth. Consequently as spectators who take up the subject position constructed by the cinematic apparatus and who willingly engage in a reading of the film text, we never pause to ask, Who is telling the story? Instead we experience the spectacle, at least intermittently, as our own.

According to Jacques Aumont, we are caught up in a kind of "turnstile" effect (alternating between the Imaginary and the Symbolic) that allows us both to *believe*[15] the image as real and to disengage ourselves from it sufficiently to endow it with meaning, thereby ensuring the film's coherence as meaningful discourse distinct from unformulatable experience.[16] Aumont's model of the way in which film activates an interplay between the Imaginary and the Symbolic is reminiscent of Jean-Pierre Oudart's theory of suture in film, but it poses the subject position less as an "antimony of reading and *jouissance*"[17] than as that which enables transit between these two processes.[18] But more significantly, Oudart's conception of the suturing process in film is rigidly dependent upon shot-reverse shot structure which, despite his insistence on its centrality in classical narrative cinema, has been shown to occur in only 30 percent to 40 percent of all cuts.[19]

By contrast, Aumont offers a much more flexible conception according to which the spectator, constantly recuperated into the imaginary space of the film through the work of the turnstile effect on the articulation of shots, is subjected to an ongoing variation of characters' points of view and "nobody's" point of view. To elaborate briefly, the turnstile effect has three interrelated aspects: The first of these involves the construction of a coherent imaginary space through the *dynamic composition* of a series of partial views (both characters' points of view and nobody's point of view) around a central locus definable as the subject position; the second aspect, the guiding story, is presented *through* the system of represented points of view; the imposition of meaning arising from the combined operation of these two aspects gives rise to the third, the *predicative point of view.*

This point of view clearly locates the author's voice, or what Branigan has called the "point of over-view" within the represented text. To the extent that it can be called an entity, it is the enunciator, the narrating *agent* within the representation. It derives from the organization of fictional space and can be said to be responsible for the way in which we experience that space and the events that occur within it. In short, it imparts judgment.

What is perhaps most significant about Aumont's notion of a predicative point of view is that it is grounded in a theory of representation, whereas Branigan, along with other theorists who have proposed versions of textual authorship, continues to subsume representation under narration. For Aumont, film is first of all representation and then narrative. His theory of the turnstile effect presumes the priority of representation. And, as we have seen, his enumeration of the three features of point of view progresses from the accumulation of partial views around a centralized point to their organization as narrative.

Aumont's emphasis is important because representation appears to be an essential key to the effective functioning of the cinematic apparatus. As Jean-Louis Baudry has convincingly pointed out, the apparatus may successfully *realize* its illusions only if we, the spectators, are able to forget both the apparatus and the ostensible producers of the spectacle.[20] And, indeed, the oversight is achieved through the elaborate accumulation of points of view that merge into the author-subject position associated with the placement of the camera. Together they produce the site of the spectator's position before the spectacle. The turnstile effect and the rapid shifts from character point of view to "nobody's" point of view converge in the onward force of the narrative to efface the agency of narration. One could say that the position of the enunciator is virtually collapsed into that of the spectator. But, as we know, this does not mean that the *voice* of the narrating agent is undetectable. It manifests itself to the critical viewer as a series of positionings and repositionings, at once dictated by the film's representation and dictating the spectator's orientation toward that representation. It is the cumulative result of these representations that predicates a point of overview and, for the traditional auteur critic, the signature of the auteur director.

But, as Caughie reminds us, we must also look outside the text if we are to understand fully the nature of the film author. We must look not just to the tradition of authorship described by Foucault that has enabled us to locate and enshrine the *author*, but to the codes of production which govern the construction of film texts as well. As any student of classical narrative film realizes, the cinema is a discursive formation, the codes of which are manifested in a system of representation. To be sure, such a system allows for a certain latitude of code usage within which a strict example of an institutional mode of representation can only be a kind of degree zero, an impossible norm abstracted from the accumulation of actual texts.

It may be possible to distinguish authorial signatures in the textual process described above; easy perhaps to discard what Wollen called the noise of other influences, reduce the variant to a stylistic unity, and attribute it to an individual. Yet the text must always remain within the confines of the discursive formation. Both what is signified and how it is signified are ultimately authored by that formation. Deviation from the codes of production, beyond the latitude of the discursive formation, defies comprehension (indeed it defies invention). Or, put another way, such deviation threatens to break down the suturing process activated by codes of cinematic reading and essential to the maintenance of the cinematic apparatus and the subject position within it.

Clearly the readerly codes also derive from the same discursive formation. Thus, by placing the specific text within the context of the cinematic system of representation it is possible to understand the author as a cultural construct that emerges from a series of narrated representations in the service of signification. This series of instances is rendered meaningful by collusion between producers and spectators, who share knowledge not only of the mode of representation, but of a larger social text. In becoming meaningful, the instances cohere as a sequence to produce an apparently unified voice. That social collusion is what harnesses the *polyphony*, the many voices of a multilayered cultural discourse, and thereby establishes a *cultural collaboration* in the production of film texts.

Written on the Wind (1956 Sirk) is an interesting film to use for an illustration of the role of authorial voice, because on the one hand it is attributed to a director who meets all the criteria of Sarris's definition of the Hollywood auteur, and on the other, the film handles subjective point of view, that is, character point of view, in an unusual way. At first appearance the film seems to offer occasional subjective point of view *shots*. But as the point of view sequence develops around such shots we discover that either the camera position or the character's position has been jockeyed and, as though to emphasize the displacement, the character almost invariably appears in the shot.

We find an example of this kind of point of view manipulation in a conversation exchange between Mitch (Rock Hudson) and Hadley Sr. (Robert Keith) just after the latter's introduction to his son's new wife. The sequence begins giving every appearance that it will be a shot-reverse shot point of view exchange. A cut from a two-shot to a shot in which the camera assumes what would seem to be Mitch's position to the left of the old man sets us up for it. Only a very astute viewer might realize that the camera is actually positioned too far to the right. But instead of cutting to the reverse position, the shot continues and the camera dollies back to reveal Mitch seated in the left foreground. His place relative to the camera brings us in quite close to his reaction to the conversation. We may identify to the extent that we feel sympathy for his discomfort, but the fact remains that we *see* his discomfort. The angle of the camera suggests more the position of an onlooking party.

A summary review of the signification in *Written on the Wind* indicates that the modification of such exchanges is no accident. The film frequently plays on point of view displacement, markedly pointing out the discrepancy between camera position and alternating character positions. Here a distinction can be made: We can see the probable influence of the director in the consistent emphasis on the relation of camera and characters. But this relation takes on meaning only by virtue of its divergence from the conventional shot-reverse shot exchange. Ultimately even these decisions are choices made from the limited range of possibilities delineated by cinematic discourse and worked out by the entire production group.

The significance of the divergence in this film arises from assumptions about human behavior drawn from the social text and recognized by spectator and film producers alike. It should be added here that such assumptions do not just depend upon common understanding of human actions in the world; they are mediated through the codes of realistic acting which have evolved and changed over time. We are not, in any case, talking about actual deviations from the constraints of cinematic discourse. The conventional mode of representation, except to the extent that it has been made rigid in production and post-production formulas, as already noted, an abstraction. Creative manipulation of the codes (commonly known as style) is invited, indeed it is reponsible for producing "depth." But it is only thinkable within the confines of the system and only acceptable up to the point that it does not threaten coherence and hence comprehensibility.

The level of collaboration I am concerned with is that which includes the director (and other contributors) as a cultural *accomplice*, that which impels Sirk (as a convenient abbreviation for all involved in the production), in this case, to use the codes in the way he does. As it happens the narratorial consequence of the film's point of view displacement for our relation to characters affects the whole process of secondary cinematic identification. As spectators we seem most closely identified with Mitch Wayne (Rock Hudson) and most sympathetic to Lucy Moore Hadley (Lauren Bacall).

Lucy, however, is only as good as her unfaltering integrity. We are never allowed to identify with her. Like Mitch, we must judge her over and over.

But how exactly are we closer to Mitch? Narratively he is the pivotal character, his struggle and his morality are more developed. Nevertheless, while the camera sneaks in close to him and seems to reveal his inner thoughts, it refuses to take up his point of view. We always see him *in relation to* his circumstances; thus we are always compelled to judge him as well. Despite his strength and virtues in the midst of weakness and degeneracy, he does not come out clean. From our third party position we see Mitch's superiority cripple his friend Kyle Hadley (Robert Stack), and we are sympathetic to Kyle; we see Mitch's unresponsiveness (justified as it may be by the narrative) suffocate what remains of the presumably good and natural qualities of Marylee Hadley (Dorothy Malone's character). His contribution to both Hadleys' troubles is a theme the movie never lets us forget entirely. Thus, while supporting melodramatic convention by providing us with a morally sound hero overcoming difficult circumstances, the film subverts generic convention representationally by its recurrent hints that the hero's superiority is itself morally questionable.

A further example of the tension arising from the spectator's relation to Mitch is brought out in a short driving sequence that occurs just after Mitch has finished Kyle's fight for Marylee's dubious virtue. Although he has cause to be angry in this sequence, his aloofness toward Marylee is not much different from what it has been in other encounters between them. The sequence consists of three shots. The first is a deep focus shot, as Mitch gets into Marylee's sports car and she drives away from the camera. The second shot is from the front of the car with rear screen projection of receding oil wells. The third shot, making up most of the sequence, is taken from the passenger's side of the car. It keeps Mitch in foreground profile, under close scrutiny, once again on the left, with Marylee's contrasting defiant animation in center frame. Again a rear screen projection of oil wells serves as ironic reminder of Hadley status and Hadley pressure as it looms over both of them. Marylee's bright red dress and car place her in contrast to the subdued blues and earth tones that characterize both Mitch and the landscape, contributing to our sense of her passion, her vitality, her oppression by him and her environment. We cannot help but recognize her pain and frustration along with her viciousness and her degeneracy. Our close view of Mitch, as a result of the camera's position, shows us, first of all, his refusal to respond to her, his disgust as he looks away from her to reveal his attitude in an aside to the camera. Then, as he leans forward to light a cigarette, he cuts her off visually just as he has shut her out emotionally. She reappears (as he leans back), but her animation, her moment of genuine decency, and her fight are gone, leaving only vicious determination.

Even from this admittedly condensed example, it is clear that several things coalesce in the sequence to produce a judgment—one offered by a covert narrator but offered as our own—a "there, you can see for yourself" proposal. We see Marylee in red dress and car, and we see Mitch and the background in brown, blue, and gray tones; but we don't see the coded opposition of the colors in the sequence even though we read it. (Compare the long third shot to a reverse shot construction which might alternatively privilege each character's point of view or reduce the extent of our judgment of Mitch.) Forced as we are to watch Mitch, and from such close vantage, we have no option but to evaluate his behavior. Representationally, though not in word or deed, he fails. Thus our identification with him is thwarted ever so subtly. Concurrently, the background of endless oil derricks, Mitch's manly stoicism and practical attire, along with the implied wealth, beauty, and ostentation of car and woman elicit a set of culturally coded responses (along with Freudian innuendos) that we read so easily that we take them for granted.

The value judgments constructed into the film's representation can cohere or they can conflict; in either case, they coalesce on the level of discourse as a voice of judgment telling the spectator what to think. In this way the system of enunciation in the film creates an authorizing voice that unifies the text, helping us to grasp it as a coherent statement, guiding us through the polysemy of the accumulating images. Yet, as the organizing principle of the film's meaning, the author proves to be nothing other than a predication of the representation. The resulting point of view emerges as a discernible voice in accordance with the necessity to conform to cultural expectations for a unified signification dictated by the narrative codes. To the extent that such a unity can be called a voice, what it says is not determined by a single individual—the director can only orchestrate the film's production. On the other hand, the text from which the voice emerges is not autonomous. The author is a juncture of multiple codes (representational, narrative, iconographic, cinematic, cultural) and multiple practices (production, promotion, reading, critical reading, theoretical analysis). The collective voice generated by this nexus of codes and practices and manifested as the author-function, is ultimately a cultural voice imbued with a culturally defined world view that invades every aspect of the film's representation.

Notes

1. Edward Branigan cautions against use of the term "voice" because of its realist connotations, its inadequacy as a mark for different levels of narration, and its already rather specialized meaning in rhetoric and grammar. Edward Branigan, *Point of View in the Cinema* (Berlin: Mouton Publishers, 1984), 48. I have chosen to retain the word, with qualifications, because I have found no satisfactory replacement.
2. Peter Wollen contends that since "the director does not have full control over his work . . . the *auteur* theory involves a kind of decipherment, decryptment. A great many features of films analysed have to be dismissed because of "noise" from the producer, the cameraman or even the actors." Peter Wollen, *Signs and Meaning in the Cinema* (Bloomington: Indiana University Press, 1972), 104.
3. Roland Barthes, "Death of the Author," in *Image, Music, Text* (New York: Hill & Wang, 1977), 146.
4. Ibid., 147.
5. John Caughie, ed., *Theories of Authorship* (London: Routledge & Kegan Paul, 1981), 206.
6. Michel Foucault, "What Is an Author?" in *Language, Counter-Memory, Practice*, ed. Donald F. Bouchard (Ithaca: Cornell University Press, 1977), 121–31.
7. David A. Cook, *A History of Narrative Film* (New York: W. W. Norton, 1981), 39.
8. This is perhaps an oversimplification of the development of authorial recognition in the

history of the American cinema. Certain directors were known from the teens on; yet film was not widely respected as an art comparable to literature or drama and, for the most part, recognition went to the studios and the stars.

9. Andrew Sarris held American auteur directors superior to the European because they were compelled to express their personal styles in all sorts of projects commissioned by the studio. Andrew Sarris, "Notes on the Auteur Theory in 1962," *Film Culture* 27 (Winter 1962–63): 1–8.
10. Roland Barthes, "The Realistic Effect," *Film Reader* 3 (1978): 131–34; Gerard Genette, "Vraisemblance et motivation," in *Figures II* (Paris: Seuil, 1966), 71–86; Aristotle, *The Rhetoric*, trans. W. Rhys Roberts (New York: Random House, 1954), ch. 21.
11. Branigan, *Point of View*, 178–80.
12. Ibid., 177.
13. Ibid.
14. Ibid., 184.
15. I use the word "believe" here in much the same way Metz uses it in his adaptation of Octave Mannoni's discussion of the structures of belief in theater from "Je sais bien mais quand même . . . ," in *Clefs pour l'imaginaire ou l'autre scène* (Paris: Seuil, 1969); Christian Metz, *The Imaginary Signifier*, trans. Ben Brewster (Bloomington: Indiana University Press, 1982), 71–74.
16. Jacques Aumont, "Point de vue," *Communications* 38 (1983): 22–24.
17. Jean-Pierre Oudart, "Cinema and Suture," *Screen* 18 (Summer 1965): 42; Stephen Health, "Notes on Suture," *Screen* 18 (Summer 1965): 59.
18. Aumont's "turnstile" notion is, in some respects, more closely aligned with the original theory of suture postulated by Jacques-Alain Miller, than is Oudart's approach. For Miller the subject position is not so clearly oppositional. An unstable, evanescent phenomenon, the subject can recognize itself in relation to the world only by means of a signifying system that simultaneously causes it to disappear. The desire of the subject to overcome the lack produced by the early divisions of the self becomes the driving force of signification in the subject's interminable effort at self-procuration as well as identification. Thus for Miller, using Lacan, "the subject functions as support of the operations of abstraction and unification"; it appears in the articulation of the signifiers of discourse. Jacques-Alain Miller, "Suture," *Screen* 18 (Winter 1977–78): 25.
19. Barry Salt, "Film Style and Technology in the Forties," *Film Quarterly* 30 (Fall 1977).
20. Jean-Louis Baudry, "The Ideological Effects of the Basic Cinematographic Apparatus," trans. Alan Williams, *Film Quarterly* 28 (Winter 1974–75).

26

Lana: Four Films of Lana Turner

RICHARD DYER

Despite the enormous interest in stars, there has been very little study of them, and this (as I found when preparing a study guide for the BFI Education Advisory Service) has predominantly been sociological, concerned with how stars function in general ideological/cultural terms. Such concerns are certainly central to film studies, but we also need to know how stars function within the films themselves, that is, how the films articulate, carry, inflect or subvert the general ideological/ cultural functions. This article examines the way a single start image, Lana Turner's, is variously used in films in relation to other elements such as the construction of character, narrative, *mise-en-scène* and so on.

Why Lana Turner? In part, certainly, because I like her; but her work also illustrates certain characteristic features of the star phenomenon. The four films discussed use her in different ways. In *Ziegfeld Girl*, the Turner image sends the film off course and in effect partly cracks open its central mythology, whereas in *The Postman Always Rings Twice* (hereinafter, *Postman*) the image both holds together and also exposes contradictory elements. *The Bad and the Beautiful* elaborates upon and finally celebrates the image, while *Imitation of Life* examines and scrutinises it, holding it up to the light so as to expose it. More generally, Turner illustrates three of the ways that stars function *cinematically* (that is, within the total signifying practice of the cinema industry situated within society as a whole):

(1) Her career is marked by an unusually, even spectacularly, high degree of inter-

---

Richard Dyer's "Lana: Four Films of Lana Turner" originally appeared in *Movie*, no. 25 (Winter 1977–78), pp. 30–54. Reprinted by the permission of the author and *Movie*.

penetration between her publicly available private life and her films. The star phenomenon depends upon collapsing the distinction between the star-as-person and the star-as-performer. This does not usually mean that the incidents of a film's scenario are taken to be actual incidents in the star's life but rather that they "reveal" or express the personality or type-of-person of the star. In the case of Turner, however, not only do her vehicles furnish characters and situations in accord with her off-screen image, but frequently incidents in them echo incidents in her life so that by the end of her career films like *Peyton Place, Imitation of Life, Madame X* and *Love Has Many Faces* seem in parts like mere illustrations of her life.

(2) In the earlier films, Turner's image exemplifies one of the major forms of relationship between a star and her/his social context, namely the reconciliation of contradiction. Stars frequently speak to dominant contradictions in social life—experienced as conflicting demands, contrary expectations, irreconcilable but equally held values—in such a way as to appear to reconcile them. In part, by simply being one indivisible entity with an existence in the "real world," yet displaying contradictory personality traits, stars can affirm that it is possible to triumph over, transcend, successfully live out contradictions. In the case of Turner, this centres on her being strongly sexual, both for herself and for others (therefore in Hollywood-American terms, extraordinary) but also ordinary. As Jeanine Basinger puts it in *Lana Turner* (Pyramid Books, 1976), "She was as much the ice cream parlor as she was the perfumed boudoir." An interesting feature of Turner's career is that films and publicity seem continually to be condemning or punishing her for this daring combination, yet her survival and growth as an identification figure bespeaks the hold of such a magic reconciliation of opposites on the cinematic imagination.

(3) In Turner's later films, the processes of manufacture—the production of the image—are increasingly evident until they become an integral part of the image. With most stars, the point is to disguise the manufacturing so that they simply appear to be what their image proclaims them to be; with Turner, part of the fascination is with the manufacture itself—with her, it is actually beguiling to see the strings being pulled. This is especially true of *The Bad and the Beautiful* and *Imitation of Life*, and also of the Joe Morella and Edward Z. Epstein biography of Turner, *Lana* (W. H. Allen, 1972), which focuses as much on the fabrication of Lana as on the "reality" of Judy Turner.

Ziegfeld Girl

Ziegfeld Girl (1941) inherits from Turner's previous career her sexy-ordinary image. In the process of building on it, however, the film gets severely out of joint, turning a production-values-laden musical into quite a serious drama. The Turner parts of the film make explicit what also comes across in the Judy Garland and Hedy Lamarr parts—a fumbling, confused critique of the notion of woman as spectacle at its most glorified, to wit, the Ziegfeld girl.

The sexy-ordinary configuration of the Turner image was crystallised in four moments in her career prior to *Ziegfeld Girl:* her first film role in *They Won't Forget* (1937), her sweater-girl pin-ups, her marriage to Artie Shaw and her starlet roles taken as a whole.

In *They Won't Forget,* she plays a young woman whose every action breathes sexuality—getting her male school-teacher all flustered, telling a soda-jerk to put an egg in her malted milk "as fresh as you," and walking down the street with hips swaying and breasts bouncing. She is raped and murdered. The ordinary setting and the ordinary clothes, together with the extraordinary appeal, would be enough to enflame any real man, the film seems to imply (and we never get to know who the rapist and murderer in fact is), and insofar as the film is a message film, it seems to have been a protest against the corruption of the South rather than against rape.

The sweater girl pin-ups date from Turner's appearance in *They Won't Forget,* but they became so widespread in the subsequent buildup that their meaning became rather more generalised. They encapsulate the sexy-ordinary configuration. On the one hand, a sweater is not a glamour garment—it is something cheap, practical, available everywhere. (In none of the portraits does Turner appear to be wearing an extravagantly styled sweater or one made of costly stuff.) On the other hand, worn by Turner, it became blantly erotic, showing off the breasts, clinging to the waist. The rigid separation of women stars into homely-but-sexless (loose or flattening garments, including sweaters) or sexy-but-exotic (fetishistic fabrics, outlandish designs heightening body features) was collapsed. The girl-next-door was that never-never sex bombshell, plain-knit and voyeur's delight were one.

In February 1940, Turner eloped with Artie Shaw. Four months later, she divorced him. Although sex in a direct form was not mentioned in the coverage of these events, they are still an inflection of the sexy-ordinary configuration. Shaw was a band leader, and the bands were the courtship, dating, heterosexual romance music of the day. Turner's first marriage was at the heart of America's love-and-sex culture. It was also impulsive, although this was not necessarily viewed as a negative quality—it could be considered charmingly youthful, though it had already intimations of immaturity. More important, it was over in four months. Turner's publicly available life was going wrong; something was going sour in the heart of ordinariness.

Certain patterns of the Turner image, then, were beginning to take shape—sexiness perceived in ordinariness, but also associations of this with youth/immaturity and trouble. The starlet roles between *They Won't Forget* and *Ziegfeld Girl* do not appear to have elaborated upon this, but it is clear that the ambiguity of Turner's image was sufficient for MGM to feel equally happy casting her as a good girl (*We Who Are Young,* 1940) or a bad (*Love Finds Andy Hardy,* 1938), a sexpot (*Calling Dr. Kildare,* 1939) or a down-to-earth student (*Dramatic School,* 1938). I think one could argue, as a general rule of the functioning of stars in films, that a star's very physiognomy carries the meanings of her/his image in whatever film she or he makes, in whatever character she or he plays (cf. Lawrence Alloway: "The Iconography of the Movies" in *Movie* 7, reprinted in *Movie Reader*). Thus, short of being strenously performed against the image, it is likely that by 1940 the character played by Turner, just because it was played by her, was already sexy-ordinary, no matter whether the film made something of it or not and virtually regardless of the character as scripted.

Ziegfeld Girl is very conscious of the images of its three main stars, Turner, Garland and Lamarr. Narrative and treatment are tailored to them. Garland is established as having a vaudeville background and thus all the know-how of the born-in-a-trunk pro; she is dressed in little girl suits and has her requisite wistful follow-up to "Over the Rainbow" in "I'm Always Chasing Rainbows" as well as her jazzy, up-tempo spot, "Minnie from Trinidad." With Lamarr, everything promotes her remote, exotic beauty—she is foreign, married to a violinist (hence associated with Artistic Beauty), and has no thought of becoming a Ziegfeld girl when the star of the show (Frank Merton/Tony Martin) is stunned by her beauty as he passes her; a glistening close-up shot of her is often inserted into her scenes with other people (whereas it never is of Turner or Garland), which effectively sets her apart from the interaction; in the numbers, she is the statuesque central figure, coming closest to Ziegfeld's prescriptions for his "girls." The film's overall structure can accommodate these two images—they can be used effectively in the numbers, and fit two show businesswomen types (though, as I'll argue below, there are elements of criticism of Ziegfeld girlhood even in Lamarr and Garland). Turner (Sheila) fits less happily.

The film begins by building on the ordinary side of the Turner configuration. She is "discovered" operating a lift in a department store. Neither a pro nor an exotic beauty, she is just an ordinary working girl rocketed to stardom. This conforms with the publicity surrounding Turner's own "discovery" at a soda fountain in a Hollywood Boulevard drug store (this is inaccurate, though not drastically so), and meteoric rise to fame (it took rather longer than was publicly known). Her first act on being asked to audition for Ziegfeld is to go and buy an exorbitantly priced leopard-skin coat. This again conforms with her image as a girl who gets a real lift out of possessions. As one fan magazine of the period noted, "She glitters whether on the beach, in the drawing room, or in the studio restaurant dressed in gingham. She admits she enjoys the luxury that stardom has brought her. And she drives a fire-engine red coupé. Lana is the most spectacular personality to be thrown up by films since Clara Bow."

Thus far, *Ziegfeld Girl* is simply reproducing a facet of Turner's image. However, as both Basinger and Morella/Epstein state, during the making of the film, MGM and the director, Robert Z. Leonard, were so impressed by Turner that they expanded her role. This affects the film in three ways—building on the elements of the Turner image adds complexity to that image, the impact of her role comes into conflict with the musical's generic requirements, and her increasing centrality also calls into question the film's central motif.

Building on the image of the ordinary girl rocketed to a fame she luxuriates in brings in the complexity of response claimed by the Turner sexy-ordinary image. There is certainly a basic level of delight of the kind the fan magazine evinced. But there is also and equally pathos and condemnation. The impulsive desire to spend, and spend big, is perhaps in itself sympathetic, and is rendered more so in a key scene between Sheila/Turner and her old truck-driver boyfriend Gil (James Stewart). Her desire is located in deprivation, a deprivation the film is careful not to link with her class situation but with her unlucky experience as a child of always being the one who arrived at a party "after the ice cream ran out." We are asked to be sorry for her—doubly so when, running after Gil as he leaves in disgust, she trips on the minks she has strewn before him to proclaim her new wealth. We are here being asked to be sorry for her materialism, for what led to it in the first place and what it is doing to her now. Yet in her pursuit of wealth, she goes to the bad. She acquires a sugar daddy, Geoffrey, then, when she snubs him, she takes to drink, is suspended from the Follies, and winds up in a seedy bar with Geoffrey, now himself down and out. It is no longer clear what sort of response is being elicited. She has broken taboos on women's behaviour—losing her man by demanding he adapt to her life-style, getting drunk. These demand condemnation (by the conventions of the film's day), and I do not know how far the pathos elements let her off the hook. This ambiguity, the "bad" woman who suffers for her badness and thus becomes an identification/sympathy figure, is the emotional timbre that is caught in all her subsequent films.

As the dramatic-pathetic elements increase with Sheila/Turner's downfall, so they come to occupy the centre of the film. Not only does this mean that the other two star characters' careers are given short shrift (as narrative developments in musicals often are), but it also begins to interfere with what is a musical's *raison d'être*, the numbers. Throughout it is clear that the numbers do not quite know what to do with Turner—she has no musical gifts (or none that film has ever developed), and although she would be fine as one of the chorines in Busby Berkeley's Warners depression musicals, the kind of thing Berkeley is staging here, all haughty parading and baroque head-dresses and trains, does not suit her small frame and "common" face—not yet in her career, anyway. By the time of the last big production number, "You Gotta Pull Strings," the Sheila/Turner plot dominates everything and, since the point is that she is not in this number, having been suspended from the Follies, the emotional weight in the cross-cutting between the number and her in the theatre watching is decidedly with her. All the more so when, unable to watch any more, despite having struggled out of her alcohol-induced sick bed to be there, she leaves the auditorium and the film stays with her and not the number. As she hears the finale walk-down music strike up on stage, she holds herself up and begins to walk down the entrance stairs. Thus for the climax of the number (and of all the numbers in the film) we see Turner in the "surrounding" narrative and not the girls in the "central" number.

This final walk-down also has a further significance in the film. The walk-down is the defining motif of the Ziegfeld show—it is the moment at which the girls parade themselves and are thus "glorified." It is used five times in relation to Sheila/Turner. The first is in the first big production number, "You Stepped out of a Dream." In this, the camera follows Turner as she walks down the circling ramp. Garland and Lamarr are not similarly treated, although the latter is given a couple of cut-in close-ups of her sculptured face, and she is distinguished from both Garland and Turner by her dress, which is more *haute couture*, less show-girl in style. The effect of the camera sticking with Turner in this number, which for all three characters is their first night as Ziegfeld girls, is to stress her excitement at being a Ziegfeld girl and to associate the walk-down especially with her. The second use of the walk-down motif takes place the next morning at Turner's home (she is still living with her parents): she is trudging down the stairs until her brother says "Here comes the glamour girl!"—then she straightens up, and descends the stairs as if on stage for the walk-down. Again, in the night-club in Florida, she walks down some stairs as if she and they are in the Follies, only this time it is after quarrelling with Gil, snubbing Geoffrey, and drinking too much champagne. Each walk-down is registering a moment in her career. The next is on stage, in the

"Minnie from Trinidad" number, during which she collapses, drunk, and the last is during "You Gotta Pull Strings," as described above.

The walk-down motif in relation to Sheila/Turner links her decline—which the film also, as we've seen, explains in terms of deprivation, materialism and going to the bad—to the core of the Ziegfeld show. In this way, by association, the whole enterprise of Ziegfeld—his girls, woman as spectacle—which the film was clearly set up to celebrate, is called into question. There are intimations of this through the Garland and Lamarr characters. The only one of the three to make it to the top is Garland—but then she has her roots in vaudeville, which is signalled in the film, through the character of her father, as being a more vital and authentic entertainment tradition. (Her father is played by Charles Winniger; in the film he teams up with Al Shean in a recreation of Gallagher and Shean, one of the legendary acts on the vaudeville circuit; this happens just before the enfeebled "You Gotta Pull Strings," number and "brings the house down"; effectively, vaudeville has the last say in the film's numbers). Lamarr, on the other hand, leaves the Follies to join her husband when he gets a job; the very haughty beauty which makes her an epitome of the Ziegfeld girl also makes her "superior" to show business. Between Garland and Lamarr, Ziegfeld gets it from low and high brows.

What Sheila/Turner adds to this is sex. Clearly, despite the "Glorifying the American Girl" tag, Ziegfeld was peddling sexuality—but the glorification idea, his use of famous couturiers and chic designers, appeared to elevate his shows above the despised burlesque (which means striptease in American usage). Sheila/Turner drags it down again. Partly, the film takes on Turner's association with sexuality just by having her in it. In addition, some of the dialogue draws attention to it—for instance, when she is worrying about her make-up, Patsy (Eve Arden) wisecracks (as only Eve Arden can), "Don't worry dear, they won't be looking at your face." It is on her legs that the camera dwells in this first walk-down, aided by the wide parting in her sequined dress. And, again unlike Garland or Lamarr, it is as a pin-up that she acquires off-stage fame, even winding up on the wall of the garage where Gil works. The crystallisation of all this round Sheila/Turner and her special association with the walk-down motif puts a dent in the hypocrisy of Ziegfeld's glittering sex show. Add to that the emotional weighting given her, her virtually eclipsing the numbers by the end, and one can see how the decision to build on Turner's star image leads the film almost to overturn its own project. The brief scene of reconciliation with Gil (they are going to go to the country to breed ducks) and a perfunctory shot of Garland atop a wedding-cake-style set hardly suffice to set the film properly back on its course.

The Postman Always Rings Twice

Between *Ziegfeld Girl* and *Postman* (1946), Turner's sexy-ordinary image was consolidated. The war proved useful for this. Nothing is more ordinary in the public imagination than the serviceman. Thus the fact that, for instance, the sailors of the S.S. Idaho voted her their favourite star, that she married a serviceman in life (Stephen Crane) and in a film (*Marriage Is a Private Affair,* 1944), and herself joined the WACs in *Keep Your Powder Dry* (1945), all preserved her association with ordinariness. Equally, they preserved the association of that with other things—with plain sexiness in the case of the S.S. Idaho men. Indeed, throughout the war Turner was a major pin-up in men's magazines. The marriage to Crane (1942) went wrong—she married on impulse again, knowing next to nothing about him; he was, however, already married, so the marriage had to be annulled; then he got a divorce, but she would not remarry him and he tried to commit suicide twice; she discovered she was pregnant and they remarried; a year later (1944), they divorced, with Turner getting custody of the baby, Cheryl. Following the Shaw fiasco, it was as if Turner and marriage (ordinary marriage to ordinary men) did not go. Not that Shaw or Crane came out of it well, but both marriages set off the central Turner ambiguity—what she touches turns bad, but is that because she is bad or because she is irresistibly attracted to the bad? (And is being attracted to the bad itself badness?) *Marriage Is a Private Affair* similarly dealt with a G.I.'s marriage (after a three-day courtship) going off the rails, through his wife's (Turner's) infidelity, though all ends happily. More generally, Turner's status as sexy leading lady was confirmed by her teamings with Clark Gable in *Honky Tonk* (1941) and *Somewhere I'll Find You* (1942).

These ambiguities, the role of impulse, the play on badness and on the sexy-ordinary configuration all came in useful for the Turner character, Cora in *Postman.* Without them, the film courts incoherence in its construction of this central character.

I want to consider *Postman* chiefly in terms of the key but neglected question of how a character is constructed in a film. What I want to suggest is that there are here three different methods of character construction, which fit uneasily together. These methods are structural (we understand characters by what they do in the plot or how they function in the narrative), motivational (the reasons provided by dialogue and sometimes other elements such as performance and mise-en-scène as to why a character does such-and-such a thing) and star-based (the star's image already gives the character a certain set of traits). These methods are of course not confined to *Postman,* but I don't want here to get into generalising too hastily from *Postman,* from the methods it uses and the particular way it combines them. One general point, however, is that these methods, like nearly all others, contribute to the construction of an apparently autonomous character (rather than one acknowledged as an aspect of the film's point[s]-of-view)—corresponding, of course, to how we normally talk about characters, ascribing motives and feelings to them as if they are real people independent of us and a narrative's author.

The initial problem with *Postman* is who the film is really about. Structurally, it is a *film noir,* which means that, like nearly all *films noirs,* the narrative is centred on the male protagonist (Frank/John Garfield). His voice-over leads into the film and recurs at various points until we realise he has been telling his story to a priest in prison. Since the film ends there and a priest has been the listener, a certain status is conferred retrospectively on Frank as both the subject of the narrative and its truthful narrator. The film can then be seen as being "about" the hero's doom. The sense of doom, fate, entrapment is reinforced by the obsessive doubling of events and images in the film, both major narrative incidents (two accidents with a lorry, two attempts to kill Nick, two attempts to leave the cafe, two trials for murder) and minor details of treatment (two lipstick rolls, two vital notes in the cash register, two pushes at the car on the second attempt on Nick's life, the echoes at the lake, the name of the cafe, The Twin Oaks, and the title of the film).

In this context, the woman is a function of the ensnaring structure. The *femme fatale* need not necessarily be evil, but she is the means by which the hero gets drawn into the plot, and hence his doom (whether or not there is a "happy ending"). Indeed, it is more to the point if she is not simply and utterly evil, for it is precisely the hero's uncertainty on this point, the very unknowability of Woman, that really traps him. (Much of the pleasure of *film noir* resides in the true knowledge of the woman, as good or evil, vouchsafed the hero and hence the [male?] audience at the end—e.g. *The Maltese Falcon, The Lady from Shanghai, Chinatown.*)

At one level, Cora in *Postman* is a mere function of the film's structure. She is only there to be the means by which Frank enters the path that leads to his doom, to be the terrible object of his sexuality, terrible because his attraction to her is what leads him to the death cell. Her famous first appearance—the roll of her lipstick along the floor attracting his (and the camera's) attention, followed by a track back along the floor, up her bare legs to her white shorts and halter top—is very directly sexual, and throughout the film her brilliant white clothes are both eye-catching and a sign of the heat of the summer (with all that connotes). The wretchedness of women, in the mind of *film noir,* is that they are such a turn-on for the hero, with disastrous consequences for him (compare the logic of *They Won't Forget*). One can see Cora functioning like this throughout the film's structure.

Yet even in this first scene, it is not as simple as that. On the one hand, Cora as herself a subject is implied—the "Man Wanted" sign in the opening shots of the film hangs over the scene, we can assume she has rolled the lipstick herself, and the manner in which she does her lips while looking at him suggests a deliberate making of herself into an object of desire. On the other hand, the burning hamburger, so obviously a symbol of lighted passions, and the general atmosphere of heat suggest a sexual force generated between them both (a sense referred to by almost every reviewer as "the chemistry" "sparked" between Garfield and Turner). This sense of Cora as herself a force acting on the narrative derives from the motivational level of character construction in *Postman* being as emphatic as the structural. Cora, and Cora-and-Frank, are provided with reasons for doing things, whereas in other *films noirs* only Frank would be.

Yet as soon as this motivational level comes into play, further problems arise. If one looks at the motives Cora is provided with, they are ambiguous and contradictory almost to the point of incoherence. Why, as indicated by the film, does Cora get Frank to kill Nick? Because, pitiably, she is trapped into a marriage with a dreary older man, largely because she was fed up with other men bothering her ("I was never homey . . . I never met a man since I was fifteen who didn't want to give me an argument about it," said fiercely/ruefully to Frank but looking straight ahead to camera; the scene where Nick tells her callously that she is to spend the rest of her life looking after his paralysed sister in Canada). And because she is ambitious (her repeated statements to the effect that she wants "to make something" of herself and the cafe). And because she loves Frank (she leaves the cafe with him; her direct, i.e. "genuine," outburst in the kitchen, after she has been contemplating suicide with a kitchen knife, "If you really love me, you would . . ."), and/or is manipulating him (in an earlier kitchen scene, we get a close-up on "Can't you see how happy we'd be together?" in which her shifting eyes clearly signal manipulation). And because she is driven by a bad sexuality (the scenes on the beach; her provocative clothes; images of heat). Partly, what is happening here is that the film wants to give Cora motivations, including some that make her a sympathetic figure, but, as her (generic) function in the narrative is to be changeable and unknowable, the film has to keep giving her different, inconsistent motivations. Yet inconsistency on this scale risks being simply incoherent. The film's devices would betray themselves all too quickly without Lana Turner in the part.

Because it is Turner, the contradictions of Cora, and Cora-and-Frank, get an emphasis which amounts to a resolution (more or less—perceptions will differ on this). Cora is sexy-ordinary: her speech about not being "homey" indicates this clearly enough, as indeed does the extraordinary sexual charges she carries in so suffocatingly dull a setting. The various motivations she is provided with can be loosely organised around the badness syndrome developed in Turner's image. She is attracted to the bad (adultery, murder); this makes her pitiable (she is trapped both by her situation of marriage and by the inexorable repetitions of the plot once she strays from marriage), but it also intimates that she may herself be bad (her sexuality, her manipulation and prompting of Frank to murder). Notions of coherence of character do not permit the coexistence of such traits (except under the rubric of woman the capricious and unknowable, which is not allowable here since, on the contrary, we know too much, and of that much is sympathetic), but notions of the star reconciling or holding in tension key contradictions in the culture (and thus effectively transcending them) do permit them to a certain extent. However, in the process, certain traits are subordinated. Thus Cora's driving ambition, which is granted legitimacy at the motivational level simply in terms of the time allowed it and the straight treatment of it, lacks force since it has no place in the Turner complex. As a result, one either ignores the ambition motive, or denies it legitimacy by regarding it as falsehood or manipulation, or one merely feels that it does not fit.

The motivations of Cora-and-Frank, as a couple and as murderers, are also aided by Turner's presence, though here she is less crucial to the film's coherence. The key to their murderous relationship is impulse. In each of the scenes in which they contemplate murder, a crash of music, where before there was none, signals the thought of murder arising from nowhere rational in their minds. The first of these scenes occurs after Nick, returning drunk from the laundry, nearly crashes into a lorry. Frank blurts out, "I like to see him get plastered like that and drive off a cliff," music in; they look at each other as Cora says, "You didn't mean that, you were joking," and Frank replies "Course I was"; they kiss. The idea for murder arises spontaneously; music signals its impact; a kiss links it to passion. (In an earlier scene, Frank's suggestion of Cora wanting to make money so as to have some set aside when her husband dies is also met by music and a kiss, though murder as such is not mentioned.) The second such scene takes place in Frank's bedroom. Having elicited from him that he loves her, Cora, fingering the lapel of the dressing gown he is wearing, says, "There's one thing we could do." Frank replies, "Pray for something to happen to Nick," and Cora says, "Something like that"; music in; Frank exclaims, "Cora!" Here the link between passion and murder is clearer, but murder is not actually directly referred to.

It is clearly in Cora's mind, but she does not have to say the word for Frank to latch on. The music signals its arousal in their "chemistry." The third scene takes place in the kitchen, after Frank has discovered Cora with a kitchen knife in her hand. Here there is a more directly expressed impulsive outburst from Cora—"If you really love me, you would . . ." pause; Frank, "Alright"; music in; Cora, "No!" This last exclamation suggests that the idea for murder arose in her head with premeditation. Once again, the music suggests the intention to murder is an impulse rather than a rational or cold-blooded plan.

The film, then, does a lot of work on the notion of impulse, even without the input of Turner as Cora. The particular inflection she adds is suffering from one's own impulses. Her impulsive marriages in life had led to suffering of one kind and another, and the film roles reprised this. Consequently the pattern of impulse and entrapment in *Postman* can be read—I would argue, *was* read by Turner's fans—as a source of identification and sympathy. The attraction to bad (often meaning little more than sexual desire) can be seen as an uncontrollable, destroying impulse that anyone can identify with (especially in a sex-negative culture). Yet this means that, at the level of the star image's contribution to character, the film is about Cora at least as much as it is about Frank, even though structurally she is a mere function of his destiny. Thus, if in terms of the relationship between the motivational and star image levels, Turner serves to mask the contradictions of the *femme fatale* type (a type of course that reflects the male construction—and fear of—the female), in terms of the relationship between the structural and star levels, Turner serves to open up the tension between what women are for men and what that means for women as women. (I am not positing here either any brilliance on Turner's part—though I would never wish to denigrate her performing abilities—or an untutored feminist sensibility on the part of the director, writer or whoever; it is rather that in the relationship between her life/films and women audiences, a certain registering and defining of the female experience in this society was possible and that this happens in *Postman* simply because she is in it.) If that accounts for the film's near-incoherence and unsatisfactory feel, it also accounts for the fascination of its elusive play of fate and motivation.

The Bad and the Beautiful

In both *Ziegfeld Girl* and *Postman*, Turner's image contributes to the overall meaning of the film. partially undermining it in the former, largely coming to its rescue in the latter. With *The Bad and the Beautiful* (1953) and *Imitation of Life* (1959), the image becomes itself in part the subject matter of the film. By this time, however, the image's meaning has shifted in certain respects. The sexy-ordinary configuration has become "glamour" (or, "Lanallure"), and the badness both more extreme and more pitiable. Both these developments are reproduced, and celebrated, in *The Bad and the Beautiful*.

Glamour and ordinariness are antithetical notions. The ordinary and the everyday are by definition not glamorous. Yet glamour—or the particular inflection of the notion embodied by Turner—is based on manufacture, and can be seen to be the process—the industrial process—by which the ordinary is rendered the glamorous. The glamour industry, in which Hollywood played a decisive part, sold itself on the idea that, given its products, anyone—any woman, anyway—could become beautiful. Turner was living proof of this, and if, later in her career, none of the original material—the ordinary woman—showed through anymore, this was all the more proof that the glamour process worked. . . .

It is this element of manufactured glamour that is emphasised in *The Bad and the Beautiful*. Whenever there is a break in the filming within the film, a hairdresser or make-up artist steps in to retouch Georgia/Turner's look. (They are in fact played by Turner's personal hairdresser, Helen Young, and make-up man, Del Armstrong.) The screen test sequence opens with a close-up of her eyebrow being painted in—as any assiduous reader of the fan magazines would have known, Turner had had her eyebrows shaved off for the role of an oriental handmaiden during the filming of *The Adventures of Marco Polo* in 1938, and they never grew again. This shot is (like the casting of hairdresser and make-up man) part in-joke, but also part reinforcing the idea of the manufacture of glamour, not just by heightening beauty that is already there but also by creating artificial beauty where there is nothing.

By emphasising manufacture, the film also emphasises the star image as an illusion. This is evoked in the first shot of Georgia/Turner. A maid answers the phone and says it is Mr Shields; the camera moves across (is it to another room, or was the maid a reflection in a mirror?), showing us in quick succession first Georgia side-on in a mirror, then her back, then her face full-on in a mirror. Already the film is giddy with reflection images, reflections, moreover, of a woman preparing her appearance at a dressing table. How can we, as we watch, pick out the levels of illusion here?—the illusion of reflection, the illusion of make-up, the illusion of the film we are watching . . . Georgia/Turner puts a black lace veil over her head, then turns to listen at the telephone receiver. The camera now finally homes in on her face (rather the reflection of it), stopping at a perfectly composed glamour framing. The final frame of this brief, one-take, then, is both really Georgia (or Turner . . .), not her reflection, and yet it is also her at her most "produced."

What we have got in the final frame is the *real illusion*. For it is no part of the purpose of *The Bad and the Beautiful* to demystify glamour by foregrounding its manufacture. Rather, the processes of manufacture themselves become fascinating and . . . glamorous. The same holds true for the film's overall depiction of Hollywood. It is rather like a conjuror showing you how a trick is done by quickness of the hand—you are so impressed by the dexterity that you remain as dazzled by how the trick is done as you were before by its magic effect. (This relates to Minnelli's other films; see Jim Cook's remarks on *On a Clear Day You Can See Forever* in *Movie 24*.)

Nor is this emphasis on the glamour of illusion-manufacture meant to detract from the notion of the star's special quality or magic. On the contrary, it is the techniques of illusion that stimulate the "real magic" of the star, the "truth" of her "performance." (The oxymoronic brilliance of *The Bad and the Beautiful* will finally defeat me). In the dialogue, we have repeated insistences that Georiga is a star. This has nothing to do with talent or acting ability but, as Jonathan (Kirk Douglas) says after her screen test, the fact that, no matter how bad she may be, no one can take their eyes off her when she is on the screen. Similarly, Jonathan dismisses Lucien's objections that Georgia does not have the poise for a period costume she has designed, observing that Georgia is a star and will therefore be all right. She needs only to be tutored to bring out this innate quality. In the processing of the raw material, the hidden value—star quality—will be revealed. (The film apparently wants to insist that this is not a question of conning the public—nowhere in *The Bad and the Beautiful* is the apparatus of fan magazines, promotion and so on shown directly to have a role in star manufacture, although the press agent, Syd, is seen as a permanent member of the creative studio team.)

In the working out of the narrative, this play on reality and illusion comes to a mesmerising climax. Jonathan cannot get the right effect from Georgia in the marriage scene in the film they are shooting. When they pack up for the day, they have a quiet exchange during which Georgia gazes longingly at him. "That's the expression I want!" he says. As a result, Georgia pours her feeling for him into the role in the film. It is this that gives "truth" to her performance. Yet the film has hinted, and is soon to reveal, that he is merely manipulating her. In other words, the truth of her performance rests on a deception.

When Georgia herself realises this, discovering him at home with Lila during the premiere party, we have the famous car scene, in which, in one long take, she drives into the night, crying hysterically, with headlights glaring into her (and our) eyes, the rain lashing down, the camera twisting around her. What we seem to be getting here is the moment of real reality, assured by the notion that only untrammelled, chaotic, violent emotion is authentic. All the rest is illusion. It is the supreme masterstroke to fabricate this authenticity so completely in a studio mock-up of a car and with the epitome of star artifice, Lana Turner.

Turner's association with badness continued as a defining element of her publicly available private life between *Postman* and *The Bad and the Beautiful*. She dated countless men, most of them famous, and hence was widely rumoured to be a nymphomaniac (or, as an MGM executive quoted by Morella and Epstein revealingly put it, "Lana had the morals and the attitudes of a man. . . . If she saw a muscular stage hand with tight pants and she liked him, she'd invite him into her dressing room"). In 1947, she married Bob Topping, a wealthy heir, three days after his divorce from a previous marriage (in which she was named as co-respondent). The Presbyterian minister who married them was, with much publicity directed against Turner, suspended because Presbyterians are not allowed to marry people divorced for less than a year. In 1951, she was separated from Topping; she had an accident in her shower, variously put down to drunkenness, suicide attempt and pure accident. The films of the period, however—apart from her role as the thoroughly wicked Lady de Winter in *The Three Musketeers* (1948)—do not reflect this emphasis on badness. What does characterise them, apart from their use of Turner as a glamour object, is a tendency to team her with considerably older men, including Spencer Tracy in *Cass Timberlaine* (1947) and a visibly ageing Clark Gable in *Homecoming* (1948, their third film together, but the difference in their ages was more apparent than before).

This teaming is of a piece with the emergence in Turner's publicity, as crucially related to her association with badness, of the role of her father. Early in her career,

MGM had invented a biography for Turner, giving her a wealthy father ("a mining engineer") who had died in an accident. In fact, she came from a very poor home; her father, who had once been a miner, was a gambler and bootlegger and was murdered by one of his cronies when Turner was ten. The studio had wanted to fabricate Turner as an All American Girl—but when her image was clearly anything but harmed by her turning to the bad, it became useful to let the true story of Turner's past be known via fan magazines, biographies, etc. The inexorable link with badness, and its pitiability, were strengthened by the image of both her sordid origins and her loss of her father—this got her all ways, she was indelibly bad, but could not help it, genetically (who her father was), environmentally (the upbringing he gave her) and psychologically (loss of him at a crucial age made the passage to mature heterosexuality problematic). In a culture as drenched, even at the popular level, in naturalising, individuated explanations of personality as America in the 'forties and 'fifties, Turner and her father were a powerful image-complex. In an interview, Turner herself suggested the meaning of her father's death—"Since my life has been wayward and impulsive, always a search for something that is not there, and then disillusionment, I believe I need all the excuses I can make. The shock I suffered then may be a valid excuse for me now. It may explain things I do not myself understand" (quoted by Morella and Epstein).

The idea that Turner's relations with men are somehow related to the early death of her father gives a certain *frisson* to many of her roles—for example, Sheila has a sugar daddy in *Ziegfeld Girl*, Nick in *Postman* is old enough to be Cora's father. But this is all very oblique. With *The Bad and the Beautiful*, it is the key to the relationship between Georgia and Jonathan. (I had better stress before going any further that what follows is not a psychoanalytic reading of *The Bad and the Beautiful*, much less of Georgia and Jonathan; it is rather an analysis of a text that is, rather obviously, informed by a popular psychoanalysis, as indeed many films directed by Vincente Minnelli are.) Their fathers bring them together; her dependence upon him depends upon her rejecting her real father and replacing him with Jonathan; the question is whether she can in turn reject this surrogate father.

Their fathers bring them together, although both are dead. Georgia's father, an actor, worked for Jonathan's, a producer, just as Georgia and Jonathan are actor and producer respectively. Georgia's father drew a picture of Jonathan's father, as a demon with a pitchfork, on the (nursery?) wall of his home. It is here that Jonathan and Georgia (legs only visible, dangling from a loft) first meet. Jonathan removes the drawing from the wall, and hangs it in his office. When she goes, an unknown bit player, for an audition there, it is her turning to look at the drawing (together with her lustrous blond hair seen earlier when she is working as a stand-in) that identifies her to Jonathan. It is moreover her turning, with an identical movement of the head, to look at the drawing in Harry Pebbel's office in the film's framing story that leads into her flash-back of her relationship with Jonathan. This relationship is thus signalled at various important moments by her father's hostile feelings towards his father.

He "kills" her father. She has "built a shrine to him" (Jonathan's words) and he breaks it up, smashing the record of her father intoning a "Macbeth" soliloquy, drawing a moustache on a picture of him. As a result, she is free of her father—but by substituting Jonathan. In the scene after he has dropped her in the pool (she has gone out and got drunk through fear on the night before shooting begins), Georgia/Turner performs just like a little girl. The accoutrements of glamour are replaced by a head towel and outsize coat (it is his, but it makes her look like the archetypal little girl wearing grown-up's clothes). She sits first on the floor, then on his knee—never in an equal adult position. She speaks, in a little girl voice, such cute lines as "If we were married, I wouldn't take up much room." And he tells her, "Love is for the very young." The naughty little girl, legs dangling over the sides of the loft in the scene of their first meeting, has become the good, meek daughter. She has become his child.

The elision of the sexual and parental relationships in this development is precisely the point—it is the sexuality of daughter-father relationships, and the dangerous sexual consequences of their disruption, that is played on in the Turner image and in the Georgia-Jonathan relationship. In turn, this relates to the theme of her becoming "authentic." Just as the car scene signals an explosion of "real" feeling, so, too, with rather less stops pulled out, does the climax of the scene in her bedroom, where Jonathan smashes her father's "shrine." He has sneered at her—"Look at you, you're acting now, playing the doomed daughter of the great man"—and when he smashes the shrine, she attacks him, her hair comes loose and swings in the light. In both cases, the "real" feeling is signalled by a departure from the static, perfectly groomed look of Georgia/Turner to wild movement with textures (her hair here, her fur in the car scene) that capture and diffuse the light. And in both cases she is being required, forcibly, to reject her father (real or surrogate).

Whether she does succeed, however, in freeing herself from her second father, Jonathan—and hence, like the Turner image, from a father-fixated sexuality—is ambiguous. At the beginning of the film, just before she, together with Fred and James Lee, go into Pebbel's office, she draws a moustache on the shield outside, Jonathan's emblem, exactly the same as the moustache he, Jonathan, draws on her father's portrait (later in the film, though earlier in her "life"). She laughs with the others. This is clearly an act of defiance, doing to Jonathan what he did to her father. But perhaps it has to be read as only an act, not a real rejection. This is what the film suggests elsewhere. In the framing narrative she is dressed in black (a neat, tight-fitting suit), her hair drawn back. In the flash-backs, she wears light, usually white, clothes, and her hair hangs lustrously. The general contrast, and especially the cut back from the flashing car scene to her immobile, black figure, posed in recall, suggest repression. She is keeping unwanted desire in check, which is not the same thing as being free from it. She tells James Lee that one may grow out of first love, "but you never get over it." Directly, this means Jonathan, but, given the pattern of father references in the film, it could also mean her father—or fathers in general. Georgia has grown out of that (the "mature" repression of desire in adulthood) but not got over it (still hung up on father figures). Of Turner, only the latter was touted as being the case. In the last shot of the film, she, like Fred and James Lee, remains fascinated by Jonathan, unable just to walk out, compelled to pick up the phone to hear what his ideas are. He still exercises his hold on her.

Whether this hold is a father-son one in the case of Fred and James Lee, I'm not sure. What does seem a reasonable supposition is that Jonathan himself is free of his own father. Despite keeping up appearances (paying mourners to attend his father's funeral), he befriends the only man, Fred, who speaks against his father, pronounces his father "*the* heel" and seems to accept Georgia's father's view of him as a demon. He overthrows Pebbel, who is effectively in the position of his father, as head of the studio, and treats him with all the patronising air of the still vigorous son. Jonathan is free of his father, but Georgia really is not. Perhaps this is because psychoanalytic thought (at least of that period) only allows sons to kill fathers. Thus Georgia, like Turner, must remain pitiably locked into her perverse needs and desires.

Imitation of Life

By the time of *Imitation of Life* in 1959, the glamour emphasis in Turner's image had become uppermost. As Jeanine Basinger puts it, ". . . Turner appeared to cut loose her past. For the audience, it ceased to exist. She was their movie goddess—born and raised on film for their pleasure—the product of photogenesis." The "bad" elements continued before and after *Imitation of Life*, if anything more scandalous—four more marriages and divorces (Lex Barker 1953–57, Fred May 1960–62, Robert Eaton 1954–69, Ronald Dante 1969–69), accused of breaking up the marriage of Ava Gardner and Frank Sinatra, her daughter's involvement in various scandals (drugs, becoming a stripper, not to mention the Johnny Stompanato affair discussed below), and some film roles: *The Prodigal* (1955) as a wicked priestess, *Portrait in Black* (1960) as an adulterous murderer. However, the effect of all these is more to increase her glamorous otherness and to make her an identification figure, the suffering woman of the woman's film genre. It is these qualities that *Imitation of Life* capitalises upon. More precisely, it uses a quality of "detachment" characterising Turner's dress and acting styles.

Throughout the films and public appearances of the 'fifties, and on into the 'sixties, Turner became increasingly associated with clothes. The 1965 film *Love Has Many Faces* was sold principally on the strength of its "Million Dollar Wardrobe," and the connection between Turner and a certain kind of dress style was essential to the films she made for Ross Hunter (*Imitation of Life, Portrait in Black, Madame* X 1966). Although many different designers worked on her films, notably Edith Head (*Who's Got the Action?* 1962, *Love Has Many Faces*), Jean Louis (*Imitation of Life, Portrait in Black, Madame* X), Helen Rose (*A Life of Her Own* 1950, *The Merry Widow* 1952, *The Bad and the Beautiful, Latin Lovers* 1953, *Bachelor in Paradise* 1961) and Travilla (*The Rains of Ranchipur* 1955), *The Big Cube* 1969), and although the style very clearly belongs to American 'fifties *haute couture*, there is nonetheless a certain Lana Turner look. This is prominent in *Imitation of Life* and relates to the film's elaboration of what is implied by its title.

The signification of many of the features of the look are those of *haute couture* in general (which has still never been better analysed than by Veblen in his "Theory of the Leisure Class")—notably expensiveness (especially, with Turner, jewellery, elaborate head-dresses and hair-does) and, distinguishing the wearer from those whose clothes have to permit labour, inconvenience (for Turner, trains, folds in the skirt, off-the-shoulder dresses). Certain other features are more specifically Lana—the use of manmade fibres, so that her high style is associated with glossy, modern artifice rather than "natural" or "old-fashioned" values; a quality of hardness in the clear-cut edges of the designs and in the use of colour, which, together with a tendency towards designs that create geometrical patterns around her frame, "dehumanises" her, plays down qualities of softness, roundness, even warmth; and a certain type of creation that is frankly bizarre and unimaginable outside of movies, even of Turner, such as, from *Imitation of Life*, an outfit consisting of vermillion pants and top, pink necklace, and a piece of pink flower-printed, insubstantial material shaped like an open-fronted dress, cut away at the knees, and trailing out behind in a full spread. The emphasis, then, is on artifice (a feature of the Turner image already dwelt upon), femininity (but one conceived not in the traditional terms of softness, but in terms of elaborateness, ornamentation, plasticity) and sheer impracticality, without connection with ordinary life. The net effect in many of her films is that Turner, in her fabulous costumes, is visually detached from her surroundings—India in *The Rains of Ranchipur,* Cornwall in *Another Time Another Place* (1958), a rusty old steam ship, captained by John Wayne, in *The Sea Chase* (1955)—except in those cases where the set-up is itself equally "unreal": as high priestess of Astarte in *The Prodigal* (revealing clothes that make every movement hazardous), as the richest woman in the world in *Latin Lovers* (in Brazil), and in *Love Has Many Faces* (in Acapulco). In *A Life of Her Own* and *Peyton Place* (1957) she was associated directly with *haute couture* as, respectively, a top model and owner of the town's smartest fashion salon.

The sense that all this gives to many of her film appearances—of her being detached from the events, on show—is central in *Imitation of Life,* for in it she plays a character, Lora, who is, or becomes, a person on show, performing, presenting an image, to be thought of neither as an essence (i.e., an inner human being expressing her self through presentation) nor as interacting with others and circumstances. In the early scenes in the film, she wears ordinary, everyday clothes—blouses and skirts, a suit for interviews—but as she gradually becomes an actor and a star, her wardrobe becomes more and more Lana. If "life" is essence, interaction, vitality, reality, then Lora/Turner, in her outlandish outfits, is an imitation of it. The problem the film poses (thus bringing in the suffering element in the Turner image) is whether there is, in fact, anything but imitation in life.

The key metaphor for imitation in the film is that of acting. The fact that Lora is an actor, in the professional sense, is only part of this. We never see her on stage, except in rehearsal or taking a bow. Insofar as her profession is relevant to the metaphor of acting, it is in the way that she is set up as "an actress" quite apart from any ability to act well on a stage. Thus agent Allen Loomis takes her on because he is impressed by her impersonation of an archetypal Hollywood star (this is how she inveigles her way into his office) and he promotes her not by putting her into a play but by taking her to parties *dressed like* an actress (in particular, in mink). Ironically, the only time we get to know anything about a play she is in is when she takes a part as a social worker in a bid for realism. But Lora/Turner acts, puts on a performance, throughout the film. Detached by dress, she is further detached by acting style. Turner has a habit—in her other later films as well—of turning away from the person she is acting with to deliver a line, adopting a posture, head-on to camera although not actually looking into the camera. Even when she does not do this her acting nonetheless is poised and posed. If one takes as an example someone at the very opposite end of the scale to her, Judy Garland, one can observe how Garland hangs on her acting partner's every word, watching her/his lips or eyes, registering response in minute facial inflections. It is this that gives Garland's performances their characteristically nervy, tense and spontaneous feel. By contrast, Turner's beautifully made-up face moves very little and she does not even always look at her partner. All of this is emphasised time and again in *Imitation of Life*, until the climactic moment when, turning from her sobbing daughter Susie (Sandra Dee), she declares, staring ahead of her, that she will give up Steve (John Gavin) rather than have him come between them. Susie looks at her and says "Oh mother, stop acting!" The film here draws attention to Turner's posing acting style, making its use of the style to embody "imitation" explicit.

This use of Turner was given a further emotional charge for contemporary viewers by Turner's involvement in the trial of her daughter Cheryl for the murder of her (Turner's) boyfriend Johnny Stompanato (in 1958). More than one newspaper described her testimony as "the greatest performance of her life." Whether or not this was fair of the press, the confusion was compounded by the purely coincidental release of *Peyton Place* around the time of the trial. In it, Turner's big scene has her breaking down in sobs on the witness stand, just as she did at the Stompanato trial. There are of course further overtones of the Stompanato affair in the relationship between Steve and Susie (just as rumour had it that Cheryl had fallen for Johnny), again blurring the distinction between imitation and reality, screen and life.

Acting is only one of the many images for imitation of life used by the film. All of these (for instance, a Nat King Cole substitute to sing the title song; the use of an obviously artificial, stage-set-like backdrop for Lora's home; narrative touches such as having a job writing envelopes to give them a wholly spurious "personal touch" connect to the central metaphor of acting/performance, but unlike *The Bad and the Beautiful*, with its endless reflections and cross-references which trap everything in the paradoxes of illusionism, *Imitation of Life* does also point, in an ultimately very melancholic fashion, to the possibility, or idea of authenticity.

In fact, nearly all the possibilities pointed to by the film are also pretty well undercut or attenuated by it. Christmas, vividly evoked with bright reds, snow and Xmas trees, is exposed as sham fairly devastatingly by Sarah Jane's materialist insistence that, since he was real, Christ must have been either black or white and by Annie (Juanita Moore) and Lora's idealist evasion in terms of it being the general idea of Christ that matters. Other possible authenticities are more ambiguously dealt with. I will look at them primarily as they relate to Lora/Turner.

The possibility of self-affirmation as a source of strength is most explored through the character of Sarah Jane (Susan Kohner) and her imitation of white, but the illusoriness of self-affirmation is underlined in the same way at certain points for both her and Lora. These ways are the use of mirror reflections at moments of affirmation and/or the introduction of the "Imitation of Life" theme on the soundtrack after such declarations. Thus when Lora rings Susie after her triumph in the role of Amy, her sense of fulfilment, achievement, is shown us only in a mirror image of it. (Compare Sarah Jane's fierce "I'm white!" to probing boy-friend, shown as reflected in a shop-window.)

Another possible source of authenticity is virility, here represented by Steve. Douglas Sirk often has a character like this in his films, embodying promise of virility, to the women and impotent men of the rest of the cast—think of his use of Rock Hudson in *All That Heaven Allows*, *Written on the Wind* and *The Tarnished Angels*. The point about these characters—played by actors who are almost exaggeratedly tall, dark and handsome—is that their virility is never put to the test. They may offer the woman fulfilment (including, quite clearly, sexual fulfilment), but this remains speculative, to take place well after the end title has appeared. Sirk's films do not even end with the marriage of this male with the female protagonist, only with our assumption that this is the way all heterosexual romances end. Much less is the consummation assured. The ending of *Imitation of Life* is especially ambiguous. In one sense, it is the cobbling together of the nuclear family characteristic of the postwar film melodrama. That is to say that while we end with a nuclear family unit, it is actually made up from bits of other families (Steve is the father of neither girl; neither he nor Lora is Sarah Jane's parent). Moreover, it is shot not as father, mother and children grouped together, but as the women grouped together in the back of the car, with a cut-in shot of Steve looking on benignly from the front seat. In other words, the promise of virility that will set the seal on the family is still only a promise.

The problem with this is what exactly the film thinks of virility. Feminism has correctly exposed the oppressiveness of virility as an idea (as opposed to an idea such as energy or strength that need not be gender-specific), yet it does seem that *Imitation of Life*, and Sirk in his other films, do believe in virility as an idea. What is being critically exposed is the absence or failure of virility. In particular, the association of Steve with a certain view of the countryside (and even more a similar association between Rock Hudson and nature in *All That Heaven Allows*) seems to be presented quite straight, without undercutting, as if Sirk really believes in a natural order of virility and, possibly, the family, at least as ideals.

There is a similar problem with another of the film's alternatives to a life of imitation, namely black culture. The main lines of the Annie–Sarah Jane plot seem to be a repeat of the imitation themes in the Lora plot. The device of the black girl who can pass for white clearly demonstrates the thesis that race is a question of cultural definition, including role-playing, in which biological difference plays no significant part. Annie's investment of her self, her labour, in provision for her spectacular funeral, something which she herself by definition cannot experience, suggests the crippling role of religious mystification in black culture. Yet the film also seems to want to say that black culture *is* more authentic than white, materially and culturally.

The role of Annie and Sarah Jane in the film is to act as the material base to the superstructure of Lora's success, which is mere phenomenal form. Annie almost lives Lora's real, practical life for her. She is the bread-winner (filling in envelopes, doing cleaning jobs, paying the bills) who enables Lora to pursue her career, and she is housewife and mother to Susie. She even at one point controls Lora's relationship with Steve, by gesturing him to go when she thinks Lora should be left alone. In other words, she is the reality, the material existence, that makes Lora's appearance possible. Moreover, it is quite clear that Lora has no conception of what it means to be black; she has no understanding of the reality that makes her life possible. She sees taking the part of the social worker as doing something more "real" on the stage, yet cheerfully chats about its "coloured angle" with David (Dan O'Herlihy) in front of Annie, without consulting *her*, without even seeming to register the fact that Annie is serving them drinks. When she upbraids Sarah Jane for her Southern mammy impersonation when bringing in drinks for her (Lora's) guests, she says "I've never treated you differently"—yet we have just seen Sarah Jane using the back stairs, going to the local school (Susie is at boarding school), expected to help out her black servant mother. Lora has not personally acted differently towards Sarah Jane and yet quite clearly Sarah Jane is getting different treatment. Lora has no conception of the racist structures that underpin her position and Sarah Jane's equally.

In addition to this materialist authenticity granted to blacks, the final funeral set-piece seems to affirm, its narrative significance *vis-à-vis* Annie's life notwithstanding, the cultural authenticity of blacks. Above all, the use of Mahalia Jackson (who really is Mahalia Jackson, not someone imitating her) suggests a core of real feeling in black religion. The fact that Jackson's singing is so "genuinely" emotional that she cannot lip-synchronise herself with any precision draws attention to the artifice of the film medium which is "unable" to "capture" her untrammelled outpouring of emotion. Yet this final affirmation of the authenticity of black culture is also the high point of grief in the film. It is almost as if the film is saying that if there is anything other than imitation it is in suffering.

It is in relation to this that the use of Turner is most interesting, drawing as it does on both her "artificial" and her "suffering" image qualities. When Annie dies, Lora/Turner breaks down and cries, and it is as if some authentic feeling has broken through the hard shell of artifice elsewhere promoted by the film. It is worth comparing this with the car scene in *The Bad and the Beautiful*. In both cases, the effect is of Turner shedding her actor's artifices and giving us naked emotion. This may also be how Turner herself experienced it—we cannot know, and I do not wish to detract from her achievement in both cases. However, the effect also derives from the way both these scenes make a formal break from the rest of the film in presentation of Turner. In *The Bad and the Beautiful*, the posed, static nature of her performance is replaced for the car scene by chaotic movement. In *Imitation of Life*, her collapse on Annie's bed makes one relise that as an element of composition everywhere else in the film, she has been used in upright and detached positions, usually still. The actual movement of falling on the bed breaks this, and the break is maintained through the funeral service where she is slumped at an angle in her seat. Whilst of course in both cases this is the art of the film-makers (of whom Turner is one) and whilst the notion of "naked emotion" does not really have any validity, nonetheless this collapse into suffering, which is also a formal break in the film's compositional patterns *vis-à-vis* Turner, *means* "authenticity," shedding of artifice, reality not imitation. What is melancholy is that this authenticity is only achieved in an image of collapse, as if the only possible reality behind the imitation of life is grief.

As I have been concerned in this article principally to discuss the star as an aspect of film language, I have tried generally to hold back from spelling out the ideological significance of Turner (and the star phenomenon), but a few words on this may be in order by way of a conclusion.

In this perspective the role of Turner as an agent of coherence (*Postman*) or to reinforce such notions as impulse (her marriages, *Postman*), naked emotion and authenticity (*The Bad and the Beautiful*, *Imitation of Life*) would not be viewed as progressive. At the same time, the way her image can disrupt a film text (the overall structure of *Ziegfeld Girl*, the centrality of Frank/Garfield to *Postman*) and its foregrounding of the processes of manufacture are suggestive. In a more directly political sense, it seems to me that her combination of sexuality and ordinariness was in itself ideologically explosive (and I have not sufficiently brought out the lower class elements in this definition of ordinariness), comparable to that later embodied by Marilyn Monroe. To what extent the machinery of glamorisation, punishment and suffering defused this, I'm not sure. I tend always to see ideological struggle within the texts of films, no less in Lana Turner than anywhere else.

Faces of the American Melodrama: Joan Crawford

JEAN-LOUP BOURGET

In setting out to examine the morphology of the American melodrama, one might well follow Propp's example when he tackled the morphology of the fairy-tale, and with the botanists Linnaeus and Goethe as guides, make an a priori distinction between some basic species of the genre—reserving the right to a possible later revision of this classification.

Such a classification would have the advantage of providing us with an historical famework. As we are primarily concerned with a genre, it seems advisable not to set the focus on the *auteur* theory: we might not see the wood for the trees. In fact, an historical study of the American cinema should include two referential axes: the *auteurs* and the genres. We would have then, to give a very obvious example, on the one hand Minnelli, *auteur* of comedies, musicals and melodramas; on the other, the musical (Minnelli, Sidney Donen, Walters . . .) or the melodrama (Minnelli, Sirk, McCarey . . .) for the corresponding period.

We propose to keep within the spirit of the genre and single out a type of melodrama. Films centering around an actress would constitute such a type and we have selected those starring Joan Crawford. They belong to the category of sentimental melodrama. (By melodrama, we always understand romantic drama, which we see as quite distinct from crime melodrama. In this sense melodrama is not merely a matter of plot but of style, theme and structure). "Women's pictures" is a term frequently applied to these films, not inappropriately. It indicates clearly that the film in question is directed to an essentially female audience—an audience, so some maintain, which

---

Jean-Loup Bourget's "Faces of the American Melodrama: Joan Crawford" originally appeared in *Film Reader* 3 (February 1978), pp. 24–34. Reprinted by permission of *Film Reader*.

was particularly characteristic of World War II America but which is, at the same time, always available. In addition it implies that the heroine is, to put it simply, woman as the victim of society. Female viewers can consequently identify with the heroine. Love is the mainspring of the intrigue; a secondary interest is traditionally supplied by the emphasis given to numerous eye-catching ensembles, evening gowns, hats and so on. The title of one of the films to be dealt with in this article is symptomatic in this respect: *Mannequin*.

Making a further distinction, this time within the "women's pictures" themselves, we can compare Crawford's films with those starring Bette Davis. In style alone, the contrast is striking. They demonstrate two opposed ways of obtaining the pathetic effect. Bette Davis's nervousness corresponds to Joan Crawford's stylization. Soon, however, we become aware of a deeper opposition. This derives largely from our impression that in Joan Crawford's films, the disaster is due to circumstances, whereas in Davis's films, the latter, as well as being the victim of disaster, is herself its principle cause. Or, to look at it from a different angle: the calamity, in Crawford's case, is a result of the heroine's weakness, while with Davis it springs from her excessive strength which turns against her. The two traditions coincide in Robert Aldrich's fine gothic fantasy, *What Ever Happened to Baby Jane?* (1963), where the characters' roles conform on the whole to their usual casting as victim and tormentor respectively.

It has been claimed that Bette Davis and Joan Crawford were the first actresses to have initiated the genre.[1] We would also have to mention the melodramas starring Gene Tierney, Barbara Stanwyck, Jane Wyman, Lana Turner. Each one of these actresses has a distinct style, which is a way of being, besides, the central point of a world, some of whose features crystallize and become familiar after one has seen a certain number of their films.

The near magical and archetypal styles of these actresses affect the very notion of genre. Films which on paper are thrillers, *noir* films rather than melodramas, become on the screen romantic dramas where the criminal element is just one more motif in the symphony of gestures, decor and montage. Such is the case in *Portrait in Black* (Michael Gordon, 1960) with Lana Turner, or in *Sudden Fear* with Joan Crawford—or, even more so, in *Mildred Pierce*.

For our study of Crawford's work we have chosen films covering a production period from 1938–1957. This sampling includes, firstly, two MGM films made by the same team (script-writer, Lawrence Hazard; producer, Joseph L. Mankiewicz; director, Frank Borzage): *Mannequin* (1938) and *Strange Cargo* (1940). Then two Warner films which marked a definite comeback for the star: *Mildred Pierce* (Michael Curtiz, 1945) for which she received an Oscar, and *Humoresque* (Jean Negulesco, 1946—both produced by Jerry Wald. Finally, a Fox film, *Daisy Kenyon* (Preminger, 1947), an RKO film, *Sudden Fear* (David Miller, 1952), a Columbia film, *Autumn Leaves* (Aldrich, 1956); and a film released, but not produced, by Columbia, *The Story of Esther Costello* (David Miller, 1957).

Joan Crawford's Personality as Heroine

As might be expected, the character portrayed by Joan Crawford in these films determines and sums up their thematics to a large extent. It is worth noting that her only negative part is in *Humoresque*. Here she plays a rich and blasé femme fatale whose last victim is John Garfield, a virtuoso violinist. The fact remains, however, that in all the other films the character she portrays reveals a certain basic tension between theoretical simplicity and actual sophistication. In *Mannequin* we first see Joan Crawford in a humble Irish environment. The setting is early neo-realistic. Children yell and the light bulb flickers in a stairway; Joan's mother wears herself out for a good-for-nothing husband. The heroine of *Mildred Pierce* grows progressively richer by dint of hard work, surrounded by greasy smells mentioned several times in the dialogue (she climbs the social scale, from waitress to owner of a chain of restaurants). In *Strange Cargo*, Crawford is a cabaret-entertainer in the heart of French Guiana; in *Daisy Kenyon* and in *Autumn Leaves*, she is still middle-class. On the other hand, in the remaining films she is presented straight away as a rich and distinguished woman (*Humoresque, Sudden Fear, Esther Costello*), although in this last film reference is made to her very modest origins.

It would appear then that Joan Crawford's relationship to the "primitivist" motifs of the melodrama (those motifs symbolizing simplicity, naturalness, Nature) is often contradictory or, at least, dialectical, whereas Jane Wyman, for example, is more or less in harmony with them. In *Johnny Belinda* (Negulesco, 1948), Jane Wyman is in tune with the "primitive" landscape of Nova Scotia, Acadia/Arcadia; in *The Glass Menagerie* (Irving Rapper, 1950), she is the very soul of innocence, with all the backwardness that the latter might imply. It is precisely this quality which enabled her to play little girls, and then, without any transition, mature women (in Sirk's melodramas).

This is not the case with Joan Crawford's films. As in the great majority of American melodramas, their fundamental dialectic lies in a subtle opposition between Nature and culture. Accordingly her films contain certain primitivist motifs, but their conclusions tend towards realism: after a purifying contact with Nature, the individual returns to civilization. There are no parables inspired by Thoreau or Rousseau here. Contemporary critics clearly felt this, in writing about *Mannequin* for example. In it, Joan Crawford has to face the strong temptation of the Irish cottage; however, she succeeds in resisting it and urges Spencer Tracy to achieve greater prosperity and social standing. We know too that Spencer Tracy, Joan's second husband, is an Irishman who has made his fortune; but his career is already assured when we see him, and it is Joan's first husband, Alan Curtis, the ambitious failure, who plays the part of the traditional "villain."

In spite of the "greasy smells," *Mildred Pierce* is a hymn to economic liberalism and to the success based on it. It is not so much the Nature-culture antinomy which is central as the opposition between two cultures: free enterprise is extolled in the face of the old European-type aristocracy as it is represented in the film by Monte Beragon (Zachary Scott), with his decadent parasitism. Jack Carson's presence, moreover, helps to tip the scales, as the real vulgarity of his character is set against the ultimately theoretical vulgarity of Mildred-Crawford.

The Primitivist Motifs

As we have seen, the Irish cottage where Joan Crawford and Spencer Tracy honeymoon corresponds to a temporary phase only in the dialectic. It is simply a question of understanding the frailty of success. But the "retreat," in the 17th century sense of the word, is just a dream. The rustic setting allows Crawford and Tracy to converse; an admirably poetic dialogue besides, where human existence is compared to a soap-bubble—increasingly fragile as it expands and finally turning back into soap-suds.[2] Yet the end reassures against the blows of fate.

Daisy Kenyon takes up the cottage motif. Significantly, however, it does not occur until the very end of the film, thus acquiring maximum emphasis. Crawford hesitates between two men, the "hero," Henry Fonda, and the more ambiguous Dana Andrews. But Fonda embodies simplicity, and Dana Andrews, Washington's high society. Finally, Joan Crawford is more confused than ever. She takes refuge in her cottage which stands in the middle of a snowscape. Driven from her isolation by the incessant ringing of the telephone, she escapes in her car. Sound is used subjectively and the telephone continues to ring until her car skids and turns over. Here we have an example of one of the archetypes of the melodrama: speeding in a car, as a flight from reality, is abruptly ended by an accident which, in turn, is a revelation.[3] Joan Crawford drags herself to the cottage where the two men now wait for her, the fire crackling in the hearth. The truth has in fact been made clear to her at the moment of the accident, with the result that the cottage also becomes the symbol of Fonda's quiet confidence. He is sure of his love and of Crawford's reciprocatory feelings; knowing the decision she has already taken, he refuses to influence her. The accident and the cottage in the snow are the tangible signs of the recognition of happiness.

Strange Cargo presents another parable, again quite primitivist. During their difficult escape bid, Clark Gable and Joan Crawford must cross primeval elements, the jungle and the sea. This escape is marked by a growing spiritual illumination of a strongly religious character and Ian Hunter is its main vehicle. A mysterious figure, he once took Clark Gable's place during a previous break for freedom. He is therefore Gable's double, and Christ. Henry Fonda too, in *Daisy Kenyon*, is a Christlike personage, thanks to his gentleness and to his knowledge of the future.

In *Esther Costello*, on the contrary, the primitive setting where the story begins is shown in a light which can scarcely be called idyllic, or even positive. It should be noted that the locality is in any case imaginary, and that the Ireland of *Esther Costello* is no more "real" than that of *Mannequin*. However, both stylistically and thematically, it is realistic to the point of caricature. Joan Crawford, born at Cloncraig (Ireland), makes a pilgrimage to her origins which brings out forcefully the disparity between her childhood background and social standing in the States. The villagers, sordid half-ruffians, are all drunk and gravely salute a disgusted Joan Crawford.

The Natural Elements

Although a saving force in *Strange Cargo*, the sea is elsewhere one of those natural elements which are considered hostile and destructive. Usually, however, it is the beach that we see, itself an ambiguous motif, at times civilized and at others primitive. The beach in *Esther Costello* displays that hideous couple, Heather Sears and Lee Patterson. *Mannequin*, on the other hand, contains a fine moonlight sequence with Joan Crawford and Alan Curtis, where Joan Crawford draws a circle in the sand to express her idea of love, sufficient to itself.

In *Autumn Leaves* too, there is an admirable beach sequence. At first, it plays on Joan Crawford's awkward shyness, a "woman in her forties" trying on a new bathing suit, uncertain of its effect and afraid to leave the bathing hut. Her young lover, Cliff Robertson, has to take the forgotten price tag off the suit. She cannot swim, but gives way to Cliff Robertson's exhilarating joy of life. Their first passionate kiss takes place in the sea (the lower part of the frame being shot underwater) and is followed by a second kiss at the edge of the waves, and a third that evening.

The sea is also part of the setting for a seduction scene in *Mildred Pierce*, but here, it becomes Leviathan. We turn full-circle, from primitive nature (the sea), to hyper-culture: Zachary Scott, the old Spanish aristocrat, calls the Pacific "his ocean." In the following sequence, we see a reflection of the fireplace and the couple in a large mirror while a finished record turns, unheeded, round and round on the player. Curtiz's discretion is to be admired, although the scene is quite unambiguous. The mirror also suggests the idea of the lie, an implication which will later become reality, thus reversing the positive role of the "cottage." During the credits in *Mildred Pierce*, each title is washed over the same shot of a wave and the shot is shown again, immediately after Zachary Scott's words ("my ocean"): the sea is the accomplice of the forces of darkness, as in *Humoresque*.

In Negulesco's film, the first embrace of Crawford and Garfield dissolves into a shot of the sea. It is the finale which is particularly famous, however. Joan Crawford has been caught in her own trap, a flirtation with Garfield who, for his part, prefers music to Crawford. She has gone to find "rest and quietness" by the sea. Listening to the radio, she hears Garfield playing, quite appropriately, Wagner's *Liebestod* theme;[4] she drinks and throws her glass against the window, breaking it. The wind snatches a poster of Paul Boray (Garfield) which she catches and crumples. We see her, poster in hand and tears pouring down her face; then, back-lit, she walks in the wind towards the sea. At last, the music stops, a close-up of her face is followed by the waves and bubbles, and then the poster, left lying on the beach, is borne away by the tide. Another natural element, the storm, is used in a remarkable sequence which we shall come to later.

The Wildermann

The character who inhabits the wilderness, or who on occasion stands for it in the thematic of the plot, is that which Eugenio d'Ors, in his book on the Baroque, calls the "Wildermann." It is the name given to the man of the woods, the wild man seen on the coats-of-arms and on the inn signs in Southern Germany and usually clad in an animal skin and armed with a club. As one might well expect, this character often crops up in the melodrama, as in all kinds of literary "romance" ("romance" as Northrop Frye defines the term in *The Anatomy of Criticism*), where he normally has a positive value, somewhat like the "good savage."

The key film here is *Humoresque*, for the character played by John Garfield, which is basically the same from one film to the next, is one of the finest embodiments of the Wildermann in the cinema. The same is true of Sterling Hayden, and we might recall that the latter plays opposite Joan Crawford in *Johnny Guitar* (Nicholas Ray, 1954). Mention should be made of Garfield's appearance in Warner films such as Curtiz's *Four Daughters* (1938), which was his first film. Here he is literally and in all senses of the word the "wild man," wild not as a result of intentional cruelty, but because of his closeness to Nature and his disdain for social conventions. Finally, he is expelled from the cushioned milieu into which he has strayed.

In *Humoresque*, he plays fundamentally the same part. His innocence is emphasized by his childish pleasure in hitting the bull's-eye at darts, or in buying a striped suit in defiance of the dressing norms of high society. As Joan Crawford observes: "Bad manners, Mr. Boray—the infallible sign of talent"—and also the key to the way in which this good savage involuntarily seduces the sophisticated woman (the classic example of *Lady Chatterley's Lover* springs to mind). Again, Paul Cavanaugh, Joan Crawford's remarkably indulgent husband and very much the 18th century rake, comments on virtuoso Garfield's style: "He plays as Van Gogh painted. There is a touch of the savage in him . . . good for art."

Sudden Fear, on the other hand, sets us on the wrong track. Certainly, Jack Palance's appearance lends itself to the Wildermann role. With intent to vengeance and robbery, he tries to seduce Joan Crawford in a train and does an impersonation in the Garfield manner, half wild, half childlike. We learn that he made his stage debut as Lenny in *Of Mice and Men*—a part which, according to Northrop Frye, is precisely a parody of the Wildermann, Lenny being the "villainous" good savage. In *Sudden Fear,* Palance is rather a Casanova, a seducer and a rake, hidden behind a mask of powerful ugliness—in other words, likeable. He invites the association himself by alluding to a portrait of Casanova in the San Francisco Palace of the Legion of Honour.

Finally, in *Autumn Leaves*, Aldrich closes the circle. The Wildermann here is a wholly negative brute and stands in contrast to the apparent, rather feminine, weakness of Cliff Robertson. He is the latter's father (Lorne Greene) and is responsible for his son's mental disturbance; having deceived Cliff Robertson with his first wife, he is ready to deceive him with Joan Crawford too. Archetypes have a floating function, as has repeatedly been shown with regard to the Western, and the melodrama is no exception to the rule. In *Autumn Leaves*, as in *Tea and Sympathy*, made in the same year (Minnelli, 1956), the purely outward signs of virility are opposed to a sensitivity which is accused of being feminine, but which is in fact characteristic of the artist, the creator and thus of man.[5]

The Villains

The word "melodrama" implies "the good man" and "the villains." We have just seen that the Wildermann, normally the good savage, is susceptible of becoming the villain. But in the majority of the films starring Joan Crawford we find another category of villains, those who belong to high society. In fact, Joan Crawford's ambiguous social position is such that she, more often than not, comes into contact with this type of person. The presence of a Wildermann accentuates, by contrast, Joan Crawford's sophistication. Her simplicity is brought out all the more by the foil of the very civilized "villain."

An alibi? A defense mechanism? Two of the most notable "villains" have nothing Anglo-Saxon about them: we are dealing with Zachary Scott in *Mildred Pierce* and Rossano Brazzi in *Esther Costello*. In the latter film, David Miller's actors' direction flounders through absurd exaggeration. Presented to the viewer in his "natural" milieu, that is, a highly sophisticated one (an art gallery), Rossano Brazzi has all the subtlety of an Elinor Glyn character. He is, unfortunately, unforgettable when he kisses Joan Crawford with theatrical passion, twisted mouth and slanting look. Soon he shows great interest in the little blind deaf-mute, an orphan girl (Heather Sears) picked up by Joan Crawford, and he plans to use her both financially (by embezzling the funds she collects for the handicapped) and sexually. The Crawford-Brazzi-Sears trio sets out on a European Grand Tour whose two highpoints are Venice, a traditionally sentimental setting and, in this case, erotic, an added stimulus to Brazzi's intentions; then London. A fine sexual metaphor, in the latter town, provides the film's sole moment of interest. On a night of storm, in Joan Crawford's absence, Rossano Brazzi approaches the bed where Heather Sears is lying. There is a clap of thunder; Brazzi kisses the girl. Miller cuts on the window which opens in a gust of wind, letting the rain stream into the room. A very readable image, successful because of its very neatness. It heralds, fairly accurately, that used by Hitchcock in *North by Northwest* (1959), the train entering the tunnel. Curiously enough it is "in a tunnel" that *Esther Costello* ends, but on this occasion it serves as a cover-up for Crawford's murder of Brazzi, as well as for her own suicide, the whole being disguised as a car accident.

In *Mildred Pierce* we have the same trio and consequently a very similar type of character who tries to seduce mother and/or daughter. It is evident that this is a fundamental melodramatic triangle on which *Imitation of Life* (Sirk, 1959) offers an interesting variation: the daughter is in love with her mother's lover without being loved in return. A subject which is grotesquely caricatural in *Esther Costello* is smoothly treated in *Mildred Pierce*, thanks to Zachary Scott's well-felt interpretation. The compact structure of Curtiz's film compresses into the Joan Crawford–Ann Blyth group the two couples (mother and daughter) which are distinct in *Imitation of Life*. Ann Blyth displays the dominant feature of each daughter-mother relationship. Not only is she in love with her mother's lover, Zachary Scott, thus prefiguring the Lana Turner–Sandra Dee pattern, but she also rebels against her mother and the social status she is to inherit, establishing the same kind of tension that is enacted between Juanita Moore and Susan Kohner. And again, like Susan Kohner, she becomes a cabaret artist. This gives rise to both Joan Crawford's and Juanita Moore's descent to Hades, searching, to a background of wolf-whistles, for their respective lost daughters.

Aspect of Style

The films which we have examined fall into two stylistic groups: one the one hand, the two Borzage films (*Mannequin* and *Strange Cargo*), the Preminger film (*Daisy Kenyon*) and Aldrich's film (*Autumn Leaves*); on the other, Curtiz (*Mildred Pierce*), Negulesco (*Humoresque*), David Miller (*Sudden Fear, Esther Costello*).

The first "school" prefers to emphasize lyricism and this in a very literal sense: the songs and the flowers. Joan Crawford's emblem in *Mannequin* is the violet—"beautiful and helpless-looking" like the heroine. The title of *Autumn Leaves* is an allusion to Joan Crawford's and Cliff Robertson's love anthem.

Even when treating a subject with social implications (*Mannequin*), Borzage does so with a certain sentimental softness which transcends the realism of the situation. He is more concerned with obtaining an overall impression of fluidity than with concentrating on acute detail. In the same way, this softness of outline is achieved in *Daisy Kenyon* through the focussing, by both director and photographer, Leon Shamroy, on the three principal actors, with close-shots and subdued lighting. *Autumn Leaves* is supposedly anchored in reality: in the geographic reality of North America, and in the medical reality of the shock treatments which Cliff Robertson has to undergo. But this geography is imaginary and mythical: Joan Crawford comes from New England, terrain elect of the primitivist melodrama, where women who are no longer young are rescued by the young men of the woods. All the "realistic touches" are caught up in the flow of a very nuanced elegy—too sentimental for Aldrich's own taste, if not for ours.[6]

In the second group, *Humoresque* seems to offer a link, as it were, between MGM and Warner Brothers. To begin with, it is a remake of a famous Borzage film (1920); and then Joan Crawford's costumes are by Gilbert Adrian, the great dress designer for this actress's MGM films (*Mannequin*, for example, but not *Strange Cargo*, in which her part requires her to wear rags). Nevertheless, stylistically, *Humoresque* is closest to *Mildred Pierce*.

Curtiz, whom we consider to be a great director, depicts in his film a particularly coherent world. This is due to Zachary Scott's interpretation, to the film's elaborate composition (three successive flashbacks), and to the kind of society in which the characters evolve, with its many mirrors and staircases, its parties where sophisticated cocktails are drunk. All these features point forward to a film which was made a little later by another German-educated director: *Ruthless* (Edgar G. Ulmer, 1948). In this context, we might add that, whilst it has often been observed of Minnelli's films that the "party" scene is the author's signature, the same observation can be justly made of those films starring Joan Crawford at her most sophisticated.

Interestingly enough, Miller converges with Curtiz in the finale of *Sudden Fear.* In both cases, the motif is that of the redeeming dawn. Mildred is freed of the charge of murdering Beragon; she finds her first husband waiting for her and walks with him towards the city with its horizon of skyscrapers. In *Sudden Fear,* Jack Palance has driven his car against his accomplice (Gloria Grahame), having mistaken her for Joan Crawford, and has killed both himself and her. Joan Crawford walks away from the place of the "accident," and turning her back to the camera, on into the dawn. It is significant that in both films a townscape should appear at the end after the purgation of passion, like a promised land. America, after questioning the myth of progress, urbanization and socialization, is content with a rhetorical question, and at the end of the story reinstates the same belief. Towards the conclusion of *San Francisco* (Woody S. Van Dyke, 1936), the town, a latter-day Sodom, is destroyed, more by heaven's avenging fire than by the earthquake. But the crowd of refugees strikes up "The Battle Hymn of the Republic" and starts off in the direction of a vision of the new San Francisco, with its proud skyscrapers; a vision of Babel after Sodom?

Notes

1. Charles Higham and Joel Greenberg in *Hollywood in the Forties* (Zwemmer and Barnes, London and New York, 1968) claim that there were no films centered around an actress before those starring Greta Garbo, who was followed by Joan Crawford and Bette Davis. We are far from being convinced of this. We are thinking of Sternberg's films with Marlene Dietrich; of the films with Gloria Swanson, in which some strange mutual resemblances can be seen (she loses her pants in Dwan's *Manhandled,* 1928, and in Stroheim's *Queen Kelly,* 1928); lastly, films like Griffith's *Way Down East,* 1920, or Henry Kings' *The White Sister,* 1923, seem to be largely centered around Lillian Gish. One could even say that they are expressive variations on the theme of a face. Actresses' close-ups constitute the classic punctuation of "women's pictures"; this tradition is surely not invalidated by Joan Crawford's tear-stained face.
2. It is amusing to be reminded in this way of the popular appellations "soap opera" or "sudser."
3. See Bette Davis in *Dangerous* (Alfred E. Green, 1936), Lana Turner in *The Bad and the Beautiful* (Minnelli, 1953) and *Portrait in Black,* Kirk Douglas in *Two Weeks in Another Town* (Minnelli, 1962), etc.
4. It is Oscar Levant who had the idea of using Wagner's *Tristan* for this sequence. In this film

he plays the part of Garfield's musician friend and his companion in misery. See Negulesco's statement in Higham and Greenberg, *The Celluloid Muse* (Angus and Robertson, London, 1969).

5. At the same time, Sirk returns to the positive archetype of the Wildermann, which explains the admirable use he made of that decried actor Rock Hudson, the new embodiment of the man from the woods (particularly and literally in *All That Heaven Allows*, 1956, where he is a nursery gardener).
6. In *The Celluloid Muse*, Aldrich explains that he made *Autumn Leaves* for three reasons: he wanted to make a soap opera anyway; to dispel the idea that he could make only violent action films; to pay tribute to Joan Crawford. He describes himself as being disappointed with the result: "too soap-operaish."

Bibliography

The Films of Joan Crawford by Lawrence J. Quirk (The Citadel Press, New York, 1968) gives the credits of all films starring Joan Crawford, short summaries of their plots, a few opinions voiced by American critics at the time of release. The book is illustrated by numerous photographs.

PRINCIPAL FILMS TREATED IN THIS ARTICLE

Mannequin. 1938. 95′.
Director: Frank Borzage. Script: Lawrence Hazard, from Katharine Brush's original story. Photo: George Folsey. Editor: Frederick Y. Smith. Music: Edward Ward. Gowns: Adrian.
Cast: Joan Crawford, Spencer Tracy, Alan Curtis, Ralph Morgan.
Producer: Joseph L. Mankiewicz (MGM).

Strange Cargo. 1940. 113′.
Director: Frank Borzage. Script: Lawrence Hazard, from Richard Sale's novel. Photo: Robert Planck. Editor: Robert J. Kern. Music: Franz Waxman. Art director: Cedric Gibbons.
Cast: Joan Crawford, Clark Gable, Ian Hunter, Peter Lorre, Paul Lukas.
Producer: Joseph L. Mankiewicz (MGM).

Mildred Pierce. 1945. 111′.
Director: Michael Curtiz. Script: Ranald MacDougall and Catherine Turney, from James M. Cain's novel. Photo: Ernest Haller. Editor: David Weisbart. Music: Max Steiner. Art director: Anton Grot. Gowns: Milo Anderson.
Cast: Joan Crawford, Zachary Scott, Jack Carson, Ann Blyth, Bruse Bennett.
Producer: Jerry Wald (Warner).

Humoresque. 1946. 125′.
Director. Jean Negulesco. Script: Clifford Odets and Zachary Gold, from Fannie Hurst's story. Photo: Ernest Haller. Editor: Rudi Fehr. Music: Franz Waxman and Leo F. Forbstein. Musical advisor: Isaac Stern. Art director: Hugh Reticker. Gowns: Adrian.
Cast: Joan Crawford, John Garfield, Oscar Levant, Paul Cavanaugh, Craig Stevens.
Producer: Jerry Wald (Warner).

Daisy Kenyon. 1947. 99′.

Director: Otto Preminger. Script: David Hertz, from Elizabeth Janeway's novel. Photo: Leon Shamroy. Editor: Louis Leoffler. Music: David Raskin and Alfred Newman. Art director: Lyle R. Wheeler and George Davis. Gowns: Charles LeMaire.

Cast: Joan Crawford, Dana Andrews, Henry Fonda.

Producer: Otto Preminger (Fox).

Sudden Fear. 1952. 110′.

Director: David Miller. Script: Lenore Coffee and Robert Smith, from Edna Sherry's novel. Photo: Charles Lang, Jr. Editor: Leon Barsha. Music: Elmer Bernstein. Art director: Boris Leven. Gowns: Sheila O'Brien.

Cast: Joan Crawford, Jack Palance, Gloria Grahame, Bruce Bennett.

Producer: Joseph Kaufman (RKO).

Autumn Leaves. 1956. 108′.

Director: Robert Aldrich. Script: Jack Jevne, Lewis Meltzer and Robert Blees, from their story. Photo: Charles Lang, Jr. Editor: Michael Luciano. Music: Hans J. Salter. Art director: William Glasgow. Gowns: Jean Louis.

Cast: Joan Crawford, Cliff Robertson, Lorne Greene, Vera Miles, Ruth Donnelly.

Producer: William Goetz (Columbia).

The Story of Esther Costello. 1957. 127′.

Director: David Miller. Script: Charles Kaufman, from Nicholas Monsarrat's novel. Photo: Robert Krasker. Editor: Ralph Kemplen. Music: Lambert Williamson. Art director: George Provis and Tony Masters. Gowns: Jean Louis.

Cast: Joan Crawford, Rossano Brazzi, Heather Sears, Lee Patterson.

Producer: David Miller (Romulus/Valiant films, for Columbia).

VI

TELEVISION MELODRAMA

In recent years, cinema study has expanded its base to include the study of other media, in particular television. This shift indicates a recognition of the need to understand the powerful social and cultural impact of television on the culture. It is also a recognition that television reaches vastly more people than even the cinema did in its heyday. As Raymond Williams indicates, "In most parts of the world, since the spread of television, there has been a scale and intensity of dramatic performance which is without any precedent in the history of human culture . . . it seems probable that in societies like Britain and the United States more drama is watched in a week or weekend by the majority of viewers than would have been watched in a year or in some cases a lifetime in any previous historical period."

Differences between television and cinema are not merely a matter of statistics, of larger audiences and more frequent performances. The reception of television in the home, its "family-centered" quality, differentiates it from the public spaces of cinema viewing and is one of many factors determining the nature and style of programming. In the arena of drama alone, television can transmit theatrical plays, films, soap operas, serials, and series. Students of the medium have begun to develop a critical terminology for televison which takes into account its variety, its mixing of genres, its treatment of time and space, the conditions of reception for specific programs as well as the relationship of programs to each other, and its differences from other media. In the following essays, the writers address the issue of melodrama from the perspective of soap opera and prime-time television drama.

Tania Modleski's discussion of television soap operas has been one of the most influential in addressing the impact of this form of drama on the female viewer. Of the primary characteristics of the soap opera, she identifies how they are usually set in a small town and concentrate on the affairs of a few families with representatives of different generations who are middle class. The programs do not seek closure and do not encourage identification with one character but depend on multiple identifications. Their strategies of endless deferment resist the resolution of conflict but proliferate new conflicts. In their refusal of closure, the soap operas promise immortality.

Modleski finds the soap operas highly sensitive to social issues, but her particular focus is how they constitute an area of study and concern for feminists. Unlike many other narrative forms, the soap opera addresses a predominantly female audience and thereby provides a ground for identifying a female discourse. In its treatment of spectatorship, the soap opera does not channel the viewer into a position of identifying with a single individual whose power is conferred on the spectator but rather offers multiple and limited points of view which, according to Modleski, deprive the spectator of a sense of power. This limited power is more conducive to the spectator's awareness of conflict and contradiction. Given the limitations of perspective, the spectator is more likely to want to intervene in the course of events.

Soap opera's appeal to women derives from several sources: women's desire for connectedness, the rhythms of domestic life with their numerous interruptions and multiple activities, and women's dual involvement in household drudgery and emotional crises. The form of the soap opera is geared to involvement, interruptions, domestic affairs, and emotional conflicts. The pleasure of these texts is to be found in their leisurely pace, their explorations of and skepticism about the efficacy of language, and their immersion in collective fantasies. Modleski sees the soap opera as portraying real need and desires though often through a distorted lens.

Charlotte Brunsdon's analysis of the British soap opera "Crossroads" shares many of Modleski's assumptions. Brunsdon suggests how in the publicity, the selection of viewing times, and the narrative construction, the program is addressed to a feminine audience. She identifies the arena of the soap opera as one of personal experience, the arena identified by Marxists as marginal to wage labor and by feminists as the women's sphere of "intimate oppression." Even work relationships and male experiences are subsumed within the personal sphere.

The narrative flow in "Crossroads," as in most soap operas, is marked by interruption, repetition, and an undifferentiated sense of time. Unlike the classical cinema, space is organized around two camera fields, in some instances only one. There is no attempt to give a sense of continuous space. In general, the effect is theatrical, not cinematic. The treatment of time and space is fragmented, the multiplicity of story lines, permitting interruption and working against the usual linearity of classical cinema. The deferral of knowledge Brunsdon argues, permits a space for the viewer to interact with the text in speculative and judgmental fashion. When it comes to the constant play on deceit, the text privileges the viewer's knowledge. The dominant question of the dramas does not concern the kind of action presented but the nature of the character doing the presenting. Brunsdon suggests that the personal sphere addresses in the soap opera is not the "natural" attribute of the female but the consequences of culturally and ideologically constructed gender differences. Within this framework of ideology, the soap opera addresses the female who is competent to make sense of the dramas. Brunsdon's position suggests that she does not necessarily see these soap operas as progressive but that she finds their devaluation in large part caused by their being regarded as feminine.

Ien Ang's discussion of "Dallas" draws on film genre study and on Modleski's work. Citing the episodic nature of television, Ang distinguishes between the series, in which episodes are clearly demarcated and the continuity dependent only on the characters and situations, and the serials, in which the narratives are continuous, creating the expectation of "resolution" in the subsequent broadcast. "Dallas" is a series that most often ends with cliffhangers, but the sense of time communicated is of "everyday realism," in which life seems to flow along in "normal" fashion. This sense of time is reinforced by the sense that there is no final narrative resolution to the series, no ultimate restoration of order and balance as in classical genres. In this respect, "Dallas" can be likened to the strategies of soap opera, though Ang is quick to assert that it differs in many other ways from the daytime serials in its more elaborate use of location and camera work characteristic of prime-time television drama. Moreover, since the program is slotted for evening viewing, its audience involves not merely the largely female audience but the entire family. Hence, business life plays a larger role than in the daytime dramas.

As a prime-time soap opera, "Dallas" offers a melange of narratives, some of which intersect, others of which are parallel, and a variety of characters who vie with one another for dominance. Rather than the stress on individual characters, the drama offers the semblance of community in the Ewing family and the larger Dallas community. The treatment of the individual lives of the agents of the drama is selective rather than detailed, and the treatment of social issues is oblique rather than direct. Issues are personalized in the portrayal of the private sphere, though these may have broader public significance. In this respect and in others, "Dallas" displays the tendencies of the family tragedy melodrama, in its use of clichés, its penchant for the sensational and for emotional intensity, its concentration on personal affective experience, and its preoccupation with alcoholism and illness as metaphor.

The outside world is presented as threatening to the harmony of the Ewing family, but the tensions within the family constantly threaten to destroy equilibrium, dramatizing the inability to reconcile personal desire with familial expectation. This "tragic structure of feeling" is intensified by the endless deferment characteristic of serials whereby nothing is ever resolved. There is no progress. Ang describes the position of the viewer as one of multiple identification. Identification does not remain stable but shifts from one character to another, contributing to the sense of the insubstantiality and evanescence of experience. Only J.R., the "villain," escapes this indeterminacy, but he serves the dual function of identifying power as negative and of dramatizing that evil emanates from within the community. The mise-en-scène, too, produces contradictory meanings. On the one hand, the environment of Dallas is presented as the epitome of luxury, but it offers a counterpoint to the gloomy portrayal of social relations.

In order to perceive the contradictions posed by "Dallas," the viewer must be prepared to understand the workings of the "melodramatic imagination." Ang examines Brooks's idea that melodrama functions to overcome the sense of the meaninglessness of contemporary material life, particularly as that life is enacted in the private sphere, but finds this explanation insufficient to account for the different ways in which people experience melodrama. Melodrama speaks to the aspect of everyday life that involves care and nurture and also pleasure.

In his discussion of soap operas, Robert C. Allen attempts to construct a "reader-oriented poetics" of the soap opera, offering ways of identifying its style and the codes it employs. He examines the classical cinema's deployment of narrative, its treatment of mise-en-scène, and its positioning of the spectator in an effort to identify the ways in which the soap opera adapts and alters cinematic techniques. Referring to the reception theory, he attempts to account for the ways in which the soap opera text positions the viewers. Wolfgang Iser's notion of the "wandering viewpoint" is relevant to the way in which attention is mobilized in the dramas through constant reorientation and reevaluation of the events. Textual indeterminacy is reinforced by the interruptions in the narrative, the "gaps of time" between broadcasts and within broadcasts. In Umberto Eco's distinction between "open" and "closed" texts, the soap opera is an open text, like the modernist writings of James Joyce and Virginia Woolf, in which multiple signifying possibilities are structured into the works. Soap opera contains multiple codes which Allen identifies as stylistic, generic, textual, intertextual, and ideological, all of which come into play in the experience of the soap opera.

Rehearsing Modleski's argument for the feminist basis of soap opera, Allen finds that her feminist approach is consistent with his concern for a reader-oriented poetics, though he takes issue with her identification of the ideal soap-opera viewer as the American housewife, finding the audience to be more varied and shifting than Modleski's analysis suggests. While Allen is aware of feminist readings of soap opera, his particular concern is to identify the ways in which these dramas provide a pleasurable alternative discourse which contrasts sharply with classical forms of narrative.

Ellen Seiter's essay takes a dimmer view of recent film and television. She comments on the popularity of family melodrama in the 1980s in both film and television, though she identifies significant differences between the earlier melodramas and the current ones, as well as differences between the daytime soap operas and the prime-time serials such as "Dallas" and "Dynasty." The family melodrama has traditionally been set in a middle-class milieu and has portrayed a middle-class sensibility. The bourgeois values of the genre have frowned on ambition and excessive wealth. In the daytime serials, too, the characters, settings, and values have been middle-class, though Seiter indicates that working-class figures have been represented and allowed up the economic ladder, citing Opal Gardner's success in "All My Children." By contrast, she finds that prime-time serials focus exclusively on upper-class figures; the tendency is to elevate an image of luxury and conspicuous consumption. Even in recent films such as *Shoot the Moon*, *On Golden Pond*, and *Ordinary People*, the focus is on the upper classes through characters, milieu, and even the use of classical music.

Seiter asserts that the emphasis on the upper-class family in recent melodrama provides a way of evading the actual problems of the middle and working classes who have experienced hardship in the last two decades. Moreover, the higher class status of the characters is a strategy for dispersing another set of conflicts, mainly those between men and women, since, in the world of affluence, women and men are more equal in terms of education, opportunity, and wealth. One never finds problems with child care. The overriding form of conflict in film and prime-time television melodrama is disruptive sexual conflict which is disciplined in the interests of monogamy and heterosexuality. With the exception of soap operas, the problems of men have tended to predominate, and men have been placed at the center of the family melodrama.

The Search for Tomorrow in Today's Soap Operas

TANIA MODLESKI

I

Approximately twelve soap operas are shown daily, each half an hour to an hour and a half long. The first of them goes on the air at about 10:00 a.m., and they run almost continuously until about 3:30 p.m. (of course, the times vary according to local programming schedules). In 1975 the *New York Times Magazine* reported that 20 million people watch soap operas daily, the average program attracting 6.7 million viewers, almost 90 percent of them female. Further:

> The households break down economically and educationally in proportions similar to the population as a whole—51.3 percent with household incomes under $10,000, for instance, and 23.0 percent with incomes over $15,000. About 24.8 percent of household heads have only an elementary school education, while 56.2 percent have a high school education or better. . . . The programs gross more than $300-million a year from the makers of soaps, deodorants, cake mixes and other household products, providing a disproportionate share of network profits though nighttime budgets are much larger.[1]

With the exception of "Ryan's Hope," which takes place in a big city, the soap operas are set in small towns and involve two or three families intimately connected with one another. Families are often composed of several generations, and the proliferation of generations is accelerated by the propensity of soap opera characters to mature at an incredibly rapid rate; thus, the matriarch on "Days of Our Lives," who looks to be

---

Tania Modleski, "The Search for Tomorrow in Today's Soap Operas," from *Loving with a Vengeance. Mass-Produced Fantasies for Women* (New York: Methuen, 1982). Reprinted by permission of the author and Shoestring Press.

about 65, has managed over the years to become a great-great-grandmother. Sometimes on a soap opera one of the families will be fairly well to do, and another somewhat lower on the social scale though still, as a rule, identifiably middle-class. In any case, since there is so much intermingling and intermarrying, class distinctions quickly become hopelessly blurred. Children figure largely in many of the plots, but they don't appear on the screen all that often; nor do the very old. Blacks and other minorities are almost completely excluded.

Women as well as men frequently work outside the home, usually in professions such as law and medicine, and women are generally on a professional par with men. But most of everyone's time is spent experiencing and discussing personal and domestic crises. Kathryn Weibel lists "some of the most frequent themes":

> the evil woman
> the great sacrifice
> the winning back of an estranged lover/spouse
> marrying her for her money, respectability, etc.
> the unwed mother
> deceptions about the paternity of children
> career vs. housewife
> the alcoholic woman (and occasionally man).[2]

Controversial social problems are introduced from time to time: rape was recently an issue on several soap operas and was, for the most part, handled in a sensitive manner. In spite of the fact that soap operas contain more references to social problems than do most other forms of mass entertainment, critics tend to fault them heavily for their lack of social realism.

If television is considered by some to be a vast wasteland, soap operas are thought to be the least nourishing spot in the desert. The surest way to damn a film, a television program, or even a situation in real life is to invoke an analogy to soap operas. In the same way that men are often concerned to show that what they are, above all, is not women, not "feminine," so television programs and movies will, surprisingly often, tell us that they are not soap operas. On a recent "Phil Donahue Show," a group of handicapped Vietnam War veterans were bitterly relating their experiences; at one point Donahue interrupted the conversation to assure his audience (comprised almost entirely of women) that he was not giving them soap opera, but he thought it important to "personalize" the war experience. An afternoon "Money Movie," *Middle of the Night*, an interminable Paddy Chayevsky affair starring Frederick March, dealt with one man's life-crisis as, on the brink of old age, he falls in love with a very young Kim Novak and struggles against the petty and destructive jealousy of his sister and daughter. "This is *not* a soap opera," he reprimands the sister at one point. Since to me it had all the ingredients of one, I could only conclude that men's soap operas are not to be thought of as soap operas only because they are *for men* (or about men).

It is refreshing, therefore, to read Horace Newcomb's book, *T.V.: The Most Popular Art*, in which he suggests that far from being the nadir of art forms, as most people take them to be, soap operas represent in some ways the furthest advance of T.V. art. In other words, for all their stereotypical qualities, they combine to the highest degree two of the most important elements of the television aesthetic: "initmacy" and "continuity."

Television, says Newcomb, is uniquely suited to deal with character and interpersonal relations rather than with action and setting. Soap operas, of course, play exclusively on the intimate properties of the medium. Newcomb also points out that because of the serial nature of the programs television can offer us depictions of people in situations which grow and change over time, allowing for a greater "audience involvement, a sense of becoming a part of the lives and actions of the characters they see."[3] Thus far it is mainly soap opera which has taken advantage of these possibilities for continuity, nighttime programs, by and large, tending to "forget" from week to week all of the conflicts and lessons which have gone before.

Newcomb's book is important in that, by refusing to indulge in an anti-feminine bias against soap operas, it reveals a new way of seeing these programs which allows them to be placed in the vanguard of T.V. aesthetics (dubious as this distinction may seem to many people). My approach is different from, though in no sense opposed to Newcomb's. I propose not to ignore what is "feminine" about soap operas but to focus on it, to show how they provide a unique narrative pleasure which, while it has become thoroughly adapted to the rhythms of women's lives in the home, provides an alternative to the dominant "pleasures of the text" analyzed by Roland Barthes and others. Soap operas may be in the vanguard not just of T.V. art but of all popular narrative art.

II

Whereas the meaning of Harlequin Romances depends almost entirely on the sense of an ending, soap operas are important to their viewers in part because they never end. Whereas Harlequins encourage our identification with one character, soap operas invite identification with numerous personalities. And whereas Harlequins are structured around two basic enigmas, in soap operas, the enigmas proliferate: "Will Bill find out that his wife's sister's baby is really his by artificial insemination? Will his wife submit to her sister's blackmail attempts, or will she finally let Bill know the truth? If he discovers the truth, will this lead to another nervous breakdown, causing him to go back to Springfield General where his ex-wife and his illegitimate daughter are both doctors and sworn enemies?" Tune in tomorrow, not in order to find out the answers, but to see what further complications will defer the resolutions and introduce new questions. Thus the narrative, by placing ever more complex obstacles between desire and fulfillment, makes anticipation of an end an end in itself. Soap operas invest exquisite pleasure in the central condition of a woman's life: waiting—whether for her phone to ring, for the baby to take its nap, or for the family to be reunited shortly after the day's final soap opera has left *its* family still struggling against dissolution.

According to Roland Barthes, the hermeneutic code, which propounds the enigmas, functions by making "expectation . . . the basic condition for truth: truth, these narratives tell us, is what is *at the end* of expectation. This design implies a return to order, for expectation is a disorder."[4] But, of course, soap operas do not end. Consequently, truth for women is seen to lie not "at the end of expectation," but *in* expectation, not in the "return to order," but in (familial) disorder.

Many critics have considered endings to be crucial to narratives. Frank Kermode speculates that fictive ends are probably "figures" for death.[5] In his essay on "The Storyteller," Walter Benjamin comes to a similar conclusion:

> The novel is significant . . . not because it presents someone else's fate to us, perhaps didactically, but because this stranger's fate by virture of the flame which consumes it yields us the warmth which we never draw from our own fate. What draws the reader to the novel is the hope of warming his shivering life with a death he reads about.[6]

But soap operas offer the promise of immortality and eternal return—same time tomorrow. Although at first glance, soap operas seems in this respect to be diametrically opposed to the female domestic novels of the nineteenth century, which were preoccupied with death, especially the deaths of infants and small children, a second look tells us that the fantasy of immortality embodied in modern melodramna is not so very different from the fantasies expressed in the older works. In the latter, it is not the case that, in Benjamin's words, "the 'meaning' of a character's life is revealed only in his death";[7] rather, for women writers and readers, forced to endure repeatedly the premature loss of their children, it was the meaning of the character's death that had to be ascertained, and this meaning was revealed only in the afterlife, only in projections of eternity.

"[T]racts of time unpunctuated by meaning derived from the end are not to be borne," says Frank Kermode, confidently.[8] But perhaps for women (no doubt for men too) certain kinds of endings are attended by a sense of meaninglessness even less capable of being borne than limitless expanses of time which at least hold open the possibility that something may sometime happen to confer sense upon the present. The loss of a child was, for nineteenth century women, an example of such an unbearable ending: it was, as Helen Papashvily has called it, "a double tragedy—the loss of a precious individual and the negation of her creativity,"[9] and it threatened, perhaps more than any other experience, to give the lie to the belief in a benevolent God and the ultimate rightness of the world order. And so, it was necessary to believe that the child would join a heavenly family for all eternity.

For twentieth-century woman, the loss of her family, not through death, but through abandonment (children growing up and leaving home), is perhaps another "ending" which is feared because it leaves women lonely and isolated and without significant purpose in life. The fear, as Barbara Easton persuasively argues, is not without foundation:

> With the geographical mobility and breakdown of communities of the twentieth century, women's support networks outside the family have weakened, and they are likely to turn to their husbands for intimacy that earlier generations would have found elsewhere.[10]

The family is, for many women, their only support, and soap operas offer the assurance of its immortality.[11] They present the viewer with a picture of a family which, though it is always in the process of breaking down, stays together no matter how intolerable its situation may get. Or, perhaps more accurately, the family remains close precisely because it is perpetually in a chaotic state. The unhappiness generated by the family can only be solved in the family. Misery becomes not, as in many nineteenth-century women's novels, the consequence and sign of the family's breakdown, but the very means of its functioning and perpetuation. As long as the children are unhappy, as long as things *don't* come to a satisfying conclusion, the mother will be needed as confidante and adviser, and her function will never end.

One critic of soap opera remarks, "If . . . as Aristotle so reasonably claimed, drama is the imitation of a human action that has a beginning, a middle, and an end, soap opera belongs to a separate genus that is entirely composed of an indefinitely expandable middle."[12] It is not only that successful soap operas do not end, it is also that they cannot end. In *The Complete Soap Opera Book*, an interesting and lively work on the subject, the authors show how a radio serial forced off the air by television tried to wrap up its story.[13] It was an impossible task. Most of the storyline had to be discarded and only one element could be followed through its end—an important example of a situation in which what Barthes calls the "discourse's instinct for preservation" has virtually triumphed over authorial control.[14] Furthermore, it is not simply that the story's completion would have taken too long for the amount of time allotted by the producers. More importantly, I believe it would have been impossible to resolve the contradiction between the imperatives of melodrama—the good must be rewarded and the wicked punished—and the latent message of soap operas—everyone cannot be happy at the same time, no matter how deserving they are. The claims of any two people, especially in love matters, are often mutually exclusive.

John Cawelti defines melodrama as having

> at its center the moral fantasy of showing forth the essential "rightness" of the world order. . . . Because of this, melodramas are usually rather complicated in plot and character; instead of identifying with a single protagonist through his line of action, the melodrama typically makes us intersect imaginatively with many lives. Subplots multiply, and the point of view continually shifts in order to involve us in a complex of destinies. Through this complex of characters and plots we see not so much the working of individual fates but the underlying moral process of the world.[15]

It is scarcely an accident that this essentially nineteenth-century form continues to appeal strongly to women, whereas the classic (male) narrative film is, as Laura Mulvey points out, structured "around a main controlling figure with whom the spectator can identify."[16] Soap operas continually insist on the insignificance of the individual life. A viewer might at one moment be asked to identify with a woman finally reunited with her lover, only to have that identification broken in a moment of intensity and attention focused on the sufferings of the woman's rival.

If, as Mulvey claims, the identification of the spectator with "a main male protagonist" results in the spectator's becoming "the representative of power,"[17] the multiple identification which occurs in soap opera results in the spectator's being divested of power. For the spectator is never permitted to identify with a character completing an entire action. Instead of giving us one "powerful ideal ego . . . who can make things happen and control events better than the subject/spectator can,"[18] soap operas present us with numerous limited egos, each in conflict with the others, and continually thwarted in its attempts to control events because of inadequate knowledge of other people's plans, motivations, and schemes. Sometimes, indeed, the spectator, frustrated by the sense of powerlessness induced by soap operas, will, like an interfering mother, try to control events directly:

> Thousands and thousands of letters [from soap fans to actors] give advice, warn the heroine of impending doom, caution the innocent to beware of the nasties ("Can't you see that your brother-in-law is up to no good?"), inform one character of another's doings, or reprimand a character for unseemly behavior.[19]

Presumably, this intervention is ineffectual, and feminine powerlessness is reinforced on yet another level.

The subject/spectator of soap operas, it could be said, is constituted as a sort of ideal mother: a person who possesses greater wisdom than all her children, whose sympathy is large enough to encompass the conflicting claims of her family (she identifies with them all), and who has no demands or claims of her own (she identifies with no one character exclusively). The connection between melodrama and mothers is an old one. Harriet Beecher Stowe, of course, made it explicit in *Uncle Tom's Cabin*, believing that if her book could bring its female readers to see the world as one extended family, the world would be vastly improved. But in Stowe's novel, the frequent shifting of perspective identifies the reader with a variety of characters in order ultimately to ally her with the mother/author and with God who, in their higher wisdom and understanding, can make all the hurts of the world go away, thus insuring the "essential 'rightness' of the world order." Soap opera, however, denies the "mother" this extremely flattering illusion of her power. On the one hand it plays upon the spectator's expectations of the melodramatic form, continually stimulating (by means of the hermeneutic code) the desire for a just conclusion to the story, and, on the other hand, it constantly presents the desire as unrealizable, by showing that conclusions only lead to further tension and suffering. Thus soap operas convince women that their highest goal is to see their families united and happy, while consoling them for their inability to realize this ideal and bring about familial harmony.

This is reinforced by the character of the good mother on soap operas. In contrast to the manipulating mother who tries to interfere with her children's lives, the good mother must sit helplessly by as her children's lives disintegrate; her advice, which she gives only when asked, is temporarily soothing, but usually ineffectual. Her primary function is to be sympathetic, to tolerate the foibles and errors of others. Maeve Ryan, the mother on "Ryan's Hope," is a perfect example. "Ryan's Hope," a soap opera centered around an Irish-Catholic, bar-owning family which, unlike the majority of soap families, lives in a large city, was originally intended to be more "realistic," more socially oriented than the majority of soap operas.[20] Nevertheless, the function of the mother is unchanged: she is there to console her children and try to understand them as they have illegitimate babies, separate from their spouses (miraculously obtaining annulments instead of divorces), and dispense birth control information in the poor neighborhoods.

It is important to recognize that soap operas serve to affirm the primacy of the family not by presenting an ideal family, but by portraying a family in constant turmoil and appealing to the spectator to be understanding and tolerant of the many evils which go on within that family. The spectator/mother, identifying with each character in turn, is made to see "the larger picture" and extend her sympathy to both the sinner and the victim. She is thus in a position to forgive all. As a rule, only those issues which can be tolerated and ultimately pardoned are introduced on soap operas. The list includes careers for women, abortions, premarital and extramarital sex, alcoholism, divorce, mental and even physical cruelty. An issue like homosexuality, which could explode the family structure rather than temporarily disrupt it, is simply ignored. Soap operas, contrary to many people's conception of them, are not conservative but liberal, and the mother is the liberal par excellence. By constantly presenting her with the many-sidedness of any question, by never reaching a permanent conclusion, soap operas undermine her capacity to form unambiguous judgments.

In this respect, soap opera melodrama can be said to create in the spectator a divisiveness of feeling totally different from the "monopathic" feeling Robert Heilman sees as constituting the appeal of traditional melodrama. There, he writes, "one enjoys the wholeness of a practical competence that leads to swift and sure action; one is untroubled by psychic fumbling, by indecisiveness, by awareness of alternate courses, by weak muscles or strong counterimperatives."[21] But in soap operas, we are constantly troubled by "psychic fumbling" and by "strong counterimperatives." To take one example, Trish, on "Days of Our Lives," takes her small son and runs away from her husband David in order to advance her singing career. When she gets an opportunity to go to London to star in a show, she leaves the child with her mother. When the show folds, she becomes desperate to get back home to see her child, but since she has no money, she has to prostitute herself. Finally she is able to return, and after experiencing a series of difficulties, she locates her son, who is now staying with his father. Once she is in town, a number of people, angry at the suffering she has caused David, are hostile and cruel towards her. Thus far, the story seems to bear out the contention of the critics who claim that soap opera characters who leave the protection of the family are unequivocally punished. But the matter is not so simple. For the unforgiving people are shown to have limited perspectives. The larger view is summed up by Margo, a woman who has a mysterious and perhaps fatal disease and who, moreover, has every reason to be jealous of Trish since Trish was the first love of Margo's husband. Margo claims that no one can ever fully know what private motives drove Trish to abandon her family; besides, she says, life is too short to bear grudges and inflict pain. The spectator, who sees the extremity of Trish's sorrow, assents. And at the same time, the spectator is made to forgive and understand the unforgiving characters, for she is intimately drawn into their anguish and suffering as well.

These remarks must be qualified. If soap operas keep us caring about everyone; if they refuse to allow us to condemn most characters and actions until all the evidence is in (and, of course, it never is), there is one character whom we are allowed to hate unreservedly: the villainess, the negative image of the spectator's ideal self.[22] Although much of the suffering on soap opera is presented as unavoidable, the surplus suffering is often the fault of the villainess who tries to "makes things happen and control events better than the subject/spectator can." The villainess might very possibly be a mother trying to manipulate her children's lives or ruin their marriages. Or perhaps she is a woman avenging herself on her husband's family because it has never fully accepted her.

This character cannot be dismissed as easily as many critics seem to think.[23] The extreme delight viewers apparently take in despising the villainess testifies to the enormous amount of energy involved in the spectator's repression and to her (albeit unconscious) resentment at bring constituted as an egoless receptacle for the suffering of others.[24] The villainess embodies the "split-off fury" which, in the words of Dorothy Dinnerstein, is "the underside of the 'truly feminine' woman's monstrously overdeveloped talent for unreciprocated empathy."[25] This aspect of melodrama can be traced back to the middle of the nineteenth century when *Lady Audley's Secret*, a drama based on Mary Elizabeth Braddon's novel about a governess turned bigamist and murderess, became one of the most popular stage melodramas of all time.[26] In her discussion of the novel, Elaine Showalter shows how the author, while paying lipservice to conventional notions about the feminine role, managed to appeal to "thwarted female energy":

> The brillance of *Lady Audley's Secret* is that Braddon makes her would-be murderess the fragile blond angel of domestic realism. . . . The dangerous woman is not the rebel or the bluestocking, but the "pretty little girl" whose indoctrination in the female role has taught her secrecy and deceitfulness, almost as secondary sex characteristics.[27]

Thus the villainess is able to transform traditional feminine weaknesses into the sources of her strength.

Similarly, on soap operas, the villainess seizes those aspects of a woman's life which normally render her most helpless and tries to turn them into weapons for manipulating other characters. She is, for instance, especially good at manipulating pregnancy, unlike most women, who, as Mary Ellmann wittily points out, tend to feel manipulated by it:

> At the same time, women cannot help observing that conception (their highest virtue, by all reports) simply happens or doesn't. It lacks the style of enterprise. It can be prevented by foresight and device (though success here, as abortion rates show, is exaggerated), but it is accomplished by luck (good or bad). Purpose often seems, if anything, a deterrent. A devious business benefitting by indirection, by pretending not to care, as though the self must trick the body. In the regrettable conception, the body instead tricks the self—much as it does in illness or death.[28]

In contrast to the numerous women on soap operas who are either trying unsuccessfully to become pregnant or who have become pregnant as a consequence of a single unguarded moment in their lives, the villainess manages, for a time at least, to make pregnancy work for her. She gives it the "style of enterprise." If she decides she wants to marry a man, she will take advantage of him one night when he is feeling especially vulnerable and seduce him. And if she doesn't achieve the hoped-for pregnancy, undaunted, she simply lies to her lover about being pregnant. The villainess thus reverses male/female roles: anxiety about conception is transferred to the male. He is the one who had better watch his step and curb his promiscuous desires or he will find himself burdened with an unwanted child.

Some episodes on "The Young and the Restless" perfectly illustrate the point. Lori's sister Leslie engages in a one night sexual encounter with Lori's husband, Lance. Of course, she becomes pregnant as a result. Meanwhile Lori and Lance have been having marital difficulties, and Lori tries to conceive a child, hoping this will bring her closer to her husband. When she finds out about her sister and Lance, she becomes frantic about her inability to conceive, realizing that if Lance ever finds out he is the father of Leslie's child, he well be drawn to Leslie and reject her. Vanessa, Lance's mother and a classic villainess, uses her knowledge of the situation to play on Lori's insecurities and drive a wedge between her and Lance. At the same time, Lori's father has been seduced by Jill Foster, another villainess, who immediately becomes pregnant, thus forcing him to marry her.

Furthermore, the villainess, far from allowing her children to rule her life, often uses them in order to further her own selfish ambitions. One of her typical ploys is to threaten the father or the woman possessing custody of the child with the deprivation of that child. She is the opposite of the woman at home, who at first is forced to have her children constantly with her, and later is forced to let them go—for a time on a daily recurring basis and then permanently. The villainess enacts for the spectator a kind of reverse *fort-da* game, in which the mother is the one who attempts to send the child away and bring it back at will, striving to overcome feminine passivity in the process of the child's appearance and loss.[29] Into the bargain, she also tries to manipulate the man's disappearance and return by keeping the fate of his child always hanging in the balance. And again, male and female roles tend to get reversed: the male suffers the typically feminine anxiety over the threatened absence of his children. On "Ryan's Hope," for example, Delia continually uses her son to control her husband and his family. At one point she clashes with another villainess, Raye Woodward, over the child and the child's father, Frank Ryan, from whom Delia is divorced. Raye realizes that the best way to get Frank interested in her is by taking a maternal interest in his child. When Delia uncovers Raye's scheme, she becomes determined to foil it by regaining custody of the boy. On "The Young and the Restless," to take another example, Derek is on his way out of the house to try to intercept Jill Foster on her way to the altar and persuade her to marry him instead of Stuart Brooks. Derek's ex-wife Suzanne thwarts the attempt by choosing that moment to inform him that their son is in a mental hospital.

The villainess thus continually works to make the most out of events which render other characters totally helpless. Literal paralysis turns out, for one villainess, to be an active blessing, since it prevents her husband from carrying out his plans to leave her; when she gets back the use of her legs, therefore, she doesn't tell anyone. And even death doesn't stop another villainess from wreaking havoc; she returns to haunt her husband and convince him to try to kill his new wife.

The popularity of the villainess would seem to be explained in part by the theory of repetition compulsion, which Freud saw as resulting from the individual's attempt to become an active manipulator of her/his own powerlessness.[30] The spectator, it might be thought, continually tunes into soap operas to watch the villainess as she tries to gain control over her feminine passivity, thereby acting out the spectator's fantasies of power. Of course, most formula stories (like the Western) appeal to the spectator/reader's compulsion to repeat: the spectator constantly returns to the same story in order to identify with the main character and achieve, temporarily, the illusion of mastery denied him or her in real life. But soap operas refuse the spectator even this temporary illusion of mastery. The villainess's painstaking attempts to turn her powerlessness to her own advantage are always thwarted just when victory seems most assured, and she must begin her machinations all over again. Moreover, the spectator does not comfortably identify with the villainess. Since the spectator despises the villainess as the negative image of her ideal self, she not only watches the villainess act out her own hidden wishes, but simultaneously sides with the forces conspiring against fulfillment of those wishes. As a result of this "internal contestation,"[31] the spectator comes to enjoy repetition for its own sake and takes her adequate pleasure in the building up and tearing down of the plot. In this way, perhaps, soap operas help reconcile her to the meaningless, repetitive nature of much of her life and work within the home.

Soap operas, then, while constituting the spectator as a "good mother," provide in the person of the villainess an outlet for feminine anger: in particular, as we have seen, the spectator has the satisfaction of seeing men suffer the same anxieties and guilt that women usually experience and seeing them receive similar kinds of punishment for their transgressions. But that anger is neutralized at every moment in that it is the special object of the spectator's hatred. The spectator, encouraged to sympathize with almost everyone, can vent her frustration on the one character who refuses to accept her own powerlessness, who is unashamedly self-seeking. Woman's anger is directed at woman's anger, and an eternal cycle is created.

And yet, if the villainess never succeeds, if, in accordance with the spectator's conflicting desires, she is doomed to eternal repetition, then she obviously never permanently fails either. When as occasionally happens, a villainess reforms, a new one immediately supplants her. Generally, however, a popular villainess will remain true to her character for most or all of the soap opera's duration. And if the villainess constantly suffers because she is always foiled, we should remember that she suffers no more than the good characters, who don't even try to interfere with their fates. Again, this may be contrasted to the usual imperatives of melodrama, which demand an ending to justify the suffering of the good and punish the wicked. While soap operas thrive they present a continual reminder that women's anger is alive, if not exactly well.

III

Critics have speculated before now about why the narrative form of soap opera seems to have special appeal to women. Marcia Kinder, reviewing Ingmar Bergman's *Scenes from a Marriage*, suggests that the "open-ended, slow paced, multi-climaxed" structure of soap opera is "in tune with patterns of female sexuality."[32] While this is certainly a plausible explanation, it should be clear by now that soap opera as a narrative form also reflects and cultivates the "proper" psychological disposition of the woman in the home. Nancy Chodorow provides us with a nice description of women's work in the home and usefully contrasts it to work performed in the labor force:

> Women's activities in the home involve continuous connection to and concern about children and attunement to adult masculine needs, both of which require connection to, rather than separateness from, others. The work of maintenance and reproduction is characterized by its repetitive and routine continuity, and does not involve specified sequence or progression. By contrast, work in the labor force—"men's work"—is likely to be contractual, to be more specifically delimited, and to contain a notion of defined progression and product.[33]

We have already seen ways in which soap operas encourage women to become involved in—"connected to"—the lives of the people on the screen. A comparison with "Dallas," the popular nighttime serial, is instructive. There, the characters are highly glamorized, the difference between their world and that of the average viewer could not be greater, and the difference is continually emphasized. On soap operas, by contrast, glamour and wealth are played down. Characters are attractive enough so that their looks are not distracting, well off enough so that, as in a Henry James novel, they can worry about more exciting problems than inflation at the market. But glamour and wealth are not preoccupations as they are on "Dallas." Obviously, the soap opera world is in reality no more like the average spectator's than the world of "Dallas"; yet the characters and the settings all connote, to use a Barthesian type of neologism, averageness. This accounts for the fans' frequent contention that soap opera characters are just like them—whereas no one is likely to make such a claim about the Ewing family on "Dallas." The consequent blurring of the boundaries between fantasy and life which sometimes occurs (as, for example, when fans write letters to the "characters," giving them advice about their problems) suggests that the psychological fusion which Chodorow says is experienced by the wife/mother applies in these instances to the *viewer's* experience of the characters.

Another way in which soap opera stimulates women's desire for connectedness is through the constant, claustrophobic use of close-up shots. Often only the audience is privileged to witness the characters' expressions, which are complex and intricately coded, signifying triumph, bitterness, despair, confusion—the entire emotional register, in fact. Soap operas contrast sharply with other popular forms aimed at masculine visual pleasure, which is often centered on the fragmentation and fetishization of the female body. In the most popular feminine visual art, it is easy to forget that characters even have bodies, so insistently are close-ups of faces employed. One critic significantly remarks, "A face in close-ups is what before the age of film only a lover or a mother ever saw."[34] Soap operas appear to be the one visual art which activates the gaze of the mother—but in order to provoke anxiety about the welfare of others. Close-ups provide the spectator with training in "reading" other people, in being sensitive to their (unspoken) feelings at any given moment.

Chodorow stresses the "connectedness" of women's work in the home, but this is only half the picture. The wife's job is further complicated by the fact that she must often deal with several people with different, perhaps conflicting moods; and further she must be prepared to drop what she is doing in order to cope with various conflicts and problems the moment they arise. Unlike most workers in the labor force, the housewife must beware of concentrating her energies exclusively on any one task—otherwise, the dinner could burn or the baby could crack its skull (as happened once on "Ryan's Hope" when the villainess became so absorbed in a love encounter that she forgot to keep an eye on her child). The housewife functions, as many creative women have sadly realized, by distraction. Tillie Olsen writes in *Silences*, "More than in any other human relationship, overwhelmingly more, motherhood means being instantly interruptable, responsive, responsible. . . . It is distraction, not meditation, that becomes habitual: interruption, not continuity; spasmodic, not constant toil."[35] Daytime television plays a part in habituating women to distraction, interruption, and spasmodic toil.

These observations have crucial implications for current television theory. In his book *Television: Technology and Cultural Form* Raymond Williams suggests that the shifts in television programming from one type of show to another and from part of a show to a commercial should not be seen as "interruptions"—of a mood, of a story—but as parts of a whole. What at first appear to be discrete programming units in fact interrelate in profound and complex ways. Williams uses the term "flow" to describe this interaction of various programs with each other and with commercials. "The fact of flow," he says, defines the "central television experience."[36] Against Williams I would argue that the flow within soap operas as well as between soap operas and other programming units reinforces the very principle of interruptability crucial to the proper functioning of women in the home. In other words, what Williams calls "the central television experience" is a profoundly decentering experience.

"The art of being off center," wrote Walter Benjamin in an essay on Baudelaire, "in which the little man could acquire training in places like the Fun Fair, flourished concomitantly with unemployment."[37] Soap operas also provide training in the "art of being off center" (and we should note in passing that it is probably no accident that the nighttime "soap opera" "Dallas" and its spinoffs and imitators are flourishing in a period of economic crisis and rising unemployment). The housewife, of course, is in once sense, like the little man at the Fun Fair, unemployed, but in another sense she is perpetually employed—her work, like a soap opera, is never done. Moreover, as I have said, her duties are split among a variety of domestic and familial tasks, and her television programs keep her from desiring a focused existence by involving her in the pleasures of a fragmented life.

Interruptions may be, as Benjamin thought, one of the fundamental devices of all art, but surely soap opera relies on them to a far greater extent than any other art.[38] Revelations, confrontations, and reunions are constantly being interrupted and postponed by telephone calls, unexpected visitors, counterrevelations, catastrophes, and switches from one plot to another. These interruptions are both annoying and pleasurable: if we are torn away from one exciting story, we at least have the relief of picking up the thread of an unfinished one. Like the (ideal) mother in the home, we are kept interested in a number of events at once and are denied the luxury of a total and prolonged absorption. Commercials constitute another kind of interruption, in this case from *outside* the diegesis. Commercials present the housewife with mini-problems and their resolutions, so after witnessing all the agonizingly hopeless dilemmas on soap operas, the spectator has the satisfaction of seeing something cleaned up, if only a stained shirt or a dirty floor.

Although daytime commercials and soap operas are both set overwhelmingly within the home, the two views of the home seem antithetical, for the chief concerns of commercials are precisely the ones soap operas censor out. The saggy diapers, yellow wax buildup and carpet smells making up the world of daytime television ads are rejected by soap operas in favor of "Another World," as the very title of one soap opera announces, a world in which characters deal only with the "large" problems of human existence: crime, love, death and dying. But this antithesis embodies a deep truth about the way women function in (or, more accurately, around) culture: as both moral and spiritual guides and household drudges; now one, now the other, moving back and forth between the extremes, but obviously finding them difficult to reconcile.[39]

Similarly, the violent mood swings the spectator undergoes in switching from quiz shows, the other popular daytime television fare, to soap operas also constitute a kind of interruption, just as the housewife is required to endure monotonous, repetitive work but to be able to switch instantly and on demand from her role as a kind of bedmaking, dishwashing automaton to a large sympathizing consciousness. It must be stressed that while nighttime television certainly affords shifts in mood, notably from comedy to drama, these shifts are not nearly as extreme as in daytime programming. Quiz shows present the spectator with the same game, played and replayed frenetically day after day, with each game a self-contained unit, crowned by climactic success or failure. Soap operas, by contrast, endlessly defer resolutions and climaxes and undercut the very notion of success.

The formal properties of daytime television thus accord closely with the rhythms of women's work in the home. Individual soap operas as well as the flow of various programs and commercials tend to make repetition, interruption, and distraction pleasurable. But we can go even further and note that for women viewers reception itself often takes place in a state of distraction. According to Benjamin, "reception in a state of distraction . . . finds in the film its true means of exercise."[40] But now that we have television we can see that it goes beyond film in this respect, or at least the daytime programs do. For, the consumption of most films as well as of nighttime programs in some ways recapitulates the work situation in the factory or office: the viewer is physically passive, immobilized, and all his attention is focused on the object before him. Even the most allegedly "mindless" program requires a fairly strong degree of concentration if its plot is to make sense. But since the housewife's "leisure" time is not so strongly demarcated, her entertainment must often be consumed on the job. As the authors of *The Complete Soap Opera Book* tell us:

> The typical fan was assumed to be trotting about her daily chores with her mop in one hand, duster in the other, cooking, tending babies, answering telephones. Thus occupied, she might not be able to bring her full powers of concentration to bear on *Backstage Wife*.[41]

This accounts, in part, for the "realistic" feel of soap operas. The script writers, anticipating the housewife's distracted state, are careful to repeat important elements of the story several times. Thus, if two characters are involved in a confrontation which is supposed to mark a final break in their relationship, that same confrontation must be repeated, with minor variations, a few times in order to make sure the viewer gets the point. "Clean breaks"—surely a supreme fiction—are impossible on soap operas.

Benjamin, writing of film, invoked architecture as the traditional art most closely resembling the new one in the kinds of response they elicit. Both are mastered to some extent in a state of distraction: that is, both are appropriated "not so much by attention as by habit."[42] It is interesting to recall in this connection the Dadaist Eric Satie's concept of furniture music, which would be absorbed while people went about their business or chatted with each other. Television is the literalization of the metaphor of furniture art, but it must be stressed that this art is more than simply background noise in the way, for example, that Muzak is; soap operas are intensely meaningful to many women, as a conversation with any fan will immediately confirm.

Ironically, critics of television untiringly accuse its viewers of indulging in escapism. In other words, both high art critics and politically oriented critics, though motivated by different concerns, unite in condemning daytime television for *distracting* the housewife from her real situation. My point has been that a distracted or distractable frame of mind is crucial to the housewife's efficient functioning *in* her real situation, and at this level television and its so-called distractions, along with the particular forms they take, are intimately bound up with women's work.

IV

Given the differences in the ways men and women experience their lives, it is not surprising to find that "narrative pleasure" can sometimes mean very different things to men and women. This is an important point. Too often feminist criticism implies that there is only one kind of pleasure to be derived from narrative and that it is an essentially masculine one. Hence, it is further implied, feminist artists must first of all challenge this pleasure and then out of nothing begin to construct a feminist aesthetics and feminist form. This is a mistaken position, in my view, for it keeps us constantly in an adversary role, always on the defensive, always, as it were, complaining about the family but never leaving home. Feminist artists don't have to start from nothing; rather, they can look for clues to women's pleasure which are already present in existing forms, even if this pleasure is currently placed at the service of patriarchy. Claire Johnston, a feminist film theorist, has argued for a strategy combining "both the notion of film as a political tool and film as entertainment":

> For too long these have been regarded as two opposing poles with little common ground. In order to counter our objectification in the cinema, our collective fantasies must be released: women's cinema must embody the working through of desire: such an objective demands the use of the entertainment film. Ideas derived from the entertainment film, then, should inform the political film, and political ideas should inform the entertainment cinema: a two way process.[43]

Clearly, women find soap operas eminently entertaining, and an analysis of the pleasure these programs afford can provide feminists with ways not only to challenge this pleasure but to incorporate it into their own artistic practices.

The fact that soap operas never reach a full conclusion has usually been viewed in an entirely negative light. Here are the words of Dennis Porter, who, working from Roland Barthes' theories of narrative structures and ideology, completely condemns soap operas for their failure to resolve all problems:

> Unlike all traditionally end-oriented fiction and drama, soap opera offers process without progression, not a climax and a resolution, but mini-climaxes and provisional denouements that must never be presented in such a way as to eclipse the suspense experienced for associated plot lines. Thus soap opera is the drama of perepetia without anagnorisis. It deal forever in reversals but never portrays the irreversible change which traditionally marks the passage out of ignorance into true knowledge. For actors and audience alike, no action ever stands revealed in the terrible light of its consequences.[44]

These are strange words indeed, coming from one who purports to be analyzing the ideology of narrative form. They are a perfect illustration of how a high art bias, an eagerness to demonstrate the worthlessness of "low" art, can lead us to make claims for high art which we would ordinarily be wary of professing. Terms like "progression," "climax," "resolution," "irreversible change," "true knowledge," and "consequences" are certainly tied to an ideology; they are "linked to classical metaphysics," as Barthes observes. "[The] hermeneutic narrative in which truth predicates an incomplete subject, based on expectation and desire for its imminent closure, is . . . linked to the kerygmatic civilization of meaning and truth, appeal and fulfillment."[45] To criticize classical narrative because, for example, it is based on a suspect notion of progress and then criticize soap opera because it *isn't* will never get us anywhere—certainly not "out of ignorance into true knowledge." A different approach is needed.

Luce Irigaray, describing woman's "rediscovery" of herself, writes, "It is a sort of universe in expansion for which no limits could be fixed and which, for all that, would not be incoherence."[46] The similarities between this description and soap opera as a form are striking. They suggest the possibility that soap operas may not be an entirely negative influence on the viewer; they may also have the force of a *negation*, a negation of the typical (and masculine) modes of pleasure in our society. This challenge is, moreover, very like the one being mounted in current literary and film theory. Theorists have recently been pointing out the pleasures of the kind of text which breaks the illusion of unity and totality provided the reader or spectator by the "classic text." Hence the emphasis since the structuralists has been on "decentering the subject." But, as we have seen, women are, in their lives, their work, and in certain forms of their pleasure, already decentered—"off center." As Mark Poster remarks in his *Critical Theory of the Family*, "the feeling of being the center of creation is typical of the ego-structure of the bourgeois male."[47] This fact seems to me to be of crucial importance to anyone interested in formulating a feminist aesthetic. Indeed, I would like to argue that soap operas are not altogether at odds with an already developing, though still embryonic, feminist aesthetics.

"Deep in the very nature of soaps is the implied promise that they will last forever."[48] This being the case, a great deal of interest necessarily becomes focused upon those events which retard or impede the flow of the narrative. If, on the one hand, these constant interruptions provide consolation for the housewife's sense of missed opportunities, by illustrating for her the enormous difficulty of getting from desire to fulfillment, on the other hand, the notion of what Porter contemptuously calls "process without progression" is one endorsed by many innovative women artists. In praising Nathalie Sarraute, for example, Mary Ellmann observes that she is not

> interested in the explicit speed of which the novel is capable, only in the nuances which must tend to delay it. In her own discussions of the novel, Nathalie Sarraute is entirely anti-progressive. In criticizing ordinary dialogue, she dislikes its haste: there not being "time" for the person to consider a remark's ramifications, his having to speak and to listen frugally, his having to rush ahead toward his object—which is of course "to order his own conduct."[49]

Soap opera is similarly antiprogressive.[50] Just as Sarraute's work is opposed to the traditional novel form, soap opera is opposed to the classic (male) film narrative, which, with maximum action and minimum, always pertinent dialogue, speeds its way to the restoration of order.

In soap operas, the important thing is that there always be time for a person to consider a remark's ramifications, time for people to speak and to listen lavishly. Actions and climaxes are only of secondary importance. This may seem wilfully to misrepresent soap operas. Certainly they appear to contain a ludicrous number of climaxes and actions: people are always getting blackmailed, having major operations, dying, conducting extra-marital affairs which inevitably result in pregnancy, being kidnapped, going mad, and losing their memories. But just as in real life (one constantly hears it said) it takes a wedding or a funeral to reunite scattered families, so soap opera catastrophes provide convenient occasions for people to come together, confront one another, and explore intense emotions. One advantage of placing people in hospitals, for example, is that because they are immobilized they are forced to take the time to talk to others and listen to what others have to say to them. And friends and family members, imprisoned in waiting rooms (in some ways an apt metaphor for women's homes), can discuss their feelings about the latest tragedy, and, from there, since the waiting often seems interminable, go on to analyze the predicaments of their mutual friends, as well as the state of their own relationships. Thus, in direct contrast to the typical male narrative film, in which the climax functions to resolve difficulties, the "mini-climaxes" of soap opera function to introduce difficulties and to complicate rather than simplify the characters' lives.

Furthermore, as with much women's narrative (such as the fiction of Ivy Compton-Burnett, who strongly influenced Sarraute), dialogue in soap operas is an enormously tricky business. Again, I must take issue with Porter, who says, "Language here is of a kind that takes itself for granted and assumes it is always possible to mean no more and no less than what one intends."[51] More accurately, in soap operas the gap between what is intended and what is actually spoken is often very wide. Secrets better left buried may be blurted out in moments of intensity, or they are withheld just when a character most desires to tell all. This is very different from nighttime television programs and classic Hollywood films with their particularly naive belief in the beneficence of communication. The full revelation of a secret on these shows usually begins or proclaims the restoration of order. Marcus Welby can then get his patient to agree to treatment; Perry Mason can exonerate the innocent and punish the guilty. The necessity of confession, the means through which, according to Michel Foucault, we gladly submit to power, is wholeheartedly endorsed.[52] In soap operas, on the other hand, the effects of confession are often ambiguous, providing relief for some of the characters and dreadful complications for others. (Here too we can see how soap opera melodrama diverges from traditional melodrama, which Peter Brooks, following Eric Bentley, has defined by its impulse to excess, to the overcoming of inhibition and repression: "The genre's very existence is bound to [the] possibility, and necessity, of saying everything.")[53] Moreover, it is remarkable how seldom in soap operas a character can talk another into changing his/her ways. Ordinarily, it takes a major disaster to bring about self-awareness—whereas all Marcus Welby has to do is give his stop-feeling-sorry-for-yourself speech and the character undergoes a drastic personality change. Perhaps more than men, women in our society are aware of the pleasures of language—though less sanguine about its potential use as an instrument of power.

Not only do soap operas suggest an alternate kind of narrative pleasure experienced by women, but they also tell us a great deal about what Johnston calls women's "collective fantasies." To the dismay of many feminist critics, the most powerful fantasy embodied in soap operas appears to be the fantasy of a fully self-sufficient family. Carol Lopate complains:

> Daytime television . . . promises that the family can be everything, if only one is willing to stay inside it. For the women confined to her house, daytime television fills out the empty space of the long day when she is home alone, channels her fantasies toward love and family dramas, and promises her that the life she is in can fulfill her needs. But it does not call to her attention her aloneness and isolation, and it does not suggest to her that it is precisely in her solitude that she has a possibility for gaining a self.[54]

This statement merits close consideration. It implies that the family in soap operas is a mirror-image of the viewer's own family. But for most viewers, this is definitely not the case. What the spectator is looking at and perhaps longing for is a kind of *extended* family, the direct opposite of her own isolated nuclear family. Most soap operas follow the lives of several generations of a large family, all living in the same town and all intimately involved in one another's lives. The fantasy here is truly a "collective fantasy"—a fantasy of community, but put in terms with which the viewer can be comfortable. Lopate is wrong, I believe, to end her peroration with a call for feminine solitude. For too long women have had too much solitude and, quite rightly, they resent it. In her thought-provoking essay on the family, Barbara Easton points out that since the family is for many women their only support, those women who are abandoned to solitude by feminists eager to undermine this support are apt to turn to the right. People like Anita Bryant and Marabel Morgan, says Easton, "feed on fears of social isolation that have a basis in reality."[55] So do soap operas.

For it is important to recognize that soap opera allays *real* anxieties, satisfies *real* needs and desires, even while it may distort them. The fantasy of community is not only a real desire (as opposed to the "false" ones mass culture is always accused of trumping up), it is a salutary one. As feminists, we have a responsibility to devise ways of meeting these needs that are more creative, honest, and interesting than the ones mass culture has supplied. Otherwise, the search for tomorrow threatens to go on, endlessly.

Notes

1. Anthony Astrachan, quoted in Dan Wakefield, *All Her Children* (Garden City, N.Y.: Doubleday & Co., 1976), p. 149.
2. Kathryn Weibel, *Mirror Mirror: Images of Women Reflected in Popular Culture* (Garden City, N.Y.: 1977), p. 56.
3. Horace Newcomb, *T.V.: The Most Popular Art* (New York: Oxford University Press), 1976, p. 253.
4. Barthes, *S/Z* (New York: Hill and Wang, 1977), p. 76.
5. Frank Kermode, *The Sense of an Ending: Studies in the Theory of Fiction* (New York: Oxford University Press, 1967), p. 7.
6. Walter Benjamin, "The Storyteller," in his *Illuminations*, translated by Harry Zohn, edited by Hannah Arendt (New York: Schocken Books, 1969), pp. 100–101.
7. Benjamin, "The Storyteller," pp. 100–101.
8. Kermode, p. 162.
9. Helen Papashvily, *All the Happy Endings: A Study of the Domestic Novel in America, the Women Who Wrote It, The Women Who Read It, in the Nineteenth Century*, (New York: Harper & Brothers, 1956), p. 194.
10. Barbara Easton, "Feminism and the Contemporary Family, *Socialist Review* 8, no. 3 (1978): 30.
11. Not only can women count on a never ending storyline, they can also, to a great extent, rely upon the fact that their favorite characters will never desert them. To take a rather extreme example: when, on one soap opera, the writers killed off a popular female character and viewers were unhappy, the actress was brought back to portray the character's twin sister. See Madeleine Edmondson and David Rounds, *From Mary Noble to Mary Hartman: The Complete Soap Opera Book* (New York: Stein and Day, 1976), p. 208.
12. Dennis Porter, "Soap Time: Thoughts on a Commodity Art Form," *College English* 38 (1977): 783.
13. Edmondson and Rounds, *The Complete Soap Opera Book*, pp. 104–10.
14. Barthes, *S/Z*, p. 135.
15. John G. Cawelti, *Adventure, Mystery and Romance* (Chicago: University of Chicago Press, 1976), pp. 45–46.
16. Laura Mulvey, "Visual Pleasure and the Narrative Cinema," in *Women and the Cinema*, edited by Karyn Kay and Gerald Peary (New York: E. P. Dutton, 1977), p. 420.
17. Mulvey, p. 420.
18. Mulvey, p. 420.
19. Edmondson and Rounds, p. 193.
20. Paul Mayer, "Creating Ryan's Hope," in *T.V. Book*, edited by Judy Fireman (New York: Workman Publishing Co., 1977).
21. Robert B. Heilman, *Tragedy and Melodrama: Versions of Experience* (Seattle: University of Washington Press, 1968), p. 85.

22. There are still villains on soap operas, but their numbers have declined considerably since radio days—to the point where they are no longer indispensable to the formula. "The Young and the Restless," for example, does without them.
23. According to Weibel, we quite simply "deplore" the victimizers and totally identify with the victim (p. 62).
24. "A soap opera without a bitch is a soap opera that doesn't get watched. The more hateful the bitch the better. Erica of 'All My Children' is a classic. If you want to hear some hairy rap, just listen to a bunch of women discussing Erica.

    " 'Girl, that Erica needs her tail whipped.'

    " 'I wish she'd try to steal my man and plant some marijuana in my purse. I'd be mopping up the street with her new hairdo.' " Bebe Moore Campbell, "Hooked on Soaps," *Essence*, November, 1978, p. 103.
25. Dorothy Dinnerstein, *The Mermaid and the Minotaur* (New York: Harper & Row, 1976), p. 236.
26. "The author, Mary Elizabeth Braddon, belonged to that class of writers called by Charles Reade 'obstacles to domestic industry.' " Frank Rahill, *The World of Melodrama*, (University Park: Pennsylvania State University Press, 1967), pp. 204.
27. Elaine Showalter, A *Literature of Their Own* (Princeton, N.J.: Princeton University Press, 1977), p. 204.
28. Mary Ellmann, *Thinking About Women* (New York: Harvest Books, 1968), p. 181. Molly Haskell makes a similar point in her discussion of "The Woman's Film," in *From Reverence to Rape: The Treatment of Women in the Movies* (New York: Penguin, 1974), pp. 172–73.
29. The game, observed by Freud, in which the child plays "disappearance and return" with a wooden reel tied to a string. "What he did was to hold the reel by the string and very skilfully throw it over the edge of his curtained cot, so that it disappeared into it, at the same time uttering his expressive 'O-O-O-O.' [Freud speculates that this represents the German word '*fort*' or '*gone*.'] He then pulled the reel out of the cot again by the string and hailed its reappearance with a joyful 'da' ['there']." According to Freud, "Throwing away the object so that it was 'gone' might satisfy an impulse of the child's, which was suppressed in his actual life, to revenge himself on his mother for going away from him. In that case it would have a defiant meaning: 'All right then, go away! I don't need you. I'm sending you away myself.' " Sigmund Freud, *Beyond the Pleasure Principle*, translated by James Strachey (New York: W. W. Norton, Co., 1961), pp. 10–11.
30. Speaking of the child's *fort-da* game, Freud notes, "At the outset he was in a passive situation—he was overpowered by experience; but by repeating it, unpleasurable though it was, as a game, he took on an *active* part. These efforts might be put down to an instinct for mastery that was acting independently of whether the memory was in itself pleasurable or not." In *Beyond the Pleasure Principle*, p. 10.
31. Jean-Paul Sartre's phrase for the tension surrealism's created object sets up in the spectator is remarkably appropriate here. See *What Is Literature?* translated by Bernard Frechtman (New York: Washington Square Press, 1966), p. 133n.
32. Marcia Kinder, "Review of *Scenes of a Marriage*, by Ingmar Bergman, *Film Quarterly* 28, no. 2 (1974–75): 51.
33. Nancy Chodorow, *The Reproduction of Mothering: Psychoanalysis and the Sociology of Gender* (Berkeley: University of California Press, 1978), p. 179.
34. Porter, p. 786.
35. Tillie Olsen, *Silences* (New York: Dell Publishing Co., 1979), pp. 18–19.
36. Raymond Williams, *Television, Technology, and Cultural Form* (New York: Schocken Books, 1975), p. 95.
37. Benjamin, "On Some Motifs in Baudelaire," in *Illuminations*, p. 176.

38. Banjamin, "What Is Epic Theater?" in *Illuminations*, p. 151.
39. See Sherry B. Ortner's brilliant discussion of women's position in culture, "Is Female to Male as Nature Is to Culture," in *Woman, Culture and Society*, edited by Michelle Zimbalist Rosaldo and Louise Lamphere (Stanford, Ca.: Stanford University Press), 1974.
40. Benjamin, "The Work of Art in the Age of Mechanical Reproduction," in *Illuminations*, p. 240.
41. Edmondson and Rounds, pp. 46–47.
42. Benjamin, "The Work of Art," pp. 239–40.
43. Claire Johnston, "Women's Cinema as Countercinema," in *Movies and Methods*, edited by Bill Nichols (Berkeley: University of California Press, 1976), p. 217.
44. Porter, pp. 783–84.
45. Barthes, *S/Z*, p. 45.
46. Luce Irigary, "Ce sexe qui n'en est pas un," in *New French Feminisms*, edited by Elaine Marks and Isabelle Courtivron (Amherst: University of Massachusetts Press, 1980), p. 104.
47. Mark Poster, *Critical Theory of the Family* (New York: Continuum Books, 1978), p. 9.
48. Edmondson and Rounds, p. 112.
49. Ellmann, pp. 222–23.
50. As David Grimsted points out, melodrama may always have been deeply antiprogressive, in spite of its apparent hopefulness and thrust toward a happy ending. First, the "centrality of the villain in these plays, even though he was always eventually defeated, suggested a world where the evil and terror of which he was an incarnation were constant threats." And second, in classic melodrama (as in soap operas), virtue is always allied with the past—with fathers, mothers, rural life styles, etc., while the present is conceived of as dangerous, confusing and perhaps even "degenerate." See *Melodrama Unveiled, American Theater and Culture* (Chicago: University of Chicago Press, 1968), pp. 223–24.
51. Porter, p. 788.
52. Michel Foucault, *The History of Sexuality, Volume I: An Introduction*, translated by Robert Hurley (New York: Vintage Books, 1980), esp. pp. 57–73. In this connection, it is interesting to recall how in many detective stories, T.V. shows, and films, the detective must overcome the reluctance of an *innocent* party to yield some bit of information necessary to the solution of the crime. For an interesting discussion of Dragnet's Joe Friday as the Great Listener, see Reuel Denney, *The Astonished Muse*, (Chicago: University of Chicago Press, 1957), pp. 82–92.
53. Peter Brooks, *Balzac, Henry James, and the Mode of Excess* New Haven: Yale University Press, 1976), *The Melodramatic Imagination*, p. 42. Or, as Eric Bentley puts it, "melodrama is not so much the exaggerated as the uninhibited," See *The Life of the Drama*, New York: Atheneum, 1974, p. 206.
54. Carol Lopate, "Daytime Television: You'll Never Want to Leave Home," *Radical America* 2 (1977): 51.
55. Easton, p. 34.

Crossroads: Notes on Soap Opera

CHARLOTTE BRUNSDON

> Husband to wife weeping as she watches TV: "For heaven's sake, Emily! It's only a commercial for acid indigestion."
>
> —Joke on Bryant & May matchbox

Introduction: A Gendered Audience?

The audience for soap opera is usually assumed to be female.[1] In these notes I would like to examine this assumption, and the extent to which the notion of a gendered audience can be useful to us in the understanding of a British soap opera, *Crossroads*.

Initially, I should like to make a distinction between the subject positions that a text constructs, and the social subject who may or may not take these positions up. We can usefully analyse the "you" or "yous" that the text as discourse constructs, but we cannot assume that any individual audience member will necessarily occupy these positions.[2] The relation of the audience to the text will not be determined solely by that text, but also by positionalities in relation to a whole range of other discourses—discourses of motherhood, romance and sexuality for example. Thus it may well be that visual pleasure in narrative cinema is dependent on identification with male characters in their gaze at female characters, but it does not necessarily follow that any individual audience member will unproblematically occupy this masculine position. Indeed,

Charlotte Brunsdon's "*Crossroads*: Notes on Soap Opera" originally appeared in *Screen*, Vol. 22, no. 4 (1981), pp. 32–37. Reprinted by permission of the author and *Screen*.

feminist film criticism usefully deconstructs the gendering of this "you." As J. Winship has recently argued: "A feminist politics of representation . . . has then to engage with the social reader, as well as the social text."[3]

The interplay of social reader and social text can be considered by examining the extent to which a gendered audience is implied in programme publicity, scheduling and advertisements. The Independent Broadcasting Authority, in its 1979 annual handbook, groups *Crossroads* with other drama serials:

> TV drama serials have for many years been an essential ingredient in the programme diet of a large and devoted audience. Established favourites such as *Coronation Street* and *Crossroads* continue to develop themes and situations which often deal withe the everyday problems and difficulties to which many viewers can relate. Occasionally the more adventurous type of serial is produced.[4]

The femininity of the audience is specified, apart from the structuring dietary metaphor, in the opposition of "devoted" and "everyday" to "adventurous." There are a wide range of "spin-off materials associated with *Crossroads*—novels, special souvenir supplements, interview material, and a *Crossroads* cookbook. I will take up the question of the incoherence of *Crossroads* narratives below.

In terms of scheduling, although *Crossroads* is broadcast at different times in different regions (stripped across four evenings a week),[5] it is always broadcast within the 5:15 p.m.–7:30 p.m. slot. That is, with early evening, weekday transmission the programme is definitely not scheduled in the prime time in which it is expected to maximise on a male audience. If we accept Richard Paterson's argument that notions of the family and the domestic dominate the scheduling of British television programmes, then fathers are not expected to control television choice at this point. Paterson also suggests a relationship between scheduling and programme structure:

> Its narrative is constructed of multiple short segments, with continual repetition of narrative information, but no overall dramatic coherence in any episode. In part this structure reflects its place in the schedule: continual viewing has to be ensured even though meal times and other domestic interruptions might make it impossible to follow a coherent narrative.[6]

The broadcast slot of *Crossroads* is surrounded by magazine news programmes, panel games and other serials—all suitable for family, and interrupted, viewing. However, the advertising that frames, and erupts within, the programme is quite clearly addressed to a feminine consumer—beauty aids, breakfast cereals, instant "man-appeal" meals and cleaning products: the viewer as sexual, as mother, as wife, as housewife, in contrast to the ads for lawn mowers, car gadgets, DIY equipment or large family purchases which dominate from 8:30 p.m. on. These "extra textual" factors suggest that women are the target audience for *Crossroads*.

A Discontinuous Text

The ideological problematic of soap opera—the frame or field in which meanings are made, in which significance is constructed narratively—is that of "personal life." More particularly, personal life in its everyday realisation through personal relationships. This can be understood to be constituted primarily through the representations of romances, families and attendant rituals— births, engagements, marriages, divorces and deaths. In marxist terms this is the sphere of the individual outside waged labour. In feminist terms, it is the sphere of women's "intimate oppression." Ideologically constructed as the feminine sphere, it is within this realm of the domestic, the personal, the private, that feminine competence is recognised. However, the action of soap opera is not restricted to familial or quasi-familial institutions but, as it were, *colonises* the public masculine sphere, representing it from the point of view of the personal.

Thus in *Crossroads* we have a family run business, the Crossroads motel, with an attached garage. The motel is near a village, Kings Oak, which at various times has included a market-garden, a doctor's surgery, a post-office, an antique shop, and so on. Regular characters are members of one of three groups—the Crossroads family, the motel/garage workforce, or the village. The fictional community, clearly socially hierarchised through *mise-en-scène* and dialogue, is kept interacting through a series of interlocking economic relationships, but this business interaction is of diegetic importance only as the site of personal relationships. It is always emotionally significant personal interaction, often reported in dialogue, which is narratively foregrounded. This can be seen most clearly through the narrative construction of time and place.

There is no single linear time flow. The minimum three concurrent narratives proceed through a succession of short segments (rarely exceeding 2½ minutes). In contrast with classical narrative cinema,[7] the temporal relationship between segments is rarely encoded. Time in general moves forward, although there is repetition at the beginning of episodes. Relationships between segments can be read as in most cases sequential or simultaneous. One continuous scene can be broken into several segments—notoriously over commercial breaks and between episodes, but this is a standard intra-episodic suspense device. The lack of any overarching time scheme permits the rise and fall of different narrative threads. As each narrative has only its time of exposition, there is no loss of "real" or referential time if a narrative lapses. Similarly, the very simplicity of the use of "interruption" as the major form of narrative delay, extending dramatic action, also works against the construction of a coherent referential time. The different present tenses of the narrative co-exist, temporally unhierarchised.

Space in *Crossroads* is also organised in a way which is quite distinct from the conventions of classical narrative cinema, conventions which are carried over to some other forms of television drama. The shoestring budgets mean very restricted sets (all internal, usually no more than five in one episode) and few available camera positions.[8] Generally, sets have two distinct spaces arranged laterally to each other—that is, there are two distinct camera fields, and it is the articulation of these fields which constructs the space.[9] Some sets allow only one camera position. These camera set-ups are not variable, and camera movement is limited. Most scenes are shot in mid-shot or medium close-up, opening with either a close-up or a longer shot. The narrative does not mobilise space within any particular set, nor is there any attempt to make the different spaces of the different sets cohere. We are instead presented with a series of tableau-like views, more theatrical than cinematic. The set thus function very literally as setting or background, seen always from the same points of view, as familiar as the room in which the viewer has the television.

I am thus arguing that the diegetic world of *Crossroads* is temporally and spatially fragmented, and that this fragmentation, accompanied by repetitious spatial orientation, foregrounds that dialogue of emotional and moral dilemma which makes up the action. The coherence of the serial does not come from the subordination of space and time to linear narrativity, as it does in classical narrative cinema, but from the continuities of moral and ideological frameworks which inform the dialogue. It is these frameworks which are explored, rehearsed and made explicit for the viewer in the repeated mulling over of actions and possibilities. *Crossroads* is in the business not of creating narrative excitement, suspense, delay and resolution, but of constructing moral consensus about the conduct of personal life. There is an endless unsettling, discusion and resettling of acceptable modes of behaviour within the sphere of personal relationships.

There are two key elements in this. Firstly, structurally, the plurality of story lines, which allows the use of the narrative strategy of interruption, and secondly, diegetically, the plot importance accorded to forms of lying and deceit. Structurally, although the different physical spaces of narratives do not cohere, except in the meeting place of the motel lobby, the same set of events, or the same dilemma, will be discussed by different characters in "their own" environments. A range of different opinions and understandings of any one situation will thus be voiced. At the same time, the use of interruption, the consistent holding off of *dénouement* and knowledge, invites the viewer to engage in exactly the same type of speculation and judgement. The viewer can, as it were, practise possible outcomes—join in the debate about how a particular event is to be understood.

The use of deceit in the narrative works slightly differently. By deceit, I mean the development of a narrative line in which the audience knows that one character is consciously lying or misleading other characters. Here, the viewer is in a position of privileged knowledge in relation to the protagonists, and can see clearly what and who is "right." The drama of morality is here produced by the tension between the fact that "good" characters must continue to be trusting, to remain "good," but that they will suffer unless they "find out" about the true nature of another character, x.

In both cases, what is being set in play, or exercised, are repertoires of understandings and assumptions about personal and familial relationships, in which the notion of individual character is central. Thus although soap opera narrative may seem to ask "What will happen next?" as its dominant question, the terrain on which this question is posed is determined by a prior question—"What kind of a person is this?" And in the ineluctable posing of this question of all characters, whatever their social position, soap opera poses a potential moral equality of all individuals.

A Gendered Audience—2

Recently, Tania Modleski has argued for the textual inscription of a female (maternal) subject in American soap opera. She has suggested that the multiple narrative structure of soap opera demands multiple identification on the part of the viewer, and thus constitutes the viewer as a type of ideal mother, "a person who possesses a greater wisdom than all her children, whose sympathy is large enough to encompass the claims of all her family . . . and who has no demands of her own."[10] I will consider the related question of the type of cultural competence that *Crossroads* as soap opera narrative(s) demands of its social reader.

Just as a Godard film requires the possession of certain forms of cultural capital on the part of its audience to "make sense"—an extra-textual familiarity with certain artistic, linguistic, political and cinematic discourses—so too does *Crossroads*/soap opera. The particular competences demanded by soap opera fall into three categories:

> (1) Generic knowledge—familiarity with the conventions of soap opera as a genre. For example, expecting discontinuous and cliff-hanging narrative structures.
> (2) Serial-specific knowledge—knowledge of past narratives and of characters (in particular, who belongs to who).
> (3) Cultural knowledge of the socially acceptable codes and conventions for the conduct of personal life.

I will only comment on the third category here. The argument is that the narrative strategies and concerns of *Crossroads* call on the traditionally feminine competencies associated with the responsibility for "managing" the sphere of personal life. It is the culturally constructed skills of femininity—sensitivity, perception, intuition and the necessary privileging of the concerns of personal life—which are both called on and practised in the genre. The fact that these skills and competencies, this type of cultural capital, is ideologically constructed as natural does not mean, as many feminists have shown, that they are the *natural* attributes of femininity. However, under present cultural and political arrangements, it is more likely that female viewers will possess this repertoire of both sexual and maternal femininities which is called on to fill out the range of narrative possibilities when, for example, the phone rings. That is, when Jill is talking to her mother about her marriage (17 January 1979), and the phone rings, the viewer needs to know not only that it is likely to be Stan (her nearly ex-husband) calling about custody of their daughter Sarah-Jane (serial-specific knowledge) and that we're unlikely to hear the content of the phone call in that segment (generic knowledge) but also that the mother's "right" to her children is no longer automatically assumed. These knowledges only have narrative resonance in relation to discourses of maternal femininity which are elaborated elsewhere, already in circulation and brought to the programme by the viewer. In the enigma that is then posed—will Jill or Stan get Sarah-Jane?—questions are also raised about who, generally and particularly, *should* get custody. The question of what *should* happen is rarely posed "openly"—in this instance it was quite clear that "right" lay with Jill. But it is precisely the terms of the question, the way in which it relates to other already circulating discourses, if you like, the degree of its closure, which form the site of the construction of moral consensus, a construction which "demands," seeks to implicate, a skilled viewer.

I am thus arguing that *Crossroads* textually implies a feminine viewer to the extent that its textual discontinuities require a viewer competent within the ideological and moral framework, the rules, of romance, marriage and family life to make sense of it.

Against critics who complain of the redundancy of soap opera, I would suggest that the radical discontinuities of the text require extensive, albeit interrupted, engagement on the part of the audience, before it becomes pleasurable. This is not to designate *Crossroads* "progressive" but to suggest that the skills and discourses mobilised by its despised popularity have partly been overlooked because of their legitimation as natural (feminine).

Notes

1. For example, early research on American radio soaps either assumes a female audience, or only investigates one. (See H. Herzog, "On Borrowed Experience" in *Studies in the Philosophy of Social Science*, vol. 9, no. 65, 1941; Rudolph Arnheim, "The World of the Daytime Serial" in *Radio Research*, nos. 42–43, Lazarsfeld and Stanton (eds), New York, 1944; H Kauffman, "The Appeal of Specific Daytime Serials" in *Radio Research*, op cit.) It is of course precisely the perceived "feminine" appeal of the genre which has fuelled recent feminist interest (see for instance, Richard Dyer et al., *Coronation Street*, BFI Television Monograph no. 13, London, 1981; and Tania Modleski, "The Search for Tomorrow in Today's Soap Operas," *Film Quarterly*, vol. 33, no. 1, 1979).
2. See, for instance, Steve Neale, "Propaganda," *Screen*, vol. 18, no. 3, 1977; Paul Willemen, "Notes on subjectivity," *Screen*, vol. 19, no. 1, 1978; and David Morley, *The "Nationwide" Audience*, BFI, London, 1980.
3. J. Winship, "Handling Sex," *Media Culture and Society*, vol. 3, no. 1, 1981.
4. *Television and Radio 1979*, Independent Broadcasting Authority, London, 1979.
5. These notes are based on 1978 research when *Crossroads* was still four evenings per week, as opposed to the three at present.
6. Richard Paterson, "Planning the Family: The Art of the Schedule," *Screen Education*, no. 35, Summer 1980.
7. I recognise that "classical narrative cinema" is not monolithic. David Bordwell and Kristin Thompson in *Film Art*, New York, 1979, give an account of the conventions of the narrative fiction film in the west.
8. Production constraints of *Crossroads* are discussed by Geoff Brown, "I'm Worried about Chalet Nine," *Time Out*, 24–30 November 1978; and R. Miles, "Everyday Stories, Everyday Folk," MA Dissertation, University of Leicester, 1980.

9. I am indebted to Andy Lowe ("Narrative Spaces and Closures," unpublished paper, Media Group, Centre for Contemporary Cultural Studies, Birmingham, 1977) who originally discussed *Crossroads* in these terms.
10. Tania Modleski, op cit.

Dallas and the Melodramatic Imagination

IEN ANG

Dallas and Genre

A television serial like *Dallas* is made according to certain rules and conventions which belong to a specific genre. A genre is, one might say, a complex of themes, narrative structures and styles that groups of individual films or television programmes have in common with one another.[1] Because we know these rules and conventions, and have become familiar with them, we often know quite quickly whether a film is a Western or a thriller and we entertain certain expectations of the course of the film, although each Western or thriller has its own idiosyncrasies. But the general characteristics of the genre set limits on the individual genre film, which renders it simpler for the audience to follow. A genre is in other words a formula and each individual genre film is a specific "application" of the rules and conventions of the genre. This application can succeed to greater or lesser degree, be more or less inventive, opening new ground for the genre to a greater or lesser degree. In analysing a genre film, then, one must constantly move between the general and the particular, between the established structures and the specific application. In this chapter we shall be trying to do that with *Dallas*.

In order to discover which television genre *Dallas* should be classifed under, we must take a look at the structural characteristics of this serial. The first structural characteristic that deserves our attention is its episodic character. For as we shall see

Ien Ang, "Dallas and the Melodramatic Imagination," from *Watching Dallas: Soap Opera and the Melodramatic Imagination*, (London: Methuen, 1982). Reprinted by permission of the author and Methuen Press.

later on, this genre characteristic plays an essential role in the construction of the emotional realism stemming from the tragic structure of feeling.

The episodic character of television fiction can assume two forms: that of the *series*, in which the individual episodes are completely separate from one another from a narrative viewpoint (only the hero[ine] of the series and the basic situation are the connecting elements between the individual episodes), and the *serial*, i.e. the continuous narrative. Programmes like *Magnum* and *Charlie's Angels* are examples of series, while *Dallas*, but also *Hill Street Blues*, are examples of the serial. The separate episodes of a serial cannot in principle be watched in any order, because the precise sequence of the episodes creates a notion of the continuance of time, a continuance which is linear and irreversible. Of course each episode is more or less a separate whole: not only is there in each episode of *Dallas* one more or less central narrative line, but each episode also gets its own title and is divided off by recognizable beginning and end credits.

But in contrast to a series, in which the time between two episodes is of no narrative importance whatever, the time between two episodes in a serial does play a role—though merely an imaginary one—in the way in which viewers experience the narrative. "The characters in a serial, when abandoned at the end of an episode, pursue an 'unrecorded existence' until the next one begins," states Christine Geraghty, in a summary of the formal characteristics of the television serial.[2] The television serial thus appeals to a historical sense of time: it constructs the feeling that the lives of the characters go on during our absence—i.e. between two episodes. Thus the idea of "unchronicled growth" is aroused in viewers.

This feeling can, however, only arise if the end of an episode offers the possibility for it. The end of an episode of a serial is mostly in the shape of a so-called "cliff-hanger": the narrative is broken off at a moment of very great suspense, so that the viewers are encouraged to see the following episode if they want to know how the story goes on. In earlier film serials the cliffhanger consisted mainly in an abruptly broken off action; or at the very moment the hero threatens to be pushed over the cliff by his enemy, the words "to be continued" appear—as if to tease the audience—on the screen. The following episode then takes up the thread at the same action, at the same moment in the story. In such cases there is no question of an imaginary passage of time between two episodes.

This type of "cliffhanger" is, however, seldom used in television serials,[3] although they do occur in fact, by way of exception, in *Dallas*. Just think of the episodes that ended with an attempt on J.R.'s life or with the moment when Southfork is going up in flames. But in by far the majority of cases in *Dallas* a psychological cliffhanger is used: an episode ends most often at the moment when one of the characters lands in a new, psychologically conflictual situation. The last shot of an episode is then nearly always a close-up of the face of the character concerned, which emphasizes the psychological conflict she or he is in. In one of the following episodes—it does not necessarily need to be the very next one—we are then shown how she or he handles the conflict, but meanwhile time proceeds and life goes on as normal. The very next episode usually begins with a new day. Such a construction offers viewers the possibility of having the feeling that time in Dallas more or less keeps pace with the time in which the viewers themselves are living. This fact in itselt takes care of a specific dimension of "everyday realism"—the life of the Ewings in Dallas flows on just like our own life.

But an even more important characteristic of *Dallas* that helps to arouse this idea is the fact that there is no narrative ending in sight. The structure of the *Dallas* narrative is radically different from that of a feature film or an episode of a series such as *Kojak* or *Lou Grant*. In classic narrative theory narrative is defined in terms of the schema: order/disturbance of order/restoration of order. A narrative consists of "a movement between equilibriums which are similar but not identical";[4] at the end all the problems which have disturbed the equilibrium of the opening situation have been resolved. This narrative scheme, however, will not work for an endlessly running television serial like *Dallas*. Although in each episode problems are solved, at the same time new ones are created, which form the point of departure for the following episodes, and so on and so on.

The "endless" character of a serial is typical for a special genre of television fiction: the soap opera. Soap opera is a long-standing radio genre which was "invented" and developed at the end of the 1920s by American, mainly female, radio programme makers. The soap opera, which rapidly developed into one of the most popular entertainment forms on radio, was characterized by an accent on human relations, domesticity and daily life; it is home, garden and kitchen problems which are discussed and solved by the characters.[5] The "soaps," so called because it was mainly soap manufacturers who sponsored the programmes, shot up like mushrooms and built up a faithful following, especially among housewives—not least because they were broadcast almost every day. The soap opera was alleged to be able to provide some (surrogate) company for housewives living in isolation; they listened to their favorite soaps while doing the ironing, cooking or other domestic work.[6]

With the coming of television the soap opera finally disappeared from the American radio stations, but the genre took on a new and flourishing existence in the new medium. Although soap opera is not an exclusively American phenomenon—British, Australian and Brazilian television, for example, are richly provided with home-grown soap operas—the genre is almost totally unknown on Dutch television. *Peyton Place* and *Coronation Street* could be seen at the beginning of the 1970s on Dutch television, and they were quite popular, but the American "daytime serials," as they are officially called, have never been screened in the Netherlands—in contrast to the parodies of them, *Mary Hartman! Mary Hartman!* and *Soap!* which are esteemed mainly by an intellectual audience! Only with the arrival of *Dallas* on the screen did the Dutch television audience get handed another American soap opera.

But *Dallas* in not a daytime soap opera. Just like *Peyton Place, Dallas* is made to be shown at prime time. Of course this has its consequences. An important formal difference between *Dallas* and the daytime soap opera is the much greater attention to visualization in *Dallas*. In contrast to daytime soaps, which have always kept a radio-like character and in which the visual element is kept to a minimum (very sparse locations, very simple camera work, etc.), *Dallas* looks chic—because of the high production values which generally apply for prime time programmes—and it is made with filmic expertise. A lot of attention is paid to the visual attractiveness of the locations, the stars' costumes, and so on. This is doubtless a background which should not be neglected when accounting for its worldwide popularity. The hegemony of American television (and film) has habituated the world public to American production values and American *mises-en-scène*, such as the vast prairie or the big cities, the huge houses with expensive interiors, luxurious and fast cars and, last but not least, the healthy- and good-looking men and women, white, not too young, not too old. Such images have become signs which no longer merely indicate something like "Americanness," but visual pleasure as such. The television audience has, over the years, become familiar with all this and tends to recognize it as pleasurable; it is as though for large groups of people these American images fulfil a signal function; they imply the promise that the story will be suspenseful and exciting. As Simon Frith states: "America, as experienced in films and music, has itself become the object of consumption, a symbol of pleasure."[7]

The fact that *Dallas* is a prime time programme also has consequences for the structure of the narrative content. Prime time is the time in which the whole family usually watches television, in contrast to the morning or afternoon hours (during which housewives, pensioners and the unemployed form the largest group of viewers). A popular programme must therefore, at least according to the commercial logic of the American television industry, appeal to the whole family. In a certain sense this could explain why in *Dallas* themes from other genres such as the Western are worked in, to attract the interest of a broad mass audience. Similarly the fact that men and masculine themes such as business life play a much more central part in *Dallas* than in the average daytime soap could be connected to this.[8] Therefore *Dallas* is not a soap opera in the traditional sense.

Dallas as Prime Time Soap Opera

But in spite of the differences we have cited between *Dallas* and the daytime soaps, there are sufficient structural similarities between them to justify calling *Dallas*, as an American television encyclopedia[9] has done, a "prime time soap opera." The similarities lie in the first place in the narrative structure dictated by the endless character of the serial. Each episode of a soap opera always consists of various narratives running parallel. In every episode one of these narratives gets the greatest emphasis, but the other narratives keep "simmering" as it were in the background, to reach a climax in some subsequent episode. As one letter writer puts it:

> I watch *Dallas* pretty regularly because I find it a free serial. By that I mean that the writer can go in any direction in every episode. One time Bobby is the central figure, then it can be J.R. or Sue Ellen or another member of that "immense" family. (Letter 5)

In this sense a soap opera is therefore a continuous coming and going of mini-narratives, in an uneven rhythm. This characteristic of the soap opera can explain why many letter writers who dislike *Dallas* find it longwinded: "Every time I watch it again

I'm curious as to what has happened. But then *Dallas* ends and even more questions have arisen. I find that really stupid" (Letter 37). But this "longwindedness," this steady continuance of the story, this "indefinitely expandable middle,"[10] is essential for the soap opera as genre. Those who like *Dallas* will therefore tacitly agree to this convention. They are not expecting the definitive dénouement; quite the contrary, the (promise of) endlessness itself is a source of pleasure. "I can't get enough of it" (Letter 9), says one letter writer. According to Sheila Johnston, the primary source of involvement in a soap opera is not situated in the *suspense* of the narrative, as in many other popular television genres, but in "the creation and slow consolidation of a complex fictional world."[11] The repetitive character of *Dallas* can therefore be very important for *Dallas* fans:

> It's reassuring to see the same characters again and again. They you are far more involved in it. At least, I feel that. When I sit down to watch, I always get the idea that I belong to the family in a way too, because I have seen so much of them. I can enter into all the characters, because they are so familiar. I know them through and through. (Letter 20)

But there are other characteristics which are typical for the structure of the soap opera and which also apply for *Dallas*. Not only do different narratives exist side by side, sometimes to touch and intersect one another, and sometimes to run completely parallel. The fact that not just one (or a few) but many main characters are involved is also an important aspect of soap operas. Of none of the main characters in *Dallas* can it be said that he or she occupies the most important position from a narrative viewpoint. (In the press, it is often assumed that J.R. is the main character in *Dallas*. Although his actions do in fact often play a central part in the propulsion of the narrative, to reduce all the other characters to secondary roles shows a misjudgement of the multi-dimensionality of the *Dallas* narrative. Furthermore, considering J.R. as the main character only results from a very specific reading, which may be characterized by a masculine bias. For many letter writers the role of J.R. is not that important at all; they are not that interested in him.)

In fact the unity of the soap opera is not created by all the individual characters together, but by the community in which they live. In that community (Dallas) they each occupy an established position. This community also appears to determine which possibilities of action are open to the various characters. Not a single one of the characters escapes the "rules" of that community; in this sense the soap community is an enclosed community, like a village, a street, a hospital. Although new characters can enter the community—and that happens regularly; the soap opera steadily encroaches as it were on its surroundings in the course of years—as soon as they have made their entrance they are subjected to the laws and the logic of the community.

In *Dallas* the Ewing family forms the centre of the community. At the beginning of the serial Jock, Miss Ellie, J.R., Sue Ellen, Bobby, Pamela and Lucy have an established structural position within the family, positions ("father," "mother," "son," "daughter-in-law," "husband," "wife," "granddaughter") which are pretty unalterable. Of course later on alterations do occur in the status of the characters within the family: for example, Sue Ellen first divorces J.R. and later marries him again; and Ray Krebbs was initially not a member of the family then later turns out to be an (illegitimate) son of Jock's, so that suddenly he does belong to the family. But the fact remains that within the family itself the positions are established. The family is the central point of reference. Gillian Swanson, who has analysed the narrative structure of *Dallas*, has shown that "it is their identity as a family which is the central standard around which relations are made and according to which characters are defined and events are constructed."[12]

The Ewing family is a community within the wider community of *Dallas*, for other characters who do not belong to the family belong to that larger community. Of these characters Cliff Barnes is certainly the most important: he is the personification of the counter-forces within the larger community which try to disrupt the Ewing family. The community as a whole is therefore by no means a harmonious one—on the contrary, conflict and strife are the order of the day.

This brings us to a third important characteristic of the soap opera. This concerns the themes of the story. A soap opera follows the individual lives of the characters of a community, but it is not interested in their whole lives. In other words, it does not reveal all their doings, all their experiences. The soap opera is selective; it tells us a lot about the different characters, but it also leaves large parts of their life histories untold. A familiar complaint levelled at soap operas is, for example, that they lack social relevance: social problems and conflicts get short shrift or are not dealt with in an adequate, that is, structural way. But anyone expressing such a criticism overlooks the fact that leaving out or cutting out questions which are seen as important in the social reality is functional for the soap opera as genre. In other words, the soap opera generally ignores too concrete social or cultural references because it concerns itself with a completely different aspect of life.

According to Charlotte Brunsdon the ideological problematic of soap opera, that is, the perspective from which events in the narrative take on meaning, is that of "personal life." "More particularly, personal life in its everyday realization through personal relationships. This can be understood to be constituted primarily through the representation of romances, families, and the attendant rituals—births, engagements, marriages, divorces and deaths."[13] However, this does not imply that only the so-called private sphere of life is dealt with. Questions from the public sphere have a place too. The way in which they are handled and take on meaning is, however, always from the standpoint of the private sphere: "the action of soap opera is not restricted to the familial, or quasi-familial institutions, but as it were *colonizes* the public masculine sphere, representing it from the point of view of the personal," writes Brunsdon.[14] Thus in *Dallas* the business imbroglios to do with Ewing Oil are always shown with an eye to their consequences for the mutual relations of the family members. And the motives of Cliff Barnes in his work—first as politician and lawyer, later as owner and manager of a rival concern—are as it were shrivelled down to that one, all-prevailing motive: revenge on the Ewings. In short, in the world of the soap opera all sorts of events and situations from the public sphere occur only in so far as they lead to problems and complications in the private sphere.

The striking thing is, however, that these problems and complications assume such grotesque shapes. Personal life in soap operas is dominated by conflicts and catastrophes, which are blown up to improbable proportions. None of the following sensational problems has not yet occurred in *Dallas*: murder, suspicion of murder, marital crisis, adultery, alcoholism, rare disease, miscarriage, rape, airplane accident, car accident, kidnapping, corruption, psychiatric treatment, and so on. It is precisely this characteristic of the soap opera, this endless piling up of appalling crises, which often gives rise to incomprehension and ridicule from critics. For example, one well-known Dutch doctor and writer has lamented of *Dallas:* "I find it admirable the things these people can put up with, for . . . after a tenth of that stress I would be lying in the psychiatric hospital."[15]

As a prime time soap, then, *Dallas* combines the ideological problematic and the narrative structure of the daytime soaps with the visual style and glamour which are more usual for prime time programmes.

Dallas as Melodrama

Until now we have been describing the most important formal characteristic of *Dallas* as soap opera. Now I want to illustrate how important this formal structure is for the construction of the tragic structure of feeling—the complex of meanings which viewers can read from *Dallas*. Note: *can* read. The tragic structure of feeling as an umbrella meaning of *Dallas* emerges from the level of connotation, and not all viewers will ascribe the same connotative meanings to the programme. In other words, an arousal of the tragic structure of feeling is certainly made possible by the way in which the soap opera text itself is formally and ideologically structured, but whether this meaning is also actually ascribed depends on the cultural orientations of the viewers concerned: the expectations they have of the serial, their attitude towards the genre and television in general, the place television viewing occupies in their life, and so on. *Dallas* can also give rise to quite different reactions; the tragic structure of feeling suggested in it can also provoke ridicule and irony. Moreover, the individual viewer will probably not always make the same emotional associations when watching the programme; it is more plausible to assume that he or she can be gripped at one moment by the tragic structure of feeling, and at another moment can assume a more ironic attitude towards the text—identification and distancing constantly alternate with one another. The tragic structure of feeling is not therefore contained as it were in the nature of *Dallas*. It is a complex of meanings which is central for certain groups of *Dallas* fans, for whom a tragic look into daily life is in principle logical and meaningful.

There is a name for cultural genres whose main effect is the stirring up of the emotions: melodrama. Melodrama is a drama form which is not highly regarded in our culture and is mostly dismissed as "a sentimental, artificially plotted drama that sacrifices characterization to extravagant incident, makes sensational appeals to the emotions of its audience, and ends on a happy or at least a morally assuring note."[16] Not all soap operas or aspects of a soap opera can be regarded as melodramatic. The English soap opera *Coronation Street,* for example, has a more socio-realistic nature.[17] Most American soap operas, however, certainly are very melodramatic in character. So is *Dallas*, as I shall illustrate below.

It is difficult to persuade people to take melodrama seriously as a cultural form which is a significant expression of a lived reality, because, according to current notions, it plays on the emotions of the public in a false way: emotional straining after effect is seen as its sole aim. It is also sometimes said that melodrama is failed tragedy: the plot is so exaggerated and overdone that the story becomes ridiculous and bereft of any credibility and sensibility. The characters in a melodrama seem to be so taken up with their own violent emotions that there is no scope for reflection, intellectual distancing and relativizing.

What is unsatisfactory with these attitudes is not so much their descriptive value as the fusion of description and judgement. Melodrama is a cultural form that has been popular since the beginning of the nineteenth century, especially among the "popular" classes, and as such has also always had the status of inferior culture. And indeed, in the eyes of the literary and literate European culture of the established bourgeoisie, capitalizing on plot at the expense of giving greater depth to the characters is a reason for rejecting melodrama as "cliché-ridden" and "banal." But such a judgement is one-sided, not only because it makes absolute the norms of the European literary tradition, but also because it looks only at the surface, the outward form of melodrama. For us this last point is of particular interest. The application of literary norms to melodrama disregards the *function* of the heightened plot and the exaggerated emotions, while it is this very function that can reveal something of the attraction of melodrama. For what comes over from outside as a simplistic and easy-going penchant for the sensational can in its structure constitute the strength of the genre.

In *Dallas* too we can perceive this penchant for the sensational: the crises in the Ewings' family life succeed one another at an incredibly rapid speed, at least compared with "real" life. But although such a plot structure will be viewed by outsiders as pure sensationalism, within the fictional world of *Dallas* it is not sensational at all. On the contrary, such a plot structure is quite normal for the soap opera. To put it more strongly, soap opera would not be able to exist without murders, legal battles, extramarital affairs or serious illness. So it seems that they genre acquires its very strength from such exaggerated occurrences. This at least is the view advanced by the American television critic Horace Newcomb. "The fact that this story, in the technical reality of soap opera, is so unsensational gives us the clue to its real importance," he states.[18] In the world of soap opera the characters go through all kinds of calamities as though it were the most normal thing in life. The significance of such a plot structure is that through it "human misery" is exposed in a very emphatic manner. "Most of the problems forming the centre of soap opera plots can be defined best as being in the areas of psychical or emotional pain," says Newcomb,[19] and it seems as though it is not possible to express that pain other than by means of an overdramatizing of the narrative.

Is this the result of a lack of creativity and subtlety? I do not believe that such a personal reproach levelled at the writers of melodramatic soap operas gives us any insight into the cultural specificity of the genre, as it ignores the structural function of exaggerated plots in soap opera. Exaggerated plots can be regarded as the symbolic lumping together of the diffuse and hard-to-describe notion of "life's torments" which occur at times in every individual life. They function as metaphors for these "life's torments." And the fact that in soap operas the same types of plots are reverted to, the same sorts of narrative situations occur, should not be blamed on a lack of originality, for at this level a soap opera certainly does not try to be original. (Originality on the basis of individual creativity is a bourgeois literary value which cannot be applied to a popular genre such as soap opera.) Rather I would suggest that such plots and situations are dominant and generally current as metaphors for "life's torments" in our culture, speaking directly to the imagination of the public.

Within the framework of a popular fiction form like soap opera, exaggerated events such as kidnappings, marital dramas and chance meetings with great consequences should not be regarded and assessed for their referential value, but as bearers of the melodramatic effect. Melodrama does not seek to dramatize the unique experience of a single human character (as is mostly the case in "serious" drama). In a fascinating article on American film melodrama of the 1950s Thomas Elsaesser points out that melodrama operates on a "non-psychological conception of the *dramatis personae,* who figure less as autonomous individuals than to transmit the action and link the various locales within a total constellation. In this respect, melodramas have a myth-making function, in so far as their significance lies in the structure and articulation of the action, not in any psychologically motivated correspondence with individualized experience."[20] In other words, the "psychological credibility" of the characters in melodrama is subordinated to the functioning of those characters in melodramatic situations, so that the emotional effect is pushed to extremes. That effect can be achieved because these imagined situations are socially and culturally surrounded by myths and fantasies which endow them with a strongly emotional appeal. That appeal draws less on the bare facts of those situations than on the metaphorical role they play in the popular imagination.

Alcoholism is one such metaphor which is often used in melodrama to represent the impotence of a character. As Elsaesser remarks:

> Although alcoholism is too common an emblem in films[. . .] to deserve a close thematic analysis, drink does become interesting in movies where its dynamic significance is developed and its qualities as a visual metaphor recognized: wherever characters are seen swallowing and gulping their drinks as if they were swallowing their humiliations along with their pride, vitality and the life-force have become palpably destructive and a phoney libido has turned into real anxiety.[21]

The symbolic effectiveness of drunkenness is employed not only in films like John Huston's *Under the Volcano.* Anyone who has followed *Dallas* faithfully will know how Sue Ellen took to drink and regularly appeared drunk on the screen. Her alcoholic inclination was used as a visual externalizing of her feelings of impotence in a life situation in which she felt fettered: to be married to a man whom she loathed and who was unfaithful to her, but who at the same time had her completely in his power. Sue Ellen's alcoholism therefore has a metaphorical function here: the intention is not so much that viewers start worrying about the concrete drinking problem (from a financial point of view, for example, it will never be any problem for Sue Ellen to get a drink: pots of money), much rather, the depiction of alcoholism should enable viewers to have some idea of Sue Ellen's psychological state, of her suffering, of the emotional conflicts she is battling with.

Such a metaphor derives its strength from a *lack* of originality and uniqueness:

precisely because it constantly recurs in all sorts of popular narratives, it takes on for viewers a direct comprehensibility and recognizability. We could even say that viewers must be ready to read all sorts of events and situations in the narrative in a metaphorical way, in order to be able to understand and evaluate their full implications. Insight into the metaphorical value of the plots is the basis for the pleasure of many faithful viewers of soap operas—an insight missed by the intellectual who only watches a soap opera now and then with a mistrustful attitude and seeks to evaluate the narrative only on the basis of its literary value.

I cannot go into the question here of why exactly these events and situations fulfil a metaphorical function and precisely which common-sense meanings they contain. That would require a separate cultural-historical essay. Why, for example, in addition to murders, misfortunes or diseases, are there so many illegitimate children, unknown fathers or mothers (for whom the adult children passionately and restlessly search), or secret pasts (with fatal results for the present)? All these plot elements are incorporated in *Dallas* too! In *Dallas*, however, not only are existing metaphors adapted in the narrative in an ingenious way, but these metaphors are sometimes modernized as well, adapted to the sensibilities of the present.

An example is the metaphor of illness. It is not surprising that characters in melodramas and soap operas are so often ill, as this can propel the narrative forward in a marvellously melodramatic way. As Susan Sontag has illustrated, the phenomenon of illness is liberally surrounded by all sorts of emotionally loaded associations and images. Being ill means not only physically being out of order but also being excluded from the world of the healthy, being overcome by an unknown and uncontrollable force, etc. And some illnesses, such as tuberculosis and cancer, have a uniquely terrifying aura. Being ill therefore has far-reaching cultural consequences extending far beyond the biological fact of illness itself.[22]

In soap operas there are often cases of illness for which the diagnosis remains unknown or the physical results of which remain invisible. For example, in *Dallas* Cliff Barnes and Pamela Ewing at a certain moment are told the unpleasant news by their doctor that they are suffering from an incurable illness inherited from their father Digger, called "neurofibromatosis"—a mysterious illness which does exist according to the medical encyclopedia, but the symptoms of which in fact are not such as they are shown in *Dallas*! But only a killjoy would point that out. It is not the illness itself that is relevant for the narrative, but the dramatic consequences of it for the sick person. In the case of Pamela the illness functions as a metaphor for the drama that a powerful desire can never be fulfilled: beyond her own control, she can never achieve what she wants (to have children), for the illness prevents her. (Later the plot becomes even more involved when it emerges that Pamela is not Digger's daughter at all. . . .)

In stark contrast to the vagueness of Pamela's illness, however, is the hard realism of the illness that strikes Miss Ellie: breast cancer. From a content analysis it has emerged that the diagnosis of cancer hardly ever occurs in soap operas;[23] the illness is apparently so terrifyingly real that it cannot be fitted into the mythical world of soap opera. The fact that it does occur in *Dallas* and in such an emphatic way (two episodes were totally taken up by Miss Ellie's illness) can be regarded as "modern" or in any case as daring, the more so as Miss Ellie's breast cancer is dramatically mobilized as a metaphor for a form of "life's torment" which certainly does not enjoy any general social recognition:

the sexual objectifying of the female body by men. Miss Ellie realizes that a mastectomy has far-reaching results for her attractiveness to men. She does not believe what her husband Jock says: that it makes no difference to him (for, she muses, "he has an eye for a pretty girl"), and she tells him that men cannot understand what she is feeling. From other scenes it emerges how Miss Ellie's mastectomy releases a feeling of menace among the other female family members (Sue Ellen, Pamela and Lucy) which has to do with their sexual identity. In particular for Lucy the thought of such a mutilation of the body is so unbearable that at first she refuses to see the sick Miss Ellie and has to be persuaded by Pamela to visit her grandmother in the hospital. For Miss Ellie herself too, the illness leaves deep traces for years. Although initially she seems to recover well from the illness and has been able apparently to forget the torment, years later her mutilated body causes her to shrink from entering a new marriage—with Clayton Farlow—a fear which she has to be argued out of by Donna Krebbs ("He loves you!"). In this way a theme which has been brought into the open by feminists is recycled in *Dallas*!

As melodramatic soap opera, therefore, *Dallas*, by means of "a sentimental, artificially plotted drama that sacrifices characterization to extravagant incident," makes visible areas of internal psychological disturbance. It is now time to go into the nature of these disturbances in a little more detail.

Dallas and Family Tragedy

"What is implausible in [television melodramas] is the continual necessity for emotional display by the characters. In real life we are rarely called upon to feel so intensely, and never in such neatly escalating sequences. But the emotions dramatized by these improbable plots are not in themselves unreal, or at least they need not be," states David Thornburn in an article on television melodrama.[24] It is just as though, under the guise of the sensational, something is brought to the surface which otherwise would remain hidden. The sensational improbability of the narrative must magnify the probability of the conflicts expressed by it.

In most soap operas the conflicts forming the foundation of the dramatic development of the narrative always have to do with difficult family situations: it is the conflictual relations between family members—husband/wife, parents/children, brothers/sisters—which again and again give rise to tensions, crises and emotional outbursts. We have indicated earlier that the ideological problematic of the soap opera is personal life; we can now add that, certainly in *Dallas*, the development of personal life *within the family* is set up as the ideological norm. The family is regarded as the ideal cradle for human happiness. At least, it should be.

This focusing on the area of the personal and on the problem of psychological well-being distinguishes the soap opera in a crucial way from other genres of popular television fiction, such as the police or adventure series. These genres are preoccupied with overcoming a danger or an enemy, and there is usually little room there for emotional uncertainties or psychological conflicts relating to individual, personal existence. The (almost always male) hero is in this regard completely sure of himself. Even more, precisely this certainty forms an important ingredient of his invincibility: he never doubts, knows precisely what he has to do and never dwells on his own insignificance. He is invulnerable.

This type of popular fiction appeals to the public in a radically different way from soap opera. Just as in film melodrama, "its excitement comes from conflict not between enemies but between people tied by blood or love."[25] That is why there is no invincibility in soap operas: as a value, invincibility does not count in family relationships. Even J.R., who shrinks from nothing and no one to get his way, from time to time has to face the fact that he can lose. And that applies even more for all the other characters. No one is invulnerable, however heroic, powerful or strong he or she might be. Which is tragic.

Family life is not actually romanticized in soap operas; on the contrary, the imaginary ideal of the family as safe haven in a heartless world is constantly shattered. In *Dallas* this is done in an extremely sophisticated way. In contrast to most tradtional soap operas *Dallas* concentrates totally on the ups and downs of one family: the Ewings. All the actions in the narrative are ultimately directed at the position of this family within the *Dallas* community. And for the characters it is of particularly great significance whether they are inside or outside the family. Any new marriage, such as that between Miss Ellie and Clayton Farlow, any divorce, such as between Pamela and Bobby, or the birth of a child also inevitably causes some disturbance, because here the profile of the family is at stake. The continuance of and harmony within the Ewing family is paramount in *Dallas*. Whereas the characters of other soap operas can still find inner peace and happiness outside their family life (such as in the intimacy and camaraderie between two women friends), the belief that one can feel at home in a community not based on family relationships is doomed to failure. Sue Ellen's greatest defeat is that, after she has finally divorced J.R. and tried to build up an independent existence, she nevertheless remarries J.R. and thus—against her better judgement—projects her personal happiness again within the Ewing family. Pamela's happiness too after her divorce from Bobby is only temporary and therefore illusory: Mark, the new man in her life (who is by the way merely a compensation for Bobby, whom she still loves), turns out to be incurably ill and soon dies.

The outside world, i.e. the world outside the family, is presented in *Dallas* as a hotbed of activity threatening to the family. The relationships the Ewing women enter into with people (men) outside the family are, from the standpoint of the family, a danger to the unity of the family. The business contacts of the Ewing men in the Dallas community lead only too often to instability in the family harmony, especially through the continuing discord between J.R. and Bobby. Because the idea of personal happiness can only exist against the background of the unity of the family, this unity must always be safeguarded against attacks from outside and from inside. In short, the conflict between family-strengthening and family-undermining forces is, as Swanson's structural analysis of the *Dallas* narrative shows, the most important motor that propels this soap opera forward.[26]

Family harmony is also offered to the viewers as the norm for the assessment of the situation of the Ewings. The way in which the narrative is told scarcely allows for another point of view. The central role that Southfork plays in each episode, as the place—the haven—where family members sooner or later always return, ensures that the ranch functions as a permanent identification point. The scenes in which the whole family is at home together, at breakfast or in the living room before going to dinner, often form temporary respites in the endless series of complications. One or two of such scenes are included in each episode.[27] This was particularly true of the earlier episodes. The slow disintegration of the original family makes these family gatherings less and less frequent. In one episode there is even a dramatic scene in which Miss Ellie, the *mater familias*, is sitting quite alone at the head of a luxuriously laid dinner table—her children have not turned up, and her husband Jock is dead. . . . The viewers are thus invited to identify with the idea that the unity of the family is a living condition of prime importance. (Such an identification, however, by no means need coincide with a real attachment of the viewer to the ideology of the family; it is a component of the fantasmatic game the viewer begins when he or she enters into the narrative.)

But this norm of family harmony takes its toll. The individual family members are subjected to its demands. It is the family structure which determines which rules each of the family members must conform to; it is from the standpoint of the family that each family member is, as it were, set in a stereotyped role, such as the loving mother or the worthy son. According to Swanson this subjection of the Ewing characters to a stereotyped role forms a second important structural source of conflict.[28] They do not seem capable of becoming reconciled to the shackles of the family ideal, or they actively try to escape from them, and this leads to new, manifest problems. For example, Sue Ellen's attempts to get away from J.R. cannot be reconciled with holding the family intact: she has to leave the family in order to fulfill her own desires (and staying in the family or returning to it means giving up her desires!). Also, her initial refusal to look after her own newborn child—a refusal of the traditional mother role—does not exactly have a favourable effect on the family peace: it leads to worry for Miss Ellie, to reproach from J.R. and to the (brief) illusion for Pamela that she can take over motherhood from Sue Ellen with baby John Ross. Peace only returns when Sue Ellen accepts her duty as a mother. And above all the poisonous activities of J.R., his countless extramarital relations and his business intrigues with Ewing Oil, can certainly not be reconciled with the safeguarding of family harmony. But J.R. is pre-eminently someone who is always consciously abandoning his role of son, brother and husband whenever it suits him, and so puts the unity of the family chronically at risk.

Thus the most important characters move constantly between the two poles of a dilemma: either to go their own way in search of personal happiness, or to submit to the social fetters of the family structure. The moments when these two options are in harmony with one another are few. Just as in any soap opera, no marriage in *Dallas* is proof against the ravages of time, not even the almost idyllic marriage of Pamela and Bobby.

What is conveyed in this representation then is the eternal contradiction, the insolubility of inner conflicts, the unbridgeability as it were of the antithesis between pleasure principle and reality principle. As Laura Mulvey puts it, "beyond or beneath the dramatic mainspring of ideological contradiction that melodrama plays on, lies another contradiction: the impossibility of reconciling desire with reality. The melodrama recognizes this gap by raising problems, known and recognizable, and offering a personal escape similar to that of a daydream: a chance to work through inescapable frustrations by positing an alternative ideal never seen as more than a momentary illusion."[29] It is this disturbing "truth" over personal life that viewers are confronted with. What could provide better soil for the tragic structure of feeling?

Soap Opera, Melodrama and the Tragic Structure of Feeling

But this tragic structure of feeling within *Dallas* would impose itself in a less forceful way on devoted viewers if the conflicts the characters have to go through were not presented in a specifically melodramatic way. "Characters caught in the world of melodrama are not allowed transcendent awareness or knowledge," says Mulvey.[30] In other words, although the problems of characters develop from a conflict set structurally in the narrative, the characters themselves are not aware of that structure. They fight for a happier life in the direct immediacy of existence and are not capable of sizing up their objective position. "The melodramatic characters act out contradiction, achieving actual confrontation to varying degrees and gradually facing impossible resolutions and probably defeats," according to Mulvey.[31] And precisely this *gradual* facing of one's own impotence makes it the more tragic: illusions and ideals are steadily undermined.

The dialogues in *Dallas*—dialogue is *the* narrative instrument of soap opera—never contain any critical and conscious (self) reflection. The characters never ponder on their position in the world, they never philosophize from a detached point of view on themselves and their relations to others. The conversations the characters have with one another, on the other hand, always express the living through or digesting of a conflict, in the here and how. There is never question of an intellectual exposition and exchange of ideas; each spoken word reflects the subjective inner world of a character—his or her desires, fears, moral preferences, etc. But at the same time the dialogues between the characters are not often examples of frank and honest communication. Often they don't say everything, or don't say what they mean, or mean more than they say. In this sense the dialogues in *Dallas* are often elliptical. The status of the spoken word is therefore relativized, as though there are always things which cannot or may not be said. The essence of a situation is not expressed, but lies as it were concealed behind the facial expression of the character who at the end of a scene—as so often in *Dallas*—is shown in close-up and held for a few seconds, before the first shot of the following scene.[32] This melodramatic method produces an enlargement of the tragic structure of feeling: the close-ups emphasize the fact that the character ultimately does not have control of her or his own life, not so much because of the machinations of some superhuman divinity, but because of contradictions inherent in human society itself.

The end of the narrative is always a problem for melodrama. It is often pointed out that a melodrama is only effective when it has an "open" end: at first sight there may be the possibility of a happy ending, but so many future conflicts are already brewing that the happy end itself is not credible. In fact the end of a melodrama is not actually so important; the main thing is what happens before. As Mulvey notes, "the strength of the melodramatic form lies in the amount of dust the story raises along the road, a cloud of over-determined irreconcilables which put up a resistance to being neatly settled in the last five minutes."[33]

However, for the soap opera this problem of the last five minutes is must less acute. It is inherent in the form of soap opera that in principle it goes on endlessly.[34] The soap opera can, therefore, because it is always going along the road, raise an infinite amount of dust without worrying about clearing it up. This lack of an end, this constant deferment of the ultimate "solution," adds a new dimension to the tragic structure of feeling. The endless repetition of the slogan at the end of each episode of *Soap*! that tragicomic parody of soap opera, is a striking illustration of this: "Confused? You won't be after the next episode of . . . *Soap*!" But one is nevertheless confused yet again.

Tania Modleski has pointed out in this connection that in soap opera the so-called "hermeneutic code" prevails.[35] This code consists of all those elements in a narrative which pose a problem or effect a delay in the solution of a problem: obstacles, errors, devious behavior, deceptions, half-truths, and so on. In a classic, linear narrative the hermeneutic code is ultimately conquered by the final solution, the moment of complete truth. But in a soap opera delay is the rule, the normal course of affairs. And so the viewer is manoeuvred into a position of permanent expectation which, in the words of Roland Barthes, refers to "disorder: disorder is[. . .] what is forever added on without solving anything, without finishing anything."[36] This position of eternal expectation strengthens a feeling of aimlessness and directionlessness; it "creates a feeling that things are constantly happening (becoming more complicated) in the narrative, but that, at the same time, nothing ever really happnes."[37] The idea of progress, which is connected with the idea of a fundamental difference between past and present, is absent. The characters in *Dallas* live in the prison of an eternally conflictual present. This places the viewer in a curious position. She knows that the soap opera will never end and that the agony will never let up. Whereas in other narratives the assurance and confirmation of a happy end is a source of pleasure, in soap opera it is precisely the tragic knowledge of the *holding off* of an end satisfactory to all the characters which is the basis for narrative pleasure.

Furthermore, the viewer's position towards the individual characters is also ambiguous. As we have said, in a soap opera various narratives always intersect one another. Whereas at one moment we can sympathize with Sue Ellen's marital woes and get a glimpse of her having a good cry at her psychiatrist's, the next moment we are witness to Pamela's dilemma about whether to tell Bobby of her illness. All the characters live their own lives without necessarily having anything to do with or being in touch with the problems, actions and plans of the others. They are wrapped up in their own preoccupations and view any situation purely and simply from their own subjective standpoint. Viewers, however, know "everything" about each of them and thus find themselves in a powerful, omniscient position. But strangely enough this power is based on a realization of powerlessness, because they know that the relational structure in which the life of all the characters is embedded is immovable and leads to all kinds of tensions, without the characters themselves being aware of them.

An example: Miss Ellie hesitates to tell Jock that she has breast cancer, because she is afraid that then he will turn away from her. (She experiences exactly the same fear, as we have noted, much later when Clayton has asked her to marry him.) At the same time Jock does not know how he can tell Miss Ellie that he was married before, because he is frightened of her reaction. In both there is doubt and uncertainty, and therefore mistrust, without their knowing it of one another, which leads repeatedly to all kinds of irritations and misunderstandings. Viewers, however, are informed of both secrets and must, in order to be able to continue to follow the narrative, put themselves in the position of both. This appeal to "multiple identification"[38] means that viewers cannot simply identify with one character in order to understand and judge all the developments from that character's point of view, as is mostly the case in an adventure story.

This floating viewer position is strengthened even more by the fact that the characters are sometimes particularly inconsistent in their behaviour and within a short period can completely change their attitude. An American television critic has noted that a total instability of behavioural codes prevails in *Dallas*,[39] so that neither the characters themselves nor the viewers know where they stand. For example, instead of handing her over to the police, J.R. puts Sue Ellen's sister Kristin on the plane out of Dallas with a thick wad of banknotes, after he has learned that she was the one who had tried to shoot him. And so Sue Ellen's feelings for J.R. after the attempt on his life veer right round: although she hated him before, she suddenly realizes that she does in fact love him . . . only to find out some weeks later that J.R. does not deserve her love. There is a lack of "any secure sense of what constitutes the status quo," says Sheila Johnston.[40] And Modleski comes to the conclusion that soap operas implicitly announce a frightful truth about life: "soaps continually insist on the insignificance of the individual life."[41] The world of the soap opera is therefore totally ambiguous. It is a world in which the area of the personal is all-prevailing, but in which at the same time all personal lives are perverted. For not a single individual in a soap opera is free to construct his or her own life history. On the contrary, it is the structures and contradictions in which they are caught that determine developments.

In *Dallas*, however, one figure escapes these shackles: J.R. This villain constantly ignores the laws and rules of society and bends developments to his own will. Through his dishonest dealings and intrigues he is the most important cause of misery in *Dallas*. Modleski points out that the villain has an essential function in the soap opera narrative: he or she is the one who does not submit but resists. But paradoxically enough, J.R.'s actions tend to strengthen the tragic structure of feeling. He demonstrates that power can only be coupled with badness and immorality, while those who want to live a "good" life are constantly bereft of power and doomed to suffer. But that does not mean that the villain always wins. On the contrary, because in the soap opera ambivalence and temporality are the rule, J.R. has to keep on trying to get his way. According to some it is precisely this unremitting and indefatigable attempt to break out which explains the attraction of the villain. As Horace Newcomb says, "what we see in J.R. is a refusal to give up. He persists."[42]

But the villain fulfils a second function in the world of soap opera. Not only is he not an outsider, set apart from an otherwise harmonious community, but he also belongs to the community. Moreover, he is the one who brings the community to life and sees to it that things happen. The evil is therefore woven into the order of the community itself, so that the community by definition is conflictual because it bears the core of the conflict within itself: harmony only exists as unattainable Utopia. Thus, the Ewing family and *Dallas* would certainly cease to exist if J.R. were put out of action: family life, in the logic of *Dallas*, can only exist by the grace of the one who regularly jeopardizes the very survival of the family!

Finally, let us return to the meaning of the glamorous *mise-en-scène* which characterizes *Dallas*. The Ewings are very rich people and can afford everything material: luxury homes, splendid clothes, exclusive dinners, expensive presents, etc. This wealth does not, however, seem to have many fundamental consequences for the general plot structure of *Dallas* as soap opera: here money has more of an *instrumental* function for the composition of conflict and agony. Money as such is never the source of agony in *Dallas*; rather the ease with which millions of dollars are thrown about gives an extra sensational and bombastic dimension to the interpersonal conflicts with which *Dallas* is preoccupied. It is therefore questionable whether the glamorous *mise-en-scène* does primarily fulfil a *narrative* function, as expressed in the phrase "money can't buy happiness," which according to some critics is the ideological message of programmes like *Dallas*. Such an explanation ignores the fact that the visual excess of *Dallas* can also produce meanings which are relatively independent of the narrative. The sun-drenched prairie around Southfork, the luxurious swimming pool, the tall, spacious office buildings, the chic restaurants and the elegant women and handsome men—they seem rather to belong to the optimistic image world of advertising, an optimism that does not fit in with the pessimistic world of soap opera, so that the *mise-en-scène* in itself produces a chronic contradiction. It intensifies in this way the claustrophobic sphere of the closed community in which the characters live, in which hysteria can break out any moment, but is also curbed time and again. For in *Dallas* life always goes on normally, whatever happens.

The Melodramatic Imagination

It is thus the combination of melodramatic elements and the narrative structure of soap opera that evokes a tragic structure of feeling. This tragic structure of feeling does not, however, consist of being bowed down by the Great Tragedy of Man, as is expressed, for example, in classical Greek tragedy, but of a half-conscious realization of the tragic side of ordinary everyday life. Not high-flown *Weltschmerz*, but a completely pedestrian form of suffering. In Newcomb's words, it is a matter here of the simple idea that survival is "complicated by ambiguity and blurred with pain even in its most sought-after accomplishments."[43]

But I have said earlier that the tragic structure of feeling, which is inscribed in the meaning-structure of *Dallas*, will not automatically and obviously agree with the meanings viewers will apply to *Dallas*. That will only happen if they are sensitive to it. In other words, the tragic structure of feeling suggested by *Dallas* will only make sense if one can and will project oneself into, i.e. recognize, a *melodramatic imagination*. Viewers must therefore have a certain cultural competence or orientation to understand and evaluate *Dallas* in a melodramtic way. As Charlotte Brunsdon has so aptly put it: "Just as a Godard film requires the possession of certain forms of cultural capital on the part of the audience to 'make sense' [. . .] so too does [. . .] soap opera."[44] In the case of *Dallas*, the melodramatic imagination seems central to that cultural orientation.

The melodramatic imagination is characterized by Peter Brooks as a type of imagination in which a (semi-desperate) attempt is made "to bring into the drama of man's quotidian existence the higher drama of moral forces."[45] The melodramatic imagination should be regarded as a psychological strategy to overcome the material meaninglessness of everyday existence, in which routine and habit prevail in human relationships as much as elsewhere. In other words it is a matter of making "the world we inhabit one charged with meaning, one in which interpersonal relations are not merely contacts of the flesh, but encounters that must be carefully nurtured, judged, handled as if they mattered."[46] The melodramatic imagination is therefore the expression of a refusal, or inability, to accept insignificant everyday life as banal and meaningless, and is born of a vague, inarticulate dissatisfaction with existence here and now. This then is the tragic structure of feeling: it is not about the great suffering which plays such a prominent role in the history of humankind and which is generally known as human tragedy—the sufferings of war, concentration camps, famine, etc.—but is rather about what is usually not acknowledged as tragic at all and for that very reason is so difficult to communicate. There are no words for the ordinary pain of living of ordinary people in the modern welfare state, for the vague sense of loss, except in half-ironic, half-resigned phrases such as: "You win some, you lose some." By making that ordinariness something special and meaningful in the imagination, that sense of loss can—at least for a time—be removed. It is in this world of the imagination that watching melodramatic soap operas like *Dallas* can be pleasurable; *Dallas* offers a starting point for the melodramatic imagination, nourishes it, makes in concrete.

We may wonder about the social and historical roots of the melodramatic imagination. No single form of imagination, as a way in which the everyday, practical consciousness makes sense of an accounts for the living experiences it is confronted with, just appears out of the blue. To which cultural-historical circumstances does the melodramatic imagination form a fantasmatic answer? Here we can only go into this question briefly.

Peter Brooks connects the melodramatic imagination to the fragmented character of modern society, in which no single system of values is capable any longer of functioning as the binding element for the great variety of events and impressions. The melodramatic is, he says, "a form of the tragic [. . .] for a world in which there is no longer a tenable idea of the sacred."[47] In a life in which every immanent meaning is constantly questioned and in which traditions no longer have a firm hold, a need exists for reassurance that life can in fact have meaning and therefore life is worth the trouble, in spite of all appearances to the contrary. According to Brooks the explanation can also be found here for the tendency to sentimental exaggeration which is so characteristic of melodrama. It is as though the melodramatic imagination must impress itself so emphatically because what it wants to express is so uncertain, so difficult to grasp, and therefore too so difficult to justify. When the meaning of life threatens to elude us, the "larger than life" emotions of the melodramatic imagination offer an anchor.

Other authors have ascribed a specific function to the serial as fiction form on the basis of such considerations. The French semiologist Violette Morin points out, for example, that the popularity of the television serial could derive from the fact that the life depicted in it seems to proceed *more slowly* than real life. According to her this effect is achieved by cramming each scene with meaning, even when it is not directly of interest for the continuance of the narrative. "People eat, talk, walk about in a TV serial in tune with the rhythm of a constant semantic 'braking'; as if they were afraid to be happy at living, as if they were more slow, more cautious than in real life and at all events more healthy in their attitude to the pace of life than everyday existence."[48] According to Morin, this slow-motion idea of life responds to a desire to slow down, to put the brakes on the hasty nature of modern life. We could conclude from this that the serial form is an extremely suitable vehicle for the melodramatic imagination, because in itself it ascribes more meaning to everyday things than is usual in real life.

But such explanations, in which the melodramatic imagination is linked to the characteristics of modern society, are not specific enough. They take into consideration solely some general, formal characteristics of modern daily life, such as the fragmenting of experience, the transitory nature of time and the break with tradition, and therefore abstract from the socio-cultural differences between the living conditions of different groups of people. It is, however, precisely the concrete, practical living situations of people which demand psychological assimilation and which form the raw material for imagination and fantasy. Not everyone living in an urban, industrialized society will be equally sensitive to the melodramatic imagination. The routes followed by people's imaginative strategies are formed during the course of their personal and subcultural histories and slowly rub through, as it were, into their practical consciousness.

If, as is said of soap opera, it is a "woman's genre" because it is mainly women who like watching it, then that would suggest that it is mainly women who are susceptible to the melodramatic imagination, a type of imagination which appears to express mainly a rather passive, fatalistic and individualistic reaction to a vague feeling of powerlessness and unease. This "susceptibility," however, has not so much to do with the material social situation of women (housewives)—this would imply a sociological reductionism—as with the way they have become accustomed to facing situations psychologically and emotionally. The ideologically dominant association of the "women's area" with a concern for the private sphere and with the caring function is an important determining factor in this, for example.[49]

Moreover, we must not overrate the role of the melodramatic imagination in everyday consciousness. Commonsense thinking is not one-dimensional. On the contrary, it is of a very heterogeneous nature.[50] And there are many other ways in which experiences can be lived and assimilated: a melodramatic manner of perceiving the world can alternate with a humorous, romantic, rebellious or other imaginative strategy. The sense of the melodramatic, the tragic structure of feeling, surfaces only occasionally, often cutting in on a sober acceptance of daily existence. Mostly, too, people only experience melodramatic *moments*. Such a moment can, for example, occur when someone is watching *Dallas*. Then *Dallas* is pleasurable because it makes the melodramatic imagination present and palpable.

Of course this does not mean that there are no other ways of experiencing pleasure from *Dallas*. Viewers can also read it in a completely different way; they can attend to other aspects of the text and respond to them: the ingenious way in which the plots are intertwined, the mythical Western elements, the technical discussions on oil, J.R.'s venomous humour, and so on. *Dallas* offers points of contact for many types of imagination.

In conclusion, then, we can say that the pleasure of *Dallas* consists in the recognition of ideas that fit in with the viewers' imaginative world. They can "lose" themselves in *Dallas* because the programme symbolizes a structure of feeling which connects up with one of the ways in which they encounter life. And in so far as the imagination is an essential component of our psychological world, the pleasure of *Dallas*—as a historically specific symbolizing of that imagination—is not a *compensation* for the presumed drabness of daily life, nor a *flight* from it, but a *dimension* of it. For only through the imagination, which is always subjective, is the "objective reality" assimilated: a life without imagination does not exist.

Pleasure and Theory

But the above is theoretical construction. And theoretical constructions by definition never coincide with immediate experience: they can only shed light on that experience in a onesided way. The capricious and contradictory nature of experience is nullified by this.

As immediate experience, pleasure in *Dallas* is a more or less "spontaneous" phenomenon: a person enjoys watching it, or otherwise, in some way or other. Experiencing pleasure is not a conscious, directed activity (although one can strive for it), but something that "happens," something which comes over the viewer according to his or her feelings. The experience is diffuse, bound to time and context, heterogeneous: so much is going on in the viewer's head.

In analysing the pleasure of *Dallas* we have started with the premise that the programme is a text with a specific structure. Pleasure is then connected with the way in which viewers read the text from a specific subject position. But generally viewers do not approach *Dallas* as text. For them watching it is first and foremost a *practice*. Certainly, in this practice the *Dallas* text occupies a central place, but the practice itselt comprises more than that. Therefore it is somewhat misleading—or at any rate inadequate—to deduce the pleasure of *Dallas* totally from its characteristics as text. Watching *Dallas*, just like watching television in general, is a cultural practice which has much of the nature of a habit: it is directly available, casual and free. And a habit is always difficult to explain in intellectual terms, because it feels so natural and self-evident.

A theoretical construction has the character and the effect here, then, of a rationalization. And is it not a fact that we can talk of the experience of pleasure only by means of rationalizations? Pleasure eludes our rational consciousness. This applies not only for theoreticians who want to explain this pleasure, but also for the "witness" or "reporters" of pleasure, on which the theoreticians base their explanations. It seems as though the letter writers—my "reporters"—realize that. Some of them do their very best to express in words why they like watching *Dallas*; they recite reason after reason, in order ultimately, quite unexpectedly, to end their account with expressions of uncertainty such as:

> I don't know, but I like watching it. (Letter 4)
>
> I don't know exactly what it is but *Dallas* really draws me; there is, I find, a sort of charm radiating from the actors and from the thing itself. I just really love watching it. (Letter 13)
>
> In a word, there's a bit of everything in that film. Perhaps it's crazy to think so but that's what I see in it. (Letter 16)
>
> Finally I must just say that, funnily enough, last year I just couldn't stand *Dallas*. Unfortunately I can't say why. (Letter 17)
>
> I think *Dallas* is a serial for sensitive people, but of course I could be completely wrong. (Letter 18)
>
> I hope my story has been of some use to you, but I find it really difficult to state exactly why I like *Dallas*. (Letter 20)
>
> Looking into it more closely, I can imagine you haven't got much from my reaction because it's a bit shallow as an analysis, but I'll send it anyway. (Letter 22)
>
> Here are some opinions from my brother and from a girl living in our house. They like watching it, amusing and good-looking people are in it and it is well produced. According to them. My father just says it's shit. I hope this has been some use to you. Unfortunately there's not much you can say about it. (Letter 37)

It is as though the pleasure of *Dallas* eludes the rational consciousness of these letter writers. They do their utmost to give explanations for that pleasure, but somehow they know that the explanations they can put into words are not the whole story, or even perhaps the "right" story.

Pleasure is therefore obviously something uncertain and precarious. "Everyone can testify that the pleasure of the text is not certain: nothing says that this same text will please us a second time; it is a friable pleasure, split by mood, habit, circumstance, a precarious pleasure," writes Roland Barthes.[51] A theoretical (re)construction can therefore never fully comprehend pleasure, because theory makes it something substantial and presumes it to be permanent and static. Nor do we have to agree with Barthes when he asserts that "we are scientific because we lack subtlety"[52] (scientific subtlety may in fact exist, but this is of a different order from the subtlety of pleasure) to be able to conclude that any theoretical look at pleasure by definition falls short. A conclusion which, however paradoxical it might sound, gives rise to optimism.

Notes

1. For the theoretical problems and consequences of the use of the concept of genre in film theory, see S. Neale, *Genre*, BFI, London, 1980.
2. C. Geraghty, "The continuous serial: a definition," in R. Dyer (ed.), *Coronation Street*, BFI, London, 1980, p. 10.
3. ibid., pp. 14–15.
4. Todorov, quoted in Geraghty, "The continuous serial . . .," p. 13.
5. For a history of soap opera, see M. Edmonson and D. Rounds, *The Soaps*, Stein & Day, New York, 1973; M. G. Cantor and S. Pingree, *The Soap Opera*, Sage, Beverly Hills, 1983.
6. For the function of soap operas for housewives, see H. Herzog, "What do we really know about daytime serial listeners?" in P. F. Lazarsfeld and F. N. Stanton (eds), *Radio Research*, Duel, Sloan & Pearce, New York, 1944; D. Hobson, *Crossroads. The Drama of a Soap Opera*, Methuen, London, 1982, chapter 6.
7. S. Frith, *Sound Effects: Youth, Leisure and the Politics of Rock n' Roll*, Pantheon, New York, 1982, p. 46.
8. See also E. Seiter, "Men, sex and money in recent family melodramas," *Journal of the University Film and Video Association*, vol. XXXV, no. 1, winter 1983.
9. T. Brooks and E. Marsh, *The Complete Directory to Prime Time TV Shows*, Ballentine, New York, 1981, p. 178.
10. T. Modleski, "The search for tomorrow in today's soap operas," *Film Quarterly*, fall 1979, p. 12.
11. S. Johnston, "Crossroads: approaches to popular television fiction," paper read at BFI Summer School 1981, p. 10.
12. G. Swanson, "*Dallas*, part 1," *Framework*, no. 14, spring 1981, p. 62.
13. C. Brunsdon, "Crossroads: notes on soap opera," *Screen*, vol. 22, no. 4, 1981, p. 34.
14. ibid., p. 34.
15. W. Brakman, in a radio interview, 9 January 1982.
16. D. Thornburn, "Television melodrama," in R. Adler and D. Cater (eds), *Television as a Cultural Force*, Praeger, New York, 1976, p. 78.
17. See M. Jordan, "Convention and realism," in Dyer (ed.), *Coronation Street*.
18. H. Newcomb, *TV: The Most Popular Art*, Anchor Books, New York, 1974, p. 137.
19. ibid.
20. T. Elsaesser, "Tales of sound and fury," *Monogram*, no. 4, 1972, p. 2.
21. ibid., p. 14.
22. S. Sontag, *Illness as Metaphor*, Vintage Books, New York, 1979.
23. M. B. Cassata *et al.*, "In sickness and in health," *Journal of Communication*, vol. 29, no. 4, autumn 1979, pp. 73–80.
24. Thornburn, "Television melodrama," p. 83.
25. L. Mulvey, "Notes on Sirk and melodrama," *Movie*, no. 25, winter 1978, p. 53.
26. Swanson, "*Dallas*, part 1."
27. See E. Tee, "Dallas: het gezin van de week," *Skrien*, no. 118, May/June 1982.
28. Swanson, "*Dallas*, part 1."
29. L. Mulvey, "Sirk and melodrama," *Australian Journal for Screen Theory*, no. 4, 1978, p. 30.
30. Mulvey, "Notes on Sirk and melodrama," p. 54.

31. ibid.
32. See also J. Feuer, "Melodrama, serial form and television today," *Screen*, vol. 25, no. 1, 1984, p. 11.
33. Mulvey, "Notes on Sirk and melodrama," p. 54.
34. When a soap opera is terminated it is not because the narrative has run out, but mostly for external, commercial or organizational reasons. The narrative must then be turned off in an arbitrary way, which is usually very unsatisfactory for viewers: questions always remain open, narrative lines broken off.
35. Modleski, "The search for tomorrow . . .," p. 12.
36. Barthes, *S/Z*, Hill and Wang, New York, 1974, p. 76.
37. E. Seiter, "Promise and contradiction: the daytime television serials," in *Filmreader* 5, Evanston, 1982, p. 158.
38. Modleski, "The search for tomorrow . . .,"p. 14.
39. M. J. Arlen, "Smooth pebbles at Southfork," in M. J. Arlen (ed.), *The Camera Age*, Farrar, Straus & Giroux, New York, 1981.
40. Johnston, "Crossroads . . .," p. 11.
41. Modleski, "The search for tomorrow . . .," p. 14.
42. H. Newcomb, "Texas: a giant state of mind," *Channels of Communication*, April/May, 1981, p. 41.
43. Newcomb, *TV: The Most Popular Art*, p. 178.
44. Brunsdon, "Crossroads . . .," p. 36. The concepts cultural competence and cultural capital are borrowed from Pierre Bourdieu.
45. P. Brooks, "The melodramatic imagination. The example of Balzac and James," in D. Thornburn and G. Hartman (eds), *Romanticism. Vistas, Instances, Continuities*, Cornell University Press, Ithaca/London, 1973, p. 218. See also P. Brooks, *The Melodramatic Imagination*, Yale University Press, New Haven, 1976.
46. Brooks, "The meldoramatic imagination," p. 219.
47. ibid., p. 211.
48. V. Morin, "The television serial: life in slow motion," in *Il Feuilleton in Televisione*, RAI, Venice, 1977, p. 48.
49. Cf. Brunsdon, "Crossroads . . ."; according to Brunsdon soap opera demand cultural competences which in our culture are mainly possessed by women.
50. But each person acquires so many divergent experiences and impressions that it is impossible to process them all in a theoretically consistent and logical system. On the contrary, the daily consciousness does not concern itself with (rational) logic. Antonio Gramsci pointed this out in his notes on "common sense": A. Gramsci, *Selections from the Prison Notebooks*, Lawrence & Wishart, London, 1973.
51. Barthes, *The Pleasure of the Text*, Hill and Wang, New York, 1975, p. 52.
52. ibid., p. 61.

31

A Reader-Oriented Poetics of the Soap Opera

ROBERT C. ALLEN

The term "encrustation," which I have borrowed from Tony Bennett and others to describe the accretion of meanings around soap operas, needs here to be qualified in order to reflect not only the discursive loading that has occurred in aesthetic and social science discourses but also the concomitant "unloading" of other potential meanings of soap operas. Specifically, soap operas have been denied any status as fictive textual system, even though they are an aesthetic phenomenon of sufficient subtlety and complexity to have successfully engaged the imaginations of millions of readers for over half a century. Content analysis denies the soap opera's textuality by reducing it to quantitative data, while it denies the soap opera's fictive status by assuming that readers regard episodes as they would aspects of the "real world." The critics working within the problematic of traditional aesthetics refuses to engage the soap operas as aesthetic object. Even writers on popular culture who have elevated some categories of television programming to the status of art have found it difficult, if not impossible, to admit soap operas to the new canon—even where it would be logical for them to do so.[1]

In light of the detextualized status of the soap opera in social scientific and aesthetic discourses, it is necessary to reestablish its textuality, even at the risk of overemphasizing formal properties that probably would not be recognized as such by most readers who are not "professional" readers (that is, academics). This retextualizing operation will be a poetic one in that it will seek to give an account of the soap opera as textual

Robert C. Allen, "A Reader-Oriented Poetics of the Soap Opera," from *Speaking of Soap Operas* (Chapel Hill: University of North Carolina Press, 1985).

system in terms of the general laws that govern its production and reception. Where the toal of traditional aesthetics is the evaluation of individual works according to their correspondence to an aesthetic canon, the goal of poetics is the establishment of the normative features of particular types of aesthetic products. Thus our examination of the soap opera as aesthetic object focuses on the distinctive features of the soap opera form in general, rather than on individual episodes. Furthermore, the problem of defining that autonomous, isolated aesthetic object, so important in traditional aesthetics, is for our purposes obviated by a poetics of soap operas. As Todorov notes with regard to literary poetics:

> Each work is therefore regarded only as a manifestation of an abstract and general structure, of which it is but one of the possible realizations. Whereby this science [poetics] is no longer concerned with actual literature but with a possible literature, in other words, with that abstract property that constitutes the singularity of the literary phenomenon: literariness. The goal of this study is no longer to articulate a paraphrase . . . but to propose a theory of the structure and functioning of literary discourse, a theory that affords a list of literary possibilities, so that existing literary works appear as achieved particular cases.[2]

My insistence in this chapter upon the soap opera as a governing set of structural principles by which the reader is able to recognize any specific instance as a soap opera and through which the reader engages with the soap opera as a textual system transcending any specific episode is to some degree a strategic maneuver, a deliverate attempt to force attention upon aspects of the soap opera that have been hidden for so long. More than forty years ago Adorno encountered the refusal of empiricist mass communications research to regard "art as something objective in itself," rather than merely a stimulus, a set of statistically (if not behaviorally) measurable responses, or an "inaccurate" copy of reality. Forty years later the assertion of the distinctive and quantitatively irreducible textuality of the fictive narratives audiences encounter on television is still, unfortunately, necessary. "Critical studies" in American mass media does *not* indicate a concern for the analysis of textual production and reception, but rather points out a general orientation that is "critical" of the dominant empiricist model.[3]

If the elaboration of the soap opera as textual system is to be more than a mere formalist exercise or rhetorical counter to the antitextualism of empiricism, however, it must be tempered by a concern for both the functions the soap opera is designed to serve by the institution that produces it and the manner by which it is engaged by its readers. In recognition of the latter, the poetic operation conducted here will be a reader-oriented one. To Jonathan Culler poetics is inherently concerned not only with texts but with reading strategies as well, since poetics constructs hypotheses regarding the "conditions of meaning" within texts and "hypotheses about the conditions of meaning are claims about the conventions and interpretive operations applied in reading."[4] In bringing to bear upon soap operas a reader-oriented poetics this analysis is not so much applying a single critical model as it is taking into account the insights of a number of critics and theorists who have contributed to a general reorientation of literary studies away from the "work" and the "author" and toward the "text" and its "readers."[5] Thus it will be advancing hypotheses regarding what Wolfgang Iser calls the *verbal* and *affective* dimensions of the soap opera textual system.

Obviously referring to literary, and not televised, texts, *verbal* describes the text's "intersubjectively verifiable instructions for meaning production," or what might be called its formal properties. The verbal aspect guides the reader's response, encouraging certain meanings and eliminating others. As a verbal structure, the text exists as a signifying potentiality, analogous to a peculiarly tuned musical instrument: a range of sound production is possible, but some sounds are easier to produce than others. Not until this verbal structure is engaged by the reader, until its potential is actualized, is meaning constructed. This fulfillment of "that which has been pre-structured by the language of the text" Iser calls its *affective* aspect. The meanings produced by the interaction of the reader and textual structure are neither totally private and arbitrary nor totally determined by the verbal aspect of the text, but are situated somewhere between the two. The text initiates "performances" of meaning, in which both text and reader play crucial roles. The verbal aspects of the text prevent its realization in the mind of the reader from being entirely idiosyncratic; *General Hospital* is not fifteen million different texts because it has that many readers. At the same time, however, the relative indeterminacy of the text's verbal structure produces a range of actualizations, and it is this indeterminacy—the part of meaning production not controlled by the text—that allows us to say that *General Hospital* means different things to different viewers. Thus, understanding how the soap opera signifies and gives aesthetic pleasure requires that we consider both its "verbal" structure—its formal properties—and the mechanisms by which readers of soap operas construct meaning on the basis of those properties.[6]

Visual and Auditory Style

To the content analyst, the visual and auditory articulation of the soap opera's narrative is a transparent and hence insignificant feature. Content analysis presumes not only that events and objects in the soap opera world mean the same as they do in "real life" but also that the viewer experiences them as if they were real. Yet the apparent transparency of soap opera style renders it neither natural nor meaningless. For the viewer there is no preexistent soap opera world that is represented on television; it is only as sound and images on the screen that the world of *General Hospital* or *As the World Turns* is known. Soap opera style represents the crystallization of a set of stylistic conventions taken over from Hollywood filmmaking practive (called by film scholars the classical Hollywood narrative style). While every type of American narrative television has adapted the Hollywood style to some degree, the soap opera has reproduced that style in what is perhaps its most austere form.[7]

The hallmarks of the Hollywood style are economy, transparency, and accessibility. Its overall aim is to produce a seamless, possible world, detached from our own yet governed by a real-world sense of plausibility. It is into this world that we are immersed for the duration of the film. The Hollywood style positions the spectator as the ideal, quasi-omniscient observer of the events in this complete fictional world, or diegesis.

Our interest in this world is secured through the story that unfolds within it. The Hollywood style focuses our attention on the story by hiding the patently artificial means by which the story is related and its world constructed on the screen. Every element of style functions in the Hollywood cinema not for its own sake but as part of this reciprocal process of perfecting the illusion of the "reality" of the narrative world while simultaneously disguising the techniques of illusion making.

The Hollywood style can be expressed as a set of rules governing every category of cinema style—rules derived not only inductively, through their observation in individual films, but deductively from normative precepts laid down since the 1920s in various manuals, guidebooks, and periodicals in which the "pros" related the techniques of "good" (read, "Hollywood") filmmaking practice. For example, one basic difference between the narrative diegesis as constructed in film and that in literature is that a filmic narrative possesses an explicit spatial dimension, while the "space" of a literary narrative is purely imaginary. Hence a number of rules prescribe how space should be used in Hollywood films. Space functions primarily to contain narratively significant elements; the greater the narrative significance of the element, the greater the space it occupies on the screen and the less "other" space there is to look at. In the shot construction of a typical scene in a Hollywood film the amount of space represented on the screen diminishes rapidly from shot to shot, while the relative scale of objects depicted increases proportionally. In a dialogue scene set in an Empire State Building office, the first shot (the establishing shot) might well be the exterior of the building. The second shot (the master shot) is likely to be the office in which the dialogue is to take place, with both characters shown in the same shot. As the dialogue begins, we can expect alternating close-ups of each as he or she delivers lines, varied occasionally, perhaps, by a reaction shot. By the time we have reached the narratively significant dialogue in the scene, the only space represented is that of each character's head and torso. Our attention might be even further directed toward this space by rendering out-of-focus what little background space is contained in the shot. Certainly, not every Hollywood scene is constructed in this way, but the above description does represent a paradigm of normative spatial representation and object scale in Hollywood films and dramatic television. The effect of this paradigm is to focus the attention of the viewer on that information necessary to propel the narrative forward, even if in the process it depicts space in a manner entirely different from how we perceive it in "real life."

In the soap opera the conventions of diminishing space and increasing scale are maintained, but operate within a greatly compressed range. The production situation of the soap opera (studio television) and the economics of soap opera production (the need to turn out the equivalent of several feature films each week as cheaply as possible) greatly restrict the spaces represented. It is a commonplace to refer to the soap opera as a world of interiors. Although *Ryan's Hope* is set in Manhattan and *Capitol* in Washington, the only views we regularly get of these cities occur in the title sequences. The development of portable broadcast-quality video recording equipment in the 1970s enabled soap operas to "open up" their interior worlds, but the locations to which audiences have been taken in these "remotes" have been exotic rather than domestic, carefully bracketed and segregated from the depiction of ordinary space in Port Charles or Henderson. So long as exterior space is kept offscreen, the spatial worlds of soap operas can be represented as an aggregate of atomistic interiors whose relationship to each other in space is constructed in the mind of the viewer. To "open up" these domestic worlds, however, would necessitate the creation of explicit geographic connections and, hence, spatial congruities. The British soap opera *Coronation Street* has solved this problem by constructing a standing exterior set of the one-block section of the street on which all of the regular characters live—a solution more feasible in the depiction of a British working-class neighborhood than of an automobile-dependent, middle-class American suburb. In American soaps establishing shots of exterior locales are frequently eliminated and their function collapsed with that of the master shot. Thus the world of the soap opera is represented spatially through the close-up and the two-shot, a strategy that has the effect of focusing viewer attention almost exclusively on facial expression and figure relationships, respectively.

Editing is potentially the most disruptive of all cinematic elements. Each cut breaks spatial and temporal continuity and threatens to evoke the difference between cinematic convention and "real-life" perception, thus distracting the viewer from the narrative. For this reason, Hollywood editing conventions constitute an elaborate regulatory system, whose aim is to produce "invisible" editing. Changes in camera location are disguised by cutting on action. Screen direction and background are kept constant through the 180-degree rule (two successive shots of the same action must be from camera positions less than 180 degrees apart). Eyeline-matches link one character's offscreen glance with the object of that glance and both with the gaze of the viewer.

Editing in soap operas is, if anything, more "invisible" than in the typical Hollywood production. In Hollywood films and in prime-time dramatic television programs shot on film, the continuous space and time of a scene is an illusion constructed in the editing room. The entire scene is acted out in master-shot, then in a two-shot, then in individual close-ups, and so forth, so that the appearance of continuity must be reconstituted by the editor. Broadcast live until the mid-1960s, soap operas are now recorded "live tape," meaning that while scenes might be recorded out of their eventual sequence in the episode, each scene is enacted and recorded on video tape only once. Editing is done at the time of recording, by switching between the shots being simultaneously taken by three television cameras. Thus, unless something goes wrong (an actor flubs a line, for example) the time of enactment is the same as that of presentation, its continuity represented rather than reconstructed.

Another important function of Hollywood editing is to indicate changes in point of view. Most of the time in Hollywood films the viewer is an unseen, nonparticipating observer of the action in the diegesis, the camera acting as the viewer's eye. Occasionally, however, point of view will switch to that of a character in the diegesis, and, while in this "subjective" mode, the viewer's vision and that of the character are synonymous. Obviously, it is essential that third- and first-person perspectives are clearly differentiated, so that our visual relationship vis-a-vis the narrative is not called into question. A Hollywood editing convention called glance/object editing brackets subjective point of view, visually announcing the restriction of "our" sight to that of a single character and then reassuring us with an unambiguous return to a more omniscient vantage point. Glance/object editing involves a three-shot strategy. In shot 1 we see a close-up of a character looking into offscreen space. Shot 2 shows us the object of that glance as the character would see it. In shot 3 third-person point of view is restored with a close-up of the character. The subjective shot is sandwiched between two major objective shots, leaving no doubt as to whose eyes we are looking through and when that visual doubling ceases.

Because the glance/object editing strategy requires the instrusion of the camera into the diegetic space of the scene, its use is even more severely restricted in soap operas than in Hollywood films. The alternation between objective and subjective vision in such "mainstream" Hollywood films as *Psycho, Notorious*, and *Stagecoach* is extremely rare in soap operas. Subjectivity is more frequently achieved auditorially through interior monologue. We might "hear" the character's inner speech, but we see the facial expression of that character from our omniscient and undisclosed point of view. Visual subjectivity is reserved in soap operas for prolepses (flashbacks), but even there what we see from a character's memory is almost always rendered in third person, so that we see the character in his or her own recollection. The more complete bracketing of subjectivity from normative representation in soap operas endows its use with all the more significance. Because we so seldom experience the world of the soap through the eyes of a character in that world, subjective vision endows both the subject and the object of that vision (the character and what he or she sees) with special meaning.

The soap opera's distillation of Hollywood style is also apparent in camera movement. Although not as potentially distracting as editing (since spatial and temporal continuity are preserved), camera movement can call attention to the means of cinematic representation and away from the diegesis. Hence camera movements in Hollywood films are usually "motivated" by figure movement within the shot. Two characters are depicted walking down the street talking to each other, and the camera tracks along in front of them to enable us to see their faces in frame. Their movement hides the fact of "our" movement. Hollywood films are full of examples of elaborate unmotivated camera movements, however: the opening shots of *Scarface* and *Touch of Evil*, the between-the-legs tracking shot in *42nd Street*, swooping crane shots in several Hitchcock films, among many others. All but the most acrobatic of them go relatively unnoticed by the viewer, however. Camera movement as such is probably more prominent in soap operas than in Hollywood films (a convention of "live" television practice carried over into "live-tape"), but it is very seldom unmotivated. Shots are "reframed" to allow for figure movement; pans tie one acting area to another. In soap operas, though, the unmotivated camera movement, like the subjective point of view shot, is meaningful because of its marginalization within normative practice. Its rarity immediately privileges the "content" of the shot: an unmotivated camera movement usually signifies "something important and unusual is about to happen."

The auditory component of Hollywood style assures that sounds will be limited to those that are narratively significant—again, even if this means violating laws of physics. For example, the establishing shot of a dialogue scene set in Times Square might contain a high level of ambient noise. by the time the dialogue has begun in two-shot or close-up, however, that ambient noise level has dropped to an almost inaudible level in order that the narratively significant dialogue can be heard. The soap opera's infrequent use of location shooting obviates the problem of unwanted diegetic noise, while its studio production situation assures that all dialogue will be clearly heard. As in the movies, the soap opera's nondiegetic musical score supports the narrative: smoothing transitions, covering ellipses, and helping to reduce indeterminacy in a particular scene by encouraging one reading over another. The serial nature of soap operas, however, enables music to function differently from Hollywood scores in two respects. Music can be used an an auditory signature, announcing each episode of a soap—a convention widely used in other types of television programming and dating back to the early days of radio. Also a piece of music can be associated with a particular character or relationship (sometimes called "theme" music). This is common enough in movie scores, but the serial nature of soap operas enables a "theme" to be woven through many episodes over a period of weeks or months, musically linking a given scene to its paradigm.

In most other respects soap opera style can be seen as a continuation, if not condensation, of Hollywood stylistic practice, in which elements of style function in support of diegetic illusion. Objects exist as aspects of decor or as props. Settings are utilitarian. Hollywood lighting is subtly nuanced compared with the necessarily flat television lighting style of most soap operas.[8]

Soap Opera Narrative Structure

One frequently hears that soap operas are constructed not to be watched but to be listened to. This is another way of saying that the "zero-degree" visual style of soap operas carries no meaning, that dialogue is all. It is also said, usually by those trying to watch soap operas for the first time, that the elongation of plot lines over months, if not years, renders any given episode virtually static in narrative terms. Why, they ask, would anyone want to watch a soap opera five days each week when watching one episode per month is sufficient to "keep up with the story"? If one regards what Barthes calls the hermeneutic code—the causal chain of events that eventually leads to the "end" of the story—as the sole source of appeal for soap opera viewers, then it is difficult to explain why anyone would want to watch or even listen to soap operas more than once each month.

One of the fundamental insights of structural linguistics is that language and narrative are structured along two axes: a syntagmatic (combinatory) axis and a paradigmatic (associative) axis. As noted previously, one of the distinctive syntagmatic features of the soap opera is its absence of ultimate narrative closure; it is, in fact, one of the few narrative forms predicated upon the impossibility of closure. More will be said about the consequences of the syntagmatic openness of the soap opera shortly. But what is frequently overlooked in discussions of the soap opera is its paradigmatic complexity—a complexity that makes the soap opera unique among visual narratives and unmatched in literary narrative except for the most elaborate of epic novels.[9]

PARADIGMATIC STRUCTURE

The source of the soap opera's paradigmatic complexity is its large community of interrelated characters. The Hollywood film or traditional novel is structured around a limited number of characters, a few of whom are marked more specifically as protagonists or antagonists. The events of the narrative "happen" to them, and the fates of minor characters hinge on that of the heroes and heroines. Soap opera narratives, on the other hand, contain upwards of forty regularly appearing characters, and while some are more prominent than others at any given time, none can be singled out as the motor of the narrative. A great deal might happen to individual characters—multiple marriages, pregnancy, amnesia, temporary blindness, disabling accidents, and so forth—but very little happens to alter the nature of the community. The soap opera community is a self-perpetuating, self-preserving system little affected by the turbulence experienced by its individual members or the fate of any one character. The naive viewer might attend only to the constant state of crisis experienced by individual characters, but the experienced viewer is watchful for the paradigmatic strands that bind the community of characters together and the sometimes glacially slow but far more significant alterations in this network. "Who a character is" is as much a function of his or her place in this paradigmatic system as what he or she "does" in a syntagmatic sense.

It is only by reference to the paradigmatic complexity of the soap opera that some of its most distinctive narrative features can be explained. Consider, for example, the high degree of redundancy in soap operas. What we might call interepisodic redundancy—the reiteration on Tuesday of plot developments from Monday—is to a large degree explicable as a device to keep nondaily viewers "up" on narrative developments. Such redundancy is also a function of the fact that soap operas must negotiate a narrow path between moving the story along too quickly, and thus "using it up" too soon, and stretching subplots out for longer than the audience will tolerate. But soap operas also contain a great deal of intraepisodic redundancy: the repetition of information from character to character within each daily episode. Unless we presume that soap writers and producers feel required to refresh the memories of the viewers every ten minutes, intraepisodic redundancy cannot be explained as a syntagmatic device. As an illustration of intraepisodic redundancy, let us presume that in scene one of a soap episode we learn from a conversation between Lucy and her friend Debbie that Lucy is pregnant with Rick's child. In scene three, Debbie tells her husband Chris of Lucy's pregnancy. In scene five, Chris warns his friend Billy against becoming too involved with Lucy.

Such references to Lucy's pregnancy might continue for days or weeks without anything "happening" to move this subplot closer to resolution. The same information—Lucy is pregnant with Rick's child—is passed along from character to character to character. In terms of the syntagmatic, or story, dimension of the soap, such exchanges *are* redundant, since the audience already knows that Lucy is pregnant and Rick is the father, and since such redundant dialogue scenes do not move the story forward at all. Paradigmatically, however, such exchanges are far from redundant. The experienced reader of the soap is able to read these exchanges as invokings of the paradigmatic network. It makes a difference that Lucy chose to confide in Debbie about her plight because Debbie was once married to Rick. Debbie's telling Chris of Lucy's revelation is read against the background of Debbie's inability to conceive a child and Chris's recurrent infidelity, and so forth. Reduced to its syntagmatic axis, the soap opera becomes an endless string of excruciatingly retarded subplots, related in episodes whose redundancy gives them an almost Sisyphean tiresomeness. To the experienced reader, however, soap operas' distinctive networks of character relationships open up major sources of signifying potential that are simply unreadable to the naive reader.

Thus our previous discussion of soap opera's adaptation of the classical Hollywood narrative style and its narrative function needs to be qualified in light of the soap opera's paradigmatic complexity. Obviously, one function of the close-up soap operas is to concentrate our attention on dialogue and the narrative information contained therein. In addition, the style of the soap opera, built on close-ups and two-shots, functions paradigmatically to a degree quite unnecessary in Hollywood films. A pause, gesture, glance, or facial expression rendered in close-up may be syntagmatically insignificant but laden with potential paradigmatic meaning. To give but one example, in August 1981 Kelly and Morgan, two young characters on *Guilding Light*, were married. Nearly one entire episode was devoted to the wedding ceremony, which was attended by most of the show's regular characters. Throughout the wedding scene shots of the nuptial couple were intercut with close-ups of various wedding guests. Some of those characters given close-ups during the scene had played little or no part in the Kelly-Morgan subplot that had brought about their marraige. Nor was there any indication that a character's being singled out in a close-up functioned to anticipate his or her subsequent involvement in the Kelly-Morgan "story." How then was the viewer to read the relationship between shots of the wedding ceremony and close-ups of various other characters? To the naive viewer these characters were simply "there"—at the ceremony—but the experienced viewer knew that what tied these characters to Kelly and Morgan was their own relationship, past or present, to the institution of marriage. Without a single word of dialogue to indicate it, this particular plot event was plugged into *Guiding Light*'s extensive paradigmatic system. To be sure, this strategy at the "verbal" level may or may not have been "affectively" engaged by an individual viewer. The scene still had meaning even to the most naive viewer at the syntagmatic level. Still, to the competent reader, listening to this scene would hardly have been the same experience as viewing it, and in this case the function of the close-up was to stimulate a very different kind of narrative response from that usually evoked by the close-up in Hollywood films.

The complexity of the network of character relationships in soap operas derives in large part from the fact that, unlike characters in prime-time series, soap opera characters have both histories and memories. Thus the soap opera's paradigmatic system possesses both synchronic and diachronic dimensions. Certainly, character relationships change during the course of other types of narratives as well. Paul's relationship with his mother at the end of *Sons and Lovers* is read against the background of that relationship's history as it has evolved to that point in the book. The text might initiate this movement back across portions of the text already read by a reference to an earlier event, but it cannot specify what will be recalled. The text provides the reference, but the reader provides the context in which the recalled event is embedded. In soap operas, this reservoir of relational possibilities is more extensive than in any other narrative form. A viewer may read current relationships against the background of their status a year ago, five years ago, or, in some cases, more than thirty years ago. And unlike *Sons and Lovers*, that thirty-year period is not just text time but reading time as well, since it has literally taken thirty years for the viewer to "read" the text of *Guiding Light* up to that point.

The diachronic "depth" of the paradigmatic structure of the soap opera suggests another fundamental difference between it and other forms of narrative. Summarizing recent research of the temporality of fiction, Shlomith Rimmon-Kenan (following Genette) discusses two types of duration: story duration (the days, months, years depicted in the narrative) and text duration (the "amount" of text devoted to the relating of various "pieces" of story time). She aludes to a third kind of duration against which the first two might be measured—the actual time it takes to read the text—but this "reading duration" is not taken up because it "varies from reader to reader, providing no objective standard."[10] (This is, of course, a key difference between the experience of reading a novel and that of watching a film. The temporal dimension of the cinema or television is specific; running time is the same as reading time.)

Reader-response theorists have only begun to explore the concept of reading duration except to note that we can never perceive a narrative text "all at once," except when we are no longer reading it, and then the events depicted in the first chapter (or reel) are separated from us by the time it took to get from there to the end of the story. But whether reading duration is approximate, as in the case of the novel, or exact, as in the case of a film, it is presumed to occur at one historical moment. Iser points out that our understanding of the text changes as we "travel" along from beginning to end during the reading process, because the horizon constituted by our knowledge of the text to that point changes and with it the relationship between any particular narrative event and the rest of the text.[11]

The soap opera raises the possibility, unanticipated by Iser, that the reader's own extratextual horizons might change during the course of reading a narrative text. Our memory of the death of Joanne Tate's first husband in *Search for Tomorrow* is of a previous point in the text, but it can also be a memory of ourselves as readers of that text some twenty years ago. And, to make matters even more complex, in this case it is also a memory of the actress as she portrayed the same character twenty years before—Mary Stuart has been playing the role of Joanne Tate since *Search for Tomorrow* began in 1951. The context of a recalled portion of a soap opera text is twofold: the "verbal" context within the text and the affective context of the reader's initial encounter with that textual segment. The relationship of a reader to a soap opera text is in the truest sense of the term a diachronic one, in which not only does the text change with each daily episode but the reader and his or her world changes *while* the reading act occurs. We often divide literature, television shows, and films into genres on the basis of their appeal to readers of particular age groups—as in "children's literature," the "teen novel," "children's programming." With the soap opera, we have a text that might have been begun by a reader in adolescence, but which, thirty years later, is still being read *by the same reader,* who is now a mother of adolescent children. This does not make the soap opera different in kind from other narratives, but it does mean that what can be assumed away in the case of the novel or the film must be regarded as an important constituent element of the soap opera.

We have already noted the complexity of the relationship between the soap opera and its "real-life" social context. At this point we might notice that, to some extent, the paradigmatic dimension of the soap opera text helps to explain what many have seen as the peculiar social structure of its diegetic world. As content analysts have pointed out, the number of middle-class "professional" people (both men and women) is disproportionately high compared to their distribution in American society. One study found that over half the adult males in soap operas are doctors. Not surprisingly, the workplaces depicted in soap operas are those associated with middle-class occupations and leisure: hospitals, doctors' offices, law firms, corporate headquarters, restaurants, bars, and nightclubs. Because of the importance of interpersonal relationships in soaps, the workplaces depicted in them must allow for frequent contacts with other characters and opportunities to discuss matters not directly related to work—specifically to invoke the paradigmatic network of character relationships that binds any single event in the text to the community at large. This helps to explain the preference for hospital nursing stations, waiting rooms, executive suites, and nightclubs as regular settings for interaction between soap opera characters. Soap operas are, in a sense, "about" talk, and in the working world of the soap opera the opportunity to talk is associated with middle-class occupations.

The paradigmatic function of the middle-class work environment of the soap opera is itself an effect of larger, essentially ideological forces. The compression of social reality in the soap opera into a middle-class universe facilitates a suppression of material concerns in general. The economic exchanges that are so much a part of the lives of its viewers have little or no part in the soap opera world. Money seldom changes hands as a part of everyday life in the soap opera world; the cost of products is almost never mentioned; the businesses for which soap opera characters work (or, more likely, which they own) seldom actually produce goods; characters almost never worry whether there will be enough money at the end of the month to pay bills.

Similarly, soap operas' emphasis on paradigmatic structure is not unrelated to their notorious exclusion of minority-group characters. Despite the inclusion of black families in some soaps, the world of the soap opera is overwhelmingly white. The problem of including blacks and other racial groups in soaps is one not of working them into plot lines but of dealing with the paradigmatic consequences of their entry into the community of the soap opera world. There are three major types of relationships between soap opera characters: kinship, romantic, and social. Much of the appeal of soap operas resides in the complexity and overlap among these categories of actual and potential relationships for any particular character. Mistaken parentage has been a stock device in soap operas for decades. On *Guiding Light* the revelation that Quintin McCord was actually the son of Henry Chamberlain reverberated throughout the entire network of character relationships: Vanessa Chamberlain, for example, was transformed from a potential romantic partner to Quintin's half-sister. Enemies can become brothers; sisters, merely close friends; fathers, foster-fathers; and so on—all at the drop of a discovered birth certificate.

Unless a particular soap were to embrace interracial romance, marriage, and parentage as a community norm, the admission of a nonwhite character into full membership in the soap community would be impossible, since two of the three relational modes would be all but closed to him or her. Some soaps have teased audiences with actual or potential interracial romances—in one case effecting an interracial marriage only to dissolve it before consummation—but in all soaps black characters are relegated to a paradigmatic ghetto, always marked by their relational impoverishment. Once again, the paradigmatic dilemma as regards race in soap operas is itself an effect of external forces—specifically the producers' desire not to "upset" large numbers of their target audience (white women) by extending the normative boundaries of the soap opera world too far.

SYNTAGMATIC STRUCTURE

The soap opera trades an investment in an ultimate narrative telos—the most characteristic feature of traditional narratives—for a series of overlapping "mini-closures," which resolve a particular narrative question but are in no way read as moving the overall story toward its eventual end. This absolute resistance to final closure is illustrated by the termination of *Love of Life,* one of the first successful television soaps, which was canceled by CBS in 1981. Even as the show drew toward its final episodes, there was no attempt to impose an overall ending; *Love of Life* did not so much end as it expired definately in medias res. Given the decentered nature of soap opera narrative and its diffusion through a network of interrelated characters, any attempt to pull all the paradigmatic strands together in some sort of synthetic grand finale, à la Wilkie Collins, would have smacked of the most transparent sort of deus ex machina.

Although I doubt that either Iser or Jauss anticipated its application to soap operas, reader-response theory does provide a means of positioning the reader and the reading process relative to the syntagmatic openness of the soap opera form. Drawing on Husserl, Iser contends that each sentence in a literary narrative can be said to contain a "retrospective section," which answers the expectations aroused by previous sentences, and a "hollow section," which creates new expectation to be confirmed, modified, or frustrated in subsequent sentences. At any given moment, the reader's relationship to the text constitutes a "wandering viewpoint," an intersection between protension (expectation) and retention (retrospection). Each sentence prefigures a horizon of expectations, which, as it is read, immediately becomes the background for the next sentence, over and over again in a syntagmatic chain of questions and answers, which are themselves new questions. As the reader encounters more and more pieces of text, those already read retreat further into the background. But the retained significance of that background is constantly being restructured in light of new text. "That which is remembered becomes open to new connections, and these in turn influence the expectations aroused by the individual correlates in the sequence of sentences." The wandering viewpoint of the reader of a fictional narrative—his or her participation in the dialectic of protension and retention, determination and expectation—positions the reader not outside the aesthetic object contemplating it but at a constantly changing point somewhere within the text constructing it.

> There is no escaping this process, for—as has already been pointed out—the text cannot at any one moment be grasped as a whole. But what may at first sight have seemed like a disadvantage, in comparison with our normal modes of perception, may now be seen to offer distinct advantages, in so far as it permits a process through which the aesthetic object is constantly being structured and restructured. As there is no definite frame of reference to regulate this process, successful communication must ultimately depend on the reader's creative activity.[12]

In the case of the soap opera, then, we have a text that not only is ungraspable as a whole at any one moment but is also a "whole" only by reference to a given moment. The traditional narrative privileges a reading position just "on the other side of" the text: the moment of teleological insight toward which all protensions have been directed and in light of which all ambiguities are retrospectively dissolved. The classic example is the closed-room murder mystery with its stock revelation scene, beyond which there is in a very real sense nothing left to be said. The soap opera privileges that ever-changing moment when the reader comes to the text once again. The "text" of *Guiding Light* comprises all the episodes ever broadcast since 1937—a text probably no one has ever "read" in its entirety and which today one could not reread, even if one had the months to devote to the task—but it is a text the last page of which is never the final page. The final page never comes, nor does the reader read on in anticipation of its coming. If, with Juri Lotman, we can characterize a literary text as acting like "a sort of living organism, which is linked to the reader, and also instructs him by means of a feedback system," then we can characterize the soap opera as functioning not only like a living organism but one which grows by regular increments to enormous proportions.[13] The syntagmatic openness of the soap opera creates a higher degree of what we might call protensive indeterminacy than is the case in many other types of narrative, particularly where the fate of individual characters is concerned. In the traditional narrative, the hero or heroine functions with respect to the narrative's point of closure; thus, our expectations of what will happen to that character are governed by that relationship. We do not expect Hercule Poirot to be the victim of the murderer it is his "job" (in both an occupational and narrative sense) to unmask. Certainly our expectations in this regard can be violated: the murder of the heroine of *Psycho* in the first reel has all the more shock value because we do not expect *her* to be killed. But because our perspective on the world of the traditional narrative is usually tied to that of one or two central characters, we expect, at the very least, that they will survive as long as the story itself does.

Protensive indeterminacy is perhaps most limited in the prime-time television series format. Our expectations of what will happen to Lucy Ricardo or Kojak during the course of any given episode are rigidly bound by our knowledge that that character will return next week totally unaffected by whatever happened this week. In the soap opera, however, because our wandering viewpoint "wanders" not only syntagmatically but paradigmatically as well (from character to character to character) there are no such limits to what can "happen" to a given character and thus none to our expecations. Soap operas regularly kill off even the most central of characters: Adam Drake on *Edge of Night*, Nancy Hughes on *As the World Turns*, among others. Nor does apparent death necessarily mark absolute determinacy where a particular character is concerned: characters can die or they can *die*. On *Edge of Night* several years ago, Nicole Drake disappeared after a boating mishap in the Caribbean, only to be discovered alive and well in Paris more than two years (reader time) later. Bill Bauer has now "died" three times on *Guiding Light*, and on the same show Roger Thorpe was resurrected twice before given his "final" (?) death. A soap character can also be kept in a sort of protensive limbo—a potential but not active character. On *As the World Turns*, Penny has been absent from the world of Oakdale for more than a decade, but she is kept "alive" by having her call home occasionally, usually on a holiday. Similarly, the character of Laura Spencer on *General Hospital* disappeared into one of the most famous of soap opera limbos when the actress who plays her, Genie Francis, signed a contract with another television network. Is she dead? Will she return? Tune in next week.

The syntagmatic movement of the reader's wandering viewpoint along the forward frontiers of the text is not that of the driver of a sportscar down a superhighway but rather that of the uncertain tourist provided with a rather sketchy map, who frequently stops to look back where he or she has been, occasionally takes a side road, and constantly tries to glimpse what lies around the next bend. The textual space the reader traverses in this process is not that of the superhighway but rather the rural backlanes, where the pavement suddenly stops and then starts back again, where the journey forward is halting rather than continuous. It is precisely at these places where the textual "pavement" is broken that the readers's active involvement in the text is most clearly seen. What the text leaves unsaid is, nevertheless, made to signify within the imagination of the reader.

The reader inserts himself or herself into the text through these necessary gaps, filling them in part—but only in part—according to his or her own frames of reference. The structuring gaps of the text, then, mark the point of intersection between the horizon represented within the text and the horizon brought to the text by the reader. Put another way, there the "reality" of the reader confronts the pseudoreality of the fictive text. But just as the text does not merely take over "real-life" conventions in the construction of its world, the reader cannot simply impose his or her referential system upon the text. The process of "gap filling" is regulated by the text itself.

Syntagmatic gaps are constituent parts of any communication. The spaces between words mark necessary textual potholes to be negotiated by the reader/listener. In the literary text, structuring gaps occur at all syntagmatic levels (between words, sentences, paragraphs, scenes, chapters), and the "size" of these gaps range correspondingly from the seemingly insignificant and, to the reader, unnoticed to those which require a considerable and conscious "filling-in" process.

The role of gaps in the construction of textual meaning is most clearly seen where those gaps are large and regular features of a text, and where they are imposed upon the reader and controlled by the text. In the serial novels of Dickens or Collins, for example, textual segments were separated not only spatially (a partially blank page marking the gap between the end of one chapter and the beginning of the next) but temporally as well: the reader could not "jump over" the gap until the next serial installment was published. The serial story results in a special relationship between reader and text, one in which, in Iser's words, "the reader is forced by the pauses imposed upon him to imagine more than he could if his reading were continuous." The narrative anticipation that causes us frantically to flip from the last page of one chapter to the first of a new one was, in the serialized novel, attenuated, as New Yorkers anxiously and eagerly awaited the arrival of the ship from London carrying the episode of *The Old Curiosity Shop* in which Little Nell succumbs. Iser points out that readers in the nineteenth century found serialized novels read in installments more enjoyable than the same text published as a whole. He attributes this curious fact to a sort of *narrativus interruptus:* the strategic suspension of the text at crucial narrative nodes. "the result is that we try to imagine how the story will unfold, and in this way we heighten our own participation in the course of events."[14]

Syntagmatic gaps play an even more important structuring role in the soap opera. Each episode of a soap opera is, of course, separated from the next by a twenty-four-hour "gap" during the week and an even longer one over the weekend. Soap opera writers take advantage of this hiatus in reading activity by leaving a major narrative question unanswered at the end of each episode, saving the greatest narrative indeterminacy for the end of Friday's episode. The anticipation thus provoked produces in some soap opera readers the modern-day equivalent of Dicken's American readers greeting the packet at the dock: when Pope John Paul II was wounded in an assassination attempt in May 1981 the Associated Press reported that a St. Louis television station received three hundred calls from irate soap opera fans protesting the preemption of regular afternoon programming in favor of press coverage of events in Rome.

Within each episode the syntagmatic structure of the soap opera is regulated by the gaps inserted in the text at regular intervals to allow for commercial messages. Unlike the gaps between chapters of a novel, however, the commercial gaps of a soap opera are of a specific temporal duration beyond the control of the reader and, moreover, are "filled" with another textual system, that of the commercial advertisement itself. Sandy Flitterman has suggested that one function of some soap opera ads is to provide a text with a tight and closed narrative structure to offset the effects upon the reader of the soap opera's resistance to such closure. The ultimate answer to the question posed in the soap opera text just before the commercial might be weeks or months in coming (if it ever does), but the reader can take comfort in the knowledge that the mini-narrative launched by "ring-around-the-collar" will be satisfactorily resolved before the indeterminacy of the soap opera text is resumed.[15] One disadvantage of the closed structure of a narrative advertisement for sponsors is that once a commercial is "told," it loses much of its narrative appeal; the sixteenth retelling of the *Wisk* story ends exactly like the first. Thus the repetition of ads leaves plenty of room in the commercial gap for soap opera readers to fill it with retensive and protensive ruminations about the soap opera text. In a literary narrative, opportunities for such ruminations can be created by the reader just by lifting the eyes from the page for a moment or pausing at the end of one line before beginning the next. The viewer of a film or television program has no such "gap-creating" power. One can look away from the screen, but the text continues.

Within these gaps the viewpoint of the reader is free to wander both syntagmatically and paradigmatically. Previously related portions of a subplot can be reviewed in light of more recent events and expectations formed as to future developments. To a degree subsequent textual segments of a given subplot carry the reader across the gaps between them, guiding his or her viewpoint toward the subplot's eventual, if only partial, resolution. Much less guidance is provided by the text in relating an event from one subplot to one in another. Given the paradigmatic complexity of the soap opera, however, there are always many virtual relationships to be actualized by the viewer if he or she chooses to do so. The mere syntagmatic juxtaposition of two apparently unrelated scenes represents a paradigmatic indterminacy for the reader: could the relationship between them be more than sequential? The text is frequently silent in this regard, but sometimes it encourages the construction of specific relationships between scenes or entire subplots. An example is provided by the 1981 *Guiding Light* Kelly-Morgan subplot. The 18 August 1981 episode is devoted largely to informing various members of the community of their wedding plans. Scattered among these scenes, however, are scenes of another couple's wedding plans, to which those of Kelly and Morgan are implicitly contrasted. The Kelly-Morgan marriage represents the fulfillment of young love, initially thwarted by another's deceit. Noela, who regarded Kelly as a ticket out of her drab working-class existence, tried to trick him into marrying her by making him believe he had fathered her child one night when he was drunk. When the ruse is discovered, Noela settles for marrying Floyd, a hospital janitor, with whom she had been carrying on a secret liaison for months and who is the real father of her baby. The two weddings are related oppositionally throughout the episode, principally through alternating scenes depicting the reactions of other members of the *Guiding Light* community to each of them. The news of the Kelly-Morgan wedding occasions unmitigated joy; that of Noela and Floyd's elicits shock, anger, or indifference.

The textual role of the commercial "gap" brings to light another key difference in reading situation between commercial television and literature or film—a difference particularly pronounced in the soap opera. In both literature and cinema the relationship between reader and text is essentially a private one. Unless the text is read aloud, the reader of a novel does not immediately share the reading experience with anyone else, even if the reading act occurs in a public place. Public viewings of films are made into private reading situations by shrouding the reader in darkness. Television, however, allows for public *or* private viewing, public *or* private reading. Soap opera audience research indicates that some audience groups—most notably college students—prefer to watch soaps with other viewers, thus making a public viewing situation in a dorm lounge or union television room into a social reading act.

Interpretation of a particular textual segment may be "assisted" by vocalized responses. Commercial "gaps" provide additional opportunities for the development of an interreader social discourse. More competent readers can acquaint new viewers with portions of the text the latter might not have seen. A reader's private interpretation of an action, scene, or line of dialogue can be compared to that of other readers, with the result that new expectations are formed and new paradigmatic relationships actualized. Ironically, the subjects of many soap opera commercial messages—laundry products, diapers, household cleaners—encourage the use of commercial gaps for social soap opera reading among college-age viewers, since these products are largely irrelevant to their life-styles.

The Soap Opera Text: Closed or Open?

Semiotician Umberto Eco distinguishes between "open" and "closed" narrative texts. Closed texts, says Eco, "apparently aim at pulling the reader along a predetermined path, carefully displaying their effects so as to arouse pity or fear, excitement or depression at the due place and at the right moment. Every step of the 'story' elicits just the expectation that its further course will satisfy. They seem to be structured according to an inflexible project." The open text, on the other hand, has built into it multiple levels of interpretation. Whereas the closed text is a sraightforward, linear pathway of stimulus and anticipated response, the open text is a "structured maze" of possible readings. The closed work offers an extremely limited set of interpretive possibilities, but the very narrowness of the text's interpretive pathway means that readers for whom the text was not intended or who are oriented toward the text by assumptions other than those of its author frequently stray from its "path" and produce aberrant readings. In the open work, while the possibility of pluri-signification is built in, so is the notion of the Model Reader—the reader with sufficient knowledge of the codes at work in the text to be able to read it competently. The open work is not open to any interpretation, for the reader, says Eco, is "strictly defined by the lexical and syntaxical organization of the text." So while the possibility of aberrant interpretations of the closed text remains always open, the multiple interpretations of the open text have been foreseen by the author and are hence to some extent closed off. To Eco, the novels of Joyce and Woolf are "open," while those of Ian Fleming and Harold Robbins are "closed."[16]

Ellen Seiter uses Eco's open/closed dichotomy as the basis for a feminist reading of soap operas. Accepting Eco's inclusion of the soap opera in the catgory of closed texts, she suggests "possible ways that women can read soap operas subversively—ways which do not exclude or negate the widespread negative interpretation of soap opera viewing as escapist fantasy for women working in the home."[17] Seiter's suggestive critique once again raises the issue of the relationship between aesthetic structure and social effect—an issue to which we shall return later in this chapter and in later chapters, particularly as regards historical changes in the soap opera's textual structure. Of immediate interest to us here is the closed text model of the soap opera upon which this bifurcation of preferred versus subversive readings is based.

While it is certainly possible for women (and others) to construct reading of soap operas "against the grain," the limiting of "allowable" readings to a unitary decoding, anticipated by the text and its authors, overlooks the television soap opera's signifying complexity. Eco's notion of the closed text presumes its orientation toward narrative closure: the interpretive pathway constructed by the author for the reader leads in a straightforward manner to "the end." Each reduction of indeterminacy brings with it a corresponding reduction of "allowable" interpretive possibilities. As we have seen, though, the soap opera is not governed by an ultimate telos, and, hence, protensive possibilities always outrun plot resolutions. Furthermore, the elaborate network of character relationships in the soap opera builds in the very pluri-significative possibilities Eco reserves for the open text. The complex paradigmatic structure of the soap opera outlines its Model Reader "as a component of its structural strategy," even though this is a term Eco reserves for open works. It is just that the Model Reader of *Guiding Light* is more likely to be a working-class woman than a male literary critic.

The reading competencies Eco speaks of with regard to the Model Reader of *Ulysses* or, we might suppose, his own novel, *The Name of the Rose*, involve three types of codes: textual, lexical, and intertextual. The more adept the reader is at the operation of these codes, the better he or she is able to negotiate the "structural maze" of the open text. Obviously, the lexically impoverished high-school student finds many passages of *Ulysses* unintelligible. Understanding that novel also requires the reader to "decode" certain textual strategies—shifts in narrational perspective, for example. And the Model Reader will be able to "plug into" the many intertextual codes employed in *Ulysses:* Irish history and legend, Catholic liturgy, Greek myth, other literary and nonliterary genres, and so forth.

The aim here is not to elevate the soap opera to the status of the elite artwork—the place, intentionally or not, Eco reserves for the open work—but rather to show that the soap opera shares with works Eco designates as open (and hence complex) certain constitutive features. Eco's analysis of such "open" works as *Ulysses* does help to point out the plural interpretive strategies employed by the reader in understanding any narrative work. Following Barthes and others, Eco calls the strategies codes—a term used here in a loose sense to indicate the interpretive mechanism linking signifier to referent. The process of reading soap operas, like that of reading *Ulysses*, involves the operation of multiple codes. As does *Ulysses*, the soap opera most fully engages its Model Reader, and, conversely, the soap opera (like *Ulysses*) contains an interpretive threshold below which the reader cannot fall and still "understand what's going on," except in the most superficial sense. This minimal interpretive threshold in the soap opera is based upon intratextual familiarity rather than extratextual lexical and literary skills—the soap opera is, after all, designed to reach the largest possible audience. Above this threshold, however, the reader may engage in multiple decoding strategies—plugging soap opera events and relationships into personal frames of reference via the operation of a number of different codes.

Like the open texts Eco speaks of, the soap opera text anticipates, to some degree, this pluri-signification, but it cannot totally control which codes will be engaged by the reader at any given moment of the interaction of those codes. It is what Iser calls the "overflow of possibilities" inherent in the decoding of any narrative work carried to a remarkable degree in the television soap opera that must account in large measure for its longevity as a form, the size of its audience, and the diversity of that audience. In fact, the soap opera represents an "over-coded" narrative form: characters, events, situations, and relationships are invested with signifying possibilities greatly in excess of those necessary to their narrative functions.

The Variety of Soap Opera Codes

The notion of codes helps us to recognize that the plurisignification of the soap opera, like that of other complex narratives, is achieved not willy-nilly but via certain generalizable interpretive pathways. Through these codes, the reader relates the text to his or her own world and experience, relates features of the text to one another, and relates the text to other texts.

STYLISTIC CODES

As we have seen, the stylistic codes of the soap opera represent the distillation of the classical Hollywood narrative style, a tightening of stylistic conventions to the point that a marginal or nonnormative usage is immediately marked as significant by the viewer. The transparency of this style draws the viewer into the world of the soap opera and draws attention away from both authorial intention and the means of representation of this world. Through the soap opera's adaptations of the stylistic codes of Hollywood representation, individual images on the television screen are firmly anchored to the textual diegesis and that diegesis endowed with a visual and auditory "fullness." These codes also assure the stability of the relationship of viewer to text; our knowledge of the world of the soap opera may be always limited, but it is never problematic. The occasional excursions into subjective point of view and duplicitous narration made within the framework of the Hollywood cinema (represented by *The Lady in the Lake* and *Stagefright*, respectively) would be unthinkable in the soap opera. Such stylistic license would irremediably rupture the contract between viewer and text—although, as we shall see in another chapter, this relationship did not become solidified until the advent of televised soap operas. Thus, these stylistic codes encourage the reader to read the audio and visual signifiers of the soap opera text in terms of their referents within the diegesis of the text.

GENERIC CODES

Other codes encourage the viewer to read a particular text or textual feature as one belonging to a larger category of texts the viewer knows as "soap operas." To the soap opera viewer the soap opera genre constitutes a portion of his or her horizon of expectations against which any particular text is read, in the same way that labeling a film a "musical" evokes certain characteristic features of that genre. Obviously, these "codes" are more at the level of specificity of conventions than linguistic or cinematic codes. Included in this category would be the soap opera's characteristic use of time and space—the attenuation of events (rather than their compression, as in most other narrative forms) and the construction of a world that is for the most part an interior one; a community-centered rather than character-centered fictive world; a serial narrative punctuated by commercial "gaps"; lack of overall narrative closure; and a complex network of character interrelationships. These conventions or codes are what enable any new "soap opera" to be read as such by its viewers, and they provide the basis upon which normative judgments about a new show or developments in an old one are formed.

TEXTUAL CODES

One misconception soap opera nonviewers often have is that all soap operas are alike. Although all soap operas do share certain stylistic and generic traits, each has its own narrative patterns, community of characters, history, and stylistic peculiarities. These marks of difference between one soap opera and the next may be imperceptible to the naive viewer, but they are unmistakable to the competent reader. Far from being undiscriminating, most soap opera viewers express strong likes and dislikes for certain soaps. Each soap opera generates its own set of expectations, its own parameters in narrative, paradigmatic relationships, and style recognized by the audience and used by them to derive meaning from each episode.

The most obvious example of what we are calling here textual codes is that which governs the system of character relationships in a given soap. At one level a marital infidelity "means" the same thing whether it occurs in *General Hospital* or *One Life to Live*, but the superficial meaning of a situation common to all soap operas is instantly overwhelmed by the deeper significance of that event in the specific character network in which it occurs. Some soap operas bear stronger marks of visual difference than others. Sets on *The Young and the Restless* are lit so that much of the decor is in shadow. This stylistic strategy is read by its viewers as "normal," while viewers of other soaps often find *The Young and the Restless* "gloomy."

Because the soap opera text has a history, it can be said to construct—to borrow terminology from Jauss—a textual horizon of expectations for its readers: the sum of its textual codes against which any new textual feature is received. The textual horizon of the soap opera appears largely undifferentiated to the reader, but it is what gives each soap opera world its specificity. Each episode, each new character, each new plot line becomes a "theme" to be assessed against the horizon supplied by the reader's perception of the text to that point. The importance of this horizon in the construction of meaning can best be seen when there is a considerable distance between it and a theme. Soap opera viewers can easily sense when a new development in a soap opera does not seem to "fit," which, given frequent changes in writers and producers, is not uncommon. The responses provoked by the distance between horizon and theme may be several. The soap's textual horizon might be expanded or altered to accommodate the theme. For example, a character who had been portrayed as a villain gradually takes on more and more redeeming qualities, so that over a period of time a marked personality change occurs. The viewer refigures the textual horizon of the soap so as to include not only that character change but the possibility of such character changes as features of the soap's world. Soap opera texts are full of such character transformations.

On the other hand, the theme might be at such odds with the soap's horizon that some viewers stop watching or switch to other soaps. In recent years some soap operas have introduced whole groups of new, younger characters in an attempt to cash in on adolescent and college-student interest in soap operas. In the process these soaps have no doubt lost some older viewers for whom such demographic shifts in the soap opera community represent too drastic a change. But in the case of the soap opera—unlike most other categories of narrative texts—a further response to theme/horizon distance is possible. The writers and producers of a particular soap can respond to the feedback they receive from viewers by expunging the "theme" from the soap opera text. A plot line that was to last for several months can be foreshortened; a new character can be written out; or a familiar character scheduled for departure can be resuscitated.

INTERTEXTUAL CODES

Like all cultural products, soap operas exist within networks of other texts to which they inevitably in some way refer, so that the reader is constantly comparing the text being read with the encyclopedia of other texts he or she has experienced. What I have referred to thus far as the generic code, which allows readers to place a text within the general category of the soap opera, might be seen as one type of intertextuality. Chapter 6 [of his *Speaking of Soap Operas*] is largely devoted to a discussion on the intertextual horizon against which the first soap opera were read, particularly that portion of the horizon constituted by popular discourse aimed at American women.

In more recent years soap opera writers have exploited intertextual relationships in several ways. In their never-ending seach for new plot twists, writers have based plotlines on popular movies, novels, other television programs, press reportage of the Mafia, religious cults, and terrorism, among other topics. Well-known actors from television and the movies have made cameo appearances in soap operas, either as "themselves," or, in the case of Elizabeth Taylor in *General Hospital*, as a soap opera character.

One of the most notable instances of soap opera intertextuality occurred during the 1980–81 television season on *General Hospital*. Producer Gloria Monty introduced a major subplot that made reference not to any particular intertext but to an entire narrative genre: science fiction. An archvillain obtained a weather-altering device (the "Ice Princess") with the power to turn the climate of Port Charles into that of Siberia. After an elaborate global search, the device was found and the plot foiled by two of the show's most popular young characters. The success of the "Ice Princess" plot (or its perceived success, since Monty has always insisted that the audience was primarily attracted by the love affair between the two characters and not by the trappings of science fiction) fostered imitation, and soon other soaps were featuring diabolical dwarfs, rescues from desert islands, and treks across Africa.

In setting up resonances between soap opera characters and situations and those in other texts, however, writers risked bringing the intertextual codes being employed into conflict with the textual codes that keep any new event anchored in a world familiar to the viewer. For example, *Guiding Light*'s response to *General Hospital*'s intertextuality was to institute a gothic-romance subplot, complete with mysterious mansion, intimidating housekeeper, handsome-but-enigmatic master of the house, and poor-but-willing ingenue. But the world of the gothic romance is not that of the soap opera. The gothic romance isolates the heroine in an alien environment controlled by forces she cannot, at first, understand. The soap opera world is that of the community, governed by the dynamics of human interaction. While the gothic subplot was prominent, *Guiding Light* was split into two worlds with few connections between them. Eventually, the gothic plot was absorbed into the world of *Guiding Light*, but most of its gothic elements had to be jettisoned in the process: the ingenue and the master of the house marry; he turns out to be the long-lost son of a prominent Springfield family; the Mrs. Danvers character is sent to live with her sister in Scotland, and so forth. In short, the pull toward intertextual meaning meets a corresponding resistance from textual codes, whose function it is to preserve the autonomy of the soap opera world so carefully constructed for so long.

The soap opera "renaissance" of recent years has produced a new form of soap opera intertext: information about soap opera actors and the "behind the scenes" world of soap opera production in newspaper columns, specialized magazines, and television shows. Since the mid-1970s, an entire industry hyping the soap opera has emerged, one which rivals in scope, if not in size, the promotional infrastructure of Hollywood in its heyday. Several syndicated newspaper columnists now cover the soap opera "beat." Soap actors regularly make public appearances at shopping centers, arranged by agencies that do nothing else. Some soap actors have their own publicity agents. A half-dozen fan magazines are devoted largely to soap operas. In 1982 a half-hour, syndicated, "magazine-format" televsion program of soaps, *Soap World*, was introduced.

Representative of the function served by these soap intertexts is *Soap Opera Digest*, a biweekly magazine. It was begun in the early 1970s as a means of keeping viewers who worked outside the home up to date with plot developments on their favorite soaps. Today, in addition to plot summaries of all daytime soaps, *Soap Opera Digest* contains articles on and interviews with soap actors, photographic essays, articles on how soap operas are produced, and a readers' forum in which viewers can express their views about soap operas, among other features. Its focus is the soap opera actor and the character he or she plays.

Soap Opera Digest reflects and contributes to the transformation of some soap actors into "stars." Richard Dyer defines a star as a "structured polysemy" constructed around a performer. Essential to the polysemic nature of stardom is the development of a persona beyond that assumed by an actor in his or her roles.[18] From the beginning of soap operas in the 1930s through the 1950s, soap opera producers (particulary Procter and Gamble) actively discouraged actors from developing off-screne (and, earlier, off-speaker) images, perhaps believing that this would detract from the "realism" of the soap world, but also realizing (as did early film producers) that the more a character became known to the public also as an actor, the greater his or her potential leverage at contract renewal time.

More recently, however, networks, production companies, and sponsors have realized the offsetting benefits of promoting soap actors and through them the soaps in which they star. Rick Springfield, Dr. Noah Drake in *General Hospital*, is equally well known as a rock-and-roll performer. Other soap actors (Tony Geary and Genie Francis among them) have firmly established extra–soap opera personas. *Soap Opera Digest* provides a prime vehicle for promoting both the character as star and the actor as character. Because of that magazine and other sources, the referentiality of some characters is doubled: Dr. Noah Drake can be read as that character and as Rick Springfield, the separate but related persona constructed from other images. Although stories about soap opera actors in *Soap Opera Digest* are frequenty written as exposés of the "real" person behind the character, the intertext used by the soap opera viewer is not the actor as person but merely another image of an existing image. Obviously, there is a "person" behind the character/actor/star, but this person is almost never known directly by the viewer; both character and performer's persona are constructed textual images that comment upon one another. Their difference lies in the codes employed in understanding them.

IDEOLOGICAL CODES

As we have seen, one of the primary ways any narrative text is made to "mean" is the filling in of textual gaps by the reader, the imposition of the individual's frames of reference upon the world of the text. The term "ideological," as applied to this process, designates the structured but largely unarticulated body of beliefs, assumptions, and values which forms the basis upon which the reader fills in textual gaps. Eco calls this set of codes "common frames." The viewer constantly compares soap opera actions with "what should happen" in such a situation: what is plausible, veristic, morally correct, and so forth, according to both the textual codes of the soap opera world and the viewer's own world of experience and values. For content analysts, ideological codes are the only ones employed in understanding soap operas, but in fact they are but one set of codes among several simultaneously employed by the viewer. The viewer realizes that even when his or her expectations are based upon experience, they are being applied *not* to a real-life situation but to a fictive construct.

In 1975, Sari Thomas conducted extensive interviews with a sample of forty soap opera viewers. Working from a theoretical model developed by Sol Worth and Larry Gross, Thomas suggested that soap opera viewers employed two distinct frames of reference in decoding them: attributional and inferential. According to this model, when readers encounter what they believe to be a fictional text, they decode it by attempting to assign patterns of signification (the "message") found in the text to its author. When, on the other hand, readers encounter what seems to be a nonauthored text (a natural phenomenon or a piece of unedited newsfilm, for example), they decode it by attributing meaning to it by reference to "real life," or, more accurately, their experience of real life.

Thomas does not suggest that the employment of an inferential frame of reference means those viewers regard soap operas as reality, but that they tend to rely more on what are called here ideological codes in their decoding. The viewer makes sense of soap opera characters and situations by imposing his or her own frame of knowledge, values, and experience. For example, Thomas asked her respondents to predict what would happen in a given plot line in *All My Children*. One viewer responded: "I think Chuck and Tara will stay together for the sake of the baby. Even if it is Phil's child, Chuck has really acted as the father. I don't go for that. I mean irregardless of who actually made the baby, it's the parents who raise the child that counts." Other viewers tended to base their expectations upon what Thomas would call attributional, and I would call textual, codes. (Given the invisibility and often plurality of soap opera authorship, it seems unlikely that viewers imagine a unitary communicating force behind the text itself.) For example, another viewer responded: "Chuck and Tara will stay together because this way there's always room for complication later on. If Tara and Phil actually did stay together, the whole story there would be kaput."[19]

Integrating Thomas's findings into the theoretical framework of this chapter, I would argue that attributional/inferential orientations of soap opera readers do not represent realistic/unrealistic or informed/uninformed decoding practices. Rather, the semiotic operation of the soap opera text not only allows for but encourages both these and other codes to be employed. To a greater extent perhaps than any other fiction, the soap opera text constantly walks the line between one that can be read as fiction and one that spills over into the experiential world of the viewer. The operation of the ideological codes pulls the world of the viewer and that of the text together; other codes keep them pushed apart. It is the possibility of simultaneously employing a range of codes, not in substitution for one another but in addition to one another, that renders the soap opera text "over-coded" and complex.

The Female Reader

Both Iser and Jauss have been criticized—and rightly so—for constructing an ideal reader suspiciously like themselves: educated European males.[20] Neither would deny that differences in class and gender among readers condition the activations of texts by those readers, but neither concerns himself very much with the nature of those differences or their likely or even possible effects. Obviously, in the case of the soap opera we cannot afford to presume either a genderless or a male reader, since for as long as there have been soap operas, women have constituted their primary readership. We need to examine the soap opera's *differently* gendered audience in its possible relationship to both textual structure and the position marked out for the reader within that structure. As we have seen, Ellen Seiter uses Eco's open/closed text distinction to argue that soap operas allow for the possibility of "alternative" readings unintended by their producers. In her book *Loving with a Vengeance*, Tania Modleski goes much further, suggesting that the soap opera represents a "femininely" structured textual system that engages the female reader in a unique fashion, with the result that "soap operas may be in the vanguard not just of T.V. art but of all popular narrative art."[21]

Modleski uses soap operas, along with romances and gothic novels, to point out that our notions of narrative pleasure and response to popular works remain overly narrow. Even in contemporary feminist criticism, it is frequently presumed that narrative pleasure is essentially "masculine" in nature because it involves identification with a single protagonist (usually male) and because of its orientation toward action leading to ultimate resolution, knowledge, and hence spectator/reader power.[22] The soap opera, however, is for Modleski an example of a narrative form whose structuring principles are essentially "feminine" and whose reader is positioned quite differently than in the mainstream Hollywood film or James Bond novel. Rather than make narrative closure the point from which narrative pleasure derives, the soap opera, which is predicated upon the impossibility of closure and constantly delays resolution, "makes anticipation of an end an end in itself." Whereas masculine narratives might "inscribe" in the text a reader whose omniscience is secured by the end of the book, the soap opera gives us a reader as ideal mother: one whose narrative interests are diffused among a large "family" of characters and whose power is always limited by her helplessness to bring their problems to ultimate resolution.

Thus the "immortality" of the soap opera speaks to the contemporary situation of the housewife/mother, whose life is given purpose and meaning by and through the family. The never-ending tensions and traumas suffered by soap opera families assures the continuing need for the advice and consolation of the mother. The soap opera asserts the centrality of the family, but does so by keeping its families in a state of constant disarray, always in need of the understanding of both its diegetic mothers and its mother/reader. Although denied ultimate knowledge that comes with resolution, the mother/reader is endowed with greater knowledge at any given moment than any of her "children" in the soap opera world. She is called upon not to pass judgment in most cases but, by being given "all sides" of an issue, to exercise maternal tolerance and sympathy.

To Modleski the soap opera represents a narrative form whose construction is diametrically opposed to that of the "male" film and novel. The latter favors action over dialogue and ruthlessly reduces indeterminacies in order to arrive at a single moment of closure, solution, and knowledge. The soap opera makes the consequences of actions more important than action itself, introduces complications at every opportunity, and denies the desire for ultimate control by assuming its own immortality. In the male narrative dialogue is motored by plot and serves to explain, clarify, and simplify. In the soap opera, dialogue increases indeterminacy and retards resolution. The self-knowledge that is frequently expressed through dialogue as the Hollywood film approaches resolution is largely absent from the soap opera. Talk bespeaks multiplicitous motives, the unintended ramifications of every action, and, concomitantly, the limits of self-awareness.

The work of Modleski and Seiter is complementary in several respects to the reader-oriented poetics of soap operas presented here. First, both interrogate the notion of narrative pleasure in general and the pleasures to be derived from popular texts in particular. In doing so, they demonstrate that the nature of that pleasure may differ greatly between men and women. This suggests that both the peculiar status of the soap opera as object of social science investigation and the disdain it has engendered among most critics are in part attributable to a misrecognition of this difference. The soap opera has been illegible as an aesthetic object partly because the terms by which it could be aesthetically engaged seemed foreign to most men. Feminist criticism of the past decade has raised the possibility that the narrative strategies and central stylistic features of "mainstream" fiction and film are sexually loaded, that a male reader/spectator is "inscribed" in the text. This does not mean that a female reader cannot enjoy such texts, but rather that her response is mediated by her difference from the text's implied reader. If this is the case, then the values that critics privilege in such works are likely to be sexually loaded as well.

Modleski acknowledges that criticism by sexual analogy can rapidly deteriorate into silliness, and neither she nor I would claim that the popularity and aesthetic appeal of soap operas can be explained by their attunement to the patterns and rhythms of female sexuality. As Julia Kristeva has argued, however, the feminine experience of temporality might well be different from that of male time. "Female subjectivity," says Kristeva, "would seem to provide a specific measure that essentially retains *repetition* and *eternity* from among the multiple modalities of time known through the history of civilizations."[23] Yet these temporal modalities—characteristic of the soap opera—are those least likely to be associated with works of narrative art within the discourse of traditional aesthetics. Indeed, it is their obverse—innovation and progression—that are revered in narrative fiction. Regardless of how far we might wish to go in regarding gender as a determinant of narrative pleasure, feminist criticism of the sort exemplified by the work of Modleski and Seiter proposes the *reception* of cultural texts as an essential category of critical analysis. As such, its concerns overlap to a significant degree with those of a reader-oriented poetics in general.

While her description of the soap opera reader as ideal mother is useful in differentiating the soap opera reading experience from that of other texts, Modleski comes close at some points in her analysis to reducing the soap opera reading situation to a metaphorical correspondence with the presumed life of a "housewife" and mother. Married women not working outside the home have long constituted the core of the soap opera audience, and the size and loyalty of this audience indicate that soap operas have long addressed the narrative and aesthetic needs of women working in the home and raising children. However, several important qualifications must be made to this association of the soap opera reader with the "average American housewife." First, neither the structure of the soap opera text nor the social situation of its audience has remained static. Although Modleski seems to present the "mother/reader" as a textually inscribed position to be taken up by whoever the actual reader happens to be, she comes close at times to conflating the two. What Modleski discusses as the decenteredness of soap opera form we have called here its paradigmatic complexity. The diffusion of interest and identification in the soap opera may well provide the housewive/spectator with "training in a decentered existence," but, viewed as paradigmatic complexity, it also opens up the soap opera text for a variety of responses from a number of different readerships. The soap opera represents an "over-coded" narrative form, in which characters and relationships are endowed with pluri-significative possibilities far exceeding that required by narrative function alone. It is this very indeterminacy created by the soap opera's over-coding that helps to account for the form's longevity and the breadth of its contemporary appeal. This is not to say that the soap opera is ideologically neutral or that it can be read in an infinite number of ways, but we must not confuse presumed ideological intent with either reader response or ideological effect.

. . . [S]oap operas since their inception have been concerned with aspects of American life that have been marginalized in mainstream fictive narratives: parentage, family, the emotional consequences of romance, conflicting female role expectations, and so forth. Regardless of how the viewer might feel about the *way* in which these issues are addressed in soap operas, she knows that at the very least she will find that they *are* addressed there. Modleski's conclusion that the soap opera form is "not altogether at odds with a possible feminist aesthetic" stems from her recognition of that form as an alternative to "male" narratives. As such, it provided a point of departure at least for the development of narrative strategies that "make explicit the criticisms of masculine power and masculine pleasure implied in the narrative form of the soap opera." Quite aside from its potential as a possible proto-feminist form, however, the soap opera represents an alternative basis for narrative aesthetic pleasure in general—one that values complexity, repetition, and speech over simplicity, telos, and action. A soap opera viewer might find some aspects of a soap silly or uninteresting, but she knows that the nature of narrative engagement to be found in the soap opera is different from that to be found in any other form of commercial television—perhaps in any other form of narrative.

Notes

1. For example, in an essay on television aesthetics Fred Schroeder sees the serial form as central, yet he omits discussion of the soap opera—despite its being the most fully realized embodiment of the serial narrative ever produced in any medium. In his *TV: The Most Popular Art*, Horace Newcomb comes as close as any traditional critic to opening a space within the aesthetic field for soap operas, but it winds up being a very small and ill-defined space indeed. Newcomb lists intimacy and continuity as distinguishing characteristics of television art. "Television is at its best," he says, "when it offers us faces, reactions, exploration of emotions registered by human beings." Soap operas, he admits, do fulfill this criterion of intimacy to some degree. But as an illustration of how exploitation of television's intimacy has resulted in "moments of great symbolic power," Newcomb offers not a soap opera but a BBC adaptation of *The Golden Bowl*. He devalues the prime-time series because it offers no opportunity for sustained and developing characterizations: "There is no sense of continuous involvement with these characters. They have no memory. They cannot change in response to events that occur within a weekly installment, and consequently they have no history." Again, Newcomb sees soap operas overcoming this problem, but he calls them "distorted by their own stereotypical views." It is yet another BBC serialized adaptation of an accepted literary classic that Newcomb holds up as a model of "a new work of art." See Fred Schroeder, "Video Aesthetics and Serial Art," in Horace Newcomb, ed., *Television: The Critical View*, 2nd ed. (New York: Oxford University Press, 1979), pp. 407–19; Horace Newcomb, *TV: The Most Popular Art* (New York: Anchor, 1974), pp. 248–55.
2. Tzvetan Todorov, *Introduction to Poetics* (Minneapolis: University of Minnesota Press, 1981), p. 6. Jonathan Culler counterposes the poetic programmatic with that of traditional criticism: "In this critical climate [that dominated by the precepts of New Criticism] it is therefore important . . . to take up a tendentious position and maintain that while the experience of literature may be an experience of interpreting work, in fact the interpretation of individual works is only tangentially related to the understanding of literature. To engage in the study of literature is not to produce yet another interpretation of *King Lear* but to advance

one's understanding of the conventions and operations of an institution, a mode of discourse" (*The Pursuit of Signs* [London: Routledge and Kegan Paul, 1981], p. 5).

3. Theodor W. Adorno, "Scientific Experiences of a European Scholar in America," in Donald Fleming and Bernard Bailyn, eds., *The Intellectual Migration: Europe and America, 1930–1960* (Cambridge: Harvard University Press, 1969), p. 344. In the "Ferment in the Field" issue of *Journal of Communication* (Summer 1983) not one of the thirty-five essays explicitly addresses the need for textual analysis of mass media programming.
4. Jonathan Culler, "Prolegomena to a Theory of Reading," in Susan Suleiman and Inge Crossman, eds., *The Reader in the Text: Essays in Audience and Interpretation* (Princeton: Princeton University Press, 1980), p. 49.
5. As Suleiman and Crossman note, audience-oriented or reader-response criticism "is not one field but many, not a single widely trodden path but a multiplicity of crisscrossing, often divergent tracks that cover a vast area of the critical landscape in a pattern whose complexity dismays the brave and confounds the faint of heart." See their "Introduction: Varieties of Audience-Oriented Criticism," in *The Reader in the Text*, pp. 3–45.

   On reader-response criticism (in addition to Suleiman and Crossman) see Jane P. Tompkins, ed., *Reader-Response Criticism: From Formalism to Post-Structuralism* (Baltimore: Johns Hopkins University Press, 1980); Robert Holub, *Reception Theory* (London: Methuen, 1984); and Steven Mailloux, *Interpretive Conventions: The Reader in the Study of American Literature* (Ithaca: Cornell University Press, 1982).

   The key English translations of Wolfgang Iser are *The Implied Reader: Patterns of Communication in Prose Fiction from Bunyan to Beckett* (Baltimore: Johns Hopkins University Press, 1974) and *The Act of Reading: A Theory of Aesthetic Reception* (Baltimore: Johns Hopkins University Press, 1978). Those of Hans Robert Jauss are *Toward an Aesthetic of Reception* (Minneapolis: University of Minnesota Press, 1982) and *Aesthetic Experience and Literary Hermeneutics* (Minneapolis: University of Minnesota Press, 1982).
6. Iser, *The Act of Reading*, p. 18.
7. This discussion of the classical Hollywood narrative style is based upon David Bordwell, Janet Staiger, and Kristin Thompson, *The Classical Hollywood Cinema: Film Style and Mode of Production to 1960* (London: Routledge and Kegan Paul). I am grateful to the authors for allowing me advance access to their manuscript.
8. One exception to this generalization is the lighting in *The Young and the Restless*, in which the background is left in shadow. The function of this lighting strategy, however, is not to call attention to itself but to draw the eye away from the set and toward the characters.
9. The soap opera is by no means the only popular narrative form to evince an elaborate paradigmatic structure. See, for example, Charles F. Altman, "The American Film Musical: Paradigmatic Structure and Mediatory Function," *Wide Angle* 2 (1978): 10–17; and Jane Feuer, "The Self-Reflexive Musical and the Myth of Entertainment," *Quarterly Review of Film Studies* 2 (1977): 313–26.
10. Shlomith Rimmon-Kenan, *Narrative Fiction: Contemporary Poetics* (London: Methuen, 1983), p. 51.
11. Iser, *The Act of Reading*, p. 109.
12. Ibid., pp. 109–12.
13. Quoted by Iser, p. 66.
14. Ibid., pp. 190–91. See also, Iser, "Indeterminacy and the Reader's Response in Prose Fiction," in J. Hillis Miller, ed., *Aspects of Narrative* (New York: Columbia University Press, 1971), pp. 1–45.
15. Sandy Flitterman, "The *Real* Soap Operas: TV Commercials," in E. Ann Kaplan, ed. *Regarding Television* (Frederick, Md.: University Publications of America, 1983), pp. 84–96.

16. Umberto Eco, *The Role of the Reader: Explorations in the Semiotics of Texts* (Bloomington: Indiana University Press, 1979), pp. 1–11.
17. Ellen Seiter, "The Role of the Woman Reader: Eco's Narrative Theory and Soap Operas," *Tabloid* 6 (1981). See also in *Regarding Television*, Robert C. Allen, "On Reading Soap Operas: A Semiotic Primer," pp. 97–108.
18. Richard Dyer, *Stars* (London: British Film Institute, 1979).
19. Sari Thomas, "The Relationship between Daytime Serials and Their Viewers," Ph.D. dissertation, University of Pennsylvania, 1977.
20. See Holub, pp. 96–101.
21. Tania Modleski, *Loving with a Vengeance* (Hamden, Conn.: Archon Books, 1982), p. 87. All subsequent references are to this book's chapter on soap operas, "The Search for Tomorrow in Today's Soap Operas," pp. 85–109.
22. See, for example, Laura Mulvey's influential essay, "Visual Pleasure and Narrative Cinema," *Screen* 16 (Autumn 1975): 6–18; reprinted in Karyn Kay and Gerald Pearcy, eds., *Women and the Cinema* (New York: Dutton, 1977), pp. 412–28.
23. Julia Kristeva, "Women's Time," *Signs* 7 (1981): 16.

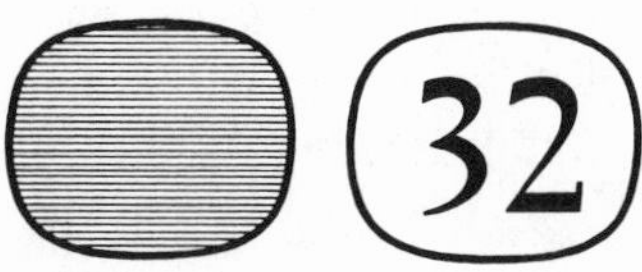

Men, Sex, and Money in Recent Family Melodramas

ELLEN SEITER

Since the late nineteen-seventies, the popularity of family melodramas has been increasing, while its conventions have undergone some diversifaction. No longer is the family melodrama the exclusive domain of women's popular culture, restricted to women's films and soap operas. Recent feature films and prime time television serials now form a significant aspect of the genre, concentrating on male protagonists in an effort to appeal to a new audience composed both men and women. These melodramas of the nineteen-eighties reveal signficant trends in terms of gender, class and the nature of the tribulations. This article is a survey of the dominant features of family melodramas today including: soap operas, prime time serials such as *Dallas* and *Dynasty*, and theatrical feature films.

Affluence as Ordinary

Family melodramas have always tended to deal with an environment, a set of characters and a narrative dilemma unquestionably indentified as middle class. From its beginning, melodrama allied itself with a middle class on the

---

Ellen Seiter's "Men, Sex, and Money in Recent Family Melodramas," originally appeared in *The Journal of Film and Video*, Vol. 35, no. 1 (Winter, 1983), pp. 17–27. Reprinted by permission to the author and *The Journal of Film and Video*.

rise, portraying a class identical to or matching its audience's aspirations. The persistence of the middle class environment in family melodramas has tended to present middle class values as universal, with no consciousness of class (or often ethnic and racial) specificity. While the middle class setting allows the drama to elide class issues, it also reinforces the primary of personal definitions rather than social ones in dealing with the family. Upward social mobility has conventionally been a concern in the melodrama only to the extent that it affects the personal happiness of its characters, serving as an obstacle, for example, to the fulfillment of love through marriage. For the most part, family melodramas have continued to voice the nineteenth century "cult of sensibility," and suggested that wealth can be a drawback in terms of personal happiness. At the same time, the middle class context is emphatically depicted through setting, cultural references, social context, and defined as the average, the typical, the ordinary.

The conventional configuration of characters on the daytime serials includes an upper class family, a middle class, professional family—providing the proliferation of doctors and lawyers—and a poor, working class family (often a widow, employed by the middle and upper class families as a servant, and her children, who have professional aspirations). While the possibility of social mobility exists through the rather free intermarriage between classes on soap operas, the divorce rate makes such arrangements extremely insecure. In the long run, characters usually remain part of the class they were born into. Because there are such strong class distinctions in the basic structure of soap operas, the narratives possess a kind of class consciousness often absent from other types of melodrama. Working class characters are shown in a variety of occupations—as waitresses, nurses, clerical workers, even police, and there is an emphasis on the key role work plays in the lives of these characters. While the material aspirations of the working class characters are sometimes treated as comic relief (just as servants furnished comic relief in nineteenth century stage melodramas) they are at least as prominent as the wealthy and middle class characters in terms of narrative interest. On *All My Children*, for example, the character Opal Gardner freed herself from life as a maid to the wealthy Wallingford family by blackmailing Professor Wallingford for enough money to open her own business, a health spa called the "Glamourama." While Opal is often used for comedy in the story, it is usually at the expense of the upper class characters. She frequently speaks about the struggle she has faced all her life being poor, the kinds of prejudice she has faced, and her relentless ambition for her daughter, Jenny. Typical of the world of soap opera, her chance for success comes through luck, conniving and an alliance with one of the members of the show's wealthy family. While Opal Gardner is strongly stereotyped as loud, brash, Southern and gauche, she is also one of the program's most popular characters, her outspokeness allowing her to break through the stuffiness of the middle and upper class worlds. Her aspirations to become middle class are taken seriously on the show, and the years of struggle and hard work involved in such upward social mobility are stressed.

The so-called soap operas of prime time, *Dallas* and *Dynasty*,[1] borrow heavily from the daytime serials, but differ from them substantially. The plot focuses entirely on an upper class family, their spouses, business rivals, or illegitimate relations. Working class characters are almost entirely absent, and all characters are white except for an occasional servant. All scenes take place in settings of fabulous wealth: mansions, ranches, limousines, executive suites, private jets. The worlds of *Dallas* and *Dynasty* are the richest on prime time television. The lack of diversity in the class of the characters on these shows may be due in part to the functional necessity of eliminating the large number of characters found on daytime soap operas, where writers have five times the amount of screen time in which to unravel their plots. The nature of content is significantly changed, however, with the virtual absence of middle and working class characters. The families of *Dallas* and *Dynasty* are not only rich, they are oil families. Both programs were created during a period of increased awareness of oil company profits and hostility toward them due to gasoline price increases. On *Dallas* and *Dynasty,* the oil business is taken out of the impersonal, corporate world of Exxon and Mobil, and placed in the realm of family inheritance and personal fortunes, accumulated through the brilliance, tenacity and sheer will of men like J. R. Ewing, (Larry Hagman) and Blake Carrington (John Forsythe). The rich and famous have always been of popular interest, especially during period of economic depression. These serials are not unusual in providing the fantasy of a life of luxury and conspicuous consumption. At the same time, *Dallas* and *Dynasty* reveal the lives of the rich and powerful to be full of strife, anxiety and personal torment.

In theatrical feature films, family melodramas have tended recently to specify the class of their characters as upper middle class, members of a professional elite, intellecutal and culturally high brow, as in *The Turning Point, An Unmarried Woman, Ordinary People, Kramer vs. Kramer, The Four Seasons, Endless Love, Making Love, Shoot the Moon* and *On Golden Pond.* In *Shoot the Moon,* for example, the setting of the family's troubles is Marin, the poshest county in California. The father, George (Albert Finney), writes award winning nonfiction. The family's financial concerns are on the order of whether Faith (Diane Keaton) can afford to build a tennis court in the backyard. In *Making Love,* the husband, Zach (Michael Ontkean), is a doctor; the wife, Claire (Kate Jackson), a television executive. The couple's courtship memories consist of listening to Gilbert and Sullivan records and reciting the poetry of Rupert Brooke. In *On Golden Pond,* Henry Fonda plays a retired university profesor, Norman Thayer. Katharine Hepburn, playing his wife Ethel, brings to the role her career-long association with the upper class. The action of *On Golden Pond* takes place at their summer home in Maine. In all these films, the characters are portrayed quite specifically as upper middle class, yet the lack of significance of the family's class is insisted upon, as in the title, *Ordinary People.* The families in these film melodramas are not set up as objects of envy or material for fantasy and escapism, they are presented as "normal" familes, just plain folks.

The naturalness of the upper middle class social milieu in these films is literalized by the introduction of landscape shots throughout many of the films, often accompanied by classical music. Vivaldi's "The Four Seasons" was used both in *Ordinary People* and *The Four Seasons* over landscape shots which recurred throughout the films as breaks in the action. *Shoot the Moon* and *On Golden Pond* punctuate emotionally charged scenes with shots of lakes and countryside. As *Endless Love* reaches its conclusion, the location changes from the city to the country. Such techniques reinforce the notion of the family as a natural order, rather than a social one, and abstract the characters from their social and economic context.

The trend in these melodramas to portray families of the upper and upper middle classes can be explained as the avoidance of serious contemporary problems which confront most families. Conventionally, the structure of melodrama limits it to the presentation of only those conflicts which can be resolved *within* the family. The world of the family melodrama is an insular, enclosed one, never looking further than its characters in locating the cause of turmoil and designating scapegoats. One reason that recent family melodramas have raised the class of their characters may be that current economic conditions have had too serious an effect on middle and working class families to be ignored in a genre so committed to realist presentation. The most conspicuous source of suffering which currently affects the nuclear family is economic in nature. Unemployment and loss of income are the stuff from which real family melodramas are made these days. This kind of suffering is economically, rather than psychologically motivated, and therefore is not adaptable to the genre in its conventional form because it logically blocks the understanding and treatment of the family in isolation. The assignment of blame, the investigation of guilt and the cure for such suffering would, of necessity, involve a world larger than the nuclear family.

The higher class status of the families in recent melodrams automatically disperses another source of conflict as well: the social inequality of men and women. In these upper middle class and upper class families, women are equal to men in terms of education, job opportunities and financial security. On *Dallas* and *Dynasty,* women and men are equally likely to be the holders of personal fortunes. When career women are introduced into these empires of high finance, they are as powerful, as successful and as ruthless as men. These prime time soap operas portray the oil business as a bastion of equal opportunity. In the upper middle class world of the feature films, women decide whether or not to work outside the home based entirely on personal factors; none of these families need a second income. When women do work, they enjoy immediate access to jobs which pay as well and are as interesting as the male characters' jobs. Child care and housework are magically taken care of or never surface as problems at all in the world of the upper middle and upper class. Just as these family melodramas avoid many problems in the family because no one is ever worried about money, they avoid the problems which men and women confront in marraige which are caused by the inequalities which women face outside the home, as well as in it.

The increased affluence of the families portrayed in these melodramas both creates sympathy and identification with the upper and upper middle classes and makes possible the continued treatment of the family in a social void. The stories of the families on prime time and in feature films can still be contained in the realm of the individual, the psychological and the emotional.

Sexuality as Disruption

While family melodramas are ultimately concerned with affirming the naturalness and rightness of the nuclear family as a social arrangement, they are also preoccupied with its disruption. An overriding anxiety is expressed in contemporary melodramas about instability and transience of the nuclear family. Since the melodrama requires that crises introduced into the family must be remediable within the family, turmoil is frequently caused by individual acts of villainy. This villainy often takes the specific form of sexual license. Indeed, sexuality has proven to be an unlimited source of narrative conflict in these melodramas—one ideally suited to the genre's requirement of individual and psychological resolutions. The primary way that the genre has renewed itself over the years has been through the introduction of problems afflicting the family which seem somehow current, particularly modern. "Social problem" films of the nineteen-fifties took themes such as mental illness, alcohol and drug abuse, and teenage rebellion (all problems which can be seen as related to sexual repression) and their effect on the family)—providing a glimpse of the destruction of normal, middle class family life only to insist on its ultimate importance.[2] Sexuality provides subject matter for the family melodrama which has the appeal of the mildly risque, can be solved in terms of individual characters, can be treated with some degree of sensationalism, and yet furnishes the occasion for the reassertion of one of the melodrama's favorite themes: the overriding importance of monogamy.

Daytime soap operas rely on the constant propagation of suffering in order to prolong their serial narrative indefinitely. Often this is accomplished nearly single-handedly by one of the notorious villainesses of the soap operas, women such as Erica (Susan Lucci) on *All My Children*, whose boundless energy is directed toward ruining everyone else's life. Erica continually meddles, deceives, double crosses and—especially—seduces. This association between villainy and sexual seduction can be found in the earliest melodramas, where the moral war being waged found its clearest form in the fight for monogamy or sexual purity over promiscuity. The power of the villainous characters often derives from their sexual desirability. The preoccupation with these characters and with sexual activity in general on soap operas has given them a reputation for being mildly pornographic in their appeal. The overriding moralism of the genre definitively limits this tendency in melodrama, however. In feature films, for example, family melodramas are nearly always rated PG—a reflection of both the audience's expectations and the inherent restrictions of the genre. The fact that nearly all characters on soap operas become involved in numerous sexual relationships as the stories run on year after year certainly enhances soap opera appeal on the level of sexual fantasy.

While sexual psychodrama is the driving force of the soap opera narrative, other subject matter is sometimes introduced which resembles the "social problem" films of the ninteen-fifties; alcohol and drug abuse, mental illness, abortion, domestic violence, rape and interracial marriage have all intruded on the soap opera world. Because soap operas span so much more time than feature films or prime time programs, they can deal with such issues over the course of months. Sometimes the material is dealt with in an appallingly exploitative way, as with Laura's rape on *General Hospital* and subsequent love affair with her rapist, Luke. Other times the material is introduced in a way that emphasizes public education, as with the theme of domestic violence on *All My Children*, which evolved into the character Leonora's pressing charges against her husband and taking refuge at a woman's shelter. The enclosure of the daytime serials within the home and the small town, close knit community, however, means that these social issues rarely take on a broader social significance except when the characters pay lip service to the idea that such a problem is widespread. These social themes are never sustained in the same way that other narrative situations are, such as romantic triangles, and tend to be dropped abruptly when they come to appear to the viewers as a kind of intrusion, an unnecessary straying from the real plot, the sexual drama. This means that social issues which affect relationships between men and women tend to be the sole domain of prime time situation comedies, or occasional made-for-television movies.

The prime time serials *Dallas* and *Dynasty* strongly resemble soap operas in terms of their obsession with sexual relationships, working out, as the plot develops, an increasingly complex matrix of relationships involving sexual liaisons and family ties. The prime time serials are steamier than daytime; the characters more sexually active. The infamous J.R. of *Dallas* is a man who propositions and sleeps with nearly every woman he meets. His villainy is reinforced by his lack of scruples about sexual matters. An important aspect of the plot involves how his wife (or ex-wife, depending on which season), Sue Ellen (Linda Gray), is able to cope with her husband's infidelities (the price she pays for her opulent lifestyle). Blake Carrington of *Dynasty* is also an expert womanizer. The irresistible sexual attraction of these men enhances their power in the business world. Often these characters conduct business entirely on the basis of personal obsessions, sexual jealousy and competition, as though the vicissitudes of monopoly capitalism were simply a series of personal vendettas. Like the daytime serials, however, *Dallas* and *Dynasty* are deeply sentimental about marraige, and the greatest esteem (if not the greatest narrative interest) is awarded to monogamous individuals.

Sexual expression has been a popular theme in recent film melodramas, which repeatedly strive to define what the limits of "appropriate" sexual expression in the nuclear family are. Because films are not subject to the same kind of censorship as television programs, they can be somewhat more explicit in their treatment of sexuality. Franco Zeffirelli's *Endless Love*, for example, raised the problem of teenage sex as a threat to family life. The film self-consciously presents the sexual activity of Brooke Shield's character in the tone of the risque, playing up the shock value of a teenage girl sleeping with her boyfriend openly in her parent's house. On one level, *Endless Love* suggests that teenage sexuality, if unleashed, can do nothing but wreak havoc with the family. In the film, all family members become embroiled in conflict, the father and brother become enraged with jealousy, the parents' once happy marriage ends in divorce, their home literally burns down, and the father dies. The destructive potential of adolescent sexual freedom in the family becomes obscured, however, as *Endless Love* transforms itself into a quite conventional love story at the end.[3] The final significance in *Endless Love* is placed not on teenage sex, but on the grand passion of two exceptional teenagers who share an eternal "endless" romance. Brooke Shields and her boyfriend become representatives of the conventional couple who will make a monogamous commitment to one another for life. As such, they represent the ultimate good, from the point of view of the family melodrama, the foundation of the nuclear family. *Endless Love* is a quite typical example of the way family melodramas may reflect anxiety about social changes—teenage sex being widely perceived in the media at the time the film was released as a kind of national crisis—but treats them only in attenuated and conventionalized ways. The depiction of the family as a group of bohemian intellecutals in *Endless Love* safely distances the problem of teenage sex, which can then be dealt with purely in terms of individual, moral and psychological issues. The character of Brooke Shields never needs to worry about unwanted pregnancy or venereal disease, only how well she keeps up her grades.

Homosexuality has, for the most part, been scrupulously avoided in the family melodrama. On daytime serials it has been introduced on rare occasions, only to be hastily dropped. One of its strongest taboos, homosexuality has appeared in the film melodrama only in disguised, ambiguous ways, accessible only to an audience ready to understand the gay subtext.[4] Recently, homosexuality has entered the domain of the family melodrama to a limited degree as a potential threat to the monogamous, child-bearing, heterosexual couple which must constantly be affirmed. One of *Dynasty*'s most sensational subplots concerned the open gayness of Blake Carrington's son, Steven. Steven's gayness is played off against his sister Fallon's nearly incestual attachment to her father. Blake Carrington reacts violently to his son's sexual preference, using all his power to stop Steven's homosexual activity, and eventually murdering Steven's gay lover "accidentally." Shortly after the murder and ensuing trial, Steven suddenly, inexplicably became heterosexual, marrying a young, scheming, fortune hunter. After one season of marriage—which was an utter failure—Steven announced at the end of the 1981–82 series that he was gay after all and he would not let his family pressure him any longer. This assertion of independence coincided, however, with his character being written out of the show. The *Dynasty* example illustrates some of the ways that homosexuality profoundly disrupts the conventions of the family melodrama and its ideal of the nuclear family. Since good sexuality must always be directed towards marriage and children in the family melodrama, homosexuality must either be associated with villainy and neuroses, or banished altogether.

Making Love (directed by Arthur Hiller, the man who gave us *Love Story*) introduced the topic of homosexuality and reconciled it with the conventions and ideology of the family melodrama. The film treats homosexuality in the framework of a story about marital infidelity—instead of "the other woman," "the other man" threatens the marriage. The character Claire is a woman who believes she has everything: a perfect marriage and a successful career. In the world of the family melodrama, this situation makes her a prime candidate for misfortune and suffering. When Claire leaves town for the weekend on a business trip, her husband becomes sexually involved with another man, Bart (Harry Hamlin). While the film does not blame Claire for her husband's wandering, this plot device reinforces the common cautionary theme that women who work outside the home can never be secure about what goes on within it. While *Making Love* is explicitly sympathetic in its portrayal of the husband, Zach, and the process of his coming out, it also presents him as an exceptional gay may who rejects the promiscuous gay lifestyle presented in the film. On the other hand, his lover Bart is criticized as childish, narcissistic, selfish, insecure and incapable of love. Bart's resistance to a monogamous relationship with Zach stems from his immaturity, the film asserts, and dooms him to a life of unhappiness. The most important thing in personal life is monogamy, *Making Love* proclaims, and homosexuality can be accepted if it duplicates the heterosexual model of the couple. Zach is validated as an exceptional man—this is the liberalness of the film that it does not matter if he is straight or gay—while Claire and Bart (woman and most gays) are presented as objects of pity—suffering and somehow pathetic. Throughout the film, Claire and Bart deliver monologues in direct address, discussing their love for Zach as though speaking to a psychotherapist. Both characters have lost him—this exceptional man—and both are victims.

Homosexuality has also entered the realm of film melodramas as jokes, passing remarks. In films such as *Julia*, *Girlfriends* and *An Unmarried Woman*, lesbianism receives mention in order to be ardently denied. The heroines of these women's films must be cleared of the slightest suspicion of a sexual element in their relationships with other women, apparently, in order to properly function as objects of identification. In *Personal Best*, the lesbian relationship between the two women athletes exists merely as a "phase" which the Mariel Hemingway character must pass through on the road to heterosexuality. Immediately after leaving her female lover, she is recuperated into what the film presents as a normal, healthy and mature relationship with a male athlete.

Anxiety about monogamy and the stability of the nuclear family repeatedly appears in recent family melodramas in their treatment of divorce. Because films such as *Kramer vs. Kramer, The Four Seasons, Shoot the Moon* and *An Unmarried Woman* began with separation or divorce, the causes of disruption in the family become obsured. Rather than dealing with why couples divorce, the films focus on the effects of divorce, particularly on children—their feelings of confusion, rejection and apprehension. The importance placed on the children's points of view in these films functions as an implicit recrimination of the parents for separating, and the lack of dramatic representation of married life before the separation increases the blame and guilt directed towards the parents. These films suggest that children are irreparably and incalculably damaged by separation and divorce; the effect on children of living in a home with parents who do not wish to remain married never surfaces at all. As the children are set up as objects of pity and sympathy, the parents' claims to independence, individual identity, satisfaction and fulfillment dwindle in importance. The parents tax our compassion far less than the children in these films.

Films dealing with divorce also underscore the children's shock and confusion about sexual matters, the result of their knowledge that their mother and father are having sexual relationships with other people. In *Kramer vs. Kramer,* this was treated humorously in the scene where the son runs into a naked woman (who is humiliated and embarrassed) as she emerges from his father's bedroom. In *Shoot the Moon, The Turning Point* and *An Unmarried Woman,* the children become alternately voyeuristic about their parents' sexual activity and harshly condemning. In the value system of the family melodrama, sexual satisfaction can never rival the importance of children's happiness, security and innocence. Parents are implicitly recriminated any time their children become conscious of their extra-marital sexual activity.

This message becomes most overt in *On Golden Pond*, one of the most popular family melodramas in recent years. The thirteen year old boy, Billy (Douglas McKeon), who comes to stay with Ethel and Norman Thayer, is presented as a victim of divorce: caught between his parents, lacking love and guidance, feeling unwanted and insecure, precocious in an unhealthy way. When he comes into contact with the Thayers and their entirely traditional marriage, his character is transformed overnight.

Exposed to such an old-fashioned kind of family, he becomes calm, polite, obedient, outgoing, compassionate and thoughtful. By adopting the Thayers as surrogate parents, the boy is cured of his bad behavior and bad manners, and finds security and contentment doing things suitable for his age. The marriage in *On Golden Pond* proves to be an ideal environment for children compared to the nightmare of the modern family. In the good old days, says *On Golden Pond*, before all this nonsense about feminism and sexual liberation, families were places of refuge and healing, and children were happy in them.

Men as the Heart of the Family Melodrama

The family melodrama has always concerned itself with the scrutiny of gender roles. There is an obsessive questioning of the behavior of characters in terms of their family relationships and a delineation of what is appropriate for mothers and fathers, wives and husbands, daughters and sons. Because the stability of the family is seen as ultimately dependent on women, female characters have tended to be objects of the harshest scrutiny in the family melodrama. This has tended to put women at the center of the narrative; it has also reinforced the notion that in terms of women's responsibility for family their work is truly never done. In the classic melodramas of the nineteen-thirties and -forties, the heroines were never let off the hook: whether they loved their children too much (*Mildred Pierce*, 1945) or not enough (*Imitation of Life*, 1934), cared too much about the home (*Craig's Wife*, 1936) or too much about a career (*A Star Is Born*, 1937), sacrificed everything for love (*Back Street*, 1932), or married for convenience (*Gilda*, 1946), were unable to have children (*Penny Serenade*, 1941), or did not want any (*Leave Her to Heaven*, 1946). At worst, family melodramas reinforce women's anxieties about their responsibility to family; at best, they reveal, by compounding contradictions with coincidence and circumstance, the impossibility for women to ever sustain such a burden.

In recent family melodramas, a discourse is going on about masculine behavior and personality, posed as the especially "contemporary" question of whether men can and should alter their behavior in the family. This has entailed a shift in the focus of the narrative, a new emphasis on male characters evident in the narrative structure and exposition, the amount of screen time allotted to male characters, the nature of that screen time (in terms of privileged dramatic time such as private moments) and the establishment of point of view through close-ups, over-the-shoulder shots, "seeing" shots, etc. The advertising for these recent family melodramas reflects this shift as well, with male characters equal if not more prominent than female characters.

In the past few years, soap operas have introduced a greater number of male characters and branched out into plot lines that belong conventionally to male action-oriented genres. The new material, international spy rings as on *General Hospital* or mad scientists stranding characters in the Amazon as on *One Life to Life* or underworld crime as on *The Young and the Restless* (and many others), resemble prime time programs much more closely than traditional soap opera material which remained within the realm of women, the family and personal life. The success of this development in terms of audience response is questionable. *General Hospital* was at the top of the ratings when the character Laura (Genie Francis) left the program to pursue a career in film and prime time television. After her departure, the plot fixed on her costar, Tony Geary, the character Luke, and a series of increasingly adventuresome escapades which required the nearly constant display of Luke's cunning, physical grace and bravery. At the same time, the show dropped out of first place in the Nielsen ratings for daytime serials and was replaced by *All My Children*, one of the few soap operas which did not experiment with such action sub-plots and retained its focus on female characters. A general trend back to traditional soap opera themes now is evident on most of the programs, another testament to the important function soap operas fill as popular culture specifically for and about women.

The primary difference between prime time programs such as *Dallas* and *Dynasty* and the daytime serials is the centrality of a male character to the narrative. The charismatic, if sometimes diabolical, characters J.R. Ewing and Blake Carrington bear little resemblance to conventional soap opera protagonists. Much of the plot revolves around masculine competition and intrigue in the business world. While women are affected by and sometimes become embroiled in these financial matters, they exist largely as appendages to the men. Often women characters exist in the story as prizes to be won by the men, rewards for the shrewdness and material success which *Dallas* and *Dynasty* are preoccupied with (even if they must occasionally raise moral objections to its consequences). In comparison to daytime soap operas, scenes between two women characters are much less frequent on *Dallas* and *Dynasty*, whereas scenes between two male characters occur more frequently. All characters on the show, but women in particular, are defined by their relationship to the central figure (J.R.'s wife, ex-wife, mistress, ex-mistress, etc.). Action takes place in the city, rather than the small town community of soap operas, and much of it in public space. Characters meet in bars, restaurants, elevators, courtrooms, lobbies and offices; establishing shots of hi-rise office buildings, from angles which are more than suggestive of their phallic symbolism, abound on both programs. While the treatment of themes such as unwanted pregnancy, paternity questions, divorce, infidelity, madness, and parent-child relations make them similar to the daytime serials, the centrality of the male protagonist alters and limits their treatment and makes them much less relevant to an audience of women.

Compared to the scrutiny which women characters receive when they are the focus of a family melodrama, the dominating male figures of *Dallas* and *Dynasty* are treated with a remarkable degree of permissiveness. When J.R. Ewing and Blake Carrington display ambition, ruthlessness, tough-mindedness, it is made clear that they have only learned how to hurt others out of an instinct for survival. The abundance of villainy on *Dallas* and *Dynasty* suggests that they have made the only possible adjustment to the dog-eat-dog world of oil barons; they are merely doing what they have to in order to maintain their power. Most of the men on these programs have powerful egos; J. R. Ewing and Blake Carrington have the most powerful of all, yet are shown to be in a constant state of struggle and vulnerability because of this. When these men behave badly, it is presented either as amusing (as on *Dallas*) or understandable because of the complexities of the character's psychological makeup (as on *Dynasty*). Never are these characters recriminated for their shortcomings the way female characters routinely are in family melodramas. Blame, guilt and incessant self-examination are entirely absent; J. R. Ewing and Blake Carrington are allowed to hurt others on a regular basis and continue to live well. At the same time, the slightest display of tenderness or kindness from a character like Blake Carrington is lavished with praise—a level of sympathy which distinguishes him from conventional melodramatic villains. These men are also extremely involved with and sentimental about their own children—always a positive attribute in the family melodrama. *Dallas* and *Dynasty* have not only placed men at the center of the melodramatic world, they have changed the conventional standards for moral judgment of the characters. J. R. Ewing and Blake Carrington live remarkably guilt-free lives compared to the soap opera heroines for whom one mistake, one instance of causing a loved one pain, results in a lifetime of self-reproach.

In feature films the trend toward placing men at the heart of the family melodrama began with *Kramer vs. Kramer* and *Ordinary People*, which showed us that if men choose to take on the historically feminine responsibility of parenting they can do an even better job of it than women, provide even more sympathy and nurturance. The masculine prerogative extends in these films to the one area where women have traditionally enjoyed control and superiority, with the result that men, once they begin participating in that sphere, take it over entirely. At the end of *Kramer vs. Kramer* and *Ordinary People*, women are banished from the nuclear family altogether, which then consists only of the idealized and sentimentalized father-son relationship.

Taken together, the films *Making Love*, *Shoot the Moon* and *On Golden Pond* offer a clear and consistent message about masculine behavior in the family and the possibilities for change in gender roles. In *Making Love*, Zach is the ideal husband: selfless, patient, supportive, nurturing—all the qualities, in fact, which are traditionally expected of a wife. Zach's relationship with Claire allows her to attain a high degree of success at work. The character Zach has enormous appeal for women, but the film insists upon the impossibility of such a fantasy; as wonderful as Zach may be, he is a man no woman can have. At the end of the film, Claire, a woman who came so close to having everything, appears destined for a lifetime of unfulfilled love. The film offers women a consoling message: "You could not ask a 'real man'—a heterosexual one—to behave this way."

On Golden Pond and *Shoot the Moon* treat the opposite type of masculine personality, the bastard. Henry Fonda's Norman Thayer and Albert Finney's George are proud, selfish, irritable and belligerent. Yet *On Golden Pond* is apologist, even nostalgic about Norman Thayer's behavior. The film encourages us to accept the Hepburn character's judgment of Thayer—that of a devoted, long-suffering wife—as a lovable old "poop." The film plays off the wife's judgment of Norman against that of his daughter, who condemns him as cold and unloving. The mother calls Chelsea (Jane Fonda) childish for failing to understand and sympathize with Norman when he behaves in a mean and punishing way. In the course of the film Chelsea, inspired by the emotional insight that the thirteen year old visitor, Billy, immediately had into Norman's character, comes to accept her mother's judgment of Norman and is reconciled with him. No one should ask men like Norman Thayer to change their behavior, or blame them when they hurt others, the film insists. Such men must be pampered, forgiven and understood so that they may reveal their truly sensitive interiors.

Shoot the Moon presents the behavior of the father George much more ambiguously and poses it as a much more serious problem within the family. Unlike *On Golden Pond*, the film does not adopt an overtly sympathetic attitude towards the central male character. George's irruption into domestic violence is the logical extension of his personality and psycholgogy as the film presents it. *Shoot the Moon* is unusual in that it makes the connection between this kind of masculine behavior and violence, and it situates domestic violence in an upper middle class environment. On one level the film seems harshly condemning of George and the type of man, the bastard personality, that he represents and implies that such men are hopeless cases. On another level, the film seems to be a warning that such men will become mad and violent if women refuse to take care of them. George is the man Norman would have become if he had not had such a good woman devoted to him through the years.

In both *On Golden Pond* and *Shoot the Moon*, the female characters are implicated in the behavior of the men. Ethel Thayer's unswerving allegiance to her husband separates her from her daughter and makes her the apologist for the most negative aspects of Norman's behavior. Ethel Thayer is clearly presented as the most mature, the wisest of the family members, yet she is defined exclusively as a man's woman. The character Faith in *Shoot the Moon* is an excellent mother, devoted to her four daughters, and a much more likeable and well-balanced personality than her husband George. Faith's continuing, sentimental affection for George even after his repeated acts of violence, however, implicate her in his behavior. Both films stress the indelibility of the marriage tie under any circumstances, and women's obligation to men regardless of their behavior. The films show the pain and destruction which traditional male behavior causes in the family, but conclude that the only hope for saving the family rests with women adhering to their nurturing, patient, forgiving roles as wives, mothers and daughters.

In terms of moral judgments, family melodramas continue to be rather soft on men and extremely harsh on women, even when women no longer hold the center of narrative interest. Limitless sympathy is suggested as the proper treatment for a man like Norman Thayer in *On Golden Pond*; for an umsympathetic mother immediate rejection from the family is proscribed as in *Ordinary People*. In the past, family melodramas were unique among genres in presenting some of the ways women are victimized socially and in the family. The erasure of women's point of view as the dominant one on the family, and the displacement of women characters signals a retrograde move for the genre, and the loss for women of a form of popular culture which has great potential for speaking to our experience.

Notes

1. *Dallas* on CBS and *Dynasty* on ABC have the highest Nielsen ratings among the prime time serials, which is the reason I have chosen them as examples. Other serials, such as *Knot's Landing* and *Falcon Crest* (both on CBS), may have more emphasis on female characters and traditional soap opera narratives.
2. Films belonging to this category are by no means limited to the nineteen-fifties. However, titles from the fifties include *Bigger Than Life* (1956), *Cat on a Hot Tin Roof* (1958), *Come Back, Little Sheba* (1953), *The Dark at the Top of the Stairs* (1960), *Rebel Without a Cause* (1955), and *The Wild One* (1954).
3. This convergence of the family melodrama and the love story formula seems particularly suited to films about adolescence and young adulthood. *Ice Castles*, *The Promise* and *You Light Up My Life* are other examples of this type of film.
4. See Richard Dyer, "Stereotyping," in *Gays in Film*, Richard Dyer, ed. (London: BFI, 1977), pp. 27–39.

EUROPEAN AND LATIN AMERICAN MELODRAMA

While critical attention has been focused primarily on Hollywood melodrama (and more recently British), there has been only sporadic attention paid to the production of melodrama in other parts of the world. This section makes no pretense of covering the globe, but it aims to suggest other traditions and other practices as well as addressing recent attempts to subvert melodramatic conventions and attitudes. Melodrama was a prominent genre in the European silent cinema, as exemplified in the French and Italian historical films, costume and social melodramas. Initially melodrama was not directed to the middle classes alone but also to the working classes. To meet the moral objections of critics and the threat of censorship in the middle of the first decade of the twentieth century, melodrama was adapted to suit the tastes and ethical concerns of the bourgeoisie.

Richard Abel's essay traces the evolution of bourgeois melodrama in the French silent cinema. Drawing on Peter Brook's *The Melodramatic Imagination*, Abel affirms that early French melodramas are preoccupied with ethical and psychic truths, and, moreover, that melodrama is not removed from realism and from ordinary life but seeks rather to heighten everyday experience. Threats to the integrity of the family are central and the ideological work of melodrama affirms the power and legitimacy of the family unit with the father or a paternal surrogate at its hẹad. While certain early film melodramas portray working-class characters and situations, the more principal direction lay in those films that were designed to attract a bourgeois clientele. The plots of these films were dependent on intrigue and intrigue, and the films were preoccupied with conflicts concerning the legitimacy of marriage as an institution, especially with questions of infidelity and libertinism which are resolved through the elimination of the discordant elements that undermine family stability.

The popularity of French melodrama continued to grow during World War I, influenced by such films as DeMille's *The Cheat* and Italian melodramas of the era. While some of these films are sensitive to wartime conflict between personal gratification and nationalism, others concentrate on the cinematic medium, experimenting with film language to express their melodramatic scenarios. The postwar era continued to see the growth of melodramas, though increasingly the films were to break their ties to the theater, as evidenced in the style of Raymond Bernard, Louis Delluc, and Germaine Dulac. In particular, their films are representative of a more psychological treatment, exploring the character's states of mind through the uses of lighting, setting, framing, and props. In the mid-1920s, with the concerted emphasis by filmmakers on creating a cinema of quality, the bourgeois melodrama was abosrbed into other genres. Abel's essay documents the importance of melodrama in the development of cinematic language and in the development of the French national cinema.

My discussion of the Italian melodramas of the early 1940s focuses particularly on Visconti's *Osessione*. Melodrama in the latter years of fascism became a vehicle for obliquely dramatizing social discontents. *Osessione*, based on James M. Cain's *The Postman Always Rings Twice*, self-consciously appropriates the American text to signify not only the failure of social institutions and personal relationships but also the failure of prevailing Italian cinematic forms. Melodrama, because of its focus on the personal and the familial, is a safe genre for presenting a critique of the status quo, as has been amply demonstrated through Sirk's films. Moreover, by centering on the private domain, it allows for the exploration of the subjective attitudes that dramatize the personal loyalties which underpin the adherence of prevailing norms.

Since fascism could not have endured through the application of mere force alone but was also dependent on consent, the melodramas help to chart how the political was also personal, part of a network of loyalties, expectations, desires, values, and behaviors in which individuals were enmeshed. The decor of the films, their use of setting, the characters, the portrayal of personal aspirations and failures create an obsessive repetitive climate which is intimately tied to repression and oppression. In the case of Visconti's film, sexuality is a central force for channeling desire, characteristic of how personal needs and desires under fascism were directed toward self-destructive ends.

In the more recent German cinema, the films of Rainer Werner Fassbinder have been identified as working self-consciously within melodramatic conventions toward the ends of demystifying German culture and society as well as the melodramatic ethos. Fassbinder openly acknowledged his dept to Douglas Sirk, situating himself within a similar context for filmmaking. After a brief period of experimenting with avant-garde theater and cinema, he turned his attention first to the making of films, and, later, to television narratives, which would have mass appeal, would make his audiences "think and feel." As a German and as a political filmmaker who was experimenting with how to make political issues accessible to his audiences, Fassbinder, like Visconti, wove the history of fascism into his allegorical narratives.

Ruth McCormick's essay on the films of Rainer Werner Fassbinder does not explicitly discuss melodrama, but her analysis of the filmmaker's work reveals the centrality of the melodramatic imagination. According to McCormick, Fassbinder's films are preoccupied with love. They are "a litany of the failures of love in the world." His characters are driven by the quest for the satisfaction of personal desire which ends usually in self-destruction. In the estranged world portrayed in his films, characters are frustrated by their internalized oppression, expressed particularly in their desire for domination. Like Sirk's characters, Fassbinder's are trapped in their illusions. The politics of his films are fueled by the personal melodramas of the characters which block them from arriving at any awareness of their predicaments. In the content and style of his films, melodrama seems to function not as consolation or containment but in cautionary fashion to demonstrate for the audience the dead end of "incorrect feeling."

Katherine Woodward examines the films of Godard, Truffaut, and Fassbinder in the context of "anti-melodrama." She defines anti-melodrama as an attempt to corrode the effects of melodrama. Anti-melodrama shares the modernist tendency to distance the spectator from the dilemmas of the characters, seeking to generate a critical awareness of characters and events. The films employ conventional melodramatic characters and incidents but undermine the spectator's visual and thematic expectations. Through a number of techniques such as reversing the order of injury and reconciliation, refusing to romanticize illness, blurring ethical distinctions, and self-consciously emphasizing spectatorship, anti-melodramas seek to make apparent and hence neutralize the conventional affective appeal of melodrama.

Melodrama is not unique to American, British, and European cinema. As Ana Lopez indicates, melodrama is also popular in Latin America, in both cinema and television. Melodrama has a long history in the Latin American cinema, a history that is indigenous and not merely an offshoot of Hollywood. Like the French New Wave cinema and the films of Rainer Werner Fassbinder, the new Latin American cinema rejected melodrama, seeing it as an instrument of domination in bourgeois culture. By rejecting this popular form, the cinema also rejected the very people it wanted to address. In their attempt to create an antibourgeois political cinema, filmmakers turned away from melodrama, and popular audiences turned away from their films in favor of television which was growing and popularizing melodrama. Through the *telenovelas* which appear to be an off-shoot of the North American soap opera but are in fact different, melodrama seems to be thriving in Latin America. However, as Lopez argues, these melodramas cannot be read as merely reproducing traditional values and attitudes but as playing a more complex role as sites of cultural resistance.

French Film Melodrama Before and After the Great War

RICHARD ABEL

Of the more or less distinct film genres that played a prominent role in early French cinema, especially in the emergence of its strategies of representation and narration, perhaps the least acknowledged has been the bourgeois family melodrama. The genre's immediate origins lay in Pathé-Frères' "realist and dramatic scenes," one of the more popular of a dozen film *séries* that the company advertised in its catalogues between 1904 and 1909.[1] In conjunction with the prewar realist films, perhaps best exemplified by Louis Feuillade's *Scènes de la vie telle qu'elle est* (1911–1912), the genre then developed through several series distributed by Pathé, particularly those starring Mistinguett and Gabrielle Robinne and directed by Georges Monca and René Leprince. As the films in these series lengthened into feature films, their scenarios came more and more to be adapted from or echo—and the films even to supplant—the bourgeois melodramas of the boulevard theaters in Belle Epoque Paris. During the war, largely as a result of restrictions on theater performances, the cinema soon came to serve as the principal arena for the presentation of melodrama—as in, for instance, Monca's "Scènes de la vie bourgeoise," starring the still renowned Gabrielle Robinne. And it was the wartime genre of bourgeois family melodramas that provided the initial impetus—through films such as Abel Gance's *Mater Dolorosa* (1917)—for what would become, after the war, a full-fledged French narrative avant-garde practice.

This preliminary historical sketch can serve as a framework for the ensuing analysis of surviving film prints from each of the principal stages in the genre's development

---

This essay is a much revised version of a chapter from Richard Abel, *French Cinema: The First Wave, 1915–1929* (Princeton: Princeton University Press, 1984), pp. 85–94.

before, during, and after the Great War. The approach taken here is less totalizing than that of Roger Icart, for instance, who sees melodrama underpinning nearly all of the "serious" film genres marketed by the early French film industry.[2] Yet its conception of a distinct genre relies, as does Icart's, on the conventions of nineteenth-century French stage melodrama, which perhaps are best described in Peter Brooks's seminal study. *The Melodramatic Imagination.*[3] Several of Brooks's concepts seem especially pertinent to these early French films. From its inception, in the aftermath of the French Revolution, Brooks writes, "melodrama takes as its concern and raison d'être the location, expression, and imposition of basic ethical and psychic truths."[4] Specifically, its characters "assume primary psychic roles, father, mother, child"; and its narrative presents first the blockage or eclipse of virtue and then its eventual confirmation and restoration—both of which features assume the family and its domestic sphere of personal relationships as the principal institution legitimizing a bourgeois social order.[5] As a corollary, melodrama strives "to make the 'real' and the 'ordinary' and 'private life' interesting through heightened utterance and gesture" as well as to "make its representations clear and legible for everyone."[6] Finally, in the specific domain of the theater, it transforms the stage into an "arena for represented, visual meaning [accompanied by music] . . . most especially at the end of scenes and acts," where meaning is resolved in *tableau*, "in a visual summary of the emotional situation."[7] As Brooks himself suggests, the twentieth-century popular art form "that most relayed and supplanted melodrama" was the cinema.[8]

Many of these melodrama conventions seem to have been specifically exploited in Pathé's "realist and dramatic scenes" or what Rémy de Gourmont called, in a famous 1907 essay on the cinema, "scenes of domestic life."[9] *A Father's Honor. The Stepmother. Child Kidnapped. The Poor Mother. Distress. The Fate of Life. The False Coin. Falsely Condemned.* These titles come from surviving prints of one-reel French films, most of them released by Pathé between 1905 and 1908.[10] All of them tell stories (drawn from "original" scenarios) of contemporary family traumas, of the threatened or actual loss to the family of a father or a child (but rarely a mother), and of the eventual restoration of the original or else a substitute family unit. The families tend to be petit bourgeois or even working-class, with the exception of the bourgeois family who can hire a detective in *Child Kidnapped* (Pathé 1906); and at least four of the films trace a nightmarish fall through accident or mistaken identity into destitution and/or criminality. *The Fate of Life* (Pathé 1908), which focuses on a father and his young daughter, is perhaps the most extreme. The daughter is hit and injured by a passing automobile; the father loses his low-level clerical job and then is mistakenly arrested for robbing the office safe; and the daughter is sent to an orphanage. Once released from prison, the father finds that his criminal record keeps him from holding even a menial job, and he is forced to join a band of thieves. When one thief attacks a lone woman in a bourgeois house they plan to rob, he turns on them and assists in their arrest. The woman promptly hires him to be her gardener and then shows him his daughter whom, coincidentally, she seems to have adopted. All these twists of fate and reversals of fortune occur in just nineteen shot-scenes.[11] The family relationship and the father's centrality to that relationship are restored, but with an unusual shift upward in socioeconomic position (at least for the daughter). What is not unusual at all, however, is that, just as the father's virtue or right wins out, it is sanctioned by the police—whose ideological function of confirmation and reconciliation recurs in no less than five of the other films.[12]

All of these film melodramas from 1905 to 1908 clearly provide some evidence of the shift recent film historians have noted during this period, from a so-called primitive "cinema of attractions" to a "cinema of narrative integration."[13] Spectacle of one kind or another and features unique to the cinema do tend in these films to be integrated into the process of narrativization. *A Father's Honor* (Pathé 1905), for instance, includes the "attraction" of an LS pan[14] as a boy is checking traps along the wooded bank of a river, a pan that ends on his discovery of the body of a young woman whose murder her father will avenge. Both *Child Kidnapped* and *The False Coin* (Pathé 1908) break scenes down into several shots, repeatedly intercutting adjacent exterior spaces by shifting the camera either 135 or 180 degrees—in one, to coincide with the entrances and exits to the kidnappers' cabin; in the other, to represent a boy's discovery of a counterfeiting operation through a café cellar window.[15] The two films also include cut-ins within a scene, in order to reveal crucial information—in one, to a CU of the kidnappers' ransom note and, in the other, to an MS of the unscrupulous café owner minting fake coins.[16] While *The Stepmother* (Gaumont 1907) and, to a lesser extent, *Distress* (Pathé 1907) and *The False Coin* present relatively detailed set decors to suggest the poverty of their central characters, others exploit the spectacle of "deep space" in various location framings.[17] *The Fate of Life*, for instance, uses a wide-open frame on a grassy slope overlooking a wall and city rooftops at the point when the unemployed father is propositioned by the thieves. *Falsely Condemned* (Pathé 1908), by contrast, creates a deep, boxed-in frame down the length of a grape arbor as the "bad guys" follow a prosperous peasant they will rob and murder in the next shot, a crime for which the postman in the film will be mistakenly arrested. And in the final shot of *A Father's Honor*, on a wooded path that stretches into the far background, two policemen chase the murder suspect toward the father, who waits with his gun (in the left foreground) to shoot him and then be congratulated for his deed. In the "deep space" of the world outside the home, most of these films imply, everyone from children to adults is vulnerable to evil characters, accidents, and misrecognition.

The one film excluded so far from this discussion, *The Poor Mother* (Pathé 1906), differs from the others in several ways; yet it perhaps most strikingly exemplifies what Brooks calls the "melodramatic mode of expression." This film tells the story of a working-class mother (she does "put-out work" on a sewing machine) in a one-room apartment who, after her young daughter dies from an accidental fall, becomes an alcoholic and eventually dies in a hospital for the indigent. In the opening scene, an insert LS of a military band marching in the street seems to function as a loosely defined POV shot to motivate the girl's attraction to the apartment window from which she leans out too far and falls. Thereafter, the girl reappears to the mother as a superimposed image in three different situations. In the first, she materializes and then disappears in the apartment itself, as if to reiterate the mother's sense of loss and clearly motivate her drinking. In the second, as the mother sits on a park bench, the girl dissolves in to replace another girl whom the mother has noticed playing nearby and set on her lap. Here a cut in from LS to AmS foregrounds the replacement and seems to heighten the emotional intensity of the mother's desire to regain her daughter. In the third, the girl materializes over her mother in the hospital bed; they reach out toward each other just before the mother falls back and dies, as if to signal a promised reunion. In earlier films such as those of Méliès, the technique of superimposition was often exploited as magical illusion and/or comic trickery; here it functions instead within a certain kind of narrative to represent an emotional situation more intensely, as the visual equivalent of "heightened utterance and gesture." The "visual summary" of this ending tableau in *The Poor Mother,* furthermore, is not unlike that of the other films. Both *The Stepmother* and *Falsely Condemned,* for instance, return in their final shots to a replication of the opening—in the one, a father and son are reunited in their home after the expulsion of a tyrannical stepmother and her daughter; in the other, the postman returns exonerated to his family and resumes his daily round. And in *Child Kidnapped,* a final, isolated MS portrait of a smiling father, mother, and daughter succinctly summarizes the ideological project these early film melodramas seem determined to serve.[18]

As Pathé's catalogue classification suggests, one path of development for French film melodrama lay in the realist films that Gaumont, now, as well as Pathé, began to market as a separate film genre around 1911. Gaumont's advertisement for Feuillade's *Scènes de la vie telle qu'elle est* can stand as a credo for this new series of film.

> These scenes are intended to be slices of life. If they are interesting and compelling, it is because of the quality of virtue which emerges from and inspires them. They eschew all fantasy, and represent people and things as they are and not as they should be. And by treating only those subjects which can be viewed by anyone, they prove more elevated and more significant as expressions of morality than do those falsely tragic or stupidly sentimental tales which leave no more trace in the memory than on the projection screen.[19]

The intention to present "slices of life" and to "represent people and things as they are," of course, invokes the French tradition of a realist or even naturalistic aesthetic as well as the nineteenth-century obsession with producing a simulacrum of reality. Yet other phrases—"the quality of virtue" and "expressions of morality"—come from the not unrelated aesthetic tradition of nineteenth-century French melodrama. This suggests that melodrama conventions were not at all foreign to the early realist film genre, and a cursory examination of such representative films as Feuillade's *Les Vipères* (1911) and Gérard Bourgeois's "social drama" for Pathé. *Le Demon du jeu* (1911), demonstrate that that is indeed the case. Like their predecessors, these films also are drawn from "original" scenarios and tell contemporary stories of traumatic losses involving a humiliating shift downward in social position; but how and why those losses occur and to whom, as well as what proves to be their eventual outcome, have changed. Although these narrative changes result in sharp differences in the work of these particular filmmakers, the films generally do narrativize similar forms of spectacle and features unique to the cinema for the increasingly overt purpose of heightening crucial emotional situations.

The title of Bourgeois's "social drama"—*Le Demon du jeu* (October 1911)—clearly indicates one of these changes in narrative.[20] A young bourgeois gentleman becomes obsessed with gambling at cards and is forced to steal from his father's office to cover his losses and then loses the money he has stolen; finally, he is refused forgiveness at the bedside of his dying father. Whereas chance or accident or misrecognition caused the dramatic plot turns for the central characters in the earlier films, here such a turn is socially or psychologically, if somewhat simplistically, determined. Although Bourgeois's film follows its predecessors by privileging a male figure as central to the family, instead of confirming the son's dignity or virtuousness and restoring family harmony, it traces a steady, inexorable descent to catastrophe.[21] Yet *Le Demon du jeu* also deploys newly emerging representational strategies to heighten the son's emotional situation. His desperate robbery attempt, for instance, is intensified by single-source arc lighting from an office side window.[22] And the "deep space" spectacle of the gambling den—which stretches into a raised adjacent room in the background and whose painted perspective ceiling is accentuated by a waist-level camera—makes it an attractive milieu not only for the young gambler but for the spectator as well.

Released concurrently with Bourgeois's "social dramas," Feuillade's first films for the *Vie telle qu'elle est* series narrate strikingly different stories, which are generally typical of the series as a whole. They focus often on single women or mothers rather than on fathers; they put in social forces that determine the dramatic plot turns; and, by the end, they seem to compromise the ideological project of restoring and confirming the family and respectable bourgeois society as the locus of virtue. In *Les Vipères* (April 1911),[23] for instance, a young widow is evicted from a run-down dwelling in a provincial town and then is hired as a domestic servant by the local gendarme to care for his invalid wife and their new son. The townspeople refuse to accept the woman and spread rumors about her and the gendarme, until finally the wife, believing them, angrily turns her out into the street again. In the recurring dimly lit central room of the gendarme's home, the position of the characters and their movements establish a sort of "staging in depth" paradigm for much of the film.[24] The invalid wife usually occupies the left-center foreground of the frame; characters enter and exit through a door to the exterior in the right background; and while the young woman ranges around the room and even seems to displace the wife at one point, she alone can occupy the right foreground, where she once arranges a white vase of flowers. The recurring central room and repeated paradigm of character position and movement produce a tightly unified, almost mechanistic structure, much more so than in the Bourgeois film; and these formal patterns seem to overdetermine the melodramatic/naturalistic "fatalism" of the story. As the rumors pass through several social sites of hostility (the school, the grocer's shop, the café), and the young woman is expelled from each, they reach the crucial site of contested possession, the family home, from which two women friends and finally the mayor persuade the wife to "evict" her as well. The final shot of *Les Vipères*, particularly through its lighting, resolves the film's meaning in a simple symbolic tableau. Through the darkness of the child's room, the young woman moves slowly in an arc from right foreground (where the crib is situated) to right background, where she pauses momentarily in the door she opens and then closes in exiting. Her decentered position in the frame, together with the briefly visible empty space of the room, seems to evacuate the home as a social site of meaning.[25]

The principal line of development for the French film melodrama, however, lay in several other prewar film series, all of which were produced and distributed by Pathé. Unlike the earlier films or those of Feuillade, most of these now were literary adaptations, drawn from recent plays written for the Paris stage—by the likes of Henry Bernstein, Henry Bataille, and Paul Hervieu—or else from theatrical adaptations of nineteenth-century novels.[26] And in order to produce them, Pathé engaged more and more major directors and actors from the theater in Paris. Georges Monca, for instance, produced a popular series of one-reel films with Mistinguett, the music hall singer and boulevard theater actress—*L'Empreinte* (1909), *Souris d'hotêl* (1910), *Fleur de pavé* (1911).[27] Along with his colleague, René Leprince, Monca then directed the three- to five-reel films of the Comédie Française star Gabrielle Robinne, some of which were distributed under the series title of *Scènes de la vie cruelle* (1912–1913).[28] Beginning in 1912, Camille de Morlhon also contributed three- to five-reel "modern dramas" drawn from his own scenarios and produced by his own company, Valetta Films, under contract to Pathé.[29] All of these series, of course, evidenced Pathé's determination, after the initiative launched by Film d'Art in 1908–09, to attract a bourgeois clientele to the cinema on a more regular basis. Not unexpectedly, their subjects generally assumed the socioeconomic context of the high and middle bourgeoisie, especially in Paris. Patrons of the boulevard theaters and Opéra could find familiar settings: Renaissance dining rooms, Louis XV bedrooms, and Empire offices.[30] There were familiar plots, too, full of lurid intrigue and sometimes violent action, usually predicated on the "eternal love triangle" or the threat of a *mésalliance* between individuals of different social classes.[31] At the center was the question of a man or woman's commitment to a particular social practice of marriage and the consequent affirmation of the bourgeois family as the locus of moral and spiritual value and, hence, social stability.

None of the films directed by Monca and Leprince apparently survives from this period, so that the Cinémathèque Française's recently rediscovered print of Monca's *Le Petit Chose* (1912) will have to be taken, for the moment at least, as representative.[32] Based on an adaptation of Alphonse Daudet's novel, *Le Petit Chose* tells the story of a prodigal son (Pierre Pradier) who is tempted away from his bourgeois family in Lyon by the libertine world of the theater in Paris. The young man fails as a lycée teacher in the capital (he cannot instill discipline) and, through his older brother Jacques (Bosc), becomes secretary to a marquis, who introdues him to the theater, where he falls in love with a seductive actress, Irma Borel (Gabrielle Robinne). In the end, on his deathbed, Jacques gets him to give up the actress and marry Camille Pierrotte (Andrée Pascal), whom his family had chosen originally as his fiancée. What is immediately striking about *Le Petit Chose* is its consistent reliance on autonomous shot-scenes (recorded by a fixed waist-level camera), some of which have insert intertitles of notes and letters. Only one scene breaks this pattern; the difference is an insert, softly masked CU photograph of Camille at which "Le Petit Chose" is gazing just before Irma arrives to win him over one last time. With the exception of several location shots—a train station, a passenger boat on the Seine, and a wooded park—most of the scenes take place within studio interiors, whose decors and lighting are frankly unexceptional. The film thus assumes a rather restrictive system of representation and narration, especially in comparison to earlier Pathé and Gaumont films, a system that depends almost exclusively on the skill of the actors and that of the director in choreographing their movement, and perhaps inadvertently reproduces the empty routine of bourgeois life. At best, Monca's direction here is little more than competent—for example, in the back-to-back shot-scenes where first Camille and then Irma come to appeal to him, "Le Petit Chose" is placed in the same left foreground position and acts in a similarly fickle, petulant fashion toward both women. The regressive theatricality often alleged against the prewar French cinema does seem to have some basis, then, not only in historical films such as Film d'Art's *Madame Sans-Gêne* (1911) and Louis Mercanton's *Queen Elizabeth* (1912), but also in bourgeois melodramas such as Monca's *Le Petit Chose*.

The same claim cannot be made against Camille de Morlhon's prewar "modern dramas," at least as evidenced by *La Broyeuse de coeurs* (1913).[33] Morlhon's film also deploys a love triangle plot in which Pierre, a prosperous businessman (Pierre Magnier), abandons his fiancée, Marthé (Suzanne Delvé), for a dancer, Ida Bianca (Léontine Massart), only to find himself abandoned in turn. This conventional narrative is enhanced, however, in several ways. Three separate moments of spectacle punctuate the last half of the film: Ida's dance performance at a special celebration Pierre has organized, the couple's automobile tour of the Pyrenées, and a bullfight in which Pierre's rival, a famous toreador, is injured. In addition, one plot twist near the beginning is repeated, with a difference, near the end: first, Marthé accidentally receives a letter Pierre has intended for Ida (revealing his deception); then, Pierre deliberately blocks the toreador's love letter from reaching his mistress before the bullfight—a deception whose discovery quickly prompts her to leave him. Although *La Broyeuse de coeurs* often relies on a automonous shot-scenes (also recorded by a waist-level camera) and includes frequent insert intertitles for letters, its strategies of representation and narration are much more varied than those of *Le Petit Chose*. Several scenes include cut-ins to closer shots; and the opening scene, in which Pierre leaves Marthé for his office, smoothly intercuts the direction of their looks within interior and exterior spaces. Moreover, the Pyrenées tour sequence is composed of ten separate shots, whose intercutting handles the automobile's direction of movement within the frame as well as its exits and entrances according to the newly emerging rules of American continuity editing.[34] Finally, the film is even more sophisticated than *Le Petit Chose* in its mise-en-scène. Ida is introduced, for instance, in the center foreground of her dressing room, but with her back to the camera, which at once underscores her importance and also delays the revelation of her identity.[35] The two concluding tableau shot-scenes neatly juxtapose Pierre's abandonment, after Ida's exit, and his return to Marthé, begging her forgiveness, by shifting the woman's position, respectively, from the right foreground in one tableau to the left foreground in the other. And the couple's reconciliation, as well as the double standard of sexual behavior it assumes, is abetted and blessed by none other than the young woman's mother.

During the Great War, as cinema audiencees were increasingly composed of women and children, the bourgeois family melodrama became even more of a staple of French film production.[36] And its popularity was supported by Italian melodramas starring Francesca Bertini and American films such as Cecil B. De Mille's *The Cheat* (1915), whose success, in part, during the late summer of 1916 depended on its French melodrama origins.[37] The genre's appeal continued to derive from theatrical adaptations—by Henri Kistemaecker, for instance, as well as Bernstein and Hervieu—and particularly from the presence of famous stage actresses and personalities. Mistinguett had two of her greatest successes in André Hugon's *Chignon d'or* (1916) and *Fleur de Paris* (1916).[38] Sarah Bernhardt posed before Jeanne d'Arc's statue and the ruined Rheims cathedral in René Hervil and Louis Mercanton's *Les Mères françaises* (1917); and in Mercanton's adaptation of Tristan Bernard's *Jeanne Doré* (1916), she gave an unusually restrained performance that is affecting even today, partly because of her ravaged face and nearly immobilized body.[39] Gabrielle Robinne soon was starring in another monthly series of films, most of them in Pathé's *Scènes de la vie bourgeoise*—such as Leprince's *Zyte* (1916), Monca's *La Proie* (1917), Jean Kemm's *La Dédale* (1917), Monca's *La Bonne Hôtesse* (1918) and *La Route du devoir* (1918).[40] Although film critic Emile Vuillermoz was beginning to attack the French film industry's reliance on such theatrical adaptations, he exempted Robinne—and her restrained "grand style" of acting—from that criticism.[41] His rival, Louis Delluc, however, considered Robinne so representative of the French theater's influence on the cinema that, by 1918, he could hold up her mannered gestures for ridicule against the robust spontaneity of the American serial queen, Pearl White.[42]

Almost none of the Pathé melodramas from this period seems to have survived, so that any analysis of specific film prints has to focus largely on contributions to the genre from other production companies, especially Film d'Art. The best extant example of the often patriotic cast to these wartime films, for instance, is Henri Pouctal's *Alsace* (1916), in which Réjane reprised the celebrated role that Gaston Leroux had written for her in his 1912 play.[43] The film's story pits the French Orbey family against the German Schwartz family in the contested province of Alsace. Left to manage the family business after the other family members have gone to Paris, son Jacques falls in love with the Schwartze's daughter Marguerite. After her husband's death, Jeanne Orbey (Réjane) returns to Alsace to thwart her son's marriage plans and then, as he falls ill, gives in to his wishes. When war breaks out, Jacques must choose between his German wife and his French mother; confronted by a German mob, he shouts, "Vive la France!" and is beaten and soon dies in his mother's arms. Here the question of social identity is defined strictly in Oedipal terms, and the crisis of nationalism blocks "normal" development and drives Jacques back into the maternal bosom of France. When *Alsace* premiered at the Gaumont-Palace, according to René Jeanne, it received a tumultuous reception and ran for two consecutive and unprecedented weeks.[44] As one eyewitness reported, it was as if Réjane incarnated the spirit of France itself, especially in striking the pose of "La Marseillaise" when she visits Jacques's tomb in the film's final shot.[45]

Alsace seems rather representative of mainstream French film practice during the war. Pouctal still relies on autonomous shot-scenes but breaks them up frequently with dialogue intertitles—although speakers are almost never alone in a shot, and no shot is ever closer than an MS. Yet he also relies occasionally on continuity editing: as in Morlhon's prewar film, for instance, adjacent interior and exterior spaces are smoothly intercut; but, unlike most American films by then, there are no scenes constructed of shot/reverse shots.[46] The juxtaposition of families and then of mother and wife is conveyed through a simple form of parallel editing, which culminates near the end in the contrasting MS tableaux of Jacques cradled against Marguerite's shoulder and then of a disconsolate Jeanne drumming her fingers on a trunk she is reluctantly considering packing. The most striking features of *Alsace*, however, as with the earlier Feuillade and Morlhon films, come in its framing and mise-en-scène. Pouctal frames and choreographs the actors' movements so as to repeatedly contrast foreground and background planes of action. A HAMS/LS presents Jacques, his cousin Suzie, and her fiancé in the LCF beside a diagonal fence and wall bordering the family property, while, in the RB, the Schwartz mother and daughters promenade up the street below. The very next scene inside the house suggests Jacques's shifting allegiance, in an MS/LS, as he takes Marguerite to an RCB window, while his aunt and uncle, seated in the LCF, react more and more angrily to his obvious courting. Pouctal's cameraman, Léonce-H. Burel, also creates some attractive lighting effects, especially in the Orbey family interiors. The opening shot describes the bourgeois drawing room as a dark-curtained background against which an ornate clock and various china pieces stand out; there the family is gathered around a central lamp, their figures modeled by strong side lighting. And it is there, accompanied by Jeanne on the piano (as well as the cinema orchestra and audience, no doubt), that they sing "La Marseillaise" for the first time in this most overdetermined of French film melodramas.

Other films within the genre, however, seem to ignore the war and instead explore the narrative and representational possibilities of film language. Through Valetta Films, for instance, Morlhon continued to produce "modern dramas" from his own scenarios; at least one of them survives, *Marise* (1917), which takes its title from his new star, Marise Dauvray.[47] In this story, which seems situated in the prewar period, Marise accepts a brief liaison with a doctor (Arquillière) in order to keep up the rent on an apartment for her dying mother. Later she becomes the model and lover of an up-and-coming young sculptor, Jacques (Paul Guidé), who just happens to be the doctor's son. Discovering his identity, Marise tries to deny her love (like Camille); but she cannot prevent a climactic recognition scene between the two men, after which Jacques pulls a large statue of Marise that he has created down on himself and dies. Here a passionate *mésalliance* exposes the deceptive norms of a bourgeois patriarchal family, at the expense of everyone involved. In its generally flatly lit, flimsy sets, *Marise* reflects the film studio shortages of wartime France, particularly at Pathé; and its actors, although usually quite restrained, still exhibit broad theatrical gestures at moments of high emotion. Perhaps surprisingly, the film's framing and cutting closely resemble that of American continuity editing, with the continued exception of shot/reverse shots. What is most interesting, however, is Morlhon's relatively accomplished deployment of different editing patterns for different sections of the film. The opening, for instance, uses a simple form of alternation to sharply differentiate the milieu of the doctor (he is hosting a party) and that of Marise and her mother. That Marise has come masked to model for Jacques initially then sets up a scene at the Paris Opéra in which the sculptor recognizes her from behind through POV shots of her shoulder. Finally, after Marise has tried to leave him, both she and Jacques separately, in short subjective sequences (including CUs and MCUs), recall their past together as well as the menacing figure of the doctor. And the intertitle that ends her sequence—"They never pitied me!"—together with the surviving print's final MCU of her all alone make it seem that Marise, rather than being condemned as an immoral temptress in the affair, should be taken as the film's ultimate victim.

Abel Gance's *Le Droit à la vie* (1917), released by Film d'Art just two months before *Marise*, tells a similar though more ideologically "correct" story.[48] Andrée Maël (Andrée Brabant) is in love with stockbroker Jacques Alberty (Léon Mathot) but is forced to marry an older finanacier, Pierre Veryal (Paul Vermoyel), in order to pay the debts of her dying mother. The financier discovers the young couple's love and then an embezzlement by one of his assistants. When the assistant shoots and wounds him, an enraged Veryal pins the blame on Jacques. Finally, in the midst of a heated trial, he confesses in a letter to Jacques's innocence and, soon after, conveniently dies so the young couple can be reunited. Gance's film is distinguished from *Marise* by its sophisticated lighting and even more complicated editing, both of which, in part, derive (as does some of its story) from *The Cheat.*[49] In several key sequences, for instance, the principal characters are isolated in close shots and sculpted against black backgrounds by side lighting from either a lamp or a fireplace. This technique seems to have been a trademark of Gance and Burel, Film d'Art's chief cameraman, a technique which soon spread, at least according to Georges Sadoul, to other French films such as Germaine Dulac's *Venus Victrix* (1917).[50] But Burel does wonders as well with exteriors, as in the garden scene where strongly slanting sunlight through the trees and several superimpositions turn Jacques and Andrée's romantic wandering into a dream. As in *Marise,* subjective images underline the moral and psychological condition of the central characters, but here they are the exclusive property of the men. The suspense of the shooting climax is heightened by a strategy of parallel editing (using crude black wipes)[51] between the three men's confrontation in one room and a progressively more unrestrained masked ball in another. The trial is then articulated almost entirely in MCUs that, in imitation of *The Cheat*, depend on frequent eyeline matches and shot/reverse shots. Finally, there is one fascinating fetishistic gesture whose repetition in MCU almost turns into a rhetorical figure early in the film. In linked sequences, first Jacques lovingly caresses Andrée's hair, and then Veryal imagines caressing her in the same way as he prepares his marriage plan. After the wedding, however, as she stands by a bedroom window, she abruptly draws away from his touch—a denial that gives rise to his jealous suspicions.

At Gaumont, one of Jacques Feyder's earliest short films. *Têtes de femmes. Femmes de tête!* (1916), involving modish Parish types, provides an ironic variation on the genre's familiar love triangle plot.[52] Gaston Ravel's scenario has a young husband (André Roanne) romancing an actress (Georgette Faraboni) while his wife (Kitty Hott) commiserates with a close friend (Suzanne Delvé). Together the two women then plan an imaginary affair for the wife in order to trick the husband into accepting her once again, in a parodic happy ending. Conventional though this story may be, the film's system of representation and narration is unconventional, to say the least. First of all, Feyder restricts the framing almost exclusively to MSs and MCUs. This counters the French tendency to rely on "deep space" tableaux and their attendant lighting effects and choreography of actor movement (which, of course, also much reduces the cost of studio decors). Instead, it focuses attention on the gestures of the actors' faces, arms, and hands—fragments of behavior that are built into narrative chains through particular patterns of editing (but without the benefit of the American practice of including establishing shots). The most common pattern in *Têtes de femmes. Femmes de têtes!* relies on intercutting adjacent spaces according to an actor's exit or entrance, usually to the right or left (although at least twice an actor rises into the frame from below). Another pattern alternates between distant spaces, as when the actress goes off on a train trip while the two women confine the husband at home (the friend has intercepted his ticket). A third pattern, which proves crucial, relies on POV shots and shot/reverse shots. The two women discover the affair at the theater, for instance, through opera glasses; and, in an economical series of POV CUs, the ticket passes from actress to husband to friend, who reads its accompanying note in bed (crammed with a breakfast tray, *Le Figaro*, and dog). A final variation on this pattern occurs at the end, as the two women leave a trail of objects—CUs of a cigar, a pair of dress gloves, and a riding crop—which the husband follows to the bedroom in consternation, only to have the friend pop out from behind a curtain and present him with a baby's cup.

The films of Morlhon, Gance, and Feyder all suggest that it was within the bourgeois family melodrama genre that some French filmmakers began to find ways of going beyond the bounds of both French and American mainstream film practice. Specifically, the genre provided the basis—as Gance kept insisting to Louis Nalpas, head of production at Film d'Art—for the creation of "psychological films."[53] Nowhere is that more clearly demonstrated than in Gance's *Mater Dolorosa* (1917), which was popular enough to be rereleased the following year as well.[54] Although an original scenario, *Mater Dolorosa* echos the dramas of Hervieu, Bernstein, and, perhaps more specifically, Henri Kistemaecker's *L'Instinct*, which Pouctal had adapted as a film the previous year.[55] Much like *Le Droit à la vie*, the film also owes a good deal to *The Cheat*. The narrative is predicated on another love triangle, this one involving Dr. Gilles Berliac (Firmin Gémier), a pediatrician, his wife Marthe (Emmy Lynn), and her lover, his closest friend, author Claude Rolland (Armand Tallier). Overcome with guilt for the affair, Claude tries to leave France, at which Marthe attempts suicide and, in a struggle with her lover, accidentally shoots him. When Gilles is informed of his friend's death and then, by chance, of his wife's infidelity (through a humpbacked blackmailer, no less, who does not reveal the lover's name), he believes the worst and leaves her, taking their young son with him. Uncertain of his fatherhood, Gilles neglects the boy and, even when the latter suddenly falls ill, refuses to care for him unless Marthe agrees to confess the lover's name. Finally, an old servant finds the letter Claude wrote before dying, which exonerates Marthe; and Gilles recognizes her suffering. The couple is reunited, the son restored to health. As in the other films belonging to the genre, the emphasis throughout this narrative is on the psychological condition and moral state of the two central characters. But here, quite explicitly, the health of the individual as well as society literally depends on the health of the bourgeois family or the condition of a marriage.

Besides the ideological implications of its narrative, *Mater Dolorosa* exhibits many of the stylistic conventions of the bourgeois family melodrama. The settings are confined to the lover's study, several rooms in the Berliac family's comfortable parkside house, the hospital ward, the doctor's apartment (only these last two deviate a bit from convention—the hospital ward, for instance, is unusually realistic in its detail), and a few exterior shots. The acting is restrained, particularly that of the men (the hospital children nickname Gilles "The Goblin"), who together create a context of cold, rigid masculinity against which Marthe's emotional outbursts prove impotent. Gance and Burel use a good deal of sidelighting and low-key spotlighting on faces and parts of figures against dark backgrounds, creating even softer images than in *The Cheat* or *Le Droit à la vie*. Here the effect serves not only to model the characters in a three-dimensional space but also to heighten one's emotional state or another's mask of repression. The lovers early on are framed in silhouette at a window—a technique that owes a debt not only to *The Cheat* but to earlier French films such as Léonce Perret's

L'Enfant de Paris (1913).[56] Generally, however, Gance eschews the "deep space" tableaux of earlier films in the genre for various patterns of continuity editing. Shot/reverse shots mark several confrontation scenes, such as that between Marthe and the blackmailer (although the eyeline matching is not always consistent); and POV shots mark others, such as the soft grey HALS of Marthe leaving the house by car, which Gilles views from a second-story window. The range of shots in the film—from LS to CU—may not be all that different from *Marise* or *Le Droit à la vie*, but the cutting within and between sequences is exceptionally clear and economical (even without intertitles), perhaps more so than that of *Têtes de femmes. Femmes de têtes!* because there are quite a number of inserts, short flashbacks, and brief subjective images, along with several sequences of parallel action. By contrast, without intertitles, André Antoine's concurrent realist melodrama, *Le Coupable* (1917), which attempts to narrate a past crime story within the context of a present trial, is almost in incomprehensible.[57]

Commenting on the film's mise-en-scène, Jean Mitry neatly sums up the judgment of French film historians:

> *Mater Dolorosa* . . . surprises, astonishes, by means of lighting effects, the skillful use of light and shadow to intensify dramatic scenes, the intimate fidelity of the decors, singling out particular details, and a thousand unusual qualities for a French film.[58]

Yet, arguably, it is through its unusual framing and editing patterns that Gance's film most deviates from standard film practice during the war and opens the way toward another kind of French filmmaking. Certain moments produce a kind of textual "excess," not only beyond the demands of the narrative but even beyond the genre's conventions of heightened emotional expressiveness—latter examples of which include the CU of Marthe looking straight at the camera as Gilles finally accepts her and the alternation of moving shots (Marthe in the car, the countryside tracking by outside) which seem to propel her as she and Gilles rush to rejoin their son. Early on, for instance, when Marthe receives word that Claude plans to leave her, his letter is presented not in POV shots as expected but framed in MCU against the circular design of a cushion and then slightly crumpled in a softly edged, iris-masked CU. Throughout, the slightest movement within the frame can resonate metaphorically, as in the MS of Marthe backing off into the darkness after the shooting, a single window opening outward (with no person visible) in an LS exterior of the apartment building, the MCU of Marthe stroking a ribbon on one of her son's now discarded outfits. As Colette first noted, Gance's film provides evidence of "a new use of the *still life*, . . . as in a [black] veil falling slowly onto the floor."[59] That particular CU comes in a sequence in which a painting of the Mater Dolorosa presents the prior figure replicated by Marthe's attitude of suffering, and whose doubled figure is then re-presented in the climactic scene of Gilles's recognition. But, more important, the emblematic CU of Marthe's black veil contrasts with an earlier MCU of the married couple kissing behind a lacy white curtain; and it is repeated soon after in two shots introduced by the intertitle "The Fallen Idol": a CU of hand picking up the black veil and an MS of Gilles (now alone) tearfully kissing it. Here, in embryo, was a sustained pattern of rhetorical figuring in which common objects took on added significance through the "magnification" of close framing and through associational editing.[60]

In his very next film, *La Dixième Symphonie* (1918), whose credits now claimed him an *auteur,* Gance quite consciously attempted to extend this new film practice.[61] This time his original scenario transformed a conventional bourgeois melodrama plot by using it as a pretext to introduce the "more significant" problem of artistic creation. Gance was inspired, writes Kevin Brownlow, by a quotation from Hector Berlioz—"I am about to start a great symphony in which my great sufferings will be portrayed"—which came to serve as a prologue to the film.[62] The composer, Enric Damor (Séverin-Mars), a widower with a grown daughter Claire (Elisabeth Nizan), marries Eve Dinant (Emmy Lynn), who has an undisclosed, compromised past—she is being blackmailed by a former lover, Frédéric Ryce (Jean Toulout), for accidentally killing his sister. When Ryce courts Claire and Eve opposes their announced marriage (without explanation), Enric believes that his wife is secretly in love with the suitor. In despair, he composes a symphony entitled "Betrayal" and then performs it on a piano for an audience of friends. In response, Eve retitles the score "The Tenth Symphony" and prepares to sacrifice her own happiness, if only Ryce will leave Claire alone. Claire discovers what is happening, and, after a flurry of threats and counterthreats, Ryce shoots himself. Claire defends Eve to her father (without telling all), and Damor relents and forgives. Two years later, André Hugon would rework this dual problem of marital fidelity and artistic inspiration, with Séverin-Mars as a poet cursed by alcoholism, in a much more male-centered melodrama, *Jacques Landauze* (1920).[63]

As an extension of or advance beyond *Mater Dolorosa, La Dixième Symphonie* achieves a good measure of success, but not without qualification. Burel's side and back lighting of faces and figures against black backgrounds, for instance, is even richer than before; and certain LS images are accentuated by two-color tinting and toning. Eyeline-matched shots mark many of the film's dramatic confrontations, but several mismatchings deliberately seem to signal deceptive moments of narration—such as when Ryce, in a near duel, shoots a bird rather than his adversary; and when Claire, in the end, threatens to shoot him. POV shots as well as subjective memory images circulate among the three central characters, shifting generally, as the film progresses, from Eve to, separately, Enric and Claire. The elliptical opening of the past accidental shooting introduces the first of a number of emblematic CUs—Eve in profile agreeing to the blackmail terms, a hand clutching a small bird, a dog's bloody paw print as a mark of guilt on the carpet. In contrast to that of *Mater Dolorosa,* however, the metaphoricity of some of these images seems, rather than implicit, explicit and forced. The image of the hand now releasing the bird, for instance, returns in the end just before Ryce shoots himself; and, when Enric earlier intercepts and reads a letter from Ryce to Eve, there is an insert shot of a house of cards collapsing.

The most elaborate instance of associational editing occurs in the sequence of Enric's performance, a sequence on whose merits film critics Louis Delluc and Emile Vuillermoz at the time were sharply divided.[64] One nexus of images depends on a kind of "narrative focalization,"[65] in which the perception and feeling of several different characters seem to merge into one shared moment of consciousness. MSs and MCUs of Enric's hands at the piano keyboard are intercut, through dissolves, with shots of various listeners leaning forward from both sides of the frame. But, then, in an excess of representation, they are further intercut with the death mask of Beethoven, intertitle quotations from Rostand and Heine, and an "Isadora Duncan" dancer (Ariane Hugon of the Opéra) in a series of natural settings or "tiny dream landscapes,"[66] each of which is masked by a horizontal vignette of Greek vase designs. Another nexus of images, however, clusters separately around Eve, whose head once, in MCU, drifts away "like a decapitated flower"[67] and who later draws a veil shimmering like gold leaf over her face. These images, too, reach a point of excess, which Delluc found extraneous and embarrassingly literary, when Eve is equated with a statue replica of the Winged Victory of Samothrace.[68] Given the self-reflexivity of this sequence—in its multiple representation of prior artistic representations of heightened emotion—the end of *La Dixième Symphonie* is schizophrenic in a different yet still gender-specific sense. Enric's agony is condensed eventually in a single POV shot (from a window) or a wooded park whose emptiness contrasts poignantly with the dreamscapes of his earlier performance. Yet Eve's suffering throughout is much greater than that of her composer husband, who never comes to know, as we and Claire do, the full extent of her discontent. Ironically, just as Enric's suffering never plumbs the depths that Eve's does, so are Gance's "high art" pretensions subsumed, by the film's end, within the "low art" generic pretext of melodrama.

Immediately after the war, the bourgeois family melodrama genre continued to be an important asset to the French film industry. Especially popular were adaptations of the plays of Bernstein, Kistemaecker, and Charles Méré. When Léon Gaumont, for instance, wanted the young aesthete, Marcel L'Herbier, to prove himself commercially after the total failure of his first film, *Rose-France* (1919), he told him to consider the success that Louis Mercanton and Gaby Deslys had made of his previous scenario for *Bouclette* (1918), and he assigned him to direct Bernstein's *Le Bercail* (1919). L'Herbier agreed, as he put it, "to practice his scales."[69] The result was that Gaumont made a tidy profit, and L'Herbier could go on making films. Film d'Art produced more family melodramas starring Emmy Lynn, whom René Jeanne aptly described as that recurring "victim of passion and motherly love"[70]—see, for instance, Henry Roussel's *La Faute d'Odette Maréchal* (1920). When the company decided to make films that could be marketable in both France and the United States, it chose as its first projects Bernstein's *La Rafale* (1920) and Kistemaecker's *Le Secret du Lone Star* (1920), both directed by Jacques de Baroncelli and starring the American actress Fanny Ward as well as Gabriel Signoret of the Comédie Française.[71] Although much of its production capital was now being spent on expensive serials and multipart films, Pathé (now Pathé-Consortium) also distributed popular melodramas such as Henry Krauss's adaptation of a Méré play, *Les Trois masques* (1921).

However, the bourgeois family melodrama also was beginning to sever its close ties to the theater as more and more filmmakers sought to distinguish the "cinematic" from the "theatrical," often by abandoning adaptations for original scenarios. Abel Gance, for one, continued to reshape the genre with his technical experiments as well as his philosophical pretensions. *J'Accuse* (1919), his first superproduction for Pathé-Cinéma, transformed the genre almost completely by thrusting the melodrama plot into the disturbing context of the war.[72] Here, even more than in *La Dixième Symphonie*, the love triangle intrigue was but a pretext for a fiercely emotional personal statement and for further cinematic experimentation. Paradoxically pacifistic and nationalistic at the same time, *J'Accuse* was a stunning commercial success, especially considering its release several months after the Armistice. Despite certain qualifications again, it was also technically and rhetorically much in advance of any other French film of 1919. A similar blend of family melodrama, personal statement, and experimentation would also mark Gance's next epic, *La Roue* (1922–23).[73]

In contrast to Gance's "epic symphonies," Raymond Bernard, a protegé of Jacques Feyder, oriented the genre toward the "chamber music" of a more intimate drama. Drawing primarily on a series of plays and scenarios by his famous father, Bernard concentrated on the psychological possibilities of the bourgeois melodrama—in *Le Secret de Rosette Lambert* (1920), *La Maison vide* (1921), and *Triplepatte* (1922). The subject of *Le Secret de Rosette Lambert* was a conventionally "cruel and violent story," adapted from Tristan Bernard's *Coeur de Lilas*.[74] In it, a businessman sets a trap for the fiancée of his new partner, James Jamier (Henri Debain), in order to ruin him. When the fiancée, Rosette Lambert (Lois Meredith), repulses him and he falls down some stairs to his apparent death, another associate, Bertrand (Charles Dullin), blackmails her, only to be unmasked by an old family friend (Camille Bert). Finally, a flashback at the end reveals that the businessman actually revived and then was killed by Bertrand. This film is unlike previous bourgeois melodramas in at least two ways. First of all, its scene construction relies heavily on MSs and MCUs of the actors, organized according to the shot/reverse shot system of American continuity editing—just as producer Henri Diamant-Berger had advocated in his book, *Le Cinéma* (1919).[75] Second, the film situates its story in quite modern decors designed by the young master architect Robert Mallet-Stevens. Mallet-Stevens's sets simply and starkly validated Bernard's psychological interest as well as creating a suitable atmosphere for informal dancing—which was then undergoing a new wave of popularity in Paris.[76] Now, for the first time, modern interiors were constructed specifically for a film and not merely chosen from the stock of traditional studio decors.[77] Despite fine acting from Debain and Dullin (in debut), however, *Le Secret de Rosette Lambert* was compromised by its star, Lois Meredith, an unknown American actress and mistress of the film's financial backer, Adolphe Osso.[78] Still, Louis Delluc could conclude that Bernard's direction and Mallet-Stevens's sets combined to produce "one of the most splendid manifestations of *photogenic plasticity* in the cinema."[79]

Bernard's next film, *La Maison vide*, which was the first to come out of his own independent production company, was an original scenario that he had devised from a banal love story.[80] In his unpublished memoirs, Bernard has confessed that his ambition in the film was to make the audience aware of subtle mental states of which the characters themselves were not always conscious.[81] Henri Fescourt remembers the film vividly:

> An impalpable story of grays. Hesitations, subtle nuances, slight incidents. A timid entomologist, suspended over his precious collection, falls in love with his secretary. Scarcely anything happens. A bouquet on a table, displaced by an angry kick, falls to the floor. A microscope that reveals darkened images. Is it the fault of the lens? No, the eye that observes, an eye darkened by a tear. . . . No hands clutching the breast, no long sighs. Very few intertitles. It was enough to watch the images and Henri Debain.[82]

Unfortunately, Bernard's choice of a title, *La Maison vide*, failed to attract audiences to the cinema, and the film ended up appealing to only a few filmmakers and critics. In

Triplepatte, Bernard would fare much better by retreating to one of his father's stock of well-known plays, which allowed Debain to mildly satirize a similar "hero of indolence and indecision."[83]

Bernard was not alone in creating "chamber music" films during this period, for the analogy (it is Henri Fescourt's) also fits a small group of films produced by other young filmmakers involved in the narrative avant-garde.[84] Several of Louis Delluc's earliest films, for instance, develop a refined psychological irony from rather conventional bourgeois melodrama plots. *Le Silence* (1920) can serve as an example, even though it survives only in the form of a published, deceptively simple scenario.[85] Pierre (Signoret) is alone in his rooms, awaiting his lover Susie (Eve Francis). Suddenly, a chance comparison of letters makes him realize that, several years before, she was the one responsible for an anonymous letter that inflamed his jealousy and incited him to shoot his young wife, Aimée (Ginette Darnys) and kill her. When Susie finally arrives late, Pierre is dead in his chair, a victim of the same revolver with which he shot his wife. Because the action takes place almost entirely within Pierre's consciousness, *Le Silence* has been aptly described as "a monologue in images."[86] The "dramatic theme" (to use Delluc's own term) unfolds through the alternation of Pierre's memories and his perceptions of certain key objects in his possession—a revolver, a bed, two photographs, and several letters. These objects are isolated and intensified, especially through CUs (the cameraman was Louis Chaix), somewhat like those in Gance's *La Dixième Symphonie;* but their significance shifts in conjunction with the series of memory flashbacks. The revolver, for instance, turns into an instrument of self-destruction when it emerges from a kind of memory store, the same drawer from which came Aimée's photograph and letters. As Jean Epstein wrote of this, his favorite Delluc film, ". . . the lens . . . discovers in the simplest and most unlikely things a new dimension of inner dynamism, of symbolic truth, of dramatic conspiracy with the action."[87]

Delluc's specific choices for this metamorphosizing pattern of rhetorical figuring may be dated, but the disjunctive intricacy of the scenario's narrative structure still seems original. The eight flashbacks or imaginary sequences, most of them concentrated in the first two-thirds of the scenario, are organized *a*chronologically so that the key revelatory moments from the past are withheld until the end. Moreover, several of the sequences themselves are organized in a highly discontinuous manner. The second flashback, as it appears in the scenario, can stand as representative:

28. Present—Pierre in front of a bed.
29. Past^{5}—FS of Pierre sick in the same bed, now in disorder.
30. Present—Pierre asks himself why he was there.
31. Past^{3}—FS of Aimée looking ill in the same bed.

Intertitle—"Aimée"

32. Past^{3}—MCU of Aimée looking ill in bed.
33. Past^{1}—FS of Pierre and Aimée leaving a church in wedding clothes and laughing.
34. Past^{2}—FS of Pierre and Aimée embracing at the rail of a ship on their honeymoon.
35. Past^{4}—FS of Aimée lying dead in the same bed; Pierre kneels at the bedside.
36. Past^{4}—MS of Pierre mad with grief, restrained by some doctors.
37. Present—Pierre smiles at the clock pendulum.[88]

In just eight (planned) shots, the film presents flashback within flashback within flashback, summarizing Pierre's life with Aimée by layering over their happiness with several different moments of loss and grief. As may be gathered from this brief excerpt, the elliptical, achronological organization within and between sequences in *Le Silence* seems astonishing for 1920. In contrast to more conventional bourgeois melodramas, this film eschews the spectacle of heightened emotion for the intricacy of an intellectual puzzle, in a tightly knit narrative that traces a process of knowing through bitter revelations and ironic reversals.

Germaine Dulac also shared Gance and Delluc's interest in the bourgeois melodrama as a pretext for experimentation, but her concern focused somewhat more narrowly on representing the subjective experience of one or more characters. That concern is evident in Dulac's earliest surviving film, *La Cigarette* (1919), whose scenario she wrote in conjunction with Baroncelli.[89] Here the love triangle plot revolves around the director of the Oriental Art Museum in Paris, Pierre Guérande (Signoret), his young wife Denise (Andrée Brabant), and a young playboy for whom, according to an intertitle, "golf and dancing take the place of a career." Assuming that Denise has tired of him and his devotion to his archeological work, Pierre mixes a poisoned cigarette in with others in a box on his desk—letting chance determine the moment of his death. Denise discovers his plan and replaces all the cigarettes in his box, however, and, in the end, the couple renew their love for each other. For much of its length, this story threatens to repeat that of an ancient Egyptian princess whose mummy Pierre has acquired for his museum and whose presence spurs first his jealousy and then his resignation. Parallel editing helps to establish the initial differences between Pierre and Denise; and certain scenes of them together (in contrast to others) are marked by eyeline mismatches, as if to signal the apparent rift between them. POV shots are given almost exclusively to Pierre as he spies on Denise and follows her to what he believes is a clandestine meeting. As in *Le Silence*, Pierre's state of mind is suggested through his perception of certain images (the cameraman again is Louis Chaix), as in the sequence where he looks first at himself in a mirror, next at a photograph of himself from twenty years before, and then at the recent photograph of his and Denise's wedding. A series of CUs of crucial objects—an Egyptian vase, a photograph of Denise, the cigarette box—suggest his plan, which is then worked out through another series of CUs—of medicine bottles, a syringe, a cigarette, and a dropped label. Some of these CUs recur just before Pierre goes to smoke the last cigarette; and the others return in the flashback revealing Denise's discovery, the only time her character is privileged with POV shots. In a clever recuperative twist, the film then seals its reassertion of traditional marriage values with the couple reunited in their garden, in MS, each smoking a cigarette.

Dulac's *La Mort du soleil* (1921–22), whose scenario was written by André Legrand, redefined the character relations of the bourgeois family melodrama by giving the heroine a professional career.[90] On the one hand, this film celebrates the struggle of Doctor Lucien Faivre (André Nox) against tuberculosis—epitomized in recurring shots of supplicating diseased children on what seems to be a barren island. On the other, it also focuses on the dilemma confronting Marthe Voisin (Denise Lorys), who is dedicated to helping Faivre as his assistant but is equally devoted to her family, especially her young daughter, who becomes a figure of contention between Faivre and Marthe's industrialist husband. Given this scenario, Dulac wanted, in her words, "to describe the inner workings of the mind, within the theme of the action."[91] Consequently, she uses the plot, with its recurrent misunderstandings, as a pretext to explore the subjective life of both Marthe and Faivre, separately and in combination. The first of these moments is an unusual conjunction of the two characters as the doctor is recovering from a stroke early on in the film. Images of Faivre's delirium and of Marthe's inner thoughts, while reading, are intercut to produce a "communion of souls" whose significance oscillates between escape, shared passion, and awakening dedication to a scientific discipline. One of the last then comes in the sequence where the two conclude their work together, summed up symbolically in an MCU of both overlapping in profile, as on a prize medallion—Faivre's face dissolves out, leaving Marthe's, which then dissolves out in turn, just as his returns.[92] Unfortunately, such scenes were cut in many cinemas, as Dulac herself explained, because "spectators [and exhibitors] were not willing to endure an action slowed down by a sensitive elaboration."[93] In "creating an enlarged emotional domain" of representation, however, films like *La Mort du soleil* as well as the more famous *La Souriante Madame Beudet* (1923)[94] came to constitute what Dulac—and most film historians—would later call "the era of Impressionism,"[95] thereby inextricably linking the bourgeois family melodrama with one particular theory of narrative film within French film practice.

By 1922, the bourgeois melodrama had been so transformed—and separated from its theatrical origins—that it no longer could be perceived as a more or less distinct French film genre. Undoubtedly, this transformation was due, at least in part, to the interests of certain narrative avant-garde filmmakers in creating an "Impressionist" cinema of subjective representation, for which the private domestic space privileged by the genre provided a crucial basis or pretext. But it also may have occurred because of a developing rivalry (or lack of cooperation) between the cinema and the theater—Gaby Morlay, the most prominent boulevard melodrama actress after the war, for instance, appeared in only a couple of silent films before her rapid rise to star status in the 1930s French cinema. Perhaps, too, Charles Pathé's 1918 warning about adaptations from the theater had proved true:

> . . . the author and director should consider not only the title of the play they want to adapt, or the intensity or violence of the series of well-linked actions, but also—and this is not current practice—the nature of the emotions that are expressed. The extreme plot situations of prominent playwrights, unless substantially amended, will fail to pass censorship, particularly in the Anglo-Saxon countries. . . . The audiences of these countries will not appreciate the spicy, risqué plots that Bernstein and, preeminently, Bataille have established as the norm.[96]

Whatever the priority of these determinants, this change was actively supported by a new mass-market film journal, *Mon-Ciné*.

Within months of its initial appearance in February 1922, *Mon-Ciné* embarked on an educational campaign to encourage the development of a "cinema of quality" in France. Its purpose was twofold and implicitly ideological: to forge a link between film and fiction (rather than theater) and to dignify the cinema by displacing the serial or *cinéroman*, in the popular taste, with the *roman-ciné* or a fictional equivalent to the bourgeois melodrama.[97] To that end, each issue of *Mon-Ciné* was devoted to the novelization of a current "serious" film, which novelization soon became as important as the film itself. Largely ignoring the work of the narrative avant-garde as well as serials and theatrical adaptations, *Mon-Ciné* singled out for praise such filmmakers as Bernard, Roussel, Feyder, Fescourt, Robert Boudrioz, and Léon Poirier.[98] Their films, especially Poirier's *Jocelyn* (1922) and *Geneviève* (1923), came closest to realizing what Maurice Roelens has described as the magazine's polemical "aesthetic of emotion"—"a [logical] series of naturally melodramatic situations, apt to arouse emotion and especially 'the voluptuousness of compassion' that one usually associates with melodrama."[99] Although terminologically vague—and thus capable of infusing various genres—this became one more answer to the question of what was peculiarly French about the French cinema.

In the course of *Mon-Ciné*'s polemic, most of the filmmakers who had come into the cinema from the theater before or during the war turned exclusively to adapting fiction or writing their own scenarios. And those theatrical melodramas that did become films were usually subsumed in one of several other genres.[100] Some, such as Hervil's *Blanchette* (1921), Feuillade's *Le Gamin de Paris* (1922), or Fescourt's *Les Grands* (1924), evoke the atmosphere and ambience of natural location shooting and are perhaps best seen as realist films. Others, such as L'Herbier's "melodrama" *El Dorado* (1921) or Julien Duvivier's *Maman Colibri* (1929), became part of the cycle of exotic or colonial films. Still others, such as Dulac's *Ame d'artiste* (1925), L'Herbier's *Le Vertige* (1926), or Perret's *La Femme nue* (1926), depend on elaborate sets and an international milieu that make them early examples of the modern studio spectacular. Otherwise, the only truly theatrical adaptation to supplant the bourgeois melodrama in the 1920s was the boulevard comedy, especially as represented by the plays of Labiche and company. But the boulevard comedy was important enough, particularly in the late 1920s, to demand separate treatment elsewhere.[101]

The exception to these changes were few and far between. One of the sole surviving examples is Germaine Dulac's *Antoinette Sabrier* (1927), produced by Cinéromans from a play by Romain Coelus, which Réjane had made popular before the war.[102] Apparently Dulac only agreed to direct this commercial project in order to have the freedom to do other, more independent films—for example, *La Coquille et le clergyman* (1927) and *L'Invitation au voyage* (1927). The love triangle plot of *Antoinette Sabrier* involves a busy petroleum industrialist (Gabriel Gabrio) who cannot decide which of two women he really loves, his wife (Eve Francis, who had not made a film in four years) or a younger woman "whom he believes to be the incarnation of Love" (Yvette Armel). According to René Jeanne and Charles Ford, the film looked much like a Comédie Française theatrical production, partly because of Dulac's obvious lack of interest.[103] Julien Bayart pinpointed at least one other reason: "the decors . . . produce an impression of artificiality, an impression of coldness accentuated even more by the way they are lit." *Antoinette Sabrier*, he concluded, "is theatrical, a terribly theatrical story."[104] In a seemingly circuitous move, as if in preparation for the transition from silent to sound films, the bourgeois family melodrama genre, or what remained of it, returned to its prewar origins.

Notes

1. The fullest collection of early Pathé catalogues can be found at the Bibliothèque de l'Arsenal in Paris. For a study of such catalogues, see Emmanuelle Toulet, "Une Année de l'édition cinématographique Pathé: 1909," *Les Premiers ans du cinéma français*, ed. Pierre Guibbert (Perpignan: Institut Jean Vigo, 1985), 133–42.
2. Roger Icart, "Le Mélodrama dans le cinéma muet français," *Les Cahiers de la Cinémathèque* 28 (1979), 191–200.
3. See also Barthélemy Amengual, "Propos Pédants sur le mélodrame d'hier et le faux mélo d'aujourd'hui," *Les Cahiers de la Cinémathèque* 28 (1979), 12–15; and Jacques Goimard, "Le 'Mélodrame': Le Mot et la chose," *Les Cahiers de la Cinémathèque* 28 (1979), 17–65. Much of the material in the next seven paragraphs was first presented in a paper entitled "Melodrama/Realism in Early French Narrative Cinema" at the Society for Cinema Studies conference, Montreal, 22 May 1987.
4. Peter Brooks, *The Melodramatic Imagination: Balzac, James, Melodrama, and the Mode of Excess* (New Haven: Yale University Press, 1976), 15.
5. Ibid., 4, 32. See also Catherine Bodard Silver, "Salon, Foyer, Bureau: Women and the Professions in France," in *Clio's Consciousness Raised*, ed. Mary Hartman and Lois W. Banner (New York: Harper & Row, 1974), 78–82; Theodore Zeldin, *France 1848–1945: Ambition and Love* (Oxford: Oxford University Press, 1979), 11–22; and especially James F. McMillan, *Housewife or Harlot: The Place of Women in French Society, 1870–1940* (New York: St. Martin's Press, 1981), 11–12.
6. Brooks, *The Melodramatic Imagination*, 14, 15. See also Martin Meisel, *Realizations: Narrative, Pictorial and Theatrical Arts in Nineteenth-Century England* (Princeton: Princeton University Press, 1983), 38–51.
7. Brooks, *The Melodramatic Imagination*, 47, 48.
8. Ibid., p. 14. Perhaps the earliest study that examines the replacement of stage melodrama by the cinema is A. Nicholas Vardac's *Stage to Screen: Theatrical Origins of Early Film, David Garrick to D. W. Griffith* (Cambridge, Mass.: Harvard University Press, 1948). Although highly selective in his coverage of early cinema (his examples are drawn almost exclusively from a few films by Edwin S. Porter and D. W. Griffith), Vardac does provide excellent descriptions, drawn from surviving promptbooks, of popular late-nineteenth- and early-twentieth-century American stage melodramas.
9. Rémy de Gourmont, "Epilogues: Cinématographe," *Mercure de France* 69 (1 September 1907), 125. This essay is reprinted in English translation in my *French Film Theory and Criticism, Vol. 1, 1907–1929* (Princeton: Princeton University Press, 1988), 47–50.
10. Prints of *A Father's Honor* and *Distress* can be found, respectively, at the Museum of Modern Art and in the Post collection of the Motion Picture Division of the Library of Congress. Prints of the other titles are preserved in the Joye collection of the National Film Archive in London. The date given for each of these films is its most likely year of release, and all but two of those dates come Pathé catalogues and *Moving Picture World*.
11. The National Film Archive print of *The Fate of Life* has no intertitles. Most of the other prints have only one. *The Stepmother*, for instance, inserts the homily "Blood is thicker than water" just before the shot-scene in which the father leaves the house, allowing the stepmother to pamper her own daughter and then brutalize her new stepson. *The Poor Mother*

uses the simple phrase "A year later" to bridge the shot-scene of the mother crying over her daughter's body in the apartment to the shot-scene of her drinking heavily in the same space. *Falsely Condemned* includes a letter in a long intertitle, which absolves the postman of murder just before he is released from prison. *Distress*, however, has four nominative intertitles: "The Theft," "The Arrest," "Work," and "The Anniversary." Whether any of these films included other intertitles now lost remains uncertain.

12. *Distress* works a variation on this story. A father is arrested for stealing bread for himself and his daughter; he escapes from prison and surreptitiously takes the daughter out of an orphanage school. While at work on a construction job, he is recognized by a policeman and, in a chase, falls from a roof to his death. The policeman then brings the daughter home to be adopted into his own family.
13. See, for instance, Noël Burch and Jorge Dana, "Propositions," *Afterimage* 5 (1974), 40–66; Noël Burch, "Film's Institutional Mode of Representation and the Soviet Response," *October* 11 (Winter 1979), 77–96; Ben Brewster, "A Scene at the 'Movies,' " *Screen* 23 (July–August 1982), 4–15; Barry Salt, *Film Style and Technology: History and Analysis* (London: Starword, 1983); André Gaudreault, "Temporality and Narrativity in Early Cinema, 1895–1908," in *Film Before Griffith*, ed. John L. Fell (Berkeley: University of California Press, 1983), 311–29; Kristin Thompson, "The Formulation of the Classical Style, 1909–1928," in David Bordwell, Janet Staiger, and Kristin Thompson, *The Classical Hollywood Cinema: Film Style and Mode of Production to 1960* (New York: Columbia University Press, 1985), 155–240; André Gaudreault, "Récit singulatif, récit itératif: Au bagne (Pathé 1905)," in *Les Premiers ans du cinéma français*, ed. Pierre Guibbert (Perpignan: Institut Jean Vigo, 1985), 233–41; Ben Brewster, "La Mise-en-scène en profondeur dans les films français de 1900 à 1914," in *Les Premiers ans du cinéma français*, 204–17; Tom Gunning, "The Cinema of Attractions: Early Film, Its Spectator, and the Avant-Garde," *Wide Angle* 8. 3/4 (1986), 63–70; Noël Burch, "Primitivism and the Avant-Garde: A Dialectical Approach," in *Narrative, Apparatus, Ideology: A Film Theory Reader*, ed. Philip Rosen (New York: Columbia University Press, 1986), 483–506; Tom Gunning, "I film Vitagraph e il cinema dell'integrazione narrativa," in *Vitagraph Co. of America*, ed. Paolo Cherchi Usai (Pordenone: Edizioni Studio Tesi, 1987), 225–39; and Richard Abel, "The Point-of-View Shot: From Spectacle to Story in Several Early Pathé Films," in *Ce que je vois de mon ciné . . .* , ed. André Gaudreault and Denise Perusse (Paris: Méridiens-Klincksieck, 1988).
14. For close textual analysis, my descriptions of specific shots depend on notational acronyms designating camera distance and angle that have become familiar and necessary in film criticism. They include the following:

ECU	Extreme close-up (the shot of an eye, a pair of eyes, or part of a body or small object)
CU	Close-up (the shot of a face or object)
MCU	Middle close-up (the shot of a person from the chest up)
MS	Middle shot (the shot of a person from the waist up)
AmS	American shot (the shot of a person from the knees or calves up)
FS	Full shot (the shot of a person from the feet up or the shot of a large object)
LS	Long shot (the shot of a full interior space or a large exterior space)
ELS	Extreme long shot (the shot of a mammoth interior space or an extensive landscape)
HA	High angle (a shot taken from above chest level, looking down)
LA	Low angle (a shot taken from below waist level, looking up)

When a film's mise-en-scène combines two or more planes of interest within the frame, I resort to a double acronym—such as MS/LS. Only one other acronym appears frequently—POV—for point-of-view shot.

15. *The False Coin* and *Falsely Condemned* are both filmed consistently by a camera positioned at close to waist level, one of the earliest instances of a practice that would become standard in Pathé and Film d'Art productions.
16. The cut in to an MS of the café owner minting fake coins occurs in the middle of an LS of the cellar with the man facing forward and working at a table in the center foreground while the boy looks through a window in the upper left-center background. It does not constitute a POV shot/reverse shot structure, therefore, but rather equates the revelation to the spectator with what the boy presumably sees.
17. Several of the Pathé sets in *The Fate of Life* and *The False Coin* are obviously painted flats and at least one wobbles noticeably from the opening and closing of a door.
18. Contrast this isolated MS which "properly" concludes *Child Kidnapped* with the MS of the outlaw shooting a pistol at the camera in Porter's *The Great Train Robbery* (Edison 1903). The latter shot, Noël Burch writes, "was not actually incorporated into the film itself but delivered to exhibitors as a separate roll which they could splice onto the beginning or the end of the film, whichever they chose." Burch, "Primitivism and the Avant-Garde," 492.
19. [Louis Feuillade], "Les Scènes de la vie telle qu'elle est," *Ciné-Journal* 139 (22 April 1911), 19. This text is reprinted in English translation in my *French Film Theory and Criticism, I*, 54–55. Another important reaslit film series was Victorin Jasset's *Les Batailles de la vie* (1911–12) for Eclair.
20. The Cinémathèque Française copy of *Le Demon du jeu* is still in a fragmentary state: it includes just eleven shots and indications for at least seven intertitles. The original print of *Le Demon du jeu* ran 430 meters—see *Pathé Bulletin Hebdomadaire* 37 (1911), 3.
21. In another well-known Bourgeois film in this series, *Les Victimes de l'alcool* (1911), a family man is lured into drinking a glass of wine in a café, quickly turns into a drunkard, loses his office job, steals the money his brother lends the family to survive, loses his wife and daughter to suicide, and ends up thrashing about wildly in the straw of an asylum cell.
22. Film historians have commonly attributed such "lighting effects" in the early French cinema to Gaumont films—see, for instance, Salt, *Film Style and Technology*, 98.
23. The Cinémathèque Française copy of *Les Vipères* runs about 330 meters, has sixteen shots, and is without intertitles. The original print was listed at 360 meters—see "Nouveautés," *Ciné-Journal* 139 (22 April 1911), 39. See also "Stories of the Films," *Moving Picture World* 8 (1 July 1911), 1527. Other representative films in this series include *La Tare* (October 1911) and *Le Destin des mères* (December 1911). For a further analysis of these early Feuillade films, see my "Before *Fantômas:* Louis Feuillade and the Development of Early French Cinema," *Post Script* 7, 1 (Fall 1987), 4–26.
24. I borrow this term from Salt, *Film Style and Technology*, 113, 116; and Brewster, "La Mise-en-scène en profondeur dans les films français de 1900 à 1914," 204–17.
25. A similar decentering marks the final shot of *La Tare* as well. Noël Burch has called such decentering, or noncentering, one of the principal characteristics of the so-called primitive cinema. Burch, "Primitivism and the Avant-Garde," 486–87. Here, in Feuillade's film, such a strategy is neither disruptive nor regressive because it serves to intensify the emotional moment that concludes the narrative.
26. Maurice Bardèche and Robert Brasillach, *Histoire du cinéma* (Paris: Denoël, 1943), 49, 51.
27. "Mistinguett," *Pathé Bulletin Hebdomadaire* 45 (1911), 2; and Jean Mitry, "Georges Monca," *Filmographie universelle XXV: France, 1910–1925* (Bois d'Arcy: Service des Archives du Film, 1981), 135–40.
28. "Mme Gabrielle Robinne," *Pathé Bulletin Hebdomadaire* 38 (1912), 15; and Jean Mitry, "René Leprince," *Filmographie universelle XXIV: France, les premiers artisans* (Bois d'Arcy: Service des Archives du Film, 1981), 44–47.
29. Georges Sadoul, *Histoire générale du cinéma III: Le Cinéma devient un art, 1909–1920*

(Paris: Denoël, 1951), 262; and Jean Mitry, "Camille de Morlhon," *Filmographie universelle XXIV*, 108–9.

30. Jean Mitry, *Histoire du cinéma I: 1895–1914* (Paris: Editions Universitaires, 1967), 280; Léon Barsacq, *Caligari's Cabinet and Other Grand Illuisons: A History of Film Design*, rev. and ed. by Elliott Stein (Boston: New York Graphic Society, 1976), 38; and Theodore Zeldin, *France 1848–1945: Taste and Corruption* (New York: Oxford University Press, 1980), 80–81.
31. McMillan, *Housewife or Harlot*, 25–26, 30. See also the distribution of character types in Michael Lebrun, "Les 'Figures imposées' du mélo," *Les Cahiers de la Cinémathèque* 28 (1979, 90–93.
32. The Cinémathèque Française print of *Le Petit Chose* is without intertitles. The original version of the film ran 795 meters in length–*Pathé Bulletin Hebdomadaire* 38 (1912), 8–9; and "Nouveautés," *Ciné-Journal* 217 (19 October 1912), 82.
33. The Cinémathèque Française print of *La Broyeuse de coeurs* runs about 850 meters and seems to include all the intertitles. See "Nouveautés," *Ciné-Journal* 243 (19 April 1913), 94. Positive nitrate prints of Morlhon's *La Fleuriste de Toneso* (1913) and *Le Sacrifice surhumain* (1914) have been found at the Cinémathèque Française but have not yet been printed on acetate filmstock for viewing purposes.
34. Similar forms of supposedly American continuity editing can be found in Feuillade's *La Tare* (October 1911) and *L'Erreur tragique* (January 1913). For the best accounts of the development of American continuity editing, see Thompson, "The Formulation of the Classical Style," 194–213; and Salt, *Film Style and Technology*, 122–27, 162–70.
35. This strategy appears even earlier in such films as Film d'Art's *Don Carlos* (1909) and Vitagraph's *A Friendly Marriage* (1911).
36. For a brief consideration of French writing on the genre, see my *French Film Theory and Criticism, I*, 102–3.
37. *Annuaire général de la cinématographie française et étrangère* (Paris: Ciné-Journal, 1917), 137; Henri Fescourt, *La Foi et les montagnes* (Paris: Paul Montel, 1959), 142; Roger Icart, "Le Melodrame dans le cinéma muet français," 194.
38. Guillaume Danvers, "Présentations," *Le Film* 5 (15 April 1916), 16–17; Danvers, "Présentations," *Le Film* 32 (21 October 1916), 19. See also Bardèche and Brasillach, *Histoire du cinéma*, 107.
39. *Jeanne Doré* advertisement, *Ciné-Journal* 331 (18 December 1915), 25. Constant Larchat, "*Mères françaises*: avant-première," *Le Film* 44 (15 January 1917), 13. "Théâtres," *Le Temps* (3 February 1917), 3. Jacques Salles, "Raymond Bernard," *L'Avant-Scène Cinéma* 256 (15 November 1980), 180. A print of *Jeanne Doré* is preserved at the Cinémathèque Française. Raymond Bernard plays the role of the young boy, as he did on the stage in 1913.
40. Danvers, "Présentations," *Le Film* 31 (14 October 1916), 14; *Pathé-Journal* 38 (1917); *Pathé-Journal* 66 (1917); "Théâtres," *Le Temps* (14 September 1917), 4; *Pathé-Journal* 1 (1918); *Pathé-Journal* 16 (1916). See also René Jeanne, *Cinéma 1900* (Paris: Flammarion, 1965), 216.
41. Emile Vuillermoz, "Devant l'écran," *Le Temps* (21 February 1917), 3; Emile Vuillermoz, "Devant l'écran," *Le Temps* (10 March 1917), 3.
42. Louis Delluc, "Cinéma et cie," *Paris-Midi* (20 May 1918), 3. The French actress who most resembled Pearl White was Suzanne Grandais, who starred in a series of films directed by Mercanton and Hervil for Eclipse before she was killed in an automobile accident in 1920.
43. The National Archive print of *Alsace* runs 3,672 feet and has English intertitles. The original French version was released in early January 1916–see "*Alsace*," *Ciné-Journal* 332 (25 December 1915), 9, 12; "Théâtres," *Le Temps* (15 January 1916), 4; and Paul Feval fils, "Nos Metteurs-en-scène: Henri Pouctal," *Le Film* 8 (6 May 1916), 12.
44. Jeanne, *Cinéma 1900*, 226–27. *Alsace* was still being screened nearly a year later—see the

Gaumont-Palace ad in *Ciné-Journal* 375 (21 October 1916), 1; "Théâtres," *Le Temps* (21 October 1916), 4; and "Théâtres," *Le Temps* (24 February 1917), 3.

45. Jacques Renaux in *La France*, quoted in Jeanne, *Cinéma 1900*, 227.
46. French film criticism during the war tended to disparage the American shot/reverse shot system—see, for instance, Colette, "La Critique des films," *Le Film* 3 (28 May 1917), 6. For further information on this attitude, see my *French Film Theory and Criticism, I*, 104.
47. The Cinémathèque Française print of *Marise* seems to be incomplete, with very few intertitles. The original version ran 1,430 meters—see *Pathé-Journal* 40 (1917); and "Présentations," *Le Film* 50 (26 February 1917), 13.
48. The Cinémathèque Française print of *Le Droit à la vie* is still incomplete and lacks intertitles. The original version premiered on 5 January 1917 and ran 1,330 meters—see Pathé ad, *Ciné-Journal* 382 (9 December 1916), 2; and "Présentations," *Le Film* 40 (16 December 1916), 13.
49. *The Cheat* was screened in Paris as *Forfaiture* during July and August 1916–see Constant Larchet, "*Forfaiture*," *Le Film* 16 (1 July 1916), 11; "Echos," *Le Film* 19 (22 July 1916), 14; and Colette, "*Forfaiture*," *Excelsior* (7 August 1916), 2. A translation of Colette's essay is reprinted in my *French Film Theory and Criticism, I*, 128–29.
50. Georges Sadoul, *Histoire générale du cinéma IV: Le Cinéma devient un art* (Paris: Denoël, 1952), 398.
51. Gance and Burel had already used a similar series of crude wipes in *Barberousse* (1917), a print of which is preserved at the National Film Archive. *Barberousse* seems to have been previewed in August 1916 and then released in April 1917—see "Théâtres," *Le Temps* (12 August 1916), 3; and "Présentations," *Le Film* 55 (2 April 1917), 16.
52. The Cinémathèque Française print of *Têtes de femmes. Femmes de tête!* runs about 600 meters and is without intertitles. The original version premiered at the Gaumont-Palace on 16 June 1916 and ran 792 meters—see "Nouveautés," *Ciné-Journal* 354 (27 May 1916), 50; Victor Bachy, "Jacques Feyder," *L'Avant-Scène Cinéma* 63 (October 1966), 454; and Charles Ford, *Jacques Feyder* (Paris: Seghers, 1973), 181.
53. The best source for the exchanges between Gance and Nalpas is Roger Icart, *Abel Gance ou le Prométhée foudroyé* (Lausanne: L'Age d'Homme, 1983), 73–74.
54. Emile Vuillermoz was the first to call *Mater Dolorosa* "a benchmark in the history of contemporary cinema"—Vuillermoz, "Devant l'écran," *Le Temps* (10 March 1917), 3. The print of *Mater Dolorosa* I saw years ago at the Cinémathèque Française was without intertitles; the newly restored print there now includes them. The National Film Archive print (which has English intertitles) is drawn from a version entitled *The Call of Motherhood*, released in London in June 1924. The original French version ran 1,490 meters—see *Pathé-Journal* 38 (1917); and "Présentations," *Le Film* 49 (19 February 1917), 10, 12. For the 1918 rerelease, see Jan de Berry, "Les Spectacles," *Paris-Midi* (12 April 1918), 3.
55. "Présentations," *Le Film* 29 (30 September 1916), 10; "Théâtres," *Le Temps* (21 October 1916), 4; and Fescourt, *La Foi et les montagnes*, 169.
56. A print of *L'Enfant de Paris* is preserved at the Cinémathèque Française. The cameraman for Perret's film was Georges Specht. Juan Arroy, "Georges Specht," *Cinémagazine* 4 (18 January 1924), 93; Sadoul, *Histoire générale du cinéma II*, 201.
57. Recently the Cinémathèque Française restored the intertitles to its print of *Le Coupable*. Although filmed in 1916, the film was not released until October 1917. *Pathé-Journal* 69 (1917); "Présentations," Le Film 78 (10 September 1917), 11; Emile Vuillermoz, "Devant l'écran," *Le Temps* (10 October 1917), 3.
58. Mitry, *Histoire du cinéma II: 1915–1925* (Paris: Editions Universitaires, 1969), 255. See also Icart, "Le Mélodrame dans le cinéma muet français," 195.
59. Colette, "*Mater Dolorosa*," *Le Film* 66 (4 June 1917), 4–5. A translation of this essay is

reprinted in my *French Film Theory and Criticism I*, 136–37. Colette's language here echoes that of an unpublished note by Abel Gance from November 1915. Icart, *Abel Gance ou le Prométhée foudroyé*, 58.

60. A number of French writers about this time begin to explore the unusual effects of framing and editing. See, for instance, Louis Aragon, "Du Décor," *Le Film* 131 (16 September 1918), 8–10; Jean Cocteau, "Carte blanche," *Paris-Midi* (28 April 1919), 2; and Jean Epstein, "Grossissement," *Bonjour Cinéma* (Paris: Editions de la Sirène, 1921), 93–108. All three essays are reprinted in English translation in my *French Film Theory and Criticism, I*, 165–68, 172–73, 235–40.
61. "*La Dixième Symphonie*," *Pathé-Journal* 44 (1 November 1918). A new tinted and toned print of *La Dixième Symphonie* is now preserved at the Cinémathèque Française. The original version, according to *Pathé-Journal*, ran 1,700 meters. See also "Présentations," *Le Film* 135–36 (21 October 1918), 26–27; and Henri Diamant-Berger, "*La Dixième Symphonie*," *Le Film* 135–36 (21 October 1918), 18.
62. Kevin Brownlow, *The Parade's Gone By* (Berkeley: University of California Press, 1976), 610.
63. A print of Hugon's *Jacques Landauze* is preserved at the National Film Archive.
64. Louis Delluc, "Notes pour moi," *Le Film* 99 (4 February 1918), 3–4; Emile Vuillermoz, "Devant l'écran: *La Dixième Symphonie*," *Le Temps* (6 November 1918), 3. Both essays are reprinted in English translation in my *French Film Theory and Criticism, I*, 143–47, 168–71.
65. The term comes from Gerard Genette, *Narrative Discourse*, trans. Jane E. Lewin (Ithaca: Cornell University Press, 1980), 189–94.
66. Vuillermoz, "Devant l'écran: *La Dixième Symphonie*," 3.
67. Colette had used this metaphor to describe Emmy Lynn at the end of her review of *Mater Dolorosa*. Colette, "*Mater Dolorosa*," 5.
68. Delluc, "Notes pour moi," in *French Film Theory and Criticism, I*, 145.
69. Jean-André Fieschi, "Autour du cinématographe," *Cahiers du Cinéma* 202 (June–July 1968), 29. See also Marcel L'Herbier, *La Tête qui tourne* (Paris: Belfond, 1979), 43–44.
70. René Jeanne and Charles Ford, *Histoire encyclopédique du cinéma, I: Le Cinéma français, 1895–1930* (Paris: Robert Laffont, 1947), 458.
71. "Les Films de la quinzaine," *Ciné-pour-Tous* 33 (17 April 1920), 8; Film d'Art advertisement, *Ciné-pour-Tous* 37 (15 May 1920), 8; Fescourt, *La Foi et les montagnes*, 328.
72. For an analysis of *J'Accuse*, see my *French Cinema*, 295–302.
73. For an analysis of *La Roue*, see my *French Cinema*, 326–39.
74. Henri Diamant-Berger, *Il était une fois le cinéma* (Paris: Jean Claude Simon, 1977), 76. Salles, "Raymond Bernard," 205. A print of *Le Secret de Rosette Lambert* is preserved at the Cinémathèque Française.
75. Henri Diamant-Berger, "Le Filmage," *Le Cinéma* (Paris: Renaissance du Livre, 1919), 145–68. Selections from this chapter are reprinted in English translation in my *French Film Theory and Criticism, I*, 185–88. Diamant-Berger himself accepted the American continuity system for *Le Mauvais Garçon* (1922), a print of which is preserved at the Cinémathèque québéçois.
76. J.-L. Croze, "*Le Secret de Rosette Lambert*," *Comoedia* (26 October 1920), 1–2; J. G.-B., "Au Cinéma: *Le Secret de Rosette Lambert*," *Le Crapouillot* (1 November 1920), 16–17; "Les Films de la quinzaine," *Ciné-pour-Tous* 53 (19 November 1920), 6; Léon Moussinac, "Intérieurs modernes au cinéma," *Cinémagazine* 1 (25 February 1921), 5–8; René Jeanne, "La Dance au cinéma," *Cinémagazine* 1 (17 June 1921), 22.
77. Mitry, *Histoire du cinéma, II*, 263. For some sense of the revolutionary change in interior decoration that occurred in Paris around 1910, and which finally became visible in French films after the war, see J. de Rovera, "Les Coulisses de l'écran," *Le Film* 170 (April 1920); and

Hilly, "Décoration d'intérieur et cinéma," *La Revue Fédéraliste* 103 (November 1927), 36–43.

78. Diamant-Berger, *Il était une fois le cinéma*, 76.
79. Louis Delluc, "Quelques films français," *Cinéa* 18 (9 September 1921), 5.
80. "Le Semaine cinématographique," *Comoedia* (21 October 1921), 4; Lionel Landry," *La Maison vide*," *Cinéa* 25 (28 October 1921), 7. Apparently no print of *La Maison vide* has survived.
81. Salles, "Raymond Bernard," 182.
82. Fescourt, *La Foi et les montagnes*, 313–14.
83. Edmond Epardaud, "*Triplepatte*," *Cinéa* 73–74 (6 October 1922), 2–3.
84. For a fuller treatment of the development of the French narrative avant-garde, see my *French Cinema*, 279–94.
85. Louis Delluc, "*Le Silence*," in *Drames du cinéma* (Paris: Editions du Monde Nouveau, 1923), 19–32. "Les Films de la quinzaine," *Ciné-pour-Tous* 49 (24 September 1920), 6. The following analysis of *Le Silence* is excerpted, with some revision, from my *French Cinema*, 314–15.
86. Marcel Tariol, *Louis Delluc* (Paris: Seghers, 1965), 60.
87. Jean Epstein, "Mémoires inédites," quoted in Tariol, *Louis Delluc*, 61.
88. Delluc, "*Le Silence*," 22–23. The numbers indicating the periods of the past—from 1 (the earliest) to 5 (the latest)—have been added.
89. P.H., "Quelques films français de la quinzaine," *Ciné-pour-Tous* 7 (1 October 1919), 2; "Les Cinémas," *Comoedia* (8 October 1919), 4. A print of *La Cigarette* is preserved at the Royal Film Archive of Belgium.
90. Auguste Nardy, "*La Mort du soleil*," *Bonsoir* (17 December 1921); Germaine Dulac folder, Bibliothéque de l'Arsenal; "Présentations," *Cinémagazine* 1 (23 December 1921), 26; "*La Mort du soleil*," *Comoedia* (17 February 1922), 4–5. A print of *La Mort du soleil*, also subtitled *Le Fleau*, is preserved at the Archives du Film, Bois d'Arcy.
91. Germaine Dulac, "*La Mort du soleil* et la naissance du film," *Cinéa* 41 (17 February 1922), 14.
92. Lionel Landry singles out these moments in his review of the film in "*La Mort du soleil*," *Cinéa* 26 (12 January 1922), 15.
93. Germaine Dulac, "Les Esthètiques, les entaves, la cinégraphie intégrale," *L'Art Cinématographique* 2 (Paris: Félix Alcan, 1926), 42. This essay is reprinted in English translation in my *French Film Theory and Criticism, I*, 389–97.
94. For an analysis of *La Souriante Madame Beudet*, see my *French Cinema*, 340–44.
95. Dulac, "Les Esthètiques, les entaves, la cinégraphie intégrale," in *French Film Theory and Criticism, I*, 394. For a fuller analysis of French writings that advocate an "Impressionist" theory of narrative cinema, see my *French Film Theory and Criticism*, I, 106–7, 201–2.
96. Charles Pathé, "Etude sur l'évolution de l'industrie cinématographique française," *Le Film* 119 (24 June 1918), 6, trans. Stuart Liebman. See also Charles Pathé, *De Pathé Frères à Pathé Cinéma*, *Premier Plan* 55 (Lyon: SERDOC, 1970), 87–97.
97. Maurice Roelens, "*Mon-Ciné* (1922–1924) et le mélodrame," *Les Cahiers de la Cinémathèque* 28 (1979), 212–14.
98. Ibid., 207–12.
99. Ibid., 211.
100. Here my approach finally coincides with the much broader concept of melodrama that Roger Icart posits in "Le Mélodrame dans le cinéma muet français," 198.
101. For an analysis of silent film adaptations of the boulevard comedy, see my *French Cinema*, 227–38.
102. "Aux Cinéromans," *Cinéa–Ciné-pour-Tous* 84 (1 May 1927), 27; Charles Ford, "Germaine

Dulac," *L'Avant-Scène Cinéma* 31 (January 1968), 30. A print of *Antoinette Sabrier* is preserved at the Cinémathèque Française.

103. Jeanne and Ford, *Histoire encyclopédique*, I, 261.

104. Julien Bayart, "Ce que dit l'écran," *Photo-Ciné* 4 (15 April 1927), 66.

The Family Melodrama in the Italian Cinema, 1929–1943

MARCIA LANDY

In discussing the new industrialism, Antonio Gramsci asserted that "the new industrialism wants monogamy: it wants man as worker not to squander his nervous energies in the disorderly and stimulating pursuit of occasional sexual satisfaction."[1] Most of the Italian films of the thirties, set in the domestic or public spheres, emphasize a puritanical ethos in greater or lesser degrees. The family appears as the source of continuity, nurturance, social stability, and, as can be seen in the films of Camerini, a haven from the conflicts in the world of work. In this context, the woman serves as a procreator, nurturer, disciplinarian of the husband, self-disciplinarian, and guarantor of the integrity of the family unit. The male is the economic provider, the inseminator, the protector of the woman's honor and hence of his own honor, the straying child who must be restrained, and the responsible paterfamilias. The family is at the intersection of economic, political, and social conflict.[2] The most ideologically challenging and aesthetically superior films of the Ventennio are the melodramas of the early 1940s that focus on the family.

Many of the melodramas are the work of a group of filmmakers identified as "calligraphers." Such directors as Mario Soldati, Luigi Chiarini, Ferdinando Maria Poggioli, and Renato Castellani were associated with this type of production. The works are characterized by a high degree of formalism, a dependence on narratives derived from earlier literary works, especially of the nineteenth century, and a seeming

Marcia Landy's "The Family Melodrama in the Italian Cinema, 1929–1943" originally appeared as "Italian Melodramas of the 1940s: *Ossessione*," in *Fascism in Film: The Italian Commercial Cinema 1929–43* (Princeton: Princeton University Press, 1986).

retreat from overt political issues. As such, the films were critized by such writers as Giuseppe De Santis in the journal *Cinema*, the forum for new directions in Italian film. While it was generally recognized that the calligraphers were attempting to experiment with film form, moving narratives in a more psychological direction and using authentic settings, it was not acknowledged that these films, because of their stylized and heavily coded forms of representation, contained a powerful political critique of existing social conditions.

Melodrama was not a genre new to Italian culture. Gramsci traces its origins to the sixteenth century whence the genre maintains a consistent course into the twentieth century.[3] Most significantly, the genre is identified with the steady growth of forms of popular culture. An examination of the sources of the film melodrama reveals its dependence on popular Italian and foreign novels. For example, Visconti used James M. Cain's best-selling *The Postman Always Rings Twice* for *Ossessione,* Poggioli used Aldo Palazzeschi's novel for his *Sorelle Materassi,* and Chiarini used a tale by Matilde Serao for his *Via delle cinque lune.*

Melodrama, more than any other form of traditional narrative, seems to be an appropriate vehicle to explore and to criticize prevailing social attitudes. In his "Tales of Sound and Fury: Observations on the Family Melodrama," Thomas Elsaesser finds that

> the family melodrama . . . more often records the failure of the protagonist to act in a way that could shape the events and influence the emotional environment, let alone change the social milieu. The world is closed and the actors are acted upon. Melodrama confers on them a negative identity through suffering, and the progressive self-immolation and disillusionment gradually ends in resignation.[4]

Elsaesser explores the forms and language of melodrama, identifying the stylistic and structural operations that characterize it. The use of strong psychological effects, the emphasis on emotional crises, the exploration of failure are embedded in a style that makes it possible to identify ideological operations. For example, the secual conflict, the presence of ruptures and discontinuities, the stylized and figurative treatment, the transformation of conflict from the social into the psychic area are keys to unlocking the ideological and political impact of the genre.[5] Moreover, the subversions of melodrama are discernible not only in the narratives but also in an examination of the historical context. In the case of the Hollywood cinema, critics have focused on the popularity of melodrama in periods of intense social or ideological crisis.[6] Relative to the historical context, melodrama can function either subversively or as escapist entertainment according to ideological necessity.[7]

An examination of the Italian melodramas of the late thirties and early forties reveals the potential of the genre as an instrument for exposing social conflict. The films explore the breakdown of social relations, using the family romance to encode the weakness of authority, the dominance of obsessional behavior, competition, the manipulative aspects of petit bourgeois life, the decadence of the upper classes, and the flimsiness and hypocrisy of male relationships. Visconti's film, *Ossessione,* is only one of a number of texts that dramatize these conflicts. There was an increasing tendency to use film and film criticism for the purposes of challenging cultural and ideological practices. These critiques provide further insights into the contradictory practices of fascism.

Recent critical work on the Hollywood film has focused on melodrama as genre and style, and as a way of looking at social relations. The power of the Hollywood film, it was conceded even by the fascist regime, was its ability to use narrative forms that transmit ideology effortlessly; however, as Visconti discovered, and the French New Wave a decade later, there were ways to demystify the genre films, to see in them contradictions and areas of resistance to the dominant discourse. The critics saw the forms themselves as capable of subversion, of turning against themselves, and of exposing their secrets, and the power of melodrama would seem to reside in the ways in which the narratives utilize psychological structures as a commentary on social life. At their center are the ways in which desire and conflict are unleashed. Thomas Schatz has described how

> the family unit seems to provide an ideal locus for the genre's principal characters and its milieu for two fundamental reasons. First, it is a preestablished constellation whose individual roles (mother, father, son, daughter; adult, adolescent, child, infant, and so on) carry with them large social significance. Second, it is bound to its community by social class. . . . Ideally, the family represents a "natural" as well as a social collective, a self-contained society in and of itself. But in the melodrama this ideal is undercut by the family's status within a highly structured socioeconomic milieu.[8]

Within the Italian cinema of the early 1940s the melodrama appears often to function in the manner described by Schatz. In the films of the thirties, whether domestic and romantic comedies, male conversion dramas, war and imperialist epics, or operatic films, the family played a major role as the guarantor of social stability, a symbol of continuity, a rationale for war, and a motivation for productivity. The only rival to the family was the public arena of heroic action, though here, too, the conflicts between fathers and sons and the subordination of women played important roles.

For example, in the 1936 *Cavalleria*, the separation of the lovers is aestheticized. Suffering is made to appear ennobling. The camerawork and the editing ritualize events; the narrative builds inexorably in linear fashion around the inevitability of loss and its compensation in war, public service, creativity. While the Italian films of the 1930s reproduce, romanticize, and naturalize ideas of social order, the melodramas of the 1940s are dark, morally ambiguous, and preoccupied with disintegration. They are also closer to the neorealistic aesthetic in their treatment of conflict and setting.[9] If the earlier films reveal the projection of the family romance into the public arena, these later dramas seem to expose this strategy, using melodrama as the vehicle of demystification.

Psychological conflict is central to the Italian films of the 1940s, particularly the conflict generated by obsessional behavior: jealousy, thwarted sexuality, fetishism, violence, and disintegrating identity. These obsessions (obsession is central to melodrama) are often tied to economic, class, and political conflicts, involving such issues as irresolvable class differences that thwart gratification, violent or manipulative responses to the confining world of work, or the desire to escape the restrictive demands of an authority figure—father, husband, mother, or wife. In all these films, one can find a desire for freedom that is distorted, misdirected, and frustrated.

The style of the films can vary from a naturalistic portrayal of milieu and social conflict to a highly stylized treatment.[10] The lighting, as in *film noir*, is expressive of ambiguity and the troubled psyche. Music is important in developing emotional intensity and tone. The iconography and gesture of the characters often provide clues to their struggles. As with the films of Douglas Sirk, the stylized treatment can serve as an alienation effect whereby the film provides a commentary on itself. In a few instances, more obvious forms of self-reflexivity invite awareness of a point of view. In most of these films, conventional virtues are inverted or destroyed.

The melodramas reveal, in spite of their different styles and narratives, the presence of opposition, if not resistance, to the prevailing trends in filmmaking as exemplified in the "escapist" film, the film of propaganda, the film of war and empire, the comic film—all the films that sought to emphasize the virtues of renunciation, service, loyalty, male camaraderie, and populism. If the group of critics gathered around the journal *Cinema*, with their predilection for French cinema and American cinema and literature, represented the most vocal forces seeking to institute different cultural and ideological practices, the melodramas of the early forties also seem to constitute a form of departure from previous practices. Though these films do not treat obvious political themes as is characteristic of the neorealist cinema, they do afford a different perspective not only on the final phase of the fascist Ventennio, but also on some of the major myths and strategies of fascist life as it was encoded in the cinema. Melodrama's preoccupation with sexual, psychological, and domestic aspects of life illuminates the forces that position individuals and classes in ideology.

In 1942, Luchino Visconti directed *Ossessione* (Obsession), based on James M. Cain's novel *The Postman Always Rings Twice*. Although many of the films of the fascist era were later forgotten *Ossessione* was not. It was identified with the film style known as neorealism.[11] Not only did the film become incorporated into the canon of neorealism, but it was credited with being a major precursor of the movement and a singificant antifascist film. In part, its reputation derives from a time when little was known about the other films of the era except the "white telephone" and propaganda films, in part because it was made by Luchino Visconti, who was identified with the resistance to fascism, and in large part because the film explores fascism, touching particularly on those aspects of ideology and practice that relate to the everyday mode of existence as opposed to its spectacular and public aspects. Self-reflexive, the film probes the immediate everyday practices that served to keep fascism in place.

A handsome stranger arrives by truck at a small gas station–restaurant owned by the fat and crude Bragana, a caricature of the petit bourgeois property-owner who sees himself as a patriarch over his small corner of the world. Gino, the young man (Massimo Girotti), enters the restaurant. He helps himself to some food as Giovanna (Clara Calamai) watches him. Bragana complains about freeloaders and berates his wife, telling her that strangers are dangerous. Gino exits but leaves money on the table for the food, which Giovanna pockets. Bragana, thinking that Gino has not paid, rushes after him. Gino, understanding what Giovanna has done, agrees to come back and do a few odd jobs to pay for the meal. He will fix the truck and the water pump.

In examining the truck, which is reparable without new parts, Gino surreptitiously places a small piece of equipment in his pocket, forcing Bragana to leave the premises in order to get the part. When Bragana and the local priest ride off, Gino and Giovanna take advantage of his absence. After lovemaking, Giovanna complains to Gino of her husband, that he is disgusting and demanding, and he invites her to come away with him. She ominously hints that if Bragana were gone, she would be free.

Gino and Giovanna attempt to escape, but Giovanna cannot leave. He, however, boards a train, and a friendly passenger who introduces himself as "lo Spagnolo" (the Spaniard), offers to pay the fare. He is an artist, a traveling entertainer. That he is called the Spaniard is significant for several reasons. His role in the film is as an outsider, as someone enjoying a freer life. His specific association with the Republican cause in Spain was expunged by the censors. Nonetheless, his character stands in opposition to the obsessional world of most of the others. If Giovanna is associated with romanticized notions of respectability and security, he is associated with nonconformity and a mobile life. He directly confronts Gino with the idea of freedom. Like the young dancer, Anita, whom Gino meets later, Spagnolo poses an alternative to the dark, static life associated with the restaurant and with Giovanna's passionate but obsessional and distorted conception of freedom and with Gino's enslavement to her.

Spagnolo invites Gino to stay with him. At a performance, Gino sees Giovanna and Bragana in the audience. They invite him to join them for a drink. Gino struggles to escape, to extricate himself from the lure of Giovanna, but his struggle ends vainly. Bragana is unaware of this drama. Deeply involved in the singing competition, he performs an aria from *La Traviata* to the acclaim of the audience. The romantic music of desire seems incongruous coming from Bragana, the coarse and coercive figure of repression and conformity, but nonetheless provides a commentary on the motif of death and thwarted sexuality. The young man who follows him to the platform accompanied and supervised by his mother also reinforces the contrast between desire and denial, between the repressive and ugly environment and the desire for escape.

The operatic arias and their performance further develop the element of reflexivity introduced in the previous scene with Spagnolo, inviting the audience to examine, not identify, with the conflicts. The scene also provides a commentary on Gino and Giovanna's entrapment in a romantic fantasy of escape that is marked by possessiveness, violence, and denial. The melodramatic aspects of opera are thus used by Visconti to indicate not only that such art is linked to bourgeois aspiration, but that romantic aspirations are a source of repression, not liberation.

Signor Bragana's victory in the singing contest leads him to drink excessively until he is barely able to maneuver. He struggles to his truck, followed by Gino and Giovanna. Out of sight of her husband, she enlists Gino's cooperation in killing Bragana. The murder scene is highly stylized: the headlights of the truck at night, the tight framing of the characters within, the highlighting of contrasts. Gino and Giovanna insist that Bragana cannot drive and they push him and the truck off the road. The death introduces a new element into the film, the role of police and of surveillance.

Gino and Giovanna are interrogated by the police at the scene of the crime, then afterward at the police commissioner's office where Giovanna is asked to sign necessary papers and collect her husband's belongings. The commissioner is suspicious about this "accidental" death and warns Giovanna that he may want to talk to her again. The return home provides a stark contrast between the brightness of the day and the darkness into which Gino and Giovanna are plunged with the *trattoria*. Giovanna begins to make plans for reopening the restaurant so that life will appear normal. Gino, however, pleads unsuccessfully with Giovanna to abandon this life. Life returns to the restaurant. Don Remigio, the priest, is uncomfortable about Gino's continued presence, and Gino himself is eager to leave. He does not want money or security. In contrast to the image of Gino's isolation and alienation, the growing crowd within the restaurant is cheerful and loquacious, enjoying themselves in singing and dancing. Gino finds Bragana's watch, and contemplates his present life. The watch, the signifier of Bragana's continued presence, has been introduced several times, a reminder of Gino and Giovanna's continued enslavement to Bragana's world, to material objects, and to conformity.

Gino sees Spagnolo on the road. Overjoyed, Gino greets him. Spagnolo renews his invitation to travel, urging Gino, as Gino had urged Giovanna, to get away. Angrily, Gino tells him that he does not want to be a vagabond. Finally, he hits Spagnolo in an effort to silence him. Sadly, Spagnolo leaves, but he is stopped by a policeman who tries to ingratiate himself in order to get information about Gino. Spagnolo refuses to be an informer.

The following sequences in a garden at Ferrara highlight the contrast between the constraints of Gino and Giovanna's world, their alienation from each other, and the beauty and open spaces of the world beyond the *trattoria*. While sitting on a bench waiting for Giovanna, who is collecting her husband's insurance, Gino meets Anita, a dancer, who invites him to accompany her to the theater. He refuses at first. When Giovanna meets Gino in the garden, she ebulliently shares her plans with him to enlarge the business. Gino accuses Giovanna of murdering Bragana for the money, and defiantly he goes to Anita's apartment. When Gino and Anita emerge, Giovanna sees them and confronts Gino, but he coldly tells her to leave him, finally striking her as a crowd observes. Anita and Gino return to her room. He confesses to her that he is tied to Giovanna forever. Seeing a policeman, he suspects Giovanna of denouncing him. He escapes to the train station only to discover the police there. He finally flags down a ride in a truck and arrives at the *trattoria*, a much different person from his first arrival, also in a truck.

From Giovanna he learns that she is expecting a child. The two reconcile and spend the night together on the beach. Gino tells her the following morning when they awaken that he feels liberated now. They decide to leave the place forever. As they return to the *trattoria* to pack, a child observes them. They drive away in the truck, hopeful and eager to escape, but Gino crashes into another truck and Giovanna is killed. Prostrate over Giovanna's body, Gino is arrested.

The film's self-conscious use of melodrama probes sexual conflict, the entrapment in romantic fantasy. Giovanna is obsessed with the banality and obstructiveness of Bragana, the father-husband who controls her life and whom she seeks to destroy. Bragana, indifferent to her, plays out his authority, expecting the world to conform to his petit bourgeois expectations. Gino, the young intruder, has his own romantic notions of escape to freedom, which are blocked by his desire for Giovanna. Giovanna's fantasy is to replace Bragana with the younger man but maintain, even improve, the style of family and business life she has known, while Gino is incapable of extricating himself, bound as he is first by passion but then later by having shared in the crime of destroying Bragana. Rather than bringing the two closer to liberating themselves, the crime mires them deeper in their own obsessions, she becoming enslaved to the business and accumulating money, he enslaved to sexual desire and to the notion of enslavement itself.

The images of inside and outside, represented by the enclosed world of the *trattoria* and the open road and movement, seem to convey the unbridgeable gap between commitment and freedom, between the world of creativity and of accumulation, between the repression of the family and the liberation from its demands, between pleasure and profit. Giovanna's desire for security becomes a prison for her and for Gino. The film amply illustrates that the more she submerges herself in commerce, the less she derives personal gratification from her desire to replace Bragana and to assume his responsibilities. Visually, the images within the *trattoria* convey a sense of imprisonment corresponding to the confines of possessive love. In terms of character development, a role reversal takes place and Giovanna becomes the jailer to Gino that Bragana had earlier been to her. Thus the myth of the family and the ennobling aspects of romantic love are here dissected and revealed to be coercive, strangulating, and threatening.

The roles of the police and of surveillance are intimately related to the maintenance of the family and the consequences of transgression. The police in the film function to raise consciousness on two levels, the symbolic and the historic. On the level of the symbolic the police represent the organized and coercive forces of society that punish violations of the law and work to maintain the status quo. The role of the police develops further the disjunctions in the film between public and private spheres. Visconti thus explores the relationship between the internalization of family positions and the external social forces that ensure and maintain continuity. In a more specific historical fashion than is evident in other films of the early thirties, Visconti evokes an image of a society in which surveillance, informing, hunting, and punishment are central aspects of life.

Through Spagnolo, Visconti develops the motifs of resistance and freedom. Spagnolo constitutes an alternative to the image of the virile male so popular in the era, and his friendship with Gino is also an indirect commentary on more classical forms of male relationships. His slight figure, his nurturant role, his avoidance of forms of coercion and dominance, seem to offer a critique of male bonding. That he is an artist is also important; he "entertains" in order to provide for minimal necessity, not, as Bragana, to compete with others. He is a man of the people, and his entertainment is a gift, part of the generosity that prompts him to befriend Gino, a generosity dramatically in contrast to Bragana's, which gives nothing away. Recognizing and exposing Gino's obsession, he does not use it as a means of control and manipulation but sees Gino's plight as an opportunity for friendship and support. Spagnolo is associated with travel and movement as Gino had been earlier; he is mainly seen out of doors.

Anita is a parallel character. She, too, is an entertainer, also single, and also itinerant. Like Spagnolo, she holds no veneration for the law and is not an informer, willing even to help Gino escape the police. She asks for nothing materially or emotionally from Gino. Unpossessive, she accepts transitoriness in contrast to Giovanna, who is obsessed with security and permanence. The conjunction of open sexuality, openness of encounter, an encumbered way of living, the antiromantic nature of Spagnolo's and Anita's attachments to Gino, contrasts sharply with the other characters' obsessional nature.

Giovanna's death at the end raises a number of issues. In designing her as a *femme fatale*, Visconti makes Giovanna a contradictory figure. On the one hand she resists subordination, on the other she is a total victim. The devouring destroyer, the instigator of transgression, is also destroyed and a victim. Giovanna's death at the end and Gino's imprisonment at the point where they finally feel unburdened is Visconti's way of subverting the happy ending and, more significantly, of underlining the precariousness of an easy alternative to the conflicts posed in the film. This ending also develops the sense of unnaturalness that Visconti has tried to stress throughout the film. The film has sought to denaturalize romance, the notion of the idealized family, and the idea of security. Through melodrama as a narrative form that can place these concepts into question, Visconti seems to be calling attention to the violence inherent in the commonplace in contradistinction to those films that make violence commonplace, glamorizing it, concealing it, and renaming it.

Notes

1. Antonio Gramsci, *Selections from the Prison Notebooks*, ed. Quintin Hoare and Geoffrey Nowell-Smith (New York: International Publishers, 1978), pp. 304–5.
2. Patrizia Pistagnesi, "La scena famigliare nel cinema fascista," in *Cinema italiano sotto il fascismo*, ed. Riccardo Redi (Venice: Marsilio, 1979), p. 101.
3. Antonio Gramsci, *Letteratura e vita nazionale* (Rome: Riuniti, 1979), pp. 94–96.
4. Thomas Elsaesser, "Tales of Sound and Fury: Observations on the Family Melodrama," *Monogram* 4 (1973), pp. 2–15.
5. David N. Rodowick, "Madness, Authority, and Ideology in the Domestic Melodrama of the 1950's," *The Velvet Light Trap*, no. 19 (1982), pp. 40–45; Sandy Flitterman, "*Guest in the House*: Rupture and Reconstitution of the Bourgeois Nuclear Family," *Wide Angle* 4 (1980), pp. 18–27.
6. See E. Ann Kaplan, *Woman and Film: Both Sides of the Camera* (New York: Methuen, 1983), pp. 38–39; Peter Brooks, *The Melodramatic Imagination: Balzac, Henry James, Melodrama, and the Mode of Excess* (New York: Columbia University Press, 1984); Michael Renov, "*Leave Her to Heaven*: The Double Bind of the Post-War Woman," *Journal of the University Film and Video Association* 35 (Winter 1983), pp. 28–36; Russell Merritt, "Melodrama: Postmortem for a Phantom Genre," *Wide Angle* 5 (1983) pp. 24–32; Christian Viviani, "Who is Without Sin? The Maternal Melodrama in American Film, 1930–39," *Wide Angle* 4 (1980), pp. 4–17; Jean Loup Bourget, "Faces of the American Melodrama: Joan Crawford," *Film Reader* 3 (February 1978), pp. 24–34.
7. Christopher Orr, "Closure and Containment: Marylee Hadley in *Written on the Wind*," *Wide Angle* 4 (1980) pp. 29–35. See also Bryan Crow, "The Cinematic and the Melodramatic in *A Woman of Affairs*," *Wide Angle* 4 (1980), pp. 44–51.

8. Thomas Schatz, *Hollywood Genres: Formulas, Filmmaking, and the Studio System* (New York: Random House, 1981), p. 227.
9. Filippo Maria De Sanctis, "La rivolta dei formalisti," in *Il cinema italiano dal fascismo all'antifascismo: Testi e documenti dello spettacolo*, ed. Giorgio Tinazzi (Padua: Marsilio, 1966), p. 169. See also Franco Venturini, "Origins of Neorealism," in *Springtime in Italy: A Reader on Neorealism*, ed. David Overbey (Hamden, Conn.: Archon Books, 1978), pp. 171–75.
10. Gian Piero Brunetta *Storia del cinema italiano 1895–1945* (Rome: Riuniti, 1979), pp. 498–513.
11. Peter Bondanella, *Italian Cinema: From Neorealism to the Present* (New York: Frederick Ungar, 1983), pp. 24–25. See also Gaia Servadio, *Luchino Visconti: A Biography* (New York: Franklin Watts, 1983), pp. 80–82; Mira Liehm, *Passion and Defiance: Film in Italy from 1942 to the Present* (Berkeley and Los Angeles: University of California Press, 1984), pp. 51–59.

Fassbinder's Reality: An Imitation of Life

RUTH McCORMICK

In psychoanalysis, only the exaggerations are true.
—Theodor W. Adorno

Fassbinder's 1979 film *The Third Generation* is "Dedicated to a true lover, and therefore, probably, to nobody." His first full-length film is called *Love Is Colder Than Death*; Marie, the heroine of his second, *Katzelmacher*, tells her Greek lover, "I know I love you, because it hurts so much"; Jeff, the director in *Beware of a Holy Whore*, is accused by more than one other character of being "incapable of love"; Hans's sister in *Merchant of the Four Seasons* tells his small daughter that he is unhappy because "no one has loved him enough"; Hanni, the rebellious teenager who urges her boyfriend to kill her father in *Jail Bait* declares after his trial, "It wasn't real love with us, it was just physical"; Petra von Kant, when Karin deserts her, screams, "I loved her!"; Effi Briest confesses on her deathbed that the harsh, unforgiving husband who ruined her life was "right all along"—that he was "as good as a man could be, who is without love"; a 1976 television drama about a repressed young man who cracks up and kills a man he thinks is his father is entitled *I Only Want You to Love Me*. In Fassbinder's films, the characters talk about love continually, but even where love may have a chance for survival (*Eight Hours Are Not a Day, Fear Eats the Soul*), it faces tremendous odds. Che Guevara once said that the revolutionary must be motivated by feelings of great love. Love is, for Fassbinder, the utopian moment in the process of change, both political and personal, the impossible which must be made possible by a radical upheaval in human attitudes. How this upheaval is to come about is never mentioned; rather, Fassbinder's films are like a litany of the failures of love in the world.

Ruth McCormick, "Fassbinder's Reality: An Imitation of Life," in *Fassbinder* (New York: Tanam Press, 1981), pp. 85–97. Reprinted by permission of the Tanam Press.

Most love scenes in Fassbinder's films are cold, even repugnant. In the early films, only in *Katzelmacher* do we see any genuine affection, and this is between Marie and Jorgos (the other sexual relationships in the film are absolutely dismal). Only when we get to *Beware of a Holy Whore* do we find another love scene which could in any way be described as sensual, let alone tender, and this one also features Hanna Schygulla (with Eddie Constantine). In *Pioneers in Ingolstadt*, there are also moments of real warmth between Hanna Schygulla and Harry Baer, which make her eventual desertion all the more moving. In fact, with the exception of those depicting the Emmi-Ali relationship in *Fear Eats the Soul*, every scene that could be properly called a "love scene" in Fassbinder's films involves Hanna Schygulla (others being those between Maria Braun and the black soldier Bill, and Willie and Robert in the first part of *Lili Marleen*). There are flickers of love between Hanni and Franz in *Jail Bait*, Petra von Kant and Karin, and Franz and Eugen in *Fox and His Friends*, but these all occur at the beginning of their relationships, and are quickly extinguished. Bolwieser and Hermann in *Despair* lust after their wives, but because of their obsessions, what might have been sensual becomes merely ridiculous. Some of the most chilling scenes in Fassbinder's films take place when two people go to bed together—Ricky and the prostitute Rosa in *American Soldier*, Hans and Irmgard (and Irmgard and Anzell) in *Merchant of the Four Seasons*, Margot and the pharmacist in *Fear of Fear*, Walter and Andree in *Satan's Brew*, Ariane and her lover in *Chinese Roulette*, and Paul and Hilde in *The Third Generation*. If love is well-nigh impossible for Fassbinder's characters, sex is usually a drag.

Is Fassbinder trying to say that modern life is absolute hell? That there are no happy marriages, families, friendships? Is it only Germany that has come to this sad state? As has been noted many times, Fassbinder's "world" is not a carbon-copy of the real one. If Ozu, for example, gives us a recognizable world, in which, although his Japanese subjects have different customs from ours, we can identify the things that happen and the conversations of the characters as close to our own daily lives, Fassbinder gives us a world that is always at least a bit exaggerated, always strange. Through the camera, we become invisible witnesses to events that could take place, but never "really" do in the way they do in a Fassbinder film. Situations are extreme, as are emotions, although they are not incredible. They are within the realm of possibility, but usually confirm our worst suspicions. Nobody behaves quite as outrageously as Walter Kranz in *Satan's Brew*, even avant-garde poets—or do they? After all, we all know that poets can be egomaniacs, and Kranz is from the land of mad artists and crazy political movements. The Christ(!) family in *Chinese Roulette* are rich and elegant, but the crippled daughter can't stand her parents, who seem to regard her as an intruder who has destroyed their love life. Their housekeeper's son plagiarizes philosophical texts, but only the daughter is well-educated enough to realize that his "writings" are not original. The mute governess bears the same name as their Franconian castle. A blind beggar comes to the door, and then drives away in a Mercedes, which both the lady of the house and her servant find amusing. Crazy? Isn't it true that many parents regard their children as inconveniences, that many children have contempt for their parents, that a good deal of "serious" writing today only rehashes work that has been done before, that the *nouveau riche* are buying up the castles of impoverished aristocrats, that just about everything is a ripoff of one kind or another? And there may be more love in *our* world than in Fassbinder's, but surely not enough, or the world wouldn't be in the terrible mess it's in.

Fassbinder does not pretend to be original, although he combines elements of his cinematic models, from Hollywood gangster films and melodramas, from favorite directors (Sirk, Walsh, Sternberg, Hawks, Bunuel, Visconti, Rohmer, Godard, Chabrol, et al.) with Freudian–Marxist–Frankfurt school social theories in a way that makes him unique among contemporary filmmakers. His films bear the mark of an *auteur*, and, despite the many developments and refinements of his style, his concerns have remained consistent from the early "gangster" films through *Berlin Alexanderplatz* and *Lili Marleen*. In fact, *Berlin Alexanderplatz*, Alfred Doblin's monumental novel of a *lumpen hero* who dreams of love and respectability, which he was finally able to make as a 15½-hour, 14-part television series in 1980, had fascinated him since he first read it when he was sixteen. This story of one man's failure to find his utopia, written and situated in the years before the rise of Hitler, appealed to him personally and, in the long run, politically. Franz Biberkopf's obsessive attraction to the psychopathic Reinhold appeared to the young man, who was trying to deal with his own emerging homosexuality, as a revelation. Biberkopf's loss of his beloved Mieze and of his optimistic ideals, which were the product of a false consciousness, seem to foreshadow Fassbinder's own belief that happiness and fulfillment are impossible in a society which propagates false notions of love and success. The failure of Franz Biberkopf could, in fact, be read as the failure of Germany itself. In any case, its basic themes and characters are repeated time and again in Fassbinder's films: personal and political failure are seen as one and the same. The pessimism of these films echoes that of Marcuse's *One-Dimensional Man* and Horkeimer and Adorno's *Dialectic of the Enlightenment*. Like these thinkers, Fassbinder cannot name the unnameable, the better society, but insists upon the importance of the utopian imagination in its realization. If Mao Zedong cautions against "incorrect thinking," Fassbinder warns against "incorrect feeling."

If one theme is consistent in all Fassbinder's films, from the early, rather misogynist "gangster" films on, it is that victims internalize their own oppression, either by clinging to false, socially determined ideas of what they should want, or by yearning for a leader, a lover, a master—someone who will make things right for them. Fassbinder's characters, like a depressing number of us, want to be led whether we realize it or not, want to be told what to think and how to feel, want to feel "loved." The first form of iternalized oppression, the yearning for the "good life" we see in films and on television, hear about from our parents and friends, and read about in books and magazines, is blatantly obvious in almost all Fassbinder's films; the second, the desire for domination, is more subtle, but stands in direct relation to the first. The young gangsters in *Love Is Colder Than Death*, *Gods of the Plague* and *American Soldier* are right out of *Berlin Alexanderplatz*, though their outward mannerisms are out of American gangster films. The "hero" of the first two films mentioned is named Franz Walsch (a bow to Raoul), and, like Biberkopf, he only wants to get together enough money to go straight and marry his girlfriend Joanna, a prostitute with bourgeois dreams. However, he allows his more streetwise friend Bruno to lure him back into working for the syndicate. Joanna/Mieze is no longer seen as an "angel," but as a possessive woman who wants to trap Franz into a dull middle-class existence, while Bruno/Reinhold, who models himself on Humphrey Bogart (or Alain Delon as Humphrey Bogart), represents a kind of freedom, however warped. The end is the same; there is no escape for Franz, no real happiness with either the man or the woman he loves. Although the film is crude, displaying political naivete in its implication that a life outside "the system" side-by-side with Bruno is preferable to a "conventional" life with Joanna, there is really no alternative to be seen; each choice only offers its own kind of prison. The hoods who ape the gangsters in American films are as incapable of real life as the women who dream of the joys of married life. Fassbinder has laid out his world-view right here, and it has yet to be changed.

"Franz Biberkopf," the seeker of love and freedom, appears many times and in many guises in Fassbinder's films, and continually meets with the same failure. Jorgos, the Greek worker in *Katzelmacher,* hopes to make a better life for himself in Germany, and even though he left a wife and two kids in Greece, wants to include the romantic Marie in his plans. Simple common sense tells us he will fail, just as his German counterparts have already failed. Kurt R in *Why Does Herr R Run Amok?* has a life Franz and Jorgos might envy—a professional job, a home, a pretty wife, a young son, respectability. It is the prison that drives him insane. All Hans in *Merchant of the Four Seasons* wanted out of life was some love and some freedom; he might as well have asked for the stars. Franz, the unemployed carnie of *Fox and His Friends,* suddenly wins a huge lottery and meets the man of his dreams, but because he's completely unaware of what makes the world go 'round (and it's not love), he ends up far worse off than when he started; along with his "love" and his money, he finally loses his illusions. Erwin Weishaupt, an orphan, becomes a woman, Elvira, for the sake of the man he loves. The sacrifice is totally ignored. He tries to return to his wife and daughter, but it is too late. No one understands a word he says, and there is no longer any place for him in the world.

In these films, form serves content in an amazingly effective way. So much has been written about Fassbinder's stylistic devices, his mirror shots in which the characters experience themselves as the "other," his framing devices, which seem to isolate and/or imprison the dramatis personae in their constricted worlds, the jarring closeups and clinical overhead shots, that to write more at this point seems superfluous. What the stories and dialogue have already made evident is "brought home" even more forcefully by the actual look of the films. In *In a Year of 13 Moons,* Elvira Weishaupt lives in such a dark world that when she ventures into the sunlight, we are almost blinded. This is, indeed, a world where nuns and suicides would be reading Schopenhauer, where the intrusion of the culture industry into a depressing apartment via television seems even more deadening than it otherwise would. On the other hand, Willie in *Lili Marleen* is almost always bathed in light. As a performer, this is her element, but the light gets stronger the closer she gets to the Nazi hierarchy, and becomes an ironic epiphany when she is ushered into Der Fuhrer's office. In the end, when she is deserted by her love, she walks off into the darkness. The terrorists in *The Third Generation* operate in darkness, surrounded by sounds they never seem to notice from a variety of electronic devices; this would seem to reflect the darkness and chaos in their own heads.

Only Fassbinder tells stories like this, and does it with dazzling proficiency. He had gathered around him a number of the most gifted people working in cinema today. As a result, he was probably the most successful of the directors in "new German cinema." He was certainly the most controversial; his films have been called "provocations," and he was probably delighted about that. He had said that he would like to make psychoanalysis available to those who can't afford it, and, like a good analyst, he used a sometimes-painful Socratic method. It is as if he were trying to blast away the preconditioning of his audience by showing them themselves (and himself in the bargain) through the mirror of cinema. He was "provoking" everyone who has bought time-honored promises of happiness, whether they be fellow leftists who thought that demonstrating, organizing, making "revolutionary" art, and "educating" the oppressed through pamphlets and documentaries would somehow bring about instant utopia, as well as conservative and apolitical men and women who still believe the advertisements, who expect "love" as part of their birthright, along with a good job, plenty of money, security, freedom and fun. Fassbinder's characters are paradigms for us all. They have all bought the promises of the consumer society, and when their dreams don't come true, they see themselves as cheated, betrayed. For some of these "Biberkopfs"—Hans, Fox, Elvira, Herr R and possibly Maria Braun—it is more than they can bear, and they kill themselves. Effi Briest, whose possibilities are more limited by the time in which she lives, simply fades away, while Martha, who has totally internalized her masochism, seems even happy when she must ultimately face a life of complete dependency.

While psychological oppression is constantly evident in these films, the social oppression of his characters is seldom shown as clearly. True, the surroundings of the characters in *Katzelmacher* and the early gangster films are tacky and depressing; Jorgos and Ali are obvious victims of racist prejudice, as is Elvira of the kind of "macho" prejudice sometimes suffered by transsexuals and "queens" in the gay community; the shocking conditions under which the young Franz must work are shown in *Jail Bait*. But it is often seen as a weakness in Fassbinder's films that more concrete forms of oppression are not seen, but take a back seat to more psychological forms of repression. Oppressed people are often depicted as victims of their own peers (immigrant workers by German workers in *Katzelmacher* and *Fear Eats the Soul;* homosexuals by other homosexuals in *Fox and His Friends* and *In a Year of 13 Moons;* and women by other women in *The Bitter Tears of Petra von Kant*, *Fear of Fear*, and *Women in New York*). Even a child becomes an oppressor (though, we suspect, with good reason) in *Chinese Roulette*. Mother Kusters is treated with almost as little sensitivity by her children and the "well-meaning" radicals as she is by the yellow press, and we are hard put to know who is oppressing the terrorists in *The Third Generation*. Even their "alienation" and political ideas are never articulated. We do know, however, that their personal lives, for the most part, are not very happy. They seem to have lost the utopian vision which had inspired earlier generations of revolutionaries, who were at least capable of ideas, and who asked questions that have yet to be answered.

At one point in *The Third Generation*, someone remarks, "The masses create their exploiters," not realizing that the group is itself being exploited for the benefit of U.S. business interests. These "rebels without a cause," isolated from the "masses" for whom they say they are fighting, are as much sitting ducks for the establishment as any of Fassbinder's deluded petit bourgeois conformists. If Fassbinder has been criticized for anything, it has been for his lack of "sympathy" for the oppressed—for women, workers, gays, and in a *cause celebre* (*Garbage, the City and Death / Shadows of Angels*), Jews—even more than for his criticisms of the "left" in Germany. The implications that are drawn by Fassbinder's critics, and that they, in turn, believe will be drawn by bigots, sexists, and conservatives of various stripes, are that women, workers, gays, Jews, etc., are not only responsible for their plight, but are, in the long run, no better than their oppressors. It is gay immigrant workers, people doubly oppressed, who beat Elvira in *In a Year of 13 Moons* when they find she is not just a transvestite, but a transsexual. Then, her male lover leaves her because she has gotten "fat and stupid." Elvira's own seeming masochism can lead to the conclusion that she deserves what she gets. Seitz, the heterosexual for whom Elvira had her operation, spent time in a concentration camp and subsequently made a fortune exploiting others. Is he a Jew? That is not as important as the fact that, as Elvira explains to a friendly prostitute, he was so warped by his experiences that a brothel he owned was called Bergen-Belsen. The prostitute later meets Seitz, and is totally charmed by him. We can't help suspecting that Robert Mendelsson's rich, aristocratic father in *Lili Marleen* disapproves of his son's engagement to a cabaret singer as much for the reason that she's "not the right sort" (not rich, not Jewish) as because she is German. Petra von Kant assumes a "male" role in her attempted domination of Karin, who in turn adopts a "conniving female" role. Eugen, true to his class, exploits poor Franz and then throws him out, but it cannot be said that Franz is not at least partially to blame for his own downfall. He has been inordinately stupid about his money, and has made very little effort to make any changes in his lumpen lifestyle to please the man he says he loves. It cannot, however, be said that Fassbinder does not consider himself as much at fault as other people in the perpetuation of domination. Implicitly in *Beware of a Holy Whore* and *Satan's Brew* and explicitly in *Germany in Autumn*, he has shown himself as a quasi-oppressor. It is very disturbing to see the latter film now, in view of the subsequent suicide of Armin Meier, the recipient of Fassbinder's tirades, but it adds to our feeling that he is trying very hard to be honest about himself, as well as about the human condition. It is possible that his insistence upon showing the all-pervasive master-slave syndrome in modern society leads to his being misunderstood, but even the anger and controversy that are raised by his treatment of social problems perhaps bring more attention to them than a good-guys–bad-guys approach, as common in most leftist films as in Hollywood, ever could. If the oppressed become oppressors, or if they passively accept their oppression, Fassbinder seems to be saying, they are suffering from a failure of imagination.

In an article on German cinema in *Vogue* (Oct. 1980), critic Andrew Sarris reports that he was taken to task by a disgruntled journalist from *Der Spiegel* for admiring any of Fassbinder's films after *Merchant of the Four Seasons*, because "people like Fassbinder are responsible for the Baader-Meinhof gang." It seems to me that this unhappy (and probably conservative) journalist is putting the cart before the horse. Like the young extremists in *The Third Generation*, Fassbinder is a child of the 'sixties. His contemporaries in Germany—and the rest of the world—who are making art in the 'seventies and 'eighties are seldom much more thrilled with the status quo than he is. The old, optimistic "social realism" of earlier leftist artists has virtually disappeared, except in a few documentaries and in what we've been able to see coming out of the People's Republic of China, and in the other aesthetic camp, even Godard is edging away from the neo-formalism of his 'seventies work, and Straub/Huillet are rediscovering their sense of humor. Fassbinder's "exaggerated" stories, his increasing irony, his fluctuating between the things he likes best about Hollywood films and ongoing stylistic investigations into new forms of cinematic language bespeak a need to communicate that is both personal and political. He is hardly promoting terrorism—only mirroring it. There is just as much alienation, and a good deal more violence, in the work of any number of American directors (Coppola, Scorsese, de Palma, Cimino, Peckinpagh, innumerable "gore 'n' horror" directors) than in Fassbinder's films, and much less social analysis or insight. Can an artist pretend to see happiness and promise where they don't exist? Fassbinder, like other German directors of his generation, sees a damaged society, totally dominated by technology and utilitarian rationality, obsessed with quantity to the detriment of quality, in which the corporately controlled mass media try to sell us everything, even our dreams. Fassbinder's people are trapped and bombarded—perhaps more than we are—but that is what gives his films their cautionary power. These gangsters and terrorists, businessmen and housewives, Franz Biberkopfs and Elvira Weishaupts, can't imagine things different from the way they are. The black man who hangs himself in *In a Year of 13 Moons* tells Elvira that he refuses to live a life that cannot be on his own terms; in a quote from Bresson's heartbreaking *Le Diable, Probablement*, the latest of Fassbinder's Franz Walsches deliberately walks into a police trap in a cemetery—there is nothing to live for now that his sweetheart and the revolution are both dead. However, there are moments of humor and tenderness in these films that say that all is not lost; their complexity and trickiness tell us to keep our eyes open; maybe things aren't as bad as they seem, if we employ all our faculties of thought, feeling, and, especially, imagination. When the ruling class starts aping Jerry Lewis and getting itself kidnapped to increase sales, they're in trouble. The world changes.

Since Fassbinder is, by his own admission, both a highly subjective artist and an unrelenting critic of the status quo, can we separate the man—the product of progressive schooling and a broken home, the avowed homosexual and avid cinephile—from the artist—frenetically busy, innovative, disciplined—from the social critic who believes that we live in a totally dominated world, and that Western bourgeois art had already exhausted all its possibilities with Verdi's *La Traviata?* What Frederic Jameson says of Walter Benjamin in his book *Marxism and Form* holds equally true for Fassbinder: "How many modern philosophers have described the 'damaged existence' we lead in modern society, the psychological impairment caused by the division of labor and by specialization, the general alienation of modern life in all its aspects? Yet for the most part these analyses remain abstract; through them there speaks the resignation of the intellectual specialist to his own maimed present, the dream of wholeness, where it persists, attaching itself to someone else's future. Benjamin is unique among those thinkers in that he wants to save his own life as well. . . ."

If Fassbinder's films are problematic, however, it is because of his dialectical imagination, which very often leads to ambiguity. As Richard Dyer points out in his article "Reading Fassbinder's Sexual Politics" (*Fassbinder*, BFI, 1980, p. 54), the films "will be very differently understood by different members of the audience according to both their structural position in society (class, gender, race, sexual orientation, etc.) and their political orientation." They are, however, and I agree, "eminently suitable for further debate." The personal and the political are so intertwined, the relations between individuals are often so symbolic of larger social relations, that Fassbinder's films, more than those of most other directors, are important in dealing with the problems of communicating with a large mass audience without resorting to an unreal "social realism" or shifting over to the clichés of the culture industry, bombarding the spectator with images to the point where (s)he loses the capacity for critical thought. One should not have to read interviews with a director in order to understand her or his films. On the other hand, audiences do not want to be preached at; that is not good politics or good psychoanalysis.

If Fassbinder can be compared to Brecht, whom he considers too cerebral ("The rational doesn't interest me"), it is in his ability to force the viewer away from the subject matter, to consider it, to feel emotions about it, and to have to take those feelings, as he says, back into the street. While he attracts an audience with the beauty of his films, with the skill of the actors, with the strangeness of the stories he tells, he challenges them to make up their own endings. Though it may be true that he offers no answers, he asks question after question. His life seems at much at stake as ours.

European Anti-Melodrama: Godard, Truffaut, and Fassbinder

KATHERINE S. WOODWARD

A fruitful way to examine many modern European films is to consider them as "anti-melodramas." The anti-melodrama centers on the assumption that today's society is suffused with a false melodramatic outlook and that a film should lead viewers to scrutinize their own melodramatic inclinations. As part of the modernist movement in film, a movement initiated particularly by the French New Wave and Brechtian dramaturgy, the anti-melodrama insists on creating an aesthetic distance between the film text and viewer; it leads the viewer to recognize the film as a specifically cinematic act, often as part of a cinematic tradition, and thus actively to analyze the film. Like virtually all modernist films, the anti-melodrama combats the passive emotional identification elicited by the melodrama. What distinguishes the anti-melodrama from other modernist films is its attempt to make viewers explicitly aware of the melodramatic perspective and then to give them new insight with which to reconsider that perspective. Rather than avoid melodrama, the anti-melodrama includes potentially melodramatic incidents and structures, then comments on the melodramatic possibilities. Among the many studies of melodrama—definitional, historical, and political—the methods films employ to explore the inadequacies of melodrama have not been sufficiently addressed.

Domestic melodrama, that is, melodrama concerning love, family, and the home, is especially central to the anti-melodramatic film. A study of three domestic anti-melodramas—R. W. Fassbinder's *Ali: Fear Eats the Soul* (Germany, 1974; abbreviated

Katherine S. Woodward's "European Anti-Melodrama: Godard, Truffaut, and Fassbinder" originally appeared in *Post Script*, Vol. 3, no. 2 (Winter 1984), pp. 34–47. Reprinted by permission of the author and *Post Script*.

henceforth as *Ali*), Jean-Luc Godard's *Every Man for Himself* (France, 1979), and Francois Truffaut's *The Last Metro* (France, 1980)—will demonstrate how filmmakers can use melodrama to express their own world view. *Every Man for Himself* and *The Last Metro* are recent works by two major founders of the modernist movement in contemporary film. *Ali*, although not as recent a film, represents Fassbinder's most direct statement about melodrama among a canon of works exploring melodramatic implications; *Ali* is loosely based on the melodramatic plot of Douglas Sirk's *All That Heaven Allows* (USA, 1956). Inclusion of *Ali* broadens a discussion of anti-melodrama beyond French film; periodic references to the way Fassbinder alters the Sirk original provide additional insight into the anti-melodramatic approach.[1]

The melodramatic perspective that the anti-melodrama counters consists chiefly of the primacy of emotion. This dependence upon emotion within the fictional world of the film, and upon the viewer's emotional identification with the fictional characters, helps to account for the structure of melodrama, its focus on strong pure feelings, particularly those caused by romantic attachments, and the division of its narrative world into a clear dichotomy of good and evil, heroes to love and villains to hate. (The melodrama confirms the intended audience's definitions of good and evil to ensure emotional rather than reflective responses.) In Fassbinder's *Ali*, the anti-melodramatic perspective serves to warn the viewer of the naivete and consequent dangers of believing in melodrama. Godard's *Every Man for Himself* is more drastic and suggests the difficulty, in the present, of feeling any emotion, melodramatic or otherwise. Truffaut's *The Last Metro*, like the others, distances the viewer from its own potentially melodramatic events but, unlike the others, provides the viewer with no real ideas to consider. Its emptiness can be explained by its failure to be a true anti-melodrama, to fuse its form and content, while at the same time its use of the form of anti-melodrama suggests the prevalence of an anti-melodramatic impulse.

An examination of closing scenes demonstrates how these three films take the viewer through melodramatic incident to a reevaluation of his/her melodramatic beliefs. The first line from Erich Segal's *Love Story* (1970), "What can you say about a 25-year-old who died," typifies the melodramatic event. Regardless of Jenny's personality or virtue—of any complexity of character or circumstance—her death will make the reader sad. Simply, the reader identifies with a bereaved husband, who, having lost his love, has lost all. But whereas melodramatic incident provides dramatic affirmation of the viewer's conventional responses and beliefs (e.g., love conquers all), the anti-melodramatic event conspicuously withholds that affirmation.

In *Ali* Emmi, an elderly German widow, marries a young Moroccan *gastarbeiter*, Ali (Brigitte Mira, El Hedi Ben Salem, respectively). The two suffer intense hostility from the community, then begin to experience marital difficulties. Near the close of the film, Fassbinder allows the viewer to feel great relief and joy at Emmi and Ali's reunion (love has conquered all), but then cuts off that emotion by having Ali fall sick. However, viewers cannot give themselves over to extreme sadness, either, because Ali does not die. The film ends with the doctor's prognosis: Ali will survive this time, but he will return to the hospital again and again; the pressures on immigrants make it nearly impossible for them even to remain physically healthy. The viewer, denied melodramatic emotion (either pure joy or pure sadness), is left contemplating how political and emotional realities intertwine; specifically, how the differences in nationality and age between Emmi and Ali inevitably will shape their love relationship. Transcendence is denied.

The contrast between the ending of Sirk's *All That Heaven Allows* and that of *Ali* underscores Fassbinder's anti-melodramatic perspective. Both contain a reconciliation and injury, but the order of these events differs. *All That Heaven Allows* tells of a middle-aged, upper-middle-class widow, Carey, who falls in love with her young gardener, Ron (Jane Wyman, Rock Hudson, respectively). She lets herself be persuaded to give up Ron for the sake of her position in society, but after he is injured (he falls from a cliff while rushing toward her to catch her attention), she runs to his bedside and permanently commits herself to him. His injury not only precedes but also causes the reconciliation between lovers. By reversing the order of reconciliation and injury, Fassbinder refuses to romanticize illness and instead insists on its reality as an unfortunate, inevitably political fate for the immigrant in a xenophobic environment. Contrary to the typical melodramatic emphasis on emotion (consider the number of soap operas which feature sick people), *Ali* shows Ali's sickness eliciting no more love or kindness than existed before.

Although *Every Man for Himself* presents less a chronology of events than a poetic assemblage of images, it too contains the seeds of melodrama: Paul reluctantly breaks up with his girlfriend, Denise, then pursues his ex-wife (Jacques Dutronc, Natalie Baye, Paule Muret, respectively). Near the close of the movie, Paul is struck by a car in front of his ex-wife and his twelve-year-old daughter (Cecile Tanner), an event fraught with the same melodramatic possibilities as the injury in *Ali* and *All That Heaven Allows*. However, Godard does not even flirt with offering the audience emotional release: not only does he refuse to present a teary reconciliation, his characters seem incapable of feeling anything at all. The ex-wife and daughter calmly walk away without trying to help Paul; the riders in the car admit knowing Paul, but still suggest that the injury they have caused is "None of our business." Even Paul, the dying man, states, "I feel nothing." The culminating image of the daughter walking past twenty violinists and cellists concretizes the gulf between strong melodramatic emotion (as signified, humorously, by the twenty instruments playing the main musical theme of the film) and modern indifference (as signified by the daughter). Godard also frustrates the viewer's expectations by refusing to inform him/her whether Paul lives or dies. This denial leads viewers to question their automatic sympathy for a person in distress. Why should the viewer care more about Paul's fate than do the characters in the film?

The scene of the car accident is orchestrated to suggest that concerns exist other than the emotional ones of love and loss. Since Paul is injured by a car, a cultural icon of modern society, his movements take on thematic reverberations: Paul's walking away from his ex-wife immediately before the accident suggests people's inability to connect (compare Ron's fall in *All That Heaven Allows* while rushing toward Carey), his walking backward suggests a lack of progress in people's lives, his refusal to look where he goes indicates the aimlessness which plagues many people today.

The use of melodramatic event in *The Last Metro*'s closing scenes at first resembles that in both *Ali* and *Every Man for Himself*. After presenting the story of a wife, Marianne, trying to protect her Jewish husband from the Nazis, and then beginning to fall in love with a fellow actor, Bernard (Catherine Deneuve, Heinz Bennent, and Gerard Depardieu, respectively), Truffaut films a love scene in a hospital ward. Adhering to a melodramatic plotline, Truffaut shows Marianne experiencing rejection from the injured Bernard, but still declaring her undying love for him. Truffaut then cuts to a curtain call to reveal that the preceding melodramatic scene has formed part of a play. However, rather than develop the viewer's sudden awareness of his susceptibility to melodramatic manipulation, Truffaut drops the anti-melodramatic perspective and ends his film with Marianne holding both her husband's and Bernard's hands. Giving Truffaut the benefit of the doubt, one could say that he maintains his anti-melodramatic perspective by leaving the ending unresolved—melodrama implies simple and clear emotions—but that lack of resolution may be simply a modern cliché. Moreover, the closing incident actually contradicts Truffaut's anti-melodramatic stance, for by leaving the viewer with the question, Which man will Marianne choose? Truffaut implies that matters of the heart are the paramount consideration.

Melodramas root the primacy of emotion in a world divided between clear heroes and tangible villains. This world may thrust suffering and sacrifice on the heroes, but in the end the heroes triumph: they defeat, escape, or transcend the forces of evil. The anti-melodramas convey a more complex view of the moral world, but, more important, they focus on deconstructing the melodramatic good/evil dichotomy to demonstrate its inadequacy.

The primary way *Ali* counters the melodramatic polarities of good and evil is to present a melodramatic moral world and then, gradually, to undercut that world by interweaving the weaknesses of its "heroes." In this way the gulf between the simplistic good/evil dichotomy and the more explanatory, complex interrelation between the two becomes explicit. At first Emmi and Ali appear as conventional good guys and stand against the evil world: they are persecuted in quick succession by Emmi's neighbors, her family, her co-workers, the grocer, even the restaurant employees.

When the two return from vacation, however, the rejection turns to exploitation, and Emmi begins to cooperate with her former persecutors. (For example, she agrees to her neighbors' request to have Ali move heavy objects for them; she agrees to babysit for her family; she agrees to spend money again at the grocer's store.) The viewer wonders why a woman who stood so steadfastly against the prejudiced stares, in perfect melodramatic fashion, lets these same people use her. When Emmi also persecutes and shows prejudice to others (she shows off Ali's muscles, encouraging her friends to touch them; she refuses to eat with the Yugoslav worker), the viewer becomes aware of how a lonely person becomes susceptible to exploitation out of a desire to be liked, and how she can hate prejudice yet act prejudiced herself out of this same need. Similarly, the viewer realizes how a person can betray a loved one (Ali has an affair), not out of evil motives or even lack of love, but out of confusion and frustration at a series of events. By gradually moving away from the melodramatic moral world he has created, Fassbinder insists upon the importance of explaining human behavior rather than of finding objects in the world to love and hate.

Another way Fassbinder counters the melodramatic vision is by structuring a world where evil cannot be escaped and, therefore, must be confronted and analyzed. Carey, in *All That Heaven Allows*, has the choice between pure good—Ron's "natural" world (a world full of nature-loving, amiable people)—and pure evil—her repressive bourgeois world. (Note that at the party given by Ron's friends, everyone immediately accepts the couple; at the earlier party given by Carey's friend, the guests grotesquely reject them.)[2] In *Ali*, on the other hand, both Emmi's and Ali's worlds contain evil, that is, prejudice, rejection and oppression, although in Ali's world the evil remains less pronounced. Fassbinder has changed the focus of his film from the simpler one of choice, as in *All That Heaven Allows*, to the more complex one of modes of coping with a good/bad world. Similarly, whereas Carey suffers because she has made an incorrect choice (she sacrifices Ron for her children and friends), Emmi and Ali suffer for no justifiable reason. Ali, a Moroccan, lives in Germany; Emmi marries Ali. The absence of poetic justice in *Ali* suggests that one has to learn to cope with injustice and evil as well as try to combat them.

In *Every Man for Himself* Godard demonstrates the inadequacy of the melodramatic dichotomy of good and evil in two ways. First, although he presents evil, especially exploitation, he refuses to present the forces of good battling this evil. By denying the viewer the possibility of identifying with heroes while hating their enemies, Godard leads the viewer to consider the reasons why people acquiesce in exploitation. The most dramatic instance of this acquiescence occurs when Isabel's pimp beats her for attempting to make independent money. At first the viewer hates the pimp and feels sorry for the victim, Isabel (Isabelle Huppert). However, Godard juxtaposes this scene with another of Isabel becoming pimp to her sister (Anna Baldaccini) and insisting on taking fifty percent of her sister's profits: she accepts the rules of exploitation and simply tries, whenever possible, to occupy the dominant position. She even tells one client that she will do anything "so long as it doesn't hurt." The viewer is left to consider what society has done to foster this materialistic, exploitative attitude. The frequent cuts between Isabel's prostitution and the normal-looking people rushing to work keeps the emphasis on the pervasiveness of the exploitation and acquiescence and away from the individual people involved.

In addition, Godard's refusal to present several of his characters in moral terms suggests that issues other than good and evil often are responsible for the ills of society. Paul and Denise, for instance, have neither strong moral nor strong immoral traits; rather, they are alienated and confused. The lack of poetic justice in Paul's accidental injury or death echoes this aimlessness. Even the exploiters (like the businessman who hires women to suck his penis under his desk and has men and women alike utter animal noises on cue) appear more sick or pathetic than despicable.

Truffaut's attitude toward good and evil in *The Last Metro* contradicts his seeming anti-melodramatic orientation. That he mediates most of the Nazi terror through radio and newspaper reports does not alter his presentation of the classic good/evil struggle: the Nazis and Daxiat (Jean-Louis Richard) are the bad guys to hate (Daxiat is a French drama critic who collaborates with the Germans, even advocating on the radio "the rooting out of the Jews" from all dramatic enterprises); the stage people are the good people to love. This over-simplification leads Truffaut to ignore the nature of the Nazi mind, the reasons for complicity on the part of some of the actors, even the reasons Bernard is both actor and resistance fighter. One need only consider the analytic scope of Bernardo Bertolucci's *The Conformist* (Italy, 1970), its study of why someone becomes a fascist, to realize what an anti-melodramatist might have done with Truffaut's topic. Truffaut even goes so far as to create a morally satisfying episode of poetic justice, with Daxiat fleeing through the ruins of burning buildings and Lucas triumphantly emerging from hiding, the Nazis defeated. Even if Truffaut has no higher analytic intentions than to evoke the climate of the Occupation,[3] he cheats the viewer who probes the anti-melodramatic surface for an insight into melodramatic emotion which should lie below.

Lastly, these three anti-melodramas share with other modernist films certain techniques of distancing the viewer from events portrayed, thus eliciting contemplation rather than emotional identification. However, the anti-melodramas transform these techniques into integral comments on the creation of melodramatic emotion. The implications of each distancing technique used, in combination with the exploration of potentially melodramatic events and moral structures, constitute the anti-melodramatic film.

Ali's primary distancing technique consists of shots showing people staring at Emmi and/or Ali, or shots framing characters within windows and doors; both kinds of shots are composed and repeated to make the viewer conscious of them as cinematic images. (For example, during an intimate goodbye on the street between Emmi and Ali, the camera rises to the nosy neighbor staring down at them from her apartment window; Emmi and Ali's wedding repast at a restaurant is filmed in long shot, through two doorways, and is intercut with repeated shots of a glaring waiter.) Not only do these stares and framings place the viewer outside the action, but their repetition throughout the film suggests the voyeurism of society at large. The world always intrudes, leaving the lovers no possibility for privacy or intimacy. When the stares penetrate Emmi's home—the camera panning the disgusted looks of Emmi's children—the film completely punctures the melodramatic belief that lovers can create "a private world of their own making."[4] The same prejudice and exploitation which exist outside the home exist inside as well.

More specifically, the staring motif indicates the inseparability of home and work. The creation of melodramatic emotion demands that love supersede the claims of work. In *Ali* the worlds of home and work become similar: in both her apartment house and her place of work, Emmi receives stares through a tangled maze of lines (a lattice screen at home, the stair bannister at work). Her work literally enters her home when a co-worker visits and proceeds to stare in disgust at Ali for more than twenty seconds. (The very duration of the stare also distances the viewer.) The staring motif thus reinforces Fassbinder's decision to replace the middle-class, non-working heroine of *All That Heaven Allows* with a working-class cleaning lady. Both emphasize intrusion: of the world upon the individual, of work upon love.

Fassbinder uses other, less major techniques to distance the viewer from the emotion of his scenes, and in each case the technique comments on melodramatic emotion. For instance, he features red blinking lights whenever Emmi and Ali dance together in the Moroccan bar, a technique which isolates the couple from the normally lit onlookers. As in melodrama, the two temporarily create their own world, but the lighting simultaneously suggests that their blissful union, as signified by the dance, is as insubstantial as the lights themselves. In *All That Heaven Allows* Sirk also uses these blinking lights, but he uses them during the scene with Carey's daughter when Carey decides to reject her lover. Contrary to Fassbinder, Sirk suggests the insubstantial nature of objections to the love relationship.

In *Every Man for Himself* Godard uses many distancing techniques to analyze melodramatic emotion. First, he quickly cuts from location to location and protagonist to protagonist without any clear time frame or plot connection. In the first few minutes of the film, for instance, he cuts from hotel suite, to cocktail lounge, to escalator, to parking lot, to soccer game, to farm, to video studio, to field, back to farm, to printing room, to street corner. This rhythm of fragmentation suggests emotions of dislocation and uprootedness rather than the idealized, pure emotions of love, hate, grief, and revenge.

Godard further splinters the melodramatic emotion by filming intimate conversations in public places, amidst the bustle and confusion of crowds. Rather than emphasize the world's intrusion in the home, as Fassbinder does, Godard shows personal relationships and the world completely entangled. Paul and Denise, and Paul and his ex-wife converse (and fight) almost exclusively in congested restaurants and street corners. (Paul and Denise also discuss their relationship by phone, completely apart from each other.) Paul has advertised his "home" for rent in the newspaper and lives in a hotel room. Denise wants to move to the country; Isabel, too, considers moving. The absence of home and the constant presence of strangers implies that rootlessness and anonymity have virtually replaced the all-controlling and continuity-providing love found in melodrama.

To explain the context out of which this rootlessness and anonymity arise, Godard uses several distancing techniques. First, Godard's camera will frequently wander away from the protagonists and focus, as if by chance, on a stranger who never even encounters Paul, Denise, or Isabel. (For instance, when Paul and Isabel first meet, the camera drifts away from them to another couple, concentrates on this other couple's conversation about sex, then abandons them for the rest of the film.) At times, the film will dissociate image and sound, continuing a protagonist's voice on the sound track while the camera moves on to a stranger in the same location (as when Denise talks to a friend about her need for the country, and the camera focuses on the woman across the street, who, dressed in a fur coat, walks by a cow.) By concentrating on unrelated strangers while duplicating a rhythm of aimlessness, these techniques suggest that the complexity and over-stimulation of the modern world contribute to the individual's lack of absorption in his/her interpersonal relations and that others exist besides the central characters. In contract, melodrama requires total absorption.

In addition to letting his camera focus on people other than the leads, Godard intercuts images of cars without human beings (or shots of trucks or trains) to suggest the dehumanization caused by the machine age. These inserts also indicate stagnation (shots of traffic jams) and loss of identity (shots of car lights blinking simultaneously). Although melodrama does show an outside world, it focuses on heroes who combat external obstacles and who retain their goodness intact. *Every Man for Himself*, through these repeated image inserts of the city environment, insists that the imperfections of the world penetrate the protagonists' psyches and that the protagonists emerge psychologically impaired.

Often Godard refuses to show both members of a conversation—the customary shot/reverse shot—to emphasize the lack of feeling between people. Sometimes one person dominates, as in the conversation between Isabel and her sister where the sister is almost never shown; at other times the two people do not connect at all, as in the sex scene between Isabel and Paul where the camera never shows Paul.

Lastly, through the distancing technique of slow motion and freeze-frame cinematography, *Every Man for Himself* suggests that people are removed from their own spontaneous feelings and try to escape their frustrations by turning to preformed images. Godard films two of Denise's embraces with men in slow motion to indicate that the characters merely repeat the image of an embrace rather than engage in an act of real love. (The tableau is then completed by the presence of onlookers in both cases, Paul's daughter and Isabel, respectively.) The slow motion occurs most frequently when Denise rides her bike—a media icon of relaxation—in order to escape the alienation of both love and work. She gains tremendous speed, then suddenly becomes stuck (via a freeze frame) and makes no progress. She cannot achieve the media ideal. The countryside itself looks like picture postcards.

The dislocation, aimlessness, and lack of involvement Godard presents through his various distancing techniques embrace the world of work as well as the world of personal relationships. Isabel's job as a prostitute constitutes a metaphor for the status of work and love (sex) in the modern age, her indifference combining the two in one image. Work specifically enters the home when Isabel becomes pimp to her sister. Similarly, Denise and Paul's relationship grew out of their working together at the studio; they break up partly over Paul's making a decision for Denise at work. By including odd, sometimes even grotesque, images of work combined with sex, as, for instance, the naked businessman talking business on the phone while rubbing Isabel's backside, Godard inspires the viewer to contemplate the similarity between work and love: exploitation and alienation dominate both. *Every Man for Himself* fuses form and content to explore not only life without melodrama, but also life without much hope for love of any kind.

In *The Last Metro* Truffaut distances the viewer by using conventional narrative techniques but draining away much of their emotional impact. First, he presents a heroine so strong and poised that she elicits none of the automatic fear and sympathy customarily evoked for the conventional woman of melodrama. Each time danger threatens her husband, Marianne takes full and swift command of the situation. She even remains safe when unaware of danger, as when her friend warns her not to sell her jewels. Truffaut also denies the viewer the emotional identification of melodrama by stripping his action of its suspenseful potential. Whereas suspense comes from the viewer's growing concern about a character's danger, Truffaut purposely shortens his scenes so emotion cannot develop. For instance, when the Gestapo comes to search the cellar, Marianne clears away Lucas's apartment furniture so quickly that the viewer has little time to develop intense fear. Similarly, rather than a big jealous scene which builds the viewer's anguish for the characters, Lucas calmly tells Bernard, "My wife is very beautiful. She loves you. How do you feel about her?" and the scene is over. *The Last Metro* lacks the grand gesture.

When probing these two distancing techniques for their anti-melodramatic comment, however, one discovers only contradictions and potential affirmation of the melodramatic position. Although the viewer does not emotionally identify with Marianne, Truffaut still focuses on the rewards of emotion. True, resentment and duty enter Marianne's love for her husband, and true also, she has sex with another man. However, monogamy is not really threatened (Marianne never desires to desert her husband), and the film affirms the possibility of strong love. Simply, Marianne has not decided which man she loves the most.

Similarly, the attitude toward the home appears slightly contradictory in *The Last Metro,* but essentially, the sanctity of the home is affirmed. Although for Lucas, home becomes a prison, it also remains a clear refuge from the Nazi enemy. Although Bernard and Marianne commit an act of adultery in the home, Marianne also fiercely defends the home for the sake of her husband. Moreover, Lucas emerges as crowned king of his home when the entire audience applauds, in a standing ovation, his coming out of hiding.

Truffaut comes closest to a clear anti-melodramatic stance in his attitude toward work. Not only do work and home completely fuse in the theatre in a far more literal way than in the usual backstage drama, Truffaut indicates that Lucas's work as surreptitious director sustains him at least as much as his wife's love. However, since the viewer has no idea of Lucas's attitude toward work before the Nazi occupation, the world has no analyzable impact on him beyond the superficial, although serious, one of restricting his freedom of movement. With the exception of his positive attitude toward work, Truffaut has created an anti-melodrama in form, but almost a melodrama in content.

The anti-melodrama demands a total fusion of form and content. According to this standard, both *Ali* and *Every Man for Himself* are successful films. Through their form, they analyze the basic premise of melodrama, the primacy of emotion. *Every Man for Himself,* however, remains less than fully satisfying because it repeats several contemporary clichés: alienation from work and other people, prevalence of exploitation in a capitalist society. *The Last Metro* fails since its form contradicts its content, and the film actually affirms much of the melodramatic ideal its form denies. Only *Ali,* of the three films, completely succeeds in using the anti-melodramatic form to convey provocative insights about the inadequacies and dangers of the melodramatic outlook.

Notes

1. In choosing these three films, I am exploring how films can create anti-melodramatic perspectives; I am not claiming these films are sufficiently representative to lead to a generic definition. Because the relationship between Sirk and Fassbinder has been well established, I will concentrate on the differences between them. For discussions of their similarities, see Tony Rayns, "*Fear Eats the Soul,*" *Sight and Sound,* vol. 43, #4 (1974), p. 245; Fassbinder, "Six Films by Douglas Sirk," *Film Comment* (Nov.–Dec., 1975), pp. 22–24; interviews with Fassbinder, such as John Hughes and Brooks Riley, "A New Realism," *Film Comment* (Nov.–Dec., 1975), pp. 14–17. For discussions of Sirk's "sabotage" of the melodramatic form, see Molly Haskell, *From Reverence to Rape: The Treatment of Women in the Movies* (Baltimore: Penguin Books, 1974), pp. 269–75; Michael Sterne, *Douglas Sirk* (Boston: Twayne Publishers, 1979), pp. 111–134.
2. Despite Sirk's possible sabotage of their clear dichotomy (for example, Fassbinder claims that the film indicates Carey will miss her bourgeois world after choosing Ron's more natural

world; see "Six Films," *Film Comment*, p. 23), the possibility of a loving world as an escape from society's evils remains strong in *All That Heaven Allows*.

3. Kevin Thomas, rev. of *The Last Metro, The Los Angeles Times*, 22 Feb. 1981, p. 23.
4. This statement was made about the essence of screwball comedy, but applies equally to melodrama. See Richard Griffith and Arthur Mayer, *The Movies: The Sixty Year Story of the World of Hollywood and Its Effect on America from Pre-Nickelodeon Days to the Present* (N.Y.: Simon and Schuster, 1957), p. 324. The relationship between comedy and melodrama in film is a fascinating topic and has not been fully explored. As examples of a difference, Ernst Lubitsch's *Design for Living* (1933) and Howard Hawks's *His Girl Friday* (1940) are both classical Hollywood films which, unlike the melodramatic film, insist upon the intermingling of love and work.

The Melodrama in Latin America: Films, Telenovelas, and the Currency of a Popular Form

ANA LOPEZ

The category "melodrama" has been discussed in multiple and often contradictory critical enterprises. It has often been used as a term of opprobium to describe simple dramatic works with strong emotional appeal intended for "popular" audiences. That the cinema emerged as the successor of the popular melodramatic theater of the 19th century perpetuated the value-laden application of the label "melodrama" to those films and other cultural artifacts that elicit excessively strong emotions and are designed for popular or "mass" audiences.

Recently, melodramas and their study have been rescued from the dust bins of negative evaluations by critics who have analyzed the melodrama as a significant form with a hidden radical potential. Perhaps because of the accessibility of the Hollywood melodrama, most of these theoretical explorations of the melodramatic have focused on North American products (with the exception of recent work on the British Gainsborough melodramas of the Forties.)[1]

But we must recognize that the melodramatic is a universal form that has been utilized and exploited by most cinemas and popular media and that there is a need to examine how the melodramatic functions in other cinematic and social systems—how it is used and how it is "read." Ultimately, although we must agree that there is such a

Ana Lopez's "The Melodrama in Latin America: Films, Telenovelas, and the Currency of Popular Thought" originally appeared in *Wide Angle*, Vol. 7, no. 3 (1985), pp. 5–13. Reprinted by permission of the author and The Johns Hopkins University Press.

thing as a "melodramatic" impulse that seems to be universal, we must also agree that this impulse only exists as specific manifestations imbedded in specific histories and social moments. In this essay, I propose to briefly examine one such manifestation of the melodramatic: how the melodrama has been activated, manipulated and reformulated by Latin American cinema and television.

In Latin America, the melodramatic has been important not only as the most popular form of narrative entertainment (with roots in older oral traditions), but also as a form that is particularly well suited to represent the sociopolitical conditions of modern Latin America from the position of the dominant classes. As a spectacle, the melodrama fosters immediacy, recognition and identification; it leads the spectator to hang on every gesture and expression of an actor or actress, to adopt his or her aspirations and to suffer from the gap between these aspirations and their realization in the ordinary world. Rhetorically, it tends to obscure the social complex by reducing it to a small number of simplified options that lure the viewer/reader into adopting pseudopolitical positions without full knowledge or even awareness of other information and possible options. The melodrama's emphasis on the centrality of the logic of emotions and its tendency to shift signification away from the "rational" towards the more "natural" realms of gesture and environments charged with meaning often coincide with the logic of the dominant social and political order in most of Latin America. The melodrama has been studied and described as a reflection of the North American capitalist system and as a principal producer of the capitalist subject (especially female ones), but it can also be seen as helping to produce the "perfect" subject of political and economic dependence in the Third World.

Is it possible that this form, the product and instrument of the dominant classes and the servant of dominant ideologies, can be utilized and read as a *positive* force for socio-cultural change in dependent societies? I believe that if we examine the history of the development and evolution of the melodramatic function in Latin American cinema and television we will find that the popular melodrama has a possible critical potential that is just beginning to be explored by cultural workers.

The melodramatic has had a long history in Latin American cinema. The earliest Latin American films were either views of everyday life or simple melodramas. But the silent Latin American cinema was quickly superseded by the technical sophistication and overwhelming quantity of Hollywood imports that very early invaded the Latin American market. It is not until the coming of sound in the early Thirties that the power of the Hollywood film over the Latin American film market was relatively weakened. Although the novelty interest of the talkies was at first very strong, Hollywood experienced serious difficulties with dubbing and succeeded in alienating a large percentage of its Latin American audience by its lack of discrimination in selecting its dubbing personnel. Although in the studios it was efficient to have Mexicans, Argentines, Cubans and Chileans dubbing in the same films, the differences in dialects were so ludicrous for Spanish speaking audiences that these films were actually booed in theaters throughout Latin America. The coming of sound thus opened a temporary space that a Latin American national film industry could take advantage of: the Latin American audience was there; all that was needed was a product they would accept. With much enthusiasm, the Argentine film industry set out to capitalize on this audience and to popularize Argentine culture, music, actors and singers through "tango" films—narrative based on the melodramatic lyrics of popular tangos which incorporated the tangos themselves as well as tango's most famous stars. Later, Argentina would develop other genres, but the nationalistic and melodramatic tango films would remain its most famous and popular products nationally and throughout the rest of Latin America.[2]

Until World War II Argentina managed to maintain its position as the dominant Latin American film industry. Although the reasons for its "fall" from relative dominance are too complex to be discussed in detail here (for example, the industry's lack of adequate capitalization, its dependence on an expensive star system and on foreign intermediaries that controlled and profited from most of the exploitation of Argentine films throughout the continent), the Argentine industry was especially upset by U.S. wartime export policies: because Argentina was classified as a "neutral" nation during most of the war, it was not allotted as much film stock as other U.S. allies in Latin America like Mexico and Brazil. Suffering from a creative crisis and without raw film stock, film production in Argentina came to a virtual standstill. Mexico, its main competitor for the Latin American market, moved in and took over that market (with the aid of extra film stock shipments received from the U.S. during the war).[3]

Mexican production of this period (its "Golden Age") was also heavily dependent on melodramatic genres. Apart from the comic *comedia ranchereras*, genres like the urban melodramas, the family melodramas and the adaptations of melodramatic novels were based upon extremely exaggerated melodramatic premises. Even the cabaret melodramas (called *cabaretera* films) focused on the cheap night clubs of the capital city and their version of B-girls. Even when Mexican production moved into its period of retrenchment in the postwar period (when there was no longer a "space" left open by Hollywood) most of its productions remained extremely melodramatic in nature.

Although the Latin American cinema managed at different moments in its history to challenge and take advantage of the United States' cinematic hegemony over Latin America, the New Latin American Cinema of the late Fifties, Sixties and Seventies challenged not only the foreign cinemas, but the old Latin American cinema itself. The "old" melodramatic forms of the Latin American cinema were rejected as complicit with the imperialist system in dominance. Critics and filmmakers argued that melodramas bore no relation to the "reality" of Latin America, and they called for more realistic and explicitly political forms of cinematic discourse. The New Latin American Cinema's rejection of the melodrama was probably best articulated by two Cuban critics, Enrique Colina and Daniel Diaz Torres, in the pages of *Cine Cubano* in an article entitled "Ideology of Melodrama in the Old Latin American Cinema."[4] According to them, the popularity of the cinematic melodrama was

> a response to the petit bourgeois values rooted in the people and systematically publicized by the erosion of an ideological superstructure.[5]

In their analysis, the old melodrama of the Latin American cinema was reflective of the economic dependence of Latin America and ultimately also responsible for the maintenance and reproduction of economic and cultural dependence.

Other critics and theorists also rejected the "old" Latin American cinema as part of a "popular" culture that was totally contaminated by bourgeois ideology. As Fernando Solanas and Octavio Getino summarized,

> Importa más llegar a un solo hombre con la verdad de una idea, que diez millones con una obra mistificatoria. Aquella libera: lo otro es ignominia.
>
> It is more important to reach one man alone with the truth of an idea, than ten million with a mystifying work. The former liberates; the other is ignomy.[6]

Through this rejection of its melodramatic past, the New Latin American Cinema also rejected its own "target" audiences, for the people it most wanted to address were precisely those popular "masses" that it theorized as victims of the ideology of the old melodrama.

In contrast to the New Latin American Cinema, which rejected the popular melodramas in favor of discourses less contaminated by bourgeois imperialist ideology, television was growing in Latin America and popularizing the form even more than the old Latin American cinema had done. Perhaps because of the relative success of national cinema industries during World War II and the immediate postwar period, Latin American countries entered early and optimistically into the television age. According to UNESCO statistics, in 1954, the world's fourth television nation (in terms of sets per population) was Cuba, the fifth was Venezuela, and tied for seventh were France, Mexico and the Dominican Republic. Argentina and Brazil tied for tenth place with West Germany, Italy and the USSR. Between 1950—the year when television services began in Cuba, Mexico and Brazil—and 1953, Latin America had more television sets than did continental Europe.[7]

Originally almost totally controlled by U.S. interests,[8] television systems in Latin America began as offshoots of radio and, like the movie industries, were modeled on the North American commercial model. In 1947, President Miguel Alemán decided that Mexico should follow the CBS model in developing its television industry (rather than the BBC model), and that decision seemed to determine the direction of most Latin American television systems. In Latin America, television remains primarily privately owned, operated for profit and geared to providing entertainment to the largest possible audience (which, like in the United States, is then sold to advertisers). From their so-called birth, most Latin American television systems have carried paid advertising and, as a result, all Latin American television services have suffered from similar weaknesses. To quote Jeremy Tumstall, these weaknesses were

> Too many stations, too many hours of programming, too many minutes of advertising . . . too few sets, too little revenue, [and] too little money to spend on programming.[9]

Given that at first there were not enough U.S. programs available for import to maintain this extensive system, Latin American television services were forced to develop forms of inexpensive and easily produced local programming in order to sustain advertising and fill broadcast time. The most prominent and enduring of these early formats were the marathon variety show and the *telenovela*.

It has been argued that the *telenovela* is the generic equivalent of the North American soap opera. Together with the *radionovela*, the form seems to have been derived by Colgate and the Sydney Ross Company in pre-Castro Cuba,[10] but *telenovelas* were always markedly different from the North American soaps. Among these differences, it is important to remark upon three crucial ones. Unlike the North

American soaps, *telenovelas* always have clear-cut stories with definite endings that permit narrative closure; they are shown during prime-time viewing hours; and they are designed to attract a wide viewing audience of men, women and children. Even the nomenclature of the form reflects a subtle distance: while the title "soap opera" is ironic and non-apologetic about its commercial roots and its claims to excessive hyperbole, the newly coined word "*telenovela*" evokes both the novelistic form and the techno-cratic respectability of the new medium of communication.

The development of the *telenovela* form diluted the direct influence of North American soap operas (or specific North American financial interests) even further. Today the *telenovela* seems to be a unique Latin American phenomenon that is also quite distinct from the much shorter North American miniseries and the more diffused prime-time soaps like *Dallas* and *Dynasty.*

In the Sixties and Seventies, empirical communication researchers began to be interested in the study of information and programming "flows" from the First and Second Worlds to the Third. Their research indicated that the one way traffic of programming from the big exporting countries to the rest of the world was dominated by entertainment material.[11] Recent research seems to indicate, however, that there is substantially less importation of television programs throughout Latin America today, especially from the United States.[12] In 1973 various Latin American nations imported between 10 and 84% of their total television programming, but as of 1979 this trend had changed and the six major nations of Latin America had reduced their imports by approximately 29% in nine years.[13] This dramatic change in program flow can be attributed to the growing popularity and success of the *telenovela*. Once they were simply used to fill in empty time between paid commercial spots, but today they occupy the time slots that were previously filled by U.S. series, and they constitute the principal television export product for Mexico, Brazil, Venezuela and Argentina.

The search for profits has led commercial Latin American television chains to exploit the *telenovela* because it has proven unbeatable in its ability to draw larger audiences and thus increase the size of the television market. A successfully exported *telenovela* can be extremely profitable, and Mexico's Televisa and Brazil's TV-Globo (both powerful multinational corporations) have used *telenovelas* to replace U.S. programming throughout the Latin American television market. For example, in seven years, profits from the smash hit *Simplemente Maria*, a 500-episode *telenovela* which was exported to all of Latin America, have already exceeded 20 million dollars.[14]

Attracting huge audiences, *telenovelas* now dominate prime-time evening hours in Latin American television. It is ironic that at the moment when the New Latin American Cinema rejected the melodrama as the embodiment of cultural dependency, television used the melodrama in order to establish a solid audience base and as a result created a nationalistic (or, at least, pan–Latin American) form with which to begin to challenge that very same cultural and economic dependence. And it is doubly ironic that it is because of the power and appeal of the melodrama that television grows and threatens the existence of the new and the old Latin American cinemas, for television had the same effects on the cinema in Latin America as it did in the U.S. and other countries. The growth of television and the "modernization" of Latin America were accompanied by a marked decrease in cinema audiences and by a diminished cultural importance of the cinema throughout the continent.[15]

The extremely simplistic stories that characterized early *telenovelas* in the Fifties have also become more complex and more responsive to national or pan–Latin American characteristics. For example, after years of dominating the market the Mexican producers of *telenovelas* were forced to contend with increased competition from Brazil, Argentina and Venezuela, and this competition has been clearly reflected in the *telenovelas* themselves. In Brazil, the principal producers of *telenovelas* (TV-Globo, TV-TUPI and TV-Exelsior) began to emphasize Brazilian themes, history and contemporary problems in their productions and, in fact, TV-Globo became the principal television producer of Brazil in the Seventies primarily because of its innovative *telenovelas*.

As a result of this pooling of cultural expertise, TV-Globo managed to consolidate the *telenovela* as a popular expression of Brazilian mass culture incorporating many of the characteristics of other popular culture forms: pop Brazilian music, the themes of popular literature (the *folletin*) and the style and techniques of the movies. Rather than remain bound to multiple-camera studio shooting, for example, the Brazilian *telenovelas* have taken their stories on location and have become more concerned with production values. The inexpensive and boring sets of early *telenovelas* are no longer enough for this very competitive market which now includes the large segment of the U.S. market that is reached by the Spanish International Network (SIN). In a recent interview broadcast on SIN, Delia Fiallo, a Cuban exile and writer of *telenovelas* who works for a Venezuelan television chain, discussed the genesis of her newest *telenovela*, *Leonela* (broadcast on SIN in 1984), and the fact that it is no longer possible to remain in the studios for the duration of an episode because the Brazilian innovations with location shooting have become the industry norm throughout Latin America.

Thematic innovations and the fact that *telenovelas* are increasingly willing to deal with social issues have also increased the popularity of the form. The totally stereotypical plots and situations described by content analysts and other communication researchers (like Antonio Pasquali, Cesar Ramon Rincón, Marta Colomina de Rivera and Jose Marques de Melo) in the late Sixties are now more of an exception than an industry norm.[16] This is not to imply that *telenovelas* have become miraculously progressive, but that they are less bound by stereotypical and ideologically contemptible characterizations and plots than they once were.[17]

Telenovelas are so prevalent and commonplace today that they have even begun to adopt somewhat self-referential practices. For example, in the Venezuelan *Leonela* (a story about machismo and its effects on women who are victimized by it) two characters, a grandmother and her daughter-in-law, sit in their living room and watch a *telenovela* at the same time that they try to discuss the daughter-in-law's future. They compare the "real" problems of the daughter-in-law to the simplistic attitudes and characters portrayed in the *telenovela* they are watching. Of course, we watch *them* framed by the rabbit-ear antenna of their television set in the foreground. If art explains ideology through difference when it manages to distance the spectator from it, as so many Latin American critics have said, then at moments like this, the melodrama of the *telenovela* might begin to serve a demystifying cultural function.

The cinema has had to react to the renewed cultural significance and popularity of the melodramatic *telenovelas*. Although the New Latin American Cinema theoretically rejected the melodrama as a form of cultural dependence, what can be said when this same form serves to promote the relative independence and nationalization of Latin American popular cultures? Faced with its own inaccessibility and lack of popular acceptance within Latin America the cinema of Latin America has become more and more concerned with the "popular." It is no longer feasible to argue for an idealistic ideological purity as did Solanas and Getino. Filmmakers today are constantly aware of the need to reach audiences in order to avoid the ghettoization and marginalization of their films. Although it is indeed true that social change can only begin in the margins of a system, it will not be effective if it remains tied to that margin. And the formerly rejected melodrama seems to have acquired a new value in the eyes of filmmakers as a tool with which to attract the kinds of audiences needed for their films. The influence of the renewed cultural significance of the melodrama through the *telenovela* (and other melodramatic forms of popular culture like the *fotonovelas*) has been subtle, but visible.

Some exemplary situations and texts may highlight the reincorporation of different kinds of "melodramas" and melodramatic strategies into this "second wave" of the New Latin American Cinema.

Although the Brazilian cinema has not had much television exposure, television's popularity has exerted a considerable influence on this cinema. Carlos Diegues' *Bye Bye Brazil* (1980) is one of several recent films to address the role of television in modern Brazilian society and to adopt some of the techniques of television production (other titles are Arnaldo Jabor's *Eu te Amo* [*I Love You*, 1981] and Antonio Calmon's *Novela das Oito* [*Eight o'clock Novela*, 1981). *Bye Bye Brazil* follows an itinerant troupe, the Caravana Rolidei, as it makes its way through rural Brazil. The Caravana is a symbol not only of the popular forms of entertainment that have become obsolete with the development of the mass media, but also of the cinema itself, a form which has lost to television its ability to reach the masses.

Although the film has been interpreted by critics as a denunciation of television and its effects on the Brazilian cinema, this critique is, as Randall Johnson points out in his new book *Cinema Novo X Five*, at best an ambiguous one, for the film incorporates television into its own diegesis and reflects it in its own mode of production.[18] In the film, the opposition between the Caravana Rolidei and television suggests that television is responsible for the destruction of folk cultures and regional cultural identity in Brazil. But the film can just as easily be read as the coming of age of the Brazilian visual popular arts. While replacing and copying folk cultures, the popular arts have also transformed the effects of cultural imperialism in order to develop new modern national cultures. When the Caravana reaches a northeastern village, for example, we see all the inhabitants (including the priest and the mayor) gathered in the town square and behaving as if hypnotized by Sonia Braga in the *telenovela*, *Dancin' Days* (a story based on the influence of John Travolta in *Saturday Night Fever* [1977] upon Rio de Janeiro disco-crazed youths).[19] But if the homogenizing television images of commercial networks like TV-Globo are destroying regional cultures and differences, the Caravana Rolidei—the film's metaphor for the Brazilian cinema—is also participating in this homogenizing activity.

Like the cinema and television, the Caravana represents an urban phenomenon trying to impose itself on the rural population. But the film's representative of that rural culture, Cico the musician, is also deeply involved with the "new" urban forms: he too incorporates television and other industrial products into his act. Ultimately, *Bye Bye Brazil* argues that there is no longer a pure version of Brazilian popular culture: Bing Crosby and Frank Sinatra must be accounted for alongside indigenous forms like Condomblé, Cinema Novo and TV-Globo.

The cultural circumstances and priorities of Cuba, when compared to Brazil or to most of Latin America, are markedly different. Both television and the cinema have been accorded a specific place and function within the revolution. But just as television has been utilized to promote the popular appreciation of films through programs like *24 por Segundo* (a very popular prime-time show of film criticism and history), the cinema has looked to television in order to increase the size and composition of its national and international audiences. Within the last decade the search for popular mass audiences has left Cuban filmmakers to adopt the still popular melodramatic forms and televisual styles and to recirculate and reformulate these discourses in order to facilitate their critical apprehension by a general public.

Although his 1968 *Lucia* was already a critique (and ambiguous celebration) of different forms of melodramatic expression (from Visconti to Hollywood naturalism), Humberto Solas' most recent film, *Cecilia* (1983), is a free adaptation of the most melodramatic novel of all Cuban literature, *Cecilia Valdes* by Cerilo Villaverde (a novel which has given rise to innumerable versions and adaptations, the most famous of which is a Spanish zarzuela or light operetta). According to Solas, the film version of *Cecilia* takes the melodrama of the novel as its basic premise, but reworks it as "a historical melodrama that supposes a marxist interpretation of life."[20]

But *Cecilia* seems to be more than just a contextualized or rewritten classical melodrama (like Sergio Giral's *The Other Francisco,* a deconstruction and rewriting of a Cuban slavery "classic" comparable to *Uncle Tom's Cabin*), for it was intended to function both as a feature length film to be distributed theatrically and as a considerably longer *telenovela* to be disseminated over the air waves. Obviously, *Cecilia* was intended to capitalize on the growing Latin American market for *telenovelas.*

In addition to this attempt to produce a very sophisticated *telenovela*, filmmakers in Cuba are also taking advantage of some television techniques in their work in order to make their films more accessible to audiences. For example, Pastor Vega in his most recent film entitled *Habanera* (1984), makes use of television techniques and of some of the conventions of the melodrama to tell a story about the position of women in Cuba today. The story focuses on a female psychologist (Daisy Granados) and on her female clientele, an odd assortment of displaced and troubled women who suffer not only from the standard psychological problems, but also from the additional burden that the revolution and revolutionary struggle place on them and their families: it takes the men away, kills them, and preoccupies them. The men have a purpose within post-revolutionary societies, but what about the women? Pastor Vega combines the thematic characteristics of the melodramatic *telenovela*—the emphasis on contemporary women, the family and problems of contemporary society—with another recent strain of popular Cuban culture—the counterespionage thriller—and makes the husband of our heroine a worker for the revolution who mysteriously travels in and out of Cuba. Stylistically, he transforms the everyday spaces of the heroine into sites of emotional signification that are explored through the insistent use of closeups. For example, in one of the many visits with patients in the psychologist's office, Vega focuses the camera in extreme closeup on the patient's face, a young girl in love with an older revolutionary, and allows the view of Havana from the fifth or sixth floor window behind her to stay in perfect focus. Every detail of her face and of her impassioned speech is thus juxtaposed and (literally) bounced off from the impassive beehive-like facades behind her.

In Cuba, Brazil, Venezuela and throughout Latin America, the melodramatic form is being used differently today and has a different cultural potential. It has always played a significant part in Latin American popular culture, but it has grown in importance proportionally with the development of television's principal melodramatic genre, the *telenovela*. The cultural trajectory of the melodrama in Latin America suggests that we must consider modifying our notions of the cultural function of the dominant forces or dominant ideology of popular culture discourses. Theorists of cultural imperialism consider popular media texts as non-contradictory expressions of dominant ideology, as instruments of manipulation.

But it is too easy to dismiss "mass culture" as unavoidably contaminated by a dominant ideology while we valorize the "purity" of some archaic and irretrievably lost folk culture: today, mass culture is an essential part of the Latin American popular culture and can no longer be factored out or ignored. Further, the texts of mass culture, including *telenovelas* and films, are not always necessarily manipulative in every context and for every reader or viewer. Popular cultures, even in authoritarian societies that actively seek to eliminate any possible counter-hegemonic spaces, are never merely transparent. Popular culture forms may represent attempts at social control, but they also have to meet the real desires and needs of real people. These texts are, after all, "popular." It is necessary to conceive of these texts of popular culture as possible sites of hegemonic resistance *and* to rethink the concept of the dominant as a possible vehicle for cultural contestation. Whereas the "dominant" in the developed world is a system that actively rewrites, incorporates and coopts differences and its own margins, we can argue that at specific moments in Latin America the establishment of dominant media/popular culture forms should be valued as itself constituting a break with cultural imperialism, although that break may still have to be splintered even further.

Notes

1. Sue Aspinall and Robert Murphy, eds., *Gainsborough Melodrama* (London: British Film Institute, 1983).
2. For more details, see Estela Dos Santos *El Cine Nacional* (Buenos Aires: Centro Editor de América Latina, 1971); Domingo di Núbila, *La Historia del cine argentino* (Buenos Aires: Edición Cruz de Malta, 1959); and Jorge Schnitman *Film Industries in Latin America: Dependency and Development* (Norwood, NJ: Ablex, 1984).
3. The technical and economic aid that the U.S. gave to Mexico was tied to several conditions, among them the agreement to make propaganda films in favor of the Allied forces. See Carl

J. Mora, *Mexican Cinema: Reflections of a Society* (Berkley: Univ. of California Press, 1982); and Jorge Schnitman, "Economic Protectionism and Mass Media Development: Film Industry in Argentia," in Emile McAnany, ed., *Communication and Social Structure* (New York: Praeger, 1981).

4. Enrique Colina and Daniel Diaz Torres, "Ideology of Melodrama in the Old Latin American Cinema," *Cine Cubano*, translated and reprinted in Zuzana Pyck, *Latin American Filmmakers and the Third Cinema* (Ottawa: Carleton University, 1978).
5. Colina and Diaz Torres, p. 65.
6. Fernando Solanas and Octavio Getino, *Cine, cultura y descolonización*—(Buenos Aires: Siglo Veinteiuno, 1973), p. 26.
7. These statistics are cited by Jeremy Turnstall, *The Media Are American* (New York: Columbia Univ. Press, 1977), pp. 174–77, 293.
8. In the Fifties and Sixties a number of U.S. companies were directly involved in Latin American television, but by the Seventies direct U.S. investments in Latin American media had drastically reduced due to the political instability of most of Latin America for this kind of investment. Other forms of influence were exercised instead.
9. Turnstall, p. 175.
10. See Elihu Katz and George Wedell, *Broadcasting in the Third World: Promise and Performance* (Cambridge, MA: Harvard Univ. Press, 1977), p. 117.
16. Tapio Varis, "Peace and Communication: An Approach to Flow Studies," *Journal of Peace Research*, 19 (1982), 243.
12. Jorge Reina Schement and Everett M. Rogers, "Media Flows in Latin America," *Communication Research*, 11, No. 2 (1984), 305–20.
13. Kaarle Nordenstreng and Tapio Varis, *Television Traffic: A One-Way Street?* (Paris: UNESCO, 1974); and Livia Antola and Everett M. Rogers, "Television Flows in Latin America," *Communication Research*, 11, No. 2 (1984), 185–203.
14. Antola and Rogers, p. 189.
15. It is somewhat reductive to blame only television for the decreases in cinema attendance throughout the continent. Perhaps more so than television, the turbulent political and economic conditions in most Latin American countries in the late Sixties and Seventies strongly contributed to decreasing movie attendance figures.
16. Antonio Pasquali, *Communicación y cultura de masas* (Caracas: Monte Avila, 1972); Cesar David Rincón, "Notas sobre el contenido de las telenovelas," in Marta Colomina de Rivera, *El huesped alienante: un estudio sobre audiencia y efecto de las radio-telenovelas en Venezuela* (Maracaibo: Universidad del Zulia, Facultad de Humanidades y Educación, 1968); and Jose Marques de Melo, "As telenovelas em Sao Paulo: estudio do publico receptor," *Communiçačao social; teoria e pesquisa* (Petropolis: Vozes, 1971).
17. The increasing ability of the *telenovela* to portray "relevant" social issues ahs to be correlated to the growth of the *fotonevela rosa* and the *fotonovela roja* which coincides with this development. Just like the *telenovela*, the *fotonovela* has developed genres through which to deal with the changing moral values of increasingly more modern (and, therefore, more alienated) societies. See Cornelia Butler Flora, "The *Fotonovela* in Latin America," *Studies in Latin American Popular Culture*, 1 (1982), 15–26; and Cornelia Butler Flora, "The *Fotonevela* as a Tool for Class and Cultural Domination," *Latin American Perspectives*, 16 (1978), 134–50.
18. Randall Johnson, *Cinema Novo X Five* (Austin: Univ. of Texas Press, 1984).
19. Even this seemingly Americanized *telenovela* has been described as a typically Brazilian production by an industry source quoted by Joseph Staubhaar: "*Dancin' Days* was basically a dramatized essay about the behavior, ideology, psychology, and values of the Rio de Janeiro middle class. It put itself, by this, in the middle of the audience universe that television

captures . . . because television is a medium of communication predominantly consumed or used by the various segments, groups, and subgroups of the middle class." "The Development of the *Telenovela* as the Preeminent Form of Popular Culture in Brazil," *Studies in Latin American Popular Culture*, 1 (1982), 147.

20. Gerardo Chijona, "*Cecilia* o la busqueda de lo nacional: entrevista con Humberto Solas," *Cine Cubano*, No. 102 (1984), p. 120.

Bibliography

Allen, Robert C. *Channels of Discourse: Television and Contemporary Criticism*. Chapel Hill: University of North Carolina Press, 1987.

Aspinall, Sue, and Robert Murphy, eds. *Gainsborough Melodrama*. Dossier no. 18. London: BFI, 1983.

Bargainnier, Earl F. "Melodrama as Formula." *Journal of Popular Culture* (1975): 726–33.

Basch, Françoise. *Relative Creatures: Victorian Women in Society and in the Novel*. New York: Schocken Books, 1974.

Bentley, Eric. *The Life of Drama*. New York: Atheneum, 1964.

———. "Melodrama." *Tragedy Vision and Form*. San Francisco: Chandler Publishing, 1965, pp. 217–31.

Bogel, Fredric V. "Fables of Knowing: Melodrama and Related Forms." *Genre* 11, no. 1 (Spring 1978): 83–109.

Booth, Michael R. *English Melodrama*. London: Herbert Jenkins, 1965.

Bourget, Jean Loup. *Le Melodrame Hollywoodien*. Toulouse: Stock, 1985.

Bright Lights, no. 6 (Winter 1977–78). Special issue on Sirk.

Cadbury, William. "Theme, Felt Life, and the Last-Minute Rescue in Griffith After *Intolerance*." *Film Quarterly*, 28, no. 4 (Fall 1974): 39–49.

Cook, Pam, ed. *The Cinema Book*. London: BFI, 1985.

Creed, Barbara. "The Position of Women in Hollywood Melodrama." *Australian Journal of Screen Theory*, no. 4 (1978): 27–31.

Cripps, Thomas. *Black Film as Genre*. Bloomington: Indiana University Press, 1978.

Cunningham. Stuart. "The 'Force-Field' of Melodrama." *Quarterly Review of Film Studies*, no. 4 (Fall 1981): 347–64.

De Lauretis, Teresa. *Alice Doesn't: Feminism, Semiotics, Cinema*. Bloomington: Indiana University Press, 1984.

Derry, Charles. "Incest, Bigamy, and Fatal Disease." *Journal of Film and Video* 35 (Winter 1983): 4–16.

Disher, Maurice Willson. *Blood and Thunder*. London: Frederick Muller, 1949.

Doane, Mary Ann. "*Caught* and *Rebecca*: The Inscription of Femininity as Absence." *Enclitic* 5, no. 2, 6, no. 1 (Fall 1981, Spring 1982): 75–89.

Doane, Mary Ann, Patricia Mellencamp, and Linda Williams. *Revision: Essays in Feminist Criticism*. Los Angeles: American Film Institute Monograph Series, 1983.

Dyer, Richard, Terry Lovell, and Jean McCrindle. "Soap Opera and Women." *Edinburgh International Festival Program*, 1977.

Eckert, Charles. "The Carole Lombard in Macy's Window." *Quarterly Review of Film Studies* 3, no. 1 (Winter 1978): 1–22.

Eisenstein, Sergei M. *Film Form*. New York: Harcourt, Brace and World, 1949.

Erffmeyer, Thomas E. "*I Only Want You to Love Me*: Fassbinder, Melodrama and Brechtian Form." *Journal of the University Film and Video Association* 35, no. 1 (Winter 1983): 37–43.

Fassbinder, Rainder Werner. "Fassbinder on Sirk." *Film Comment* (November–December 1975).

Fell, John L. *Film and the Narrative Tradition*. Norman: University of Oklahoma Press, 1974.

———. *Film Before Griffith*. Berkeley: University of California Press, 1983.

———. "Melogenre." "*North Dakota Quarterly* (Summer 1983). 100–109.

Feuer, Jane. "Melodrama, Serial Form and Television Today." *Screen* 25, no. 1 (January–February 1984): 4–16.

Film Criticism 9, no. 2 (Winter 1984–85). Special issue on melodrama.

Film Reader 3 (1978). Special issue on melodrama.

Fischer, Lucy. *Shot/Countershot: Film Tradition and Women's Cinema*. Princeton: Princeton University Press, 1989.

———. "Two-Faced Women: The 'Double' in Women's Melodramas of the 1940s." *Cinema Journal* 23, no. 1 (Fall 1983): 24–43.

Flitterman, Sandy. "*Guest in the House*: Rupture and Reconstitution of the Bourgeois Family." *Wide Angle* 4, no. 2 (1980): 18–27.

Frye, Northrop. *Anatomy of Criticism: Four Essays*. New York: Atheneum, 1957.

Geduld, Harry M., ed. *Focus on Griffith*. Englewood Cliffs, N.J.: Prentice-Hall, 1971.

Geraghty, Christine. "The Continuous Serial." In *Coronation Street*, Richard Dyer, ed. London: BFI, 1980.

Gerould, Daniel, *American Melodrama*. New York: Performing Arts Publications, 1983.

———. "Gorky, Melodrama, and the Development of Early Soviet Theatre." *Yale/Theatre* 7, no. 2 (Winter 1976): 33–44.

Gilbert, Sandra, and Susan Gubar. *The Madwoman in the Attic: The Woman Writer and the Nineteenth Century Literary Imagination*. New Haven: Yale University Press, 1979.

Gledhill, Christine. *Home Is Where the Heart Is: Studies in Melodrama and the Woman's Film*. London: BFI, 1987.

Grimstead, David. *Melodrama Unveiled: American Theatre and Culture 1800–1850*. Chicago: University of Chicago Press, 1968.

Gorbman, Claudia. "The Drama's Melos: Max Steiner and *Mildred Pierce*." *The Velvet Light Trap*, no. 19 (1982): 35–39.

Halliday, Jon. *Sirk on Sirk*. New York: Viking Press, 1972.

Haskell, Molly. *From Reverence to Rape: The Treatment of Women in the Movies*. Harmondsworth: Penguin, 1974.

Heilman, Robert B. "Tragedy and Melodrama: Speculations on Generic Form." In *Tragedy: Vision and Form*, Robert W. Corrigan, ed. San Francisco: Chandler Publishing, 1965, pp. 245–57.

———. *Tragedy and Melodrama: Versions of Experience*. Seattle: University of Washington Press, 1968.

Icart, Roger. "Le mélodrame dans le cinéma muet français." *Pour une histoire du mélodrame au cinéma*. Les Cahiers de la Cinématèque, no. 28, Perpignan, pp. 191–200.

Jacobs, Lea. "*Now Voyager*: Some Problems of Enunciation and Sexual Difference." *Camera Obscura*, no. 7 (1981): 89–109.

Johnson, Albert. "Beige, Brown or Black." *Film Quarterly* 13, no. 1 (Fall 1959): 38–43.

Journal of Film and Video 35, no. 1 (Winter 1983). Special issue on melodrama.

Kaplan, E. Ann. "The Case of the Missing Mother: Maternal Issues in Vidor's *Stella Dallas*." *Heresies*, no. 16 (1983), pp. 81–85.

———. *Regarding Television*. Frederick, Md.: University Publications of America, 1983.

———. *Women and Film: Both Sides of the Camera*. New York: Methuen, 1983.
———. *Women in Film Noir.* London: BFI, 1980.
Kehr, David. "The New Male Melodrama." *American Film* 8, no. 6 (April 1983): 43–47.
Lang, Robert. *American Film Melodrama: Griffith, Vidor, Minnelli*. Princeton: Princeton University Press, 1989.
Lesage, Julia. "Artful Rape, Artful Violence." *Jump Cut* 26 (December 1981): 51–55.
Martin, William. *Griffith: First Artist of the Movies*. New York: Oxford University Press, 1980.
Merritt, Russell. "Rescued from a Perilous Nest: D. W. Griffith's Escape from Theatre into Film." *Cinema Journal* 21, no. 1 (Fall 1981): 2–30.
Modleski, Tania. " 'Never to Be Thirty-six Years Old': *Rebecca* as Female Oedipal Drama." *Wide Angle* 5, no. 1 (1982): 34–41.
Mulvey, Laura. "Afterthoughts on 'Visual Pleasure and Narrative Cinema' Inspired by *Duel in the Sun*." *Framework*, nos. 15, 16, 17 (1981): 6–18.
———. *Visual and Other Pleasures*. Bloomington: Indiana University Press, 1989.
———. "Visual Pleasure and Narrative Cinema." *Screen* 16, no. 3 (Autumn 1975): 6–18.
Mulvey, Laura, and Jon Halliday, eds. *Douglas Sirk*. Edinburgh Film Festival 72.
Nichols, Bill. "Revolution and Melodrama: A Marxist View of Some Recent Films." *Cinema* 6, no. 1 (1970): 42–48.
Pistagnesi, Patrizia. "La Scena familiare nel cinema fascista." In *Cinema italiano sotto il fascismo*. Venice: Marsilio, 1979, pp. 99–106.
Pour une histoire du melodrama au cinema. *Les Cahiers de la Cinémathèque*, no. 28, Perpignan.
Radway, Janice. *Reading the Romance: Women, Patriarchy and Popular Literature*. Chapel Hill: University of North Carolina Press, 1984.
Rahill, Frank. *The World of Melodrama*. University Park: University of Pennsylvania Press, 1967.
Rosen, Phil. "Difference and Displacement in *Seventh Heaven*." *Screen* 18, no. 2 (Summer 1977): 89–105.
Rosenberg, James L. "Melodrama." In *Tragedy: Vision and Form*, Robert W. Corrigan, ed. San Francisco: Chandler Press, 1965, pp. 232–44.
Russ, Joanna. "Someone's Trying to Kill Me and I Think It's My Husband: The Modern Gothic." *Journal of Popular Culture* 6, no. 4 (Spring 1973): 666–91.
Screen 12, no. 2 (Winter 1977–78). Special issue on Douglas Sirk.
Screen 25, no. 1 (January–February 1984). Special issue on melodrama.
Screen 27, no. 6 (November–December 1986). Special issue on melodrama.
Smith, James L. *Melodrama: The Critical Idiom*, no. 28. London: Methuen, 1973.
Sypher, Wylie. "Aesthetic of Revolution: The Marxist Melodrama." In *Tragedy: Vision and Form*, Robert W. Corerigan, ed. San Francisco: Chandler Publishing, 1965, pp. 258–67.
Thorburn, David. "Television Melodrama." In *Television as a Cultural Force*, R. Adler and D. Cater, eds. New York: Praeger, 1976.
Vicinus, Martha. "Helpless and Unfriended: Nineteenth Century Domestic Melodrama." *New Literary History* 13, no. 1 (Autumn 1981): 129–143.
Waldman, Diane. "At Last I Can Tell It to Someone." *Cinema Journal* 23, no. 2 (Fall 1983): 29–40.
Walker, Michael. "Melodrama and the American Cinema." *Movie* 29/30 (Summer 1982): 2–38.
Wide Angle 4, no. 2 (1980). Special issue on melodrama.
Wiegand, Wilfried. "The Doll in the House: Observations on Fassbinder's Films." *Fassbinder.* New York: Tanam Press, 1981, pp. 25–55.
Williams, Alan. "Ophulsian Desire: *Lola Montes* (1955)." *Max Ophuls and the Cinema of Desire*. New York: Arno Press, 1980, pp. 137–64.
Williams, Raymond. *Modern Tragedy.* London: Chatto and Windus, 1966.
Willis, Don. "Fritz Lang: Only Melodrama." *Film Quarterly* 33, no. 2 (Winter 1979–80): 2–11.

Index